W9-AEV-272

THE WORLD OF ATOMS

AN INTRODUCTION TO PHYSICAL SCIENCE

By

J. J. G. McCUE

FORMERLY ASSOCIATE PROFESSOR OF PHYSICS
SMITH COLLEGE

With the Assistance of

KENNETH W. SHERK

PROFESSOR OF CHEMISTRY
SMITH COLLEGE

THE RONALD PRESS COMPANY · NEW YORK

PRINTED IN THE UNITED STATES OF AMERICA
Library of Congress Catalog Card Number: 56–6267

PREFACE

Books must follow sciences, and not sciences books.
BACON

There is a widely held conviction that an introductory course in science should, so far as possible, teach how a scientist goes about his work. To do that, a course must present science as a human activity, not as a body of dogma. The student must be shown how we have arrived at our beliefs in the science at hand. Nothing less will show him what science is. This book makes a serious effort to show the student why we believe in the laws and theories it discusses. Although its plan took form several years before General Education received its capitals, the book has a goal that is well described by the Harvard report, *General Education in a Free Society*. Departures from the beaten path are so extensive that they call for some rather detailed prefatory remarks.

The plan of the book is to focus on a restricted, coherent branch of physical science and to describe the chain of experiments and concepts that have led to our present theories. So far as possible, the argument should be an operational one; each concept should rest on an experiment.

In order to treat a subject for which many students feel a real curiosity, it seems well to discuss what is known about atoms. Knowledge about atoms has two facets, their structure and their chemical behavior, and an operational treatment must deal with both together. The discussion therefore involves both physics and chemistry, but not through any artificial trick of "integration." Nearly a generation has passed since the facts of chemical combination came under the sway of physical theory. In the interim, the line separating chemistry from physics has been erased, and an elementary book that recognizes the merger is really overdue.

To describe how we have come to our present beliefs, the argument is for the most part inductive. After a student understands something of the processes of science, a deductive presentation is the quickest and simplest way of attaining many of the teacher's goals, but it is in no way suitable for beginners. In those to whom the inductive background is still a mystery, the deductive approach can beget little but bewilderment.

It has proved convenient to develop the subject in very nearly a chronological order. The emphasis, however, is on broad evolution rather than on historical detail; the treatment ignores nearly all of the blind alleys, and the experiments chosen to illustrate a given development are not necessarily the only ones that influenced the course of thought. The book does contain a good deal of historical matter, and considerable pains have been taken to ensure accuracy of statement in this domain. For the scientists after Kepler, nearly all of the historical statements are based on consultation of the original books or articles. For Mendeléeff's papers, however, I have had to be content with the German versions published under his supervision, and the notes that accompany the portraits are based on the standard biographies.

The cardinal precept of the book is that it give an adequate reason for believing, or at least for entertaining, each idea as it is put forward. For example, all mention of electrons, or of the sizes of atoms, is deferred until the statement can rest on evidence that the student is able to assimilate. To present a faithful image of physics and chemistry, we must show their mathematical side; the text uses mathematics whenever the only other way of reaching the conclusion is by decree. All of the mathematical treatment rests on a single concept: proportionality. Some of the arguments, especially the mathematical ones, are too involved to be digested and reproduced on examinations by all of the students who will use the book. Nearly every student, however, can get from them a comprehension of the methods of science, and the subject matter is easier to understand when the conclusions rest on argument than it is when they are pulled out of a hat.

The general theme of the book embraces four questions: why we believe there are atoms, what we know of their structure, what we know of how they combine to form molecules, and what we know of the nucleus. The account of chemical theory stops just short of resonance, and that of nuclear physics, just short of the neutrino. Some topics that arise have not commonly been included in introductory courses. The beginner, to whom all topics are new, is not frightened by these. The Exclusion Principle is as easy to understand as the difference between mass and weight, and it elicits far more interest.

In order to develop the theme within a workable compass, the book includes, as a rule, only those topics that are necessary steps toward an understanding of what comes later; exceptions to this rule are in smaller type. There are countless opportunities for embellishment of the material, but when the learner is overloaded it is the whole picture—not just the ornamental detail—that becomes clouded. Therefore the teacher who wants to enlarge on some topics will feel a need to omit others. The necessary flexibility is provided in Sections IX and X. Chapters 57–60 of Section IX give the theory of various chemical phenomena that have been encountered in earlier sections; they may be omitted at the cost of leaving the student with some unexplained facts and a few old-fashioned ideas. There follow, nearly independently, four chapters on some aspects of organic chemistry, with emphasis on the relations between useful properties and molecular structure. These chapters put the hitherto abstract studies into contact with everyday life. Organic substances are better suited to this end than are the inorganic ones; with few exceptions, the substances familiar through daily use are organic. The seven chapters of Section X, on the nucleus, are of particular value because nuclear physics is one of the frontiers where the scientific process is now at work. Each of these three groups of chapters therefore has an important function, but none of them is indispensable.

Teachers who accept the choice of material in the book will find no difficulty in covering all of it. Each chapter is designed as a single parcel of concepts, and except for Chapter 51, each is intended as one day's assignment. Because the important ideas are recurrent ones, they need not be completely mastered the first time they appear. The pace of one chapter per assignment is therefore a completely practical one.

The exercises, which are more numerous than any one class is likely to need, have a wide range of difficulty. Many of them are intended to be easy for anyone who has read the text; a few will give the most able students something to teethe on.

There is also a gradation in the rigor of the text. Section I, which introduces the basic mechanical concepts, treats them in the uncritical way that satisfied Newton and Maxwell. Its aim is to create as little trouble as possible and get on to more appealing things. Even so, the precision of thought that it requires is at least as high as the neophyte is accustomed to, and we can hardly make a Mach or a Bridgman out of him in the first few weeks. Operational definitions are used throughout the other sections.

In order to base the discussion on definite experimental evidence, the text includes a set of descriptions of experiments. They employ only equipment that is easily obtainable, and although it is not essential that he do so, it is to be hoped that the student will see many of them performed.

The Suggestions for Further Reading provide points of departure for the writing of one or two short papers per term, a teaching device that introductory science courses have thus far done little to exploit.

The book is a somewhat abridged presentation of a course that Professor Sherk and I inaugurated at Smith College at the close of World War II, for freshmen and sophomores who did not intend to major in a science. The need was for a course with no laboratory work, and the success of the course has been such that it is still given in that manner. It would seem possible, however, to accompany the text with occasional or regular laboratory work. With this end in view, the text says enough about specific heat and Ohm's law to provide a link with laboratory treatment of those traditional topics; various others fall on the main line of discussion. Many less conventional possibilities present themselves. For instance, the hackneyed "experiment" on the density of a solid can be converted, with the help of Avogadro's number and some blocks of sulfur, into a rough measurement of the diameter of the sulfur atom.

A few remarks on small points may be in order. In the main, the units used in the text are those of the MKSA system, but it has seemed advisable to start with the coulomb instead of the ampere, and to use the calorie as well as the joule. The chemical tradition of measuring weights in grams is too strong to defy; after a brief transition period in which weights appear in newtons, the gram-weight is introduced. Special pains have been taken to avoid putting the student into a position that is likely to cause confusion of mass and weight, since there is no lack of more fruitful ways to employ his time.

Although many chemists still describe the Brönsted view of acids and bases in terms of protons, it is well not to perpetuate this usage, which became obsolete with the discovery of heavy hydrogen. For "electric intensity" and "magnetic induction," I have used the terms "electric field strength" and "magnetic field strength." The latter are more descriptive, and they are in accord with the modern practice of treating E and B as cognate. I have not replaced "orbit" by "orbital" upon the introduction of the wave-mechanical atom, since it seems doubtful that the change would have any helpful effect.

The book is written, without compromise, for those who are not studying to be scientists. In curricula that are sufficiently flexible, it should prove suitable for use with prospective scientists, who would gain from the practice of scientific thinking early in their training. At the cost of minor changes in the advanced courses, which usually go over the fundamentals anyway, the preliminary course can be left free to develop methods of thought. Once these methods are established, their later application to particular topics comes easily.

The help of certain friends and many strangers is acknowledged on the next page. My special indebtedness to Professor Sherk can more fittingly be expressed here. As my teaching colleague for two years, he played an important part in the selection of the material that has gone into the book. Had we not become separated geographically, he would have been a partner in its authorship. He has suggested most of the chemical experiments and many of the exercise questions; he has also read the chemical portions of the mansucript, offering many valuable suggestions for their improvement, and he has read all of the proofs. For any flaws that may remain, however, I must take the full responsibility.

J. J. G. McCue

Lexington, Mass.
January, 1956

ACKNOWLEDGMENTS

In its illustrative material, the book has benefited from the open-handedness of many scientists and organizations; I express heartfelt gratitude to those whose names appear beneath the photographs. Quite exceptional courtesies in this connection were extended by C. L. Andrews, Sir Lawrence Bragg, E. H. K. Dibden, C. Frondel, and the Jarrell-Ash Company.

For permission to use copyrighted passages, I am under obligation as follows: to the Cambridge University Press for the quotation from *Decadence,* by A. J. Balfour, on page 2; to Alfred A. Knopf, Inc., for that in Chapter 2, which is taken from *Einstein: His Life and Times,* by P. Frank; to the Editor of *Isis* for that in Chapter 15; to the Harvard University Press for that in Chapter 16, which is from the Foreword to the Harvard Case Histories in Experimental Science; to Friedr. Vieweg & Sohn for that at the end of Chapter 49; and to the British Association for the Advancement of Science for those in Chapters 51 and 54. The quotation at the head of Chapter 56 is from the *Proceedings of the Royal Society.*

D. L. Anderson of Oberlin, I. B. Cohen of Harvard, and R. W. Long of Houston read parts of the manuscript and made valuable suggestions for its improvement.

Mary White, who typed the manuscript, was a vigorous and effective ally in the battle against errors; I am much in her debt. My sincere thanks go also to Percy Lund, who devoted his skill and ingenuity to the drawings.

CONTENTS

LIST OF PORTRAITS

THE WORLD OF ATOMS

Science is the great instrument of social change, all the greater because its object is not change but knowledge; and its silent appropriation of this dominant function, amid the din of political and religious strife, is the most vital of all the revolutions which have marked the development of modern civilization.

A. J. Balfour (1908)

INTRODUCTION

Before setting out on a study of physical science, we shall do well to reflect on the reasons for doing so, and on the place of physical science in the general scheme of human knowledge.

In speaking of human temperament, it is common to speak of three types of people, or at least of three moods by which the lives of various people are dominated. We speak of men of action, men of feeling, and men of thought. An important part of a liberal education is an understanding of these three types, arrived at by studying history for the first type, literature for the second, and science or philosophy for the third.

Science itself, of course, is many-sided; it is useful to distinguish between the physical sciences, which deal with inanimate things, and the biological sciences, which deal with living things. The principal branches of physical science are physics, chemistry, astronomy, and geology. Physics seeks to make general statements, or "laws," that apply throughout the universe. A chemist, an astronomer, or a geologist considers that he has solved a problem when he has explained it in terms of physics. A biological scientist considers that he has solved a problem if he can explain it in terms of chemistry, or directly in terms of physics. Physics, therefore, can claim to be the fundamental science, but in our study we shall see that the physicist, in formulating the laws of the universe, has often drawn heavily on facts collected by astronomers and chemists.

Because their subject matter is so complex, and because of their need to use parts of physical science as a groundwork, the biological sciences are still in a relatively primitive state of development, comparable with that of the physical sciences a century or more ago. This fact reflects no discredit at all on the biologists, but it does imply that a broader view of the scope and methods of science can be obtained by studying its physical side. The guiding idea of this book is that the nature of physical science can best be laid bare by making a rather detailed study of a limited field. We have chosen to discuss the development of knowledge about atoms; it can be traced from its beginnings to a state of much maturity and sophistication, yet it is strongly tinged with the romance of the unseen, and it has a few remaining mysteries that today's scientists are still working to unveil.

Some of the links in the chain of atomic science were forged by chemists, some by physicists. In this domain, the distinction between physics and chemistry is now so artificial that it has no significance. It is only about fifty years, however, since the two fields of study began to overlap. In considering the earlier stages of the development, some of our work will be physics and some will be chemistry. This differentiation does not mean that we shall be studying two subjects; it illustrates, rather, that all science is one—the more advanced its development, the stronger and more complex are the bonds between its parts.

Before proceeding further, we should raise the question, "What is science, anyway?" Regardless of Webster's dictionary, science in the true sense is not a body of knowledge. Science is nothing fixed or durable. Science is, in fact, a *human activity*. It is systematic study, and physical science is systematic study of our physical environment. The details of the system of study will be discussed in the early chapters of this book and will be illustrated further in the succeeding chapters. By way of orientation, it may be well to state here that science is the collecting and correlating of facts; it must not be confused with technology, which is the body of knowledge used in the industrial arts. Technology can be, and sometimes has been, static. At other times, for example the eighteenth century, technology advances unaided by science. At present, technology is developing rapidly as a result of progress in science. In our day, science is the goose, and the advances in technology are the golden eggs. This distinction between science and technology must become widely appreciated if science is to be financed successfully from government funds.

Since technology is at the very foundation of the culture in which we are living, it is perhaps strange that a college curriculum for general education does not usually include a study of technology as such. The subject of this book, however, is a sample of physical science. A few chapters late in the book will give a glimpse of the application of chemistry to some practical ends; aside from this specimen, technology will be mentioned only in passing.

I

Mechanics

The theme that lies before us is the development of atomic science, the study of the particles that constitute matter. The scientific belief that such particles exist arose from two different studies: the study of the *mechanical* and *thermal* behavior of matter, and the study of its *chemical* behavior. Later it was found that the nature of the particles can be inferred from observations on *electrical* phenomena. We must therefore study mechanics, heat, chemistry, and electricity. Whether to begin with mechanics or chemistry is a matter of choice; we shall begin with mechanics simply because it got started, in its modern form, about 200 years before chemistry did.

Mechanics is generally considered to be the least exciting branch of physical science. Perhaps it is fortunate, therefore, that for our purposes only a few of the fundamental ideas of mechanics are necessary. In particular, the concepts of force and energy are indispensable. Luckily enough, the development of mechanics was based in large part on the study of the solar system, and for the modern student a little knowledge of the solar system is a great aid in understanding atomic affairs. Our work in this first section will serve three ends: it will introduce the basic concepts of mechanics, it will give an acquaintance with the solar system, and it will afford an excellent illustration of the use of scientific method.

1

PHYSICAL SCIENCE IN THE ANCIENT WORLD

All men are by nature imbued with a desire for knowledge.

ARISTOTLE

The major aim of this book is to set forth the meaning and methods of physical science by carefully following the development of one of its aspects, the science of atoms. The inclusion of a chapter on ancient science is prompted not simply by a desire to begin at the beginning. The science of the classical period is in itself useful for the purpose of understanding what science is. Because ancient science was relatively simple, it can teach us things about science that might not be obvious from a study of the modern world alone. This chapter will therefore outline a few of the accomplishments of the ancients, showing the extent to which science developed in their hands, and pointing out some of the inferences that can be drawn from the rise and fall of science in the ancient world.

1–1. Science in the Dawn of History. Something like five thousand years ago, in Egypt, Mesopotamia, and India, a new form of human society came into being. Small groups learned to produce food so efficiently that some workers could concentrate on other activities such as mining, fabricating, trading, or governing. City life began, and its needs soon gave rise to the invention of writing. From the Egyptian and Babylonian writings that survive, we know that in these early civilizations there was some activity that can fairly be called science.

Since these societies lived on planted crops, one of their vital needs was a system for knowing when to plant. The priesthoods worked out a satisfactory correlation between the proper time for planting and the appearance of the stars. This success no doubt seemed like real grounds for hope that a further study of the stars would disclose their influence on other human affairs. At any rate, the Babylonians did cultivate astronomy over a period of many centuries, and it did get badly mixed with astrology, theology, and magic. Many of the clay tablets that they used for books survive to show that later Babylonian astronomers had arithmetical rules for correctly predicting the appearance of the heavens years ahead. Their interests embraced far more than the calendar. We do not know the place of these men in their society, nor do we really know what motivated them. In any case, they may justly be called scientists, because by systematic study they learned to use mathematics to predict events occurring in nature.

In modern times, at least until the past few years, science has rested on the hypothesis that a given set of causes is always followed by a particular effect. So far as we know, the first people to believe in this hypothesis were the Greeks. To be sure, not all Greeks believed in it. As a matter of fact, not all Americans believe in it; if they did we should have no commercial traffic in rabbits' feet. The important thing is that an appreciable number of Greeks believed in it, and practically nobody in earlier cultures seems to have done so.

In respect to method, two distinctive features of physical science are experimentation, or at least observation, and the expression of the results in mathematical form.* The making of experiments, and the mathematical formulation of the results of experiment or observation, are both tremendous intellectual inventions, although we now take them for granted. While they may not be entirely Greek inventions, at the least we inherit them from the Greeks. If the Greeks had bequeathed nothing else to our civilization, this legacy alone should command for them our eternal respect. Nevertheless, we may ask whether the Greeks did anything with science after they acquired or developed the principles on which it rests, or whether we are justified in regarding them as mere speculators rather than as scientists.

1–2. Some General Comments on Greek Science. Before presenting examples to show that Greek science was far from being the contemptible guesswork that it is often supposed to have been, it will be well to mention some of the reasons why Greek science seems meager to us.

The first and most important reason is that science and technology are almost the only human activities that are cumulative. It is doubtful whether we are better artists or poets than the Greeks, and whether we are as moral as the early Romans, but we certainly excel them in science

* There will be no attempt in this book to make generalizations that apply to biological as well as to physical science. Although there have recently been some successes in applying mathematics to biological problems, for the present the biologist usually has to be satisfied with a more modest goal than a mathematical formula. In fact, the technique of biological investigation and the technique of most physical sciences differ so much as to cast doubt upon the validity of the commonly used phrase "*the* scientific method." It may be said in passing that, in respect to method, geology resembles biology more than it does the other physical sciences.

and technology. We do so because in science and technology we can build on the work of all previous generations; to judge a generation of scientists we must compare them not with ourselves but with their predecessors. Failure to recognize the distinction between science, which is cumulative, and other realms, in which each generation fends for itself, leads us to underestimate Greek accomplishment in science. Second, our impression of Greek science is too often based on the work of Plato and Aristotle, whose chief interests and skills lay in fields other than physical science. Third, the literary tradition has had such a hold on classical scholars that they have almost ignored the ancient scientists. Finally, the works of the best Greek scientists were at variance with the religious views of the Christians, Jews, and Moslems on whom we are dependent for the transmission of Greek learning, so that our knowledge of these scientific works is confined to a few scattered fragments.

Let us now consider what the Greek scientists actually accomplished, casting an occasional glance at the relationship between science and society during this period. Reviewing all of the scientific work of the Greeks is of course unnecessary for our purpose; the progress and decline of the ancient world's knowledge of the sun and earth will be enough. We shall see that the Greeks, using observation, experiment, and mathematics, gained a very considerable store of positive knowledge, that the Greek scientific enterprise succeeded to a degree commanding respect even in our time, and that it then withered away. A little reflection on the causes of the withering may throw some light on problems that are current today.

1–3. The Birth of Greek Science. The pre-Greek efforts yielded a considerable accumulation of recorded data and rules of thumb, but science as a striving for generalization seems to have been invented by the Greeks. In fact, its invention has traditionally been attributed to a particular Greek, Thales of Miletus, a well-traveled businessman who was in the prime of a long life about 580 B.C. According to legend, Thales discovered some geometrical generalizations, for example some of the properties of similar triangles. These properties he put to use in solving practical problems, such as finding the distance from shore of a ship at sea.* The annual flooding of the Nile had forced the Egyptians to develop schemes for surveying, and Thales' travels in Egypt had presumably started him thinking along these lines. It is commonly agreed, however, that he worked out more general statements about triangles than were known to his predecessors. We have here an illustration of what seems to be typical of the Greeks: they thought in terms of general

* Notice that "geometry" is Greek for "earth-measurement."

categories. They dealt not with an individual triangle, but with classes of triangles; not with one substance, but with matter.

Thales also thought about the nature of things, reaching the conclusion that everything is made from water. This is naïve, but not silly. Relatively recently it seemed as though everything were made from hydrogen. The important point is the attempt to explain the universe in rational terms.

Pythagoras (530 B.C.),* usually considered the inventor of mathematical proofs, also founded mathematical physics with a discovery about the strings on a musical instrument. He found that two similar strings, stretched with the same tension, sound the various musical intervals when their lengths are in simple ratios. For example, if two such strings are sounding an octave, then their lengths are in the ratio 1:2; if they are sounding a fifth, then their lengths are in the ratio 2:3. *This discovery must have been based on experiment.* With the ideas of mathematical proofs, of experimentation, and of applying mathematics to the results of experiments, science in the modern sense was fairly started.

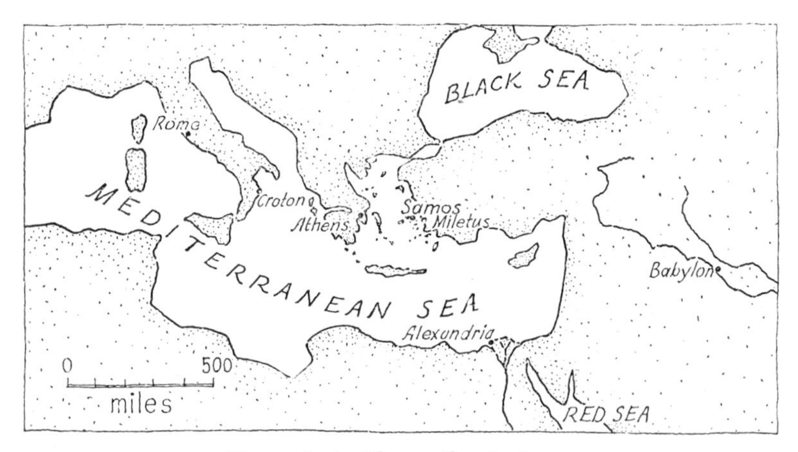

FIGURE 1–A. The cradle of science.

While the Pythagorean school was flowering in southern Italy, the Miletan school founded by Thales was still in action in Asia Minor (Figure 1–A). One of Thales' disciples used a sundial to study the motions of the sun. Another reached the conclusion that the moon shines by reflecting light given out by the sun. He was doubtless led to this conclusion by an observation that you can make for yourself: When the sun and moon are visible at the same time, notice that the bright part of the moon is the part toward the sun.

About 500 B.C., wealthy Miletus, the greatest Greek mercantile city of

* The dates of important men are mentioned in order to provide a rough scale of time. They give the year when the man was about forty years old.

its time, was conquered by the Persians, and the intellectual center of Greece shifted from Asia Minor to Athens. Anaxagoras, a contemporary and friend of Pericles and Euripides in Athens, thought the earth to be flat, but he correctly explained eclipses of the sun and the moon. Apparently basing his judgment on a huge meteorite which had recently fallen near the Dardanelles, he taught that the sun is a huge ball of white-hot stone. For this he was tried for impiety, and although acquitted he felt it wise to return to Asia Minor.

Anaxagoras' younger contemporary, Socrates (430 B.C.), must be mentioned because of his twofold influence on the progress of science, which he aided by combatting loose reasoning, but impeded by turning philosophers' attention to ethical problems, with which he himself was preoccupied.

Socrates' most distinguished pupil, Plato (390 B.C.), was also concerned largely with human affairs, but he contributed much to the logical structure of mathematics and he fostered the study of astronomy.

Aristotle (340 B.C.), one of Plato's pupils, contributed enormously to biology by careful investigation, but his work in physics was less fortunate. From our point of view, he made two major mistakes: he attempted a synthesis explaining all dynamical phenomena in terms of first principles, without having a sufficiently detailed knowledge of the phenomena, and he underestimated the importance of quantitative observation. Later in life he broke away from the Platonic tradition and developed an understanding of research which persisted in his school, the Lyceum, for years after his death. His admirable biological works date from this later period. His earlier and extensive writings on physics, which were very influential during the Revival of Learning, contribute heavily to the Greeks' reputation as poor scientists.

Aristotle died in 322 B.C., a year after the death of Alexander the Great, whose tutor he had been. The breakup of Alexander's empire caused many social changes; one of them was that Alexandria supplanted Athens as the scientific center of the western world. More significant than the change in site was the accompanying change in method. Scientists became specialists, no longer seeking to embrace all knowledge or to study the universe as a whole.

1–4. Science at Alexandria. When Alexander's empire was divided among his generals after his death, Egypt fell to one of them named Ptolemy, a progenitor of Cleopatra. Under him and his son there grew up the famous Museum, nominally a temple of the Muses, actually very much like a modern university. It was here that seventy scholars translated the Old Testament from Hebrew into Greek, giving it the form we know today.

Of the many scientists who worked at Alexandria, perhaps the greatest was Aristarchus of Samos (270 B.C.), who ranged through all of the mathematical sciences of his time but is chiefly noted for his works on astronomy, of which the only survivor is *The Sizes and Distances of the Sun and the Moon.* The details of this treatise are too involved for us to consider here, although they are interesting because they show the power of simple geometry in the hands of a master. The following description is intended only to show Aristarchus' method of attack on the problem.

* The relative distances of the sun and the moon from the earth were determined by estimating the angle A between lines of sight to the moon and the sun when just half the moon is bright, at which time the triangle in Figure 1–B has a right angle. Aristarchus estimated the angle A. Knowing two angles of the triangle, he could find the ratio of any two sides. He concluded that the sun is about 19 times as distant as the moon. (The correct value is 389 times. The error was not in the method, but in the measurement of the angle A, which is so nearly a right angle that a small error in its value results in a very large error in final calculation.)

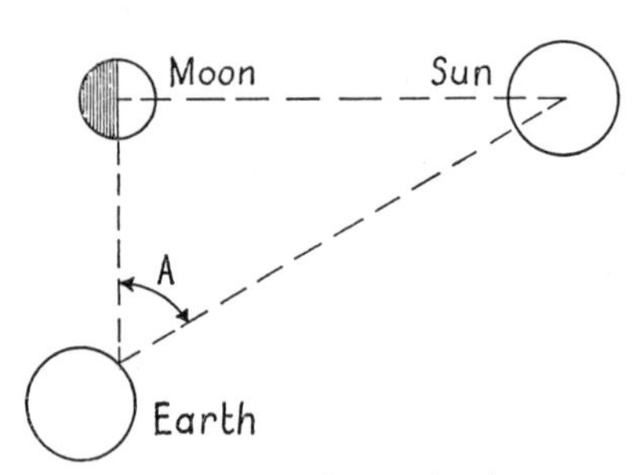

FIGURE 1–B. The earth, the moon, and the sun, when just half of the moon is bright.

During an eclipse of the sun, we see the moon pass between us and the sun. It happens that the moon is almost exactly large enough to hide the whole sun from our view; that is, the apparent size of the moon is almost exactly the same as the apparent size of the sun. An elementary argument from the similar triangles in Figure 1–C shows that

$$\frac{\text{Radius of sun}}{\text{Radius of moon}} = \frac{\text{Distance to sun}}{\text{Distance to moon}}.$$

Therefore Aristarchus reasoned that the radius of the sun is 19 times as large as the radius of the moon. Moreover, since the volume of a sphere is proportional to the cube of its radius, and $19 \times 19 \times 19$ is about 7000, he concluded that the volume of the sun is about 7000 times that of the moon.

During an eclipse of the moon, the moon passes into the earth's shadow. Aristarchus estimated the diameter of the earth's shadow on the moon to be twice the diameter of the moon. Using this ratio, and estimating the angular size of the moon as it appears from the earth, he deduced theorems relating the diameter of the moon to the diameter of the earth. From these he calculated that the volume of the earth is about 22 times the volume of the moon.

* Unless it is headed "Example" or "Experiment," material set in small type is not essential for the understanding of what comes later.

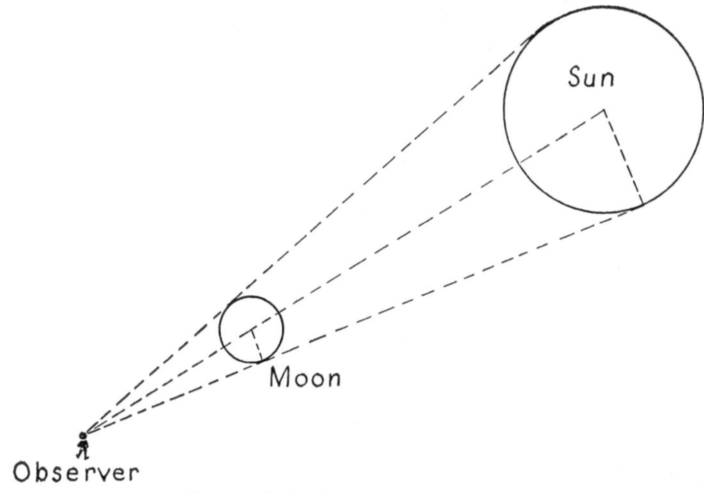

FIGURE 1-C. An eclipse of the sun.

This result implies that the sun, which according to his figures is 7000 times as large as the moon, must be about 300 times as large in volume as the earth.

Because of poor accuracy in the measurements used, these results are far from correct,* but they are of great intellectual significance because they showed that the sun is very much larger than the earth. It was perhaps this investigation that led Aristarchus to his crowning achievement, which was the assertion that the earth revolves about the sun. We shall return to this topic in Chapter 2.

It is a long step from the early idea that the earth floats on the water like a cork to Aristarchus' idea that the earth revolves about the sun. The Greeks made the step in just about three centuries. During the next century, improvement of astronomical instruments made possible much more accurate measurements, which in turn disclosed hitherto unobserved astronomical phenomena. One of the chief astronomers of this period was Hipparchus (150 B.C.), whose measurement of the mean lunar month differs from the correct value by less than one second. His work was continued by Ptolemy (A.D. 150, not a member of the ruling family) whose main accomplishment was the collection and exposition of Hellenistic knowledge of the heavens and the earth in his *Almagest* and *Geography*. In spite of living three centuries apart, Hipparchus and Ptolemy were almost collaborators. We therefore notice a striking decrease in the rate of progress, in comparison with the earlier period.

It is interesting to consider also the progress of knowledge concerning the earth itself. The idea that the earth is a sphere dates back to Pythag-

* The sun is actually over a million times as large in volume as the earth.

oras; it seems to have won general acceptance at least as early as the generation after Plato. The measurement of the diameter of the earth by Eratosthenes (235 B.C.), an Alexandrian scientist of the generation after Aristarchus, is an example of ancient science at its best.

Up the Nile, near the site of the great modern dam at Aswan, there was known to be a place where a vertical post cast no shadow at noon on the longest day of the year. Eratosthenes measured the length of shadow cast at that

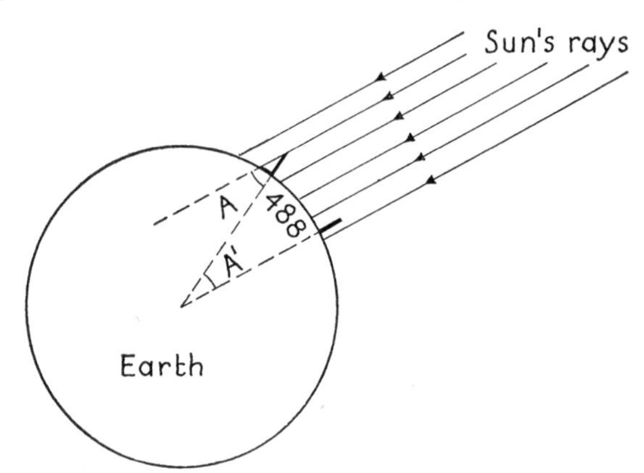

FIGURE 1–D. Eratosthenes' measurement of the size of the earth.

instant by a vertical rod at Alexandria, which he took to be 488 miles north of Aswan. The ratio of the length of the rod to the length of the shadow gave him the angle A in Figure 1–D, and this is equal to the angle A'. Clearly, then,

$$\frac{\text{Circumference of earth}}{\text{488 miles}} = \frac{360^\circ}{A'}.$$

From this the radius of the earth turned out to be 3910 miles, which is only about 40 miles smaller than the true value.*

Eratosthenes also made a map of the world as he knew it, and suggested that only the width of the ocean prevented the circumnavigation of the globe. He estimated the width of Europe and Asia to be 7600 miles, which is very close to being right. (If Columbus had known this distance and the diameter of the globe as well as Eratosthenes did, he would hardly have set out to cross the ocean.)

Ptolemy's *Geography,* written four centuries later (about A.D. 150), shows some improvement in geographical knowledge, but here too the rate of progress had obviously fallen off. Ptolemy's map of the world can be reconstructed from the latitudes and longitudes given in his book. We

* Greek measurements of distance were expressed in stadia, the stadium being a unit that had different lengths at different times and places. Here we have followed Sir Thomas Heath's opinion that the stadium used by Eratosthenes was equal to 517 English feet.

From Charles Singer, A Short History of Science, *courtesy of the Oxford University Press*

FIGURE 1–E. The world as mapped by Ptolemy.

see in Figure 1–E that it represents correctly the broad features of northern Africa, southern Asia as far as Indochina, and Europe exclusive of Scandinavia. In the roughly contemporary Roman world, however, Tacitus, writing on geographical matters, described the earth as flat, and by A.D. 600 the map of the world, as far as the most learned Europeans were concerned, had degenerated so much as to be scarcely recognizable. Further degeneration resulted in the map shown in Figure 1–F.

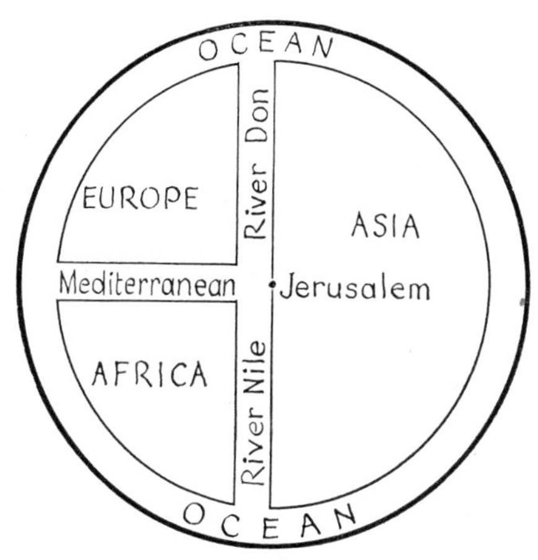

FIGURE 1–F. The world as mapped in Europe about A.D. 1000.

1–5. The Decline of Ancient Science. We see, therefore, that from 550 B.C. to about 150 B.C., the Greek world developed to a high degree the technique of scientific investigation of certain types of problems. We have mentioned cosmography and geography; very considerable progress was also made in some branches of biological science, where dissection of animals and men led to anatomical discoveries that were in some cases not repeated until the nineteenth century. We naturally inquire why this scientific activity died out. The complete answer is of course very complex, but a few of the reasons may be mentioned.

When Alexander's empire fell apart after his death, the unsettled political conditions were unfavorable to the development of science. The lot of most people was so miserable that philosophy concerned itself primarily with ethics and religion; science seemed unimportant. In Egypt, however, stability and wealth permitted the ruling Greeks to foster the development of science by the foundation and support of an institute like a university—the Museum at Alexandria. Scholars and scientists flocked there from all over the Greek world, and ancient science entered on its golden age. These scientists were specialists, not so specialized as the modern scientist, but not universal scholars like Plato and Aristotle. About 150 B.C., Rome established control over the Eastern Mediterranean, although Egypt retained a sort of independence until the time of Cleopatra. The educated Romans tried to assimilate Greek culture, and succeeded to some extent in philosophy, literature, and the fine arts, but in science they failed completely. Among the reasons for this failure were undoubtedly the following:

1. Science failed to appeal strongly to them because of their religious convictions, which emphasized the importance of conduct and minimized the importance of understanding the material world, on which the gods were alleged to exert a direct and capricious influence. Largely for military reasons, they did have a strong interest in technology, but this of course is not science.
2. Probably because they did not consider it important, they never mastered the higher branches of Greek mathematics, and therefore could not produce original work in the exact sciences.
3. Above all, they failed to recognize that science is an operation, rather than a collection of facts. They tried to take over and preserve the *results* of Greek science. This attempt failed because the body of real knowledge inevitably became more garbled and diluted with each generation, so that it became almost entirely lost long before the fall of Rome.

In the following chapter it will become clear that when physical science started to flourish again after the Renaissance, the modern scientists began just about where the ancients left off. The account just concluded has another and more important purpose, however, than a mere demonstration of continuity. The rise and fall of ancient science shows that science is not a thing that inevitably progresses. It does not grow like a weed. On the contrary, it is a delicate organism depending in a very sensitive way upon its environment. It has died before, and without the proper conditions of life it will die again.

Summary

Science is to a considerable extent an invention of the Greeks, who were apparently the first to believe that a given set of causes is always and everywhere followed by a particular effect.

Greek science employed procedures that are at the root of physical science today: observation and measurement, experimentation, and the expression of results in mathematical form.

The work of Plato and Aristotle in the physical sciences was not good, but it was extremely influential in Western Europe. Later Greek scientists, especially at Alexandria, did very impressive work in astronomy and geography, as well as in biology. Their work had little influence in Christendom until the Revival of Learning (say A.D. 1500), because scientific activity died under the Roman rule.

Thales (580 B.C.): Discovered general theorems in geometry. Tried to explain the universe in rational terms.

Pythagoras (530 B.C.): Invented mathematical proofs. Introduced mathematics into physical science (through experiments with musical strings).

Aristotle (340 B.C., pupil of Plato): Did not appreciate the importance of quantitative, i.e. mathematical, statements in physics.

Aristarchus (270 B.C.): Measured the sizes of the moon and sun (results inaccurate, but method correct). Also concluded that the earth revolves about the sun.

Eratosthenes (235 B.C.): Measured the diameter of the earth.

Hipparchus (150 B.C.): Made astronomical observations and calculations of high quality. Made improvements in astronomical instruments.

Ptolemy (A.D. 150): Compiled textbooks on astronomy and geography which preserved the Greek accomplishments in these fields. These works reached Western Europe late in the Middle Ages, via the Arabs.

Questions

1. What is science?
2. Distinguish between science and technology.
3. Mention two accomplishments of the Greek scientists.

4. State a difference between the intellectual activities at Athens and at Alexandria.
5. Give some reasons why science in the classical world died out.

Suggestions for Further Reading

O. Neugebauer, *The Exact Sciences in Antiquity* (Princeton: Princeton University Press, 1952). Deals almost entirely with Egyptian and Babylonian mathematics and astronomy, on which this author is a leading authority.

T. L. Heath, *Aristarchus of Samos* (Oxford: Oxford University Press, 1913). A history of Greek astronomy up to the time of Aristarchus, and a translation of his book *On the Sizes and Distances of the Sun and the Moon.*

M. R. Cohen and I. E. Drabkin, *A Source Book in Greek Science* (New York: McGraw-Hill Book Co., Inc., 1948). Translated excerpts from the writings of the Greek scientists.

C. Singer, *A Short History of Science to the Nineteenth Century* (Oxford: Oxford University Press, 1941). The first four chapters form a very readable account of Greek and Roman science.

G. Sarton, *A History of Science* (Cambridge: Harvard University Press, 1952 and later). A magnificent work, written by a great scholar but suited to casual browsing as well as to serious study. The first volume goes as far as Aristotle.

2

THE SOLAR SYSTEM

The most incomprehensible thing about the universe is that it is comprehensible.

EINSTEIN

The foundations of mechanics were laid by Newton, in connection with his studies of the solar system. To understand his work, we must have some knowledge of the solar system. This knowledge will also be useful in studying atomic structure, and has the additional virtue of being very entertaining in its own right.

2–1. The Heavenly Bodies. With certain exceptions (comets, meteors, satellites), the heavenly bodies may be divided into two categories: the fixed stars and the planets. The fixed stars are so called because their positions relative to one another change only minutely in the course of the centuries. They look like points of light in the dome of the heavens. The whole dome appears to rotate about an axis passing through the poles of the earth, so that in our hemisphere southerly stars rise in the east and set in the west. The northerly ones, for example those in the Big Dipper, merely move in circles about the Pole Star. The "fixed stars" therefore appear to move, but they all move together, remaining fixed *with respect to one another,* and they can be grouped for convenience into constellations. Certain other bodies, however, appear to move among the fixed stars. The most obvious example is the moon. The sun is another example, and then there are certain wandering bodies called *planets,* five of which were known in ancient times. The names of these are Mercury, Venus, Mars, Jupiter, and Saturn. Three others have been discovered in historic times, Uranus in the eighteenth century, Neptune in the nineteenth, and Pluto in the twentieth. Figure 2–A shows the motion of one of them against the background of the stars.

The classification of the sun and the moon is not obvious. The ancients classified them as planets, but the sun is now classified as a star, and the moon as a *satellite,* or attendant, of the earth.

The planets move among the constellations in very complicated and seemingly irregular ways. Most educated people now know that the planets are bodies not very different from the earth, which in fact is itself now classified as a planet. The connection between this idea and modern atomic science is sufficiently direct to justify our giving some attention to the development of the idea.

2–2. Early Work on the Planets. As far as we know, Babylonian planetary theory was a system of numerical rules for predicting the positions of the planets in the sky. The Greeks sought to express the planetary motions in terms of a geometrical model. One of Plato's pupils devised a theory that the heavenly bodies move on a set of spheres rotating within spheres, the earth being stationary at the common center of all of the spheres. Another of Plato's students accounted for the apparent motion of the fixed stars by assuming that the earth rotates on its axis, and he discovered that the theory of planetary motion could be simplified by assuming that Venus and Mercury revolve about the sun in circular orbits.

About a century later, Aristarchus extended this latter theory by taking the sun to be one of the fixed stars, about which the earth and other planets all revolve in circular orbits, with the moon revolving about the earth. Except for the shape of the orbits, this is essentially the modern view. Four centuries later, when Ptolemy (A.D. 150) compiled the *Almagest,* his compendium of Greek astronomical knowledge, the theory of Aristarchus had been abandoned in favor of one that was much more complicated, but which was more consistent with the improved observations that had been made in the meantime as better instruments were devised.

2–3. The Ptolemaic System. In the astronomical system that Ptolemy transmitted, via the Arabs, to Western Europe, two assumptions were fundamental:

NICOLAUS COPERNICUS was born in Poland, the son of a merchant and magistrate. He studied the liberal arts at the University of Cracow, then spent a decade in Italian universities, studying medicine and astronomy as well as taking the doctorate in canon law. During most of his stay in Italy, he was on leave as a canon of Frauenberg Cathedral, not far from Dantzig. The rest of his life was devoted mainly to administrative problems in his diocese, but astronomical work remained a lifelong interest. His principal work on astronomy, *De Revolutionibus Orbium Coelestium,* came from the printer as he lay dying.

In the portrait, the plant that he holds is an allusion to his training and activity as a physician.

Nicolaus Copernicus
(1473–1543)

Mount Wilson and Palomar Observatories

FIGURE 2–A. The motion of Pluto. Photographs made on two successive nights, using the 200-inch telescope at Mount Palomar. Note the position of the planet, designated by the arrow, in relation to the three closest stars.

1. The earth is at rest at the center of the universe.
2. The heavenly bodies move in circles, at constant speed.

The second assumption is based at least in part on the notion that the heavenly bodies are "perfect" and must execute the "perfect" motion, namely uniform motion in a circle. Very probably it was also based on the fact that the circle had been thoroughly investigated by the geometers, its properties were well known, and it was therefore a good tool to work with.

The gist of the Ptolemaic system may be understood by considering the way in which it accounts for two of the chief irregularities in the heavenly motions. In the first place, the sun, moon, and planets, as seen by an observer on the earth, do not appear to move at constant speed against the background of the fixed stars. For example, the sun moves faster in winter than in summer; from the spring equinox (about March 21) to the autumnal equinox (about September 21) is about 186 days, while from the autumnal equinox to the spring equinox is only about 179 days. A body moving at constant speed along a circular path will appear to move faster at some times than at others, provided the observer is not at the center of the circle. It was therefore supposed that the earth is not at the center of the circles along which the uniform motions take place. A circle with center not at the earth was called an *eccentric.* Figure 2–B gives an example.

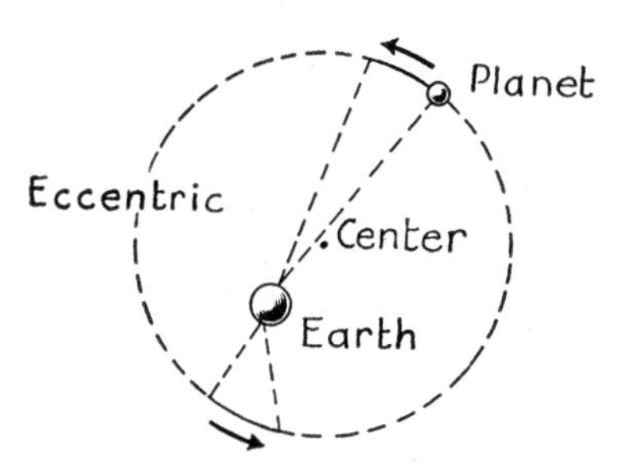

FIGURE 2–B. An eccentric. A planet moving around the dotted circle at constant speed will take the same number of days to traverse each of the arcs marked off with a solid line. To an observer on the earth, however, the planet will move through a larger angle, and will therefore appear to move faster, when it moves through the arc that is closer to the earth.

For the most part, the positions of the planets appear on successive nights to be shifting to the east, as judged against the background of the fixed stars. At some periods, however, a planet will appear to move "backwards"; that is, it will move westward with respect to the fixed stars. To account for these backward motions, called "retrogradations," one can suppose that the planet moves on a small circle, called an *epicycle,* and that the center of this small circle moves around the eccentric circle (Figure 2–C). By invoking epicycles on the epicycles, with proper

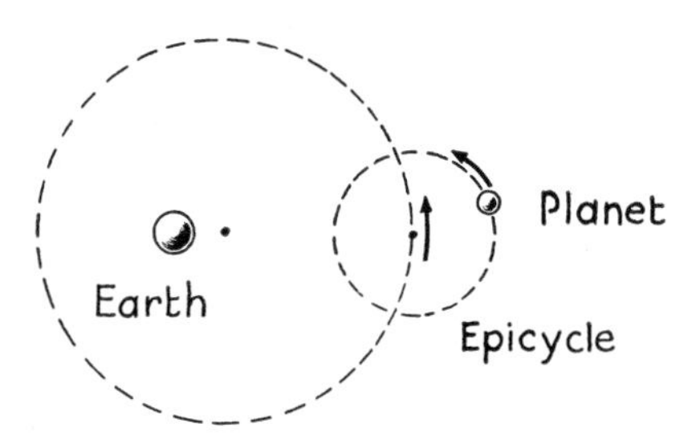

FIGURE 2–C. An epicycle. In the position shown, the planet will appear to be moving "forward"; if its speed around the epicycle is not too slow, then when it has gone halfway around the epicycle, it will appear to be moving "backward."

choice of the radii of the circles and the speeds of revolution, the motions of the planets can be described very accurately. To account for the observed motions, however, Ptolemy had to use some 80 circles.

2–4. Copernicus (A.D. 1510). Copernicus, a churchman who was invited by the Pope to interest himself in a reform of the calendar, revived the hypothesis of Aristarchus, saying that the sun is at rest, the planets, of which the earth is one, revolve about the sun, and the moon revolves about the earth. In order to account for the minor motions that Aristarchus' theory had failed to explain, Copernicus employed eccentrics and epicycles instead of simple circular orbits.

The Copernican system was not inherently more accurate than Ptolemy's; the difference between them was one of simplicity. Copernicus needed only 34 circles to describe the known motions, whereas Ptolemy needed about 80. On the other hand, there were numerous and weighty objections to the Copernican hypotheses. If the earth was whizzing around in an orbit, why did bodies not lag behind when they were thrown into the air? If the earth rotated on its axis once a day, why did loose stones not fly off of it? That the Copernican theory was taken seriously at all, in spite of these objections and the seemingly tremendous theological difficulties, shows the extent to which men's minds had been opened by the geographical, religious, and social upheavals that were going on around them. More important, to one who would understand the nature of science, it shows the premium which is placed on simplicity in a scientific theory. If two theories are equally successful in accounting for the facts, in our age the simpler one quickly wins acceptance. Nevertheless, because of the difficulties mentioned above, the Ptolemaic system died hard. It was still being taught at Harvard when Copernicus had been in his grave a hundred years. The struggle between the two theories was finally decided by the work of Kepler, with which this chapter will close.

2–5. Conic Sections. As shown in Figure 2–D, the intersection of a plane with a cone may have a variety of shapes. Aside from certain trivial cases, there are three possibilities: the ellipse, the parabola, and the hyperbola. These *conic sections* had been studied in detail by the

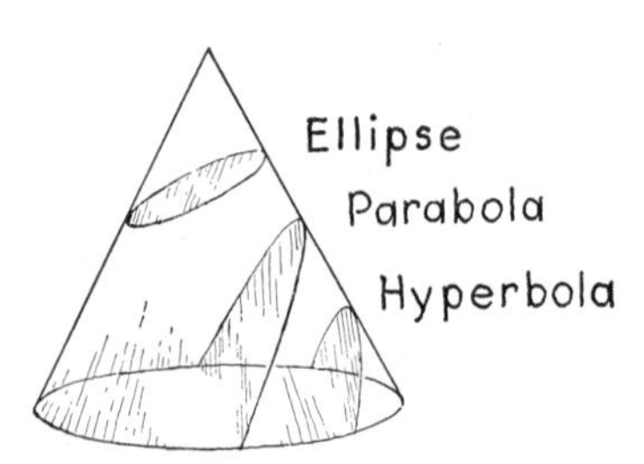

FIGURE 2–D. The intersection of a plane with a cone defines a curve which may be an ellipse, a parabola, or a hyperbola.

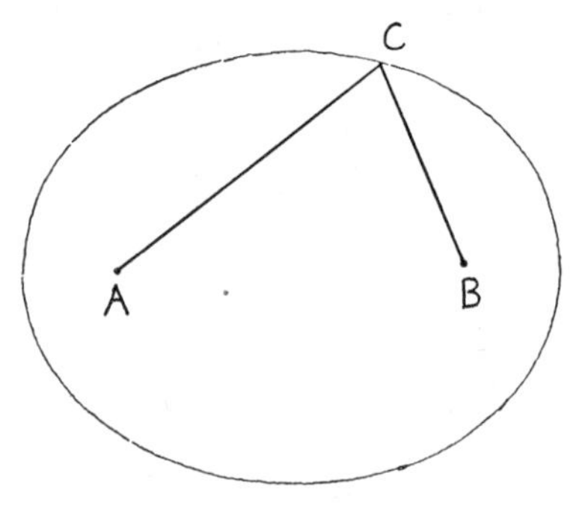

FIGURE 2–E. An ellipse and its foci.

later Greek mathematicians, notably Apollonius (Alexandria, 220 B.C.). His work was translated into Latin about 1550 and, thanks to the printing press, it soon became part of the mathematical equipment of the new scientists. It is instructive to notice how soon they were able to put these mathematical abstractions to use in the study of nature.

The ellipse can be defined without reference to any cone. It is the plane curve such that the sum of the distances from two given points to any point of the curve stays fixed. Each of the two given points is called a *focus*. In Figure 2–E, A and B are the foci, and the curve is traced in such a way that the sum $AC + CB$ does not change. An ellipse can be constructed by fastening a length of thread to tacks at A and B and drawing the thread taut with a pencil point at C. If the pencil is moved, keeping the thread taut, the point will trace an ellipse. Half the length of the thread is called the *mean radius* of the ellipse. If the tacks at A and B are moved closer together, a new ellipse can be drawn; this one will be less elongated than the previous one. The degree of flatness of the ellipse is called its *eccentricity*, a term we shall use when considering the structure of atoms. If A and B are made to coincide, the ellipse degenerates into a circle, which can be considered as an ellipse with no eccentricity.

Shortly after the knowledge of conic sections had been revived, it was found to be the key to the problem of planetary motion.

2–6. The Work of Kepler (A.D. 1610). In the latter half of the sixteenth century, while Elizabeth was Queen of England, a Danish nobleman named Tycho Brahe, working first under the patronage of his own king and then under that of the Holy Roman Emperor, spent his life making improved, and very detailed, observations on the motions of the planets. In Brahe's old age he acquired as assistant a young German named Kepler, whose defective eyesight was offset by his unexampled patience in making calculations. Kepler spent the best part of his life working over Brahe's data, supporting a large family by practicing astrology and working on a new set of navigational tables for the Emperor. Trying first one approach and then another, he sought to modify the Copernican system to make it agree with Brahe's new and refined observations on the motion of Mars. Finally he tried using elliptical orbits instead of circular ones, and it worked! After years of further toil, he announced three laws which describe the planetary motions with great accuracy. They are:

I. Each planet moves around the sun in an ellipse with the sun at one focus.
II. The line joining the planet to the sun sweeps out equal areas in equal times.
III. The square of the time of revolution (the length of the planet's "year") is proportional to the cube of the mean radius of the ellipse.

The first law needs no explanation. It does away with the need for epicycles—only one curve is needed for each planet; 6 ellipses instead of some 30 circles.

The meaning of the second law is clarified by Figure 2–F. It specifies a new kind of regularity for the motions. Suppose the planet takes a week to move from P to Q. At some later time, when the planet is in a part of the orbit farther from the sun, it will take a week to move from P' to Q', where the area $SP'Q'$ is equal to the area SPQ. Therefore the planet moves slower when it is farther from the sun. From the earthdweller's point of view, therefore, the sun will appear to move slower (with respect to the fixed stars) when it is farther from the earth. Kepler's second law takes into account the apparent change in speed of the sun without resorting to the use of an eccentric.

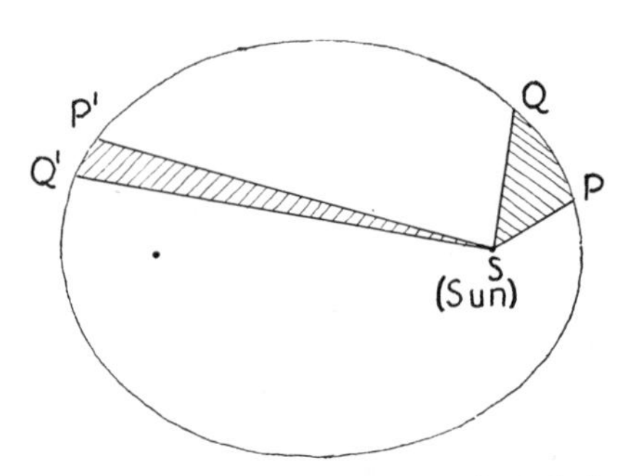

FIGURE 2–F. The meaning of Kepler's second law. The planet takes as long to travel from P' to Q' as from P to Q, the shaded areas being equal.

The third law is perhaps the most magnificent. It says that a certain relationship between the length of the planet's year and its average distance from the sun is the *same for all planets.* This shows that the planets, including the earth, constitute a definite family group—the solar system. It was not certain before this that the planets were actually related to one another in any way.

It is apparent today that after Kepler's discoveries, the world systems of Ptolemy and Copernicus did not stand a chance of survival. Even allowing for the unpleasant squares and cubes in the third law, compare

---

JOHANNES KEPLER, son of a mercenary soldier, studied theology and philosophy at the University of Tübingen, near his home in southern Germany, with the intention of being a Lutheran minister. Not being considered sufficiently orthodox for the church, he had to fall back on his minor studies in mathematics and astronomy, in order to earn a living as a teacher. Religious intolerance soon deprived him of his post, but he became assistant to Tycho Brahe at the court of the Holy Roman Empire in Prague. In 1601 he succeeded Brahe as Imperial Mathematician. The duties were partly astrological; the salary, ample but hardly ever paid.

The first and second of Kepler's famous laws appeared in his *New Astronomy, or the Physics of the Heavens* (1609); the third in *The Harmony of the Universe* (1619). He may be called the first of the modern theoretical physicists, since his great achievement lay in the distillation of general laws from a file of observations that he himself had not made.

JOHANNES KEPLER
(1571–1630)

the marvelous simplicity and unity of Kepler's description with the complexity of the eccentrics and epicycles in the earlier systems. In the history of ideas, the significance of Kepler's work is that it doomed the Ptolemaic system, in which the earth was the center of the universe, and forced man to reconcile himself to a position of less distinction.

In the history of thought, Kepler's work is equally noteworthy. Instead of being misled by the mystical views to which he was even more subject than many of his contemporaries, he patiently examined the facts of observation until he found mathematical relationships that fitted them. This deference to facts was a marked departure from the scholastic tradition.

In the history of physics, the work of Kepler is important because it led Newton to the discovery of the Law of Gravitation, from which sprang the idea that the universe is a machine. Newton also built on the work of Galileo, to which we must now turn.

Summary

Although most celestial bodies appear fixed in the dome of the heavens as it rotates overhead, a few of them wander about in a seemingly irregular way. The ones that look like wandering stars are called planets; the ancients included the sun and moon in this category. Mathematical descriptions of the planetary motions have been sought since the time of Plato. The problem became more complex as improved observations gave more details of the motions. Greek work on the subject culminated in the astronomical treatise of Ptolemy. The earth was taken to be at rest at the center of the universe, and the heavenly bodies, including the planets, were believed to move in circles at constant speed. To account for the apparent irregularities in the motions of the planets, eccentric circles and epicycles were introduced. The Ptolemaic system accounted for all the facts that were then known, but it required the use of about 80 circles.

Centuries before the time of Ptolemy, Aristarchus had put forward the hypothesis that the sun is at rest, and that the planets, of which the earth is one, move in circles about the sun. This system was revived by Copernicus about 1540, in a much more elaborate form that employed epicycles and eccentrics instead of simple circular orbits. This improved heliocentric system described the planetary motions as well as did Ptolemy's geocentric system, and it involved fewer circles. In spite of theological and physical objections to the Copernican hypothesis, it won considerable acceptance because of its relative simplicity.

The very refined planetary observations of Brahe, and the newly diffused knowledge of the Greek work on conic sections, were brought to bear on the planetary problem by Kepler. His work showed that the planets, including the earth, move about the sun in a way that can be described very simply by means of three general laws.

Questions

1. Describe the motion of the fixed stars as seen from Buenos Aires.
2. How can one tell a planet from a star?
3. With binoculars or opera glasses, look at Venus. Contrast the appearance of the planet with that of a bright star. Also compare the appearance of Venus and the moon, and account for the similarity.
4. Venus is often called "the evening star" and "the morning star," because it is always seen near the sun. Using this fact and Kepler's description of planetary motion, prove that the orbit of Venus is smaller than the orbit of the earth.
5. Make a freehand sketch of an ellipse, a parabola, and a hyperbola, all located in the plane of the paper. These curves will be of interest in later chapters.
6. (a) Construct a set of three ellipses, using the same length of thread and varying the separation of the tacks. (Use strong thread about nine inches long, with small loops in the ends.) What do these ellipses have in common? In what do they differ?
   (b) Construct another set of three ellipses, leaving the tacks fixed and varying the length of the thread. What do these ellipses have in common? In what do they differ?
7. What does the apparent motion of the fixed stars tell us about the earth?
8. State two fundamental assumptions of the Ptolemaic theory of planetary motion.
9. Describe how the apparent motion of a planet can be reconciled with Ptolemy's fundamental assumptions.
10. Compare the fundamental assumptions of Copernicus with those of Ptolemy. What is the advantage of Copernicus' theory?
11. Compare the fundamental assumptions of Kepler with those of Ptolemy and with those of Aristarchus.
12. State Kepler's laws and comment on the significance of each one.

Suggestions for Further Reading

A. Armitage, *Sun, Stand Thou Still* (New York: Henry Schuman, Inc., 1947). Also published in a paper binding under the title *The World of Copernicus,* by Mentor Books, 1951. A splendid account of Copernicus' life and work.

H. Butterfield, *The Origins of Modern Science* (London: G. Bell & Sons, Ltd., 1950). Two chapters discuss the intellectual difficulties raised by the Copernican theory and show how they were gradually overcome.

3

GALILEO'S WORK ON MOTION

> Nothing in Nature is more ancient than motion, and the volumes that the philosophers have compiled about it are neither few nor small; yet have I discovered that there are many things of interest about it, that have hitherto been unperceived.
>
> GALILEO, 1636

Modern mechanics was founded early in the seventeenth century by Galileo, who was the first man to make correct quantitative statements about moving bodies. The foundations of his work were laid by his study of how bodies fall under the action of gravity. Aristotle had stated that, other things being equal, the speeds of falling bodies are proportional to their weights. By dropping objects from a height, possibly from the Leaning Tower of Pisa, Galileo satisfied himself that Aristotle's proposition is wrong, since light and heavy bodies fall a given distance in very nearly the same time.* Then he set about finding how falling bodies do move, and he has left us a detailed account of his procedure.

3–1. The Hypothesis. Led, as he says, "by the habit and custom of nature herself . . . to employ only those means which are most common, simple and easy," Galileo framed what he conceived to be the simplest plausible hypothesis about the motion of bodies in free fall. He assumed that *the speed of a falling body is proportional to the time it has been falling*. Then followed perhaps the most important part of his work: he designed a set of experiments to test the hypothesis. Such a procedure is the keystone of the structure of modern science.

3–2. The Theory. It is hard for us to imagine the difficulties that stood in Galileo's way. He was trying to study the speeds of falling bodies, in a day when clocks only had hour hands! Two clever tricks solved the problem. In the first place, he arranged to compare short intervals of time by weighing the water that escaped, during these intervals, from a thin

* Fairly compact bodies were used, so that air resistance had little effect.

jet connected to a reservoir. This enabled him to measure time with almost * the only accurate instrument he possessed, namely, a balance. Secondly, by a set of experiments he convinced himself that a ball rolling down a straight inclined track acquires the same speed no matter how steep the track is, provided the ball always drops through the same vertical distance. In Figure 3–A, balls rolling down *AB* and out onto the level track roll along the level track at the same speed as those that have descended the track *AC*, although of course the ball spends a longer time on *AB* than on the steeper track *AC*. Imagine the track being made successively steeper, as *AD*, and finally becoming vertical. The rule just mentioned will presumably continue to hold, so that the speed acquired in the vertical fall will be the same as the speed acquired, over a longer interval of time, in descending *AB*. From this argument Galileo concluded that a ball rolling down an inclined track has the same kind of motion as a freely falling ball, except that it gains speed more slowly, and was therefore easier to study with the crude means at his disposal. He proceeded to reason out how a ball will behave on rolling down an inclined track; then he studied the actual motion and compared it with his theory.

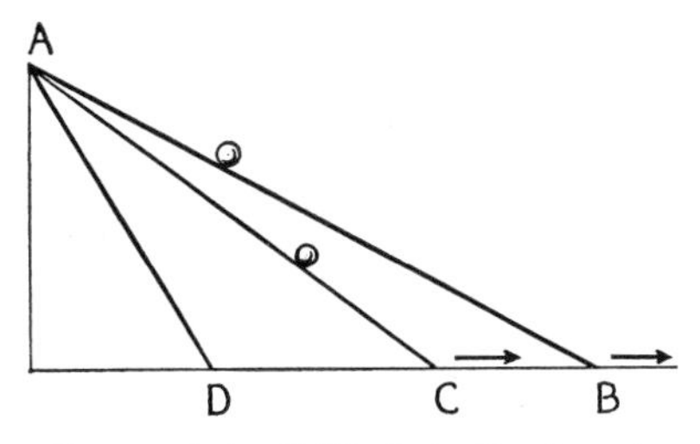

FIGURE 3–A. Galileo's inclined tracks.

It may be as well to mention ahead of time one of Galileo's great conceptual advances: He recognized the importance of *acceleration*, or what the motorist calls "pick-up." It appears in the argument below as a mathematical abstraction called a, but nowadays everyone has an intuitive feeling for it because of experience in vehicles. Notice how completely the algebraic argument is divorced from intuition.

At this point we shall drop the familiar term "speed" and use instead the word "velocity," to begin conforming with scientific usage. The concept of velocity is discussed with care in Chapters 4 and 6. Here it is enough to know that velocity is the rate at which a thing is moving; it can be expressed in miles per hour, feet per second, or any similar units.

Galileo's reasoning can be expressed in modern terms as follows, using the language of algebra for clarity. The hypothesis is that the velocity, v, of the rolling ball is proportional to the time, t, that it has been in motion. The relationship of *proportionality* means that doubling the time will double the velocity, taking a time 3 times as great will give a velocity 3 times as great, and so on. Another way of putting it is that, for any given situation, the quotient of v and t always has the same value. In symbols,

* Of course he also had a scale, or ruler, for measuring lengths.

this relation can be expressed by the equation $v/t = a$, where a is a measure of how fast the velocity is changing; we call a the *acceleration*. Since, by assumption, a is constant,* we say we are dealing with *uniformly accelerated motion*. The equation looks a little better if it is put in the form

$$v = at.$$

This simply means

$$\text{Velocity acquired} = \text{Acceleration} \times \text{Time}.$$

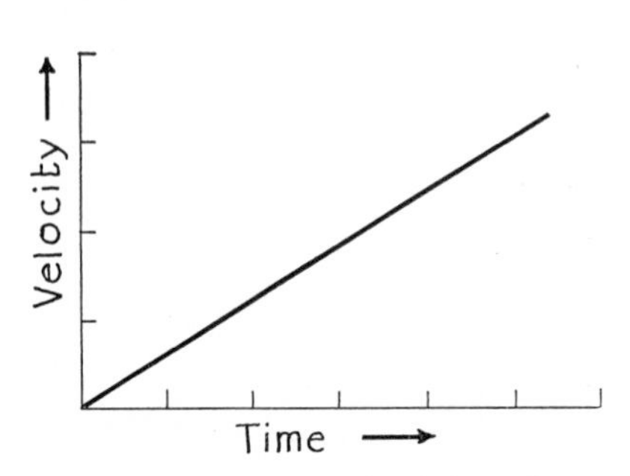

FIGURE 3–B. A graph of the velocity in uniformly accelerated motion. The body is assumed to start from rest.

Students who remember a little algebra will recall that an equation of this form has a graph which is a straight line. A typical case is shown in Figure 3–B.

The velocity of a rolling ball is very hard to measure directly, but it is relatively easy to measure the distance the ball rolls in a given time. Therefore, in order to test his hypothesis, Galileo sought to deduce from it a relationship between the

* A constant is a quantity that does not change.

GALILEO GALILEI, of the same age as Shakespeare, came from an established Florentine family that was more notable for culture than for means. After the usual classical schooling, and a start on the study of medicine, he began to specialize in mathematics and natural science. In his early years as a teacher in Italian universities, he laid much of the foundation for the science of mechanics, and became interested in the proposals of Copernicus. He was the first to study the heavens through a telescope, which he designed and made in 1609. With it, he discovered four moons revolving about Jupiter, thus undermining the Ptolemaic view and certain parts of Aristotelian doctrine, in which the educators, especially the Benedictines and Jesuits, had a vested interest. The resulting controversy was intensified by Galileo's testy temper and his gift for ridicule. In 1632, with the necessary approval from the church officials, he published *Dialogues on the Two Principal Systems of the World*, an argument between a Copernican and a defender of Ptolemy and Aristotle. His enemies raised a clamor against the book. A special papal commission charged Galileo with treating the Copernican view as a truth, rather than as a hypothesis, and with concealing from the censors the fact that he had earlier been forbidden to defend the Copernican opinion. The Inquisition forced him to deny that he believed in the Copernican system as a natural truth, and kept him under house arrest for the remainder of his life; he continued to experiment, and in this period wrote the great *Dialogues on Two New Sciences*, which describes his work on motion.

Galileo Galilei
(1564–1642)

time a ball rolls on a track and the distance it covers. As any traveler knows, the distance covered is equal to the time of travel multiplied by the average velocity.

$$\text{Distance} = \text{Time} \times \text{Average velocity}.$$

(If you fly for 3 hours at an average velocity of 200 miles per hour, you travel 600 miles.) Now in the case of uniform acceleration, the average velocity is easy to find. If the velocity starts at zero and increases uniformly, the average velocity is just half the final velocity.* After any interval, t, the final velocity is $a \times t$, so the average velocity has been $\frac{1}{2}a \times t$.

$$\text{Average velocity} = \tfrac{1}{2} \times \text{Acceleration} \times \text{Time}.$$

But, as we have already noted,

$$\text{Distance} = \text{Time} \times \text{Average velocity}.$$

The first of these equations is valid for any body starting from rest and moving with uniform acceleration, and the second is valid for *any* moving body; therefore we can substitute the first into the second as long as we confine ourselves to uniform acceleration from rest. The result is

$$\text{Distance} = \text{Time} \times (\tfrac{1}{2} \times \text{Acceleration} \times \text{Time}).$$

The distance traveled is usually denoted by s, so in symbols we have

$$s = t \times \tfrac{1}{2}at,$$

or

$$s = \tfrac{1}{2}at^2.$$

This says that s is equal to $a/2$, which is constant, times t^2, or that s is proportional to t^2. We have shown, as Galileo did, that a *uniformly accelerated body, starting from rest, traverses a distance proportional to the square of the time it travels.* The next problem is to find out whether a falling body really travels in this way.

3–3. The Experiment. Galileo had made the hypothesis that a freely falling body is uniformly accelerated, and had argued from experiment that a ball rolling down an inclined straight track moves as a falling body does. Therefore if his hypothesis is correct, a ball rolling down an inclined track will be uniformly accelerated and will, if it starts from rest, travel a distance proportional to the square of the time it rolls.

* If this is not obvious, suppose a ball starts from rest and rolls with uniform acceleration for 4 seconds. At the end of 2 seconds it will have attained half its final velocity. It will be going slower than this for the first 2 seconds, and faster during the last 2 seconds. Moreover, the rate at which the velocity increases is the same in both of the 2-second intervals. Therefore the average velocity is the same as the velocity at the middle of the path, and that is half of the final velocity.

Galileo proceeded to test this consequence of his hypothesis, and found that the distance traversed by the rolling ball actually *is* proportional to the square of the time. We can repeat his experiment, using improved equipment like that in Figure 3–C.

FIGURE 3–C. A modern version of Galileo's rolling-ball experiment. The pendulum, which ticks seconds, actuates an electrical release to start the ball. It also makes a set of lamps flash every second; by positioning each lamp so that one of its flashes is obscured by the rolling ball, the location of the ball at the end of each second can be established.

EXPERIMENT. Let a straight beam, about 12 feet long, be laid on edge and placed with one end on a table and the other end about a foot higher. In the upper surface there should be a V-shaped groove, so that a billiard ball may roll along the beam. The motion of the ball can be timed with a pendulum that ticks seconds loudly. In order to get used to the system as soon as possible, we may as well make measurements in the metric system of units. In this system the unit of time is the familiar second, but the unit of length is the *meter*, which is slightly more than a yard. If the slope of the track is adjusted so that the ball rolls 0.20 meter in the first second, then the other distances turn out as follows:

Time, seconds	1	2	3	4
Distance, meters	0.20	0.80	1.80	3.20
	(0.20 × 1)	(0.20 × 4)	(0.20 × 9)	(0.20 × 16)

By noting the validity of the figures in parentheses, we observe that the experimental results fit the equation $s = 0.20t^2$. Therefore the facts agree with the conclusion, drawn from Galileo's hypothesis, that $s = \frac{1}{2}at^2$. This agreement gives us confidence that his hypothesis is correct, i.e., that a falling body really does move with uniform acceleration.

The experiment will do a little more than simply verify that the ball rolls with constant acceleration—we can actually determine what the acceleration is in this particular case. Combining $s = \frac{1}{2}at^2$, which holds in general, with

$s = 0.20t^2$, which holds in this case, we see that in this case $\frac{1}{2}a = 0.20$, or $a = 0.40$ units of acceleration. (The proper units for expressing acceleration will be discussed in the next chapter.)

3–4. Scientific Method. Galileo's procedure in dealing with falling bodies is a clear-cut example of scientific method.* It can be summarized as follows:

1. *Observation* of the existence of a phenomenon. (Motion.)
2. *Classification* of the various instances of the phenomenon. (Some motions are "falling.")
3. *Invention of a hypothesis* which will provide a simple, and if possible quantitative, description of a class of phenomena. (Falling bodies have constant acceleration, so that $v = at$.) If a science is in an advanced state of development, the simplicity of its hypotheses may be only relative, but each will describe a large class of phenomena. Even in a mature science, the simpler the hypothesis, the more merit it is deemed to have.
4. *Construction of a theory* which brings out the implications of the hypothesis as it applies to an observable aspect of the phenomenon being studied. If possible, the implications of the hypothesis are developed mathematically, to make the theory quantitative. (The distance traversed by a falling body is proportional to the square of the time; $s = \frac{1}{2}at^2$.)
5. *Design of an experiment to test the theory.* (Measurement of the distances traversed in various times by a ball rolling down an inclined track.)

A sixth step can very often be taken: the theory can be used to predict the existence of a previously unobserved phenomenon. If this step is successful, then the theory is regarded as a good one. If, however, the theory makes predictions that are contrary to observed facts, then one of the hypotheses on which it rests must be modified, or abandoned altogether in favor of a new hypothesis. We shall later see many examples of this sixth step, in both its forms.

3–5. Where Does the Hypothesis Come From? "The scientific method sounds very neat," one may say, "but where does the hypothesis come from? Galileo seems to have drawn his out of thin air. How did he know it was correct?" The answer is, of course, that until he had gone through the whole procedure outlined above, he did not know the hypothesis to be correct. He simply had a hunch that it was correct, and he had the correct hunch because he was a genius. Hypotheses are framed by shrewd guessing, not by logic.

Even after forming a theory which turns out to be in accord with experiment, one cannot be *sure* that the theory is based on a correct

* See footnote, p. 8.

hypothesis. There is always a chance that some other hypothesis will lead to the correct conclusion. To reduce this chance as far as possible, one can draw from the hypothesis as many inferences as possible, applying it to different situations. Each inference that can be verified experimentally increases one's confidence in the hypothesis. There is always the possibility that an inference will be contradicted by an experiment. When this happens, the hypothesis is traded in for a new one. *The scientific method is very powerful, not because it is infallible, but because it is self-correcting.* In order to work effectively, the scientist must be free to make an unlimited number of mistakes, and he or his fellow scientists must be skillful enough to recognize the mistakes when they occur.

3–6. The Fruits of Galileo's Work. Having verified his hypothesis about the motion of falling bodies, Galileo extended his theory to cover the case of projectiles. These bodies, for example artillery shells or bombs, are not only rising or falling, but they are also moving horizontally. Galileo showed that as long as air resistance can be neglected, the path of a projectile is a parabola, one of Appollonius' conic sections (Article 2–5) which had recently become familiar as a mathematical abstraction. It is almost impossible now to imagine what a sensational discovery this was, combining as it did the recently discovered higher mathematics of the Greeks, and the very practical business of controlling the fire of artillery.

The main significance of Galileo's work, however, was much more far-reaching. This work on motion, and other work that he performed with his newly invented telescope, flatly contradicted various assertions that Aristotle had made. Anyone who took the trouble could verify by his own observation that Aristotle was wrong and Galileo was right. It is true that at first very few would take the trouble, but the few who were not blinded by prejudice recognized the work of Galileo and Kepler as clear proof that in science, at least, modern men need no longer follow tamely the opinions of the ancients. An English boy born in 1642, the year that Galileo died, soon completed the triumph of modern learning, in a work of such magnificence that the name of Newton stands at the head of any list of the world's greatest scientists. This work will form the subject of the next three chapters.

Summary

Having found that Aristotle's description of falling bodies is incorrect, Galileo adopted what seemed to him the simplest plausible hypothesis about the speed of a falling body. On the hypothesis, he built a theory which asserts that the distance traversed by a body falling from rest will be proportional to the square of the time it falls. Then he devised a set of experiments to see whether the theory gives a correct result, and found that it does. He therefore considered that his hypothesis had been verified.

Galileo's hypothesis is that the velocity of fall is proportional to the time of fall. This relation can be expressed algebraically in the equation $v = at$. For such a motion, the average velocity is midway between the initial velocity (zero) and the final velocity (at). Therefore the average velocity is $\frac{1}{2}at$. Multiplying the average velocity by the time of fall gives the distance the body falls. Calling this distance s, we have $s = \frac{1}{2}at \times t$, or $s = \frac{1}{2}at^2$; that is, the distance fallen is equal to some fixed quantity multiplied by the square of the time of fall.

Galileo's work, and the contemporary work of Kepler, are generally considered to have ushered in the modern age of physical science.

Questions

1. What hypothesis did Galileo make about the speed of a freely falling body?
2. How did Galileo show that the speed of a freely falling body can be studied by experimenting with a ball rolling down an inclined plane?
3. How did Galileo test his hypothesis about falling bodies?
4. If a ball on an inclined track rolls 1 foot in the first second after it starts from rest, how far will it have rolled at the end of 2 seconds? How far at the end of 5 seconds?
5. If a stone is dropped from rest, it falls approximately 16 feet in the first second. What is its acceleration? How far would the stone fall in 2 seconds?
6. A stone dropped from the roadway of the Golden Gate bridge is seen to hit the water 3.5 seconds later. Using the acceleration calculated in Problem 5, find the height of the roadway. How fast would the stone be going when it hit the water? (Neglect air resistance, which actually would have a detectable effect in this case.)
7. The text divides the typical procedure of physical science into six steps. Which of these steps do you think is the easiest? Which the hardest? Justify your answers.
8. What was the principal result of Galileo's work on falling bodies?

Suggestion for Further Reading

Galileo Galilei, *Dialogues Concerning Two New Sciences* (New York: Dover Publications, Inc., 1952). The dialogue of the Third Day is Galileo's story of his work on uniformly accelerated motion.

4

DESCRIBING MOTION

> The whole burden of philosophy seems to consist in this—from the phenomena of motions to investigate the forces of nature, and then from these forces to explain the other phenomena.
>
> NEWTON, 1686

Since the work of Newton, the material universe has been regarded as a kind of machine, and as many phenomena as possible have been treated in mechanical terms. Until the end of the nineteenth century, physical scientists of all kinds considered a phenomenon to be understood if, and only if, it had been explained in terms of mechanics. Mechanical ideas therefore play a most important part in atomic science. Since mechanics is essentially the study of motion,* motion and its allied concepts must be looked into rather carefully before we go further.

4–1. Position. The position of any point can be described by specifying its distance and direction from some other point. Distance is expressed in terms of some arbitrarily chosen standard. In most civilized countries, the standard that is used is the *meter,* which is the distance between two scratches on a certain bar of durable metal kept in a vault near Paris, when the bar is at the temperature of melting ice. The United States, among other countries, keeps a secondary standard that has been carefully compared with the international standard meter bar. Our bar, kept and used by the National Bureau of Standards, appears in Figure 4–A.

For commercial purposes in the United States, distances are measured in inches or multiples thereof, the inch being legally defined such that there are exactly 39.37 inches in a meter. For scientific purposes, it is convenient to ignore the commercial units and use the meter, because it is international. As a rule we shall follow the scientific usage, but in situ-

* Even the designer of bridges is interested in motion. He wants to insure that the bridge will *not* fall.

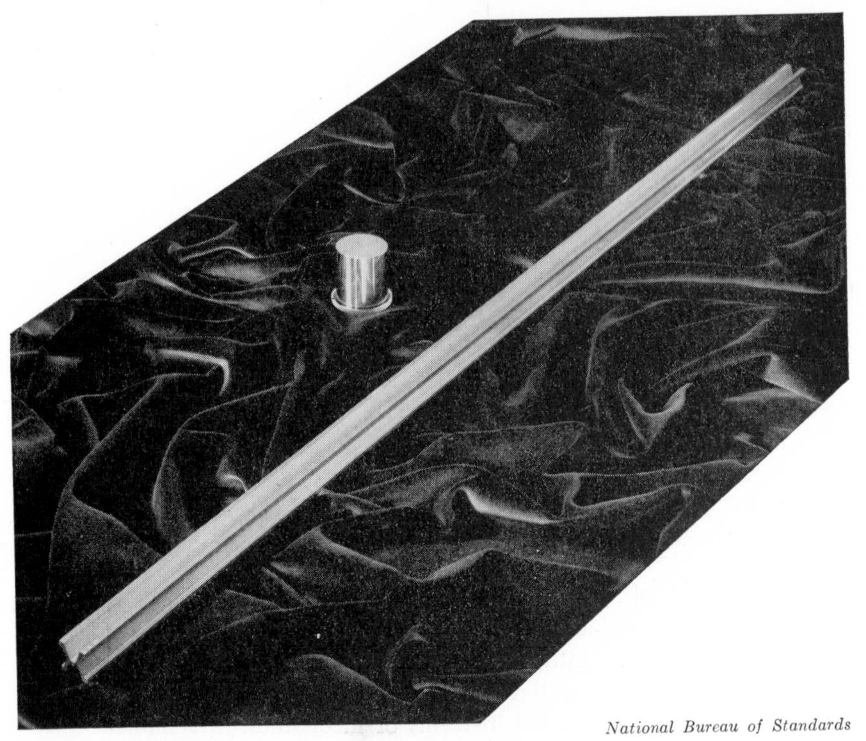

National Bureau of Standards

FIGURE 4–A. The United States standard meter bar and kilogram. Both are made of an alloy, 90 percent platinum and 10 percent iridium.

ations used purely for illustrative purposes we shall often use everyday units like the foot and the mile. Note that a meter (39.37 inches) is just slightly longer than a yard (36 inches).

4–2. Time. Any person's intuitive idea of what time is will suffice for the purposes of this discourse. The unit of time used in scientific work is the *second*, which is $1/86{,}400$ of the average interval between successive noons. (Instead of trying to put a unit of time in a vault, we use the spinning earth as a clock.)

4–3. Velocity. Motion is change of position. A commonplace but important aspect of motion is *velocity*, or rate of motion. By definition, velocity is the rate of change of position. By "rate of change" of some quantity, we mean the *change* that occurs, *divided by the time* during which the change takes place. Therefore,

$$\text{Velocity} = \frac{\text{Change in position}}{\text{Time}}.$$

In symbols,

$$v = \frac{s}{t}.$$

If you travel 100 miles in 2 hours, on a straight highway in Nebraska, your velocity along the road is 50 miles per hour. Of course if you stop for gas or dawdle a while to look at the scenery, the 50 mi/hr will only be your *average velocity*. Your velocity at any instant can be closely approximated by finding how far you move in a sufficiently short time interval, say 1 second, and dividing by that time interval, instead of using a long one like the 2 hours.

EXAMPLE. Find the average velocity of a body that moves 240 meters in 8 seconds.

$$v = \frac{s}{t} = \frac{240 \text{ m}}{8 \text{ sec}} = 30 \frac{\text{m}}{\text{sec}}.$$

Note that in order to specify the velocity we have to tell what unit it is measured in, which depends on what units of distance and time we are using.

4-4. Acceleration. Velocity is the rate at which position changes with time, and, as implied above, velocity itself often changes as time goes on. A train starting off from a station offers a familiar example. As we shall see, the rate at which velocity changes is one of the most important attributes of a motion. It is therefore given a name, acceleration. Already, in considering Galileo's work, we have used the concept of acceleration without pausing for the formal definition: *Acceleration is the rate at which velocity changes with time.* This means that the acceleration is computed as follows:

$$\text{Acceleration} = \frac{\text{Change in velocity}}{\text{Time during which the change occurs}},$$

$$= \frac{\text{Final velocity} - \text{Initial velocity}}{\text{Time during which the change occurs}}.$$

It is customary to represent the initial velocity by the symbol v_0; the last equation can then be written

$$a = \frac{v - v_0}{t}.$$

If the acceleration is not constant, then the time interval used in the calculation should be small.

EXAMPLES. If a train starts from rest and gains velocity steadily for 3 minutes, until it is going 60 mi/hr, then its acceleration has been

$$a = \frac{60 \text{ mi/hr} - 0 \text{ mi/hr}}{3 \text{ minutes}} = 20 \text{ mi/hr/min}.$$

If the train later slows down uniformly from 60 mi/hr to 40 mi/hr in 2 minutes, its acceleration is

$$a = \frac{40 \text{ mi/hr} - 60 \text{ mi/hr}}{2 \text{ minutes}} = -10 \text{ mi/hr/min}.$$

Verify for yourself that a negative acceleration indicates a slowing down. Negative acceleration is often called "deceleration."

If the velocity of a body is constant, the body clearly has no acceleration. The ball on our inclined track had a velocity that increased at a constant rate; the velocity was proportional to the time. In this case the acceleration was constant. When the velocity is constant, the motion is called *uniform motion,* but when the acceleration is constant the motion is called *uniformly accelerated motion.* Of course there are many motions in which the acceleration changes with time, but fortunately no detailed discussion of these motions will be necessary for our study.

4–5. Newton's First Law of Motion. By returning to the ball rolling down a straight track, we can very easily probe further into the nature of motion.

EXPERIMENT. To the inclined track discussed previously (Figure 3–C), a level track is attached in such a way that the ball can roll down the incline and then take off on the level track at the end of 1, 2, 3, or 4 seconds (Figure 4–B).

FIGURE 4–B. An illustration of Newton's First Law of Motion. If the ball rolls out on a horizontal track after traveling down the incline, it rolls a certain distance along the horizontal in one second, and again the same distance in the next second. On the horizontal track, it has no observable acceleration.

The level track is marked off in meters. If the ball rolls out on the level track after 2 seconds of rolling down the incline, it rolls 0.80 meter during its first second on the level track, and another 0.80 meter during the second second. As nearly as one can judge from this rather crude experiment, the ball rolls on the level track at *constant velocity.*

By experiments of this sort, Galileo discovered that a ball on a level track is in very nearly uniform motion. He imagined that if the track and the air exerted no retarding force on the ball, the motion of the ball would actually be perfectly uniform.

In 1686 Newton published his great work on mechanics, *Mathematical Principles of Natural Philosophy.* Guided by the work of Galileo, who had reached the same conclusion, Newton generalized beyond all experience to enunciate his First Law of Motion: *Every body continues in its state of rest, or of motion at constant speed in a straight line, unless it is compelled to change that state by a force acting on it.*

A more concise statement of the law is: *The velocity of a body does not change unless a force acts on the body.*

A still more condensed version is: *A body accelerates only when a force acts on it.*

Notice that the new terms, velocity and acceleration, which we have defined, enable us to state very neatly a rather complicated idea.

The law states two propositions. The first is easy to believe: If a body is at rest, then it will stay at rest unless a force acts on it to set it in motion. The second proposition is harder to believe: If a body in motion is free from the action of any force, then the body will move forever in a straight line without slowing down. Obviously, no one has ever observed an example of this sort of motion. The law goes beyond experience; whether it is true or not can only be judged by drawing conclusions from it and seeing whether they are justified by experimental evidence. We know that any body that is set sliding on a level surface eventually stops. We also know, however, that by making the surface smoother and smoother, we can make the body slide farther and farther.* We therefore come to believe that the surface does exert on the body a force, called the force of friction. We believe that if this force could be eliminated, then the body would not stop. The law is therefore more plausible than it might seem at first sight.

4–6. Mass. We know that some moving bodies, like baseballs, are easily set in motion and easily stopped. Others, for example freight trains, are hard to start or stop. The tendency of a body to resist change in its state of motion is called *inertia.* The quantitative measure of inertia is called *mass.* We can measure the mass of a body by comparing its inertia with that of some standard body.†

The body that is chosen for the standard is a lump of metal called the *kilogram,* which is kept in the vault along with the meter. For use in the United States, the National Bureau of Standards keeps the platinum-iridium cylinder that is on exhibit in Figure 4–A. This cylinder has almost

* On a level sheet of plate glass, an 8-inch cube of "dry ice" will slide several feet without any visible deceleration.

† In practice, direct measurements of this kind are not easy to make. Mass is commonly measured by some indirect method, notably those described in Chapter 8.

exactly the same mass as the international kilogram, with which it has been painstakingly compared.

If a body has twice as much inertia as the kilogram, we say that it has a mass of 2 kilograms. The word "kilogram" is therefore used in two senses; it can refer to a certain piece of metal or to a unit of mass. Later this confusing situation will be further confounded by a third use of the word.

The mass of this book is a little more than 1 kilogram.

Summary

It will be convenient for us to measure length in meters and time in seconds.

Velocity is the rate of change of position, and acceleration is the rate of change of velocity.

Motion at constant velocity is called uniform, while motion with constant acceleration (velocity growing or declining steadily) is called uniformly accelerated.

Newton's First Law of Motion asserts that a body accelerates when, and only when, a force acts on it.

Inertia is the tendency of a body to resist acceleration. The quantitative measure of inertia is called mass. A commonly used unit of mass is the kilogram, which is the mass of a certain lump of metal which is also called the kilogram.

Questions

1. Distinguish between velocity and acceleration.
2. By reference to the definitions, show that uniform motion is really just a special case of uniformly accelerated motion. (What is the acceleration when a motion is uniform?)
3. A stone dropped from rest will fall 4.9 meters in the first second. What is its acceleration, expressed in meters and seconds? (Use Galileo's formula, Article 3–2.) How far will the stone fall in 2 seconds?
4. Aristotle taught that a body in motion will come to rest unless a force keeps it moving. Newton teaches that a body in motion will continue to move uniformly unless a force acts to change the motion. Can you defend the assertion that Aristotle's proposition is based on experience, while Newton's is based on speculation? Why do we believe Newton's proposition rather than Aristotle's?

5

NEWTON'S SECOND LAW OF MOTION

Nature is pleased with simplicity.
NEWTON

The last chapter made a beginning on the scientific treatment of motion. In addition to defining concepts that are needed in the description of motion, it set forth the first of Newton's Laws of Motion. This law states a relationship between force and motion: a motion is *changed* only by force. The main business of this chapter is Newton's Second Law, which tells *how much* force is required to produce a given change in motion.

5–1. Force. The concept of force has already appeared in the statement of Newton's First Law. A careful and rigorous definition of force can be set up, but to do so would for our purposes be more difficult than profitable. It is sometimes said that a force is a push or a pull, although no logician would agree that this constitutes a real definition. A more satisfactory approach is the use of Newton's First Law as a definition of force: a force is that which causes acceleration. It will be best for us to save our logic for other problems where intuition is a less adequate guide. We shall assume that we know what a force is, just as one assumes in geometry that everybody knows what a point is.

One familiar example of a force is a *weight.* When you stand on a floor or on a set of scales, you press down on the floor or the scales with a force equal to your weight. The weight of any body is *the force exerted on it by the earth,* urging it "downward," i.e., toward the center of the earth. If your weight is not counteracted by some other force, like the upward push of the floor, you are accelerated downward.

5–2. Momentum. We have already remarked, in discussing mass, that a baseball is more easily stopped than a freight train. We also know that a freight train is more easily stopped if it is moving slowly than if it is moving fast. Considerations such as these led Newton to the concept of what we now call *momentum.* The momentum of a body is (by definition) simply the product of its mass and its velocity.

$$\text{Momentum} = \text{Mass} \times \text{Velocity}.$$

If a body has a mass of 2 kilograms and a velocity of 6 m/sec, it has a momentum of 12 kg m/sec.

5–3. Newton's Second Law of Motion. Newton's First Law says that if no force acts on a body, then the body will have no acceleration. The Second Law tells what happens to a body when a force does act on it. The law states that, if force is measured in units of the proper size, then *the rate of change of momentum is equal to the force.*

Using the definitions of momentum, rate of change, and acceleration, the Second Law can be put into a different and sometimes more convenient form by the following chain of reasoning:

$$\begin{aligned}
\text{Force} &= \text{Rate of change of momentum} \\
&= \frac{\text{Change in momentum}}{\text{Time during which the change occurs}} \\
&= \frac{\text{Final momentum} - \text{Initial momentum}}{\text{Time during which the change occurs}} \\
&= \frac{(\text{Mass} \times \text{Final velocity}) - (\text{Mass} \times \text{Initial velocity})}{\text{Time during which the change occurs}} \\
&= \text{Mass} \times \frac{\text{Final velocity} - \text{Initial velocity}}{\text{Time during which the change occurs}} \\
&= \text{Mass} \times \text{Acceleration}.
\end{aligned}$$

ISAAC NEWTON was born on a small English manor at the start of England's Civil War. Having shown a strong taste for mechanisms and mathematics, but none at all for farming, he prepared for the university and entered Cambridge at 19, staying on as fellow and professor. Before he was 25, he had invented the calculus, made optical discoveries of the first importance, and discovered his famous Law of Gravitation. In a second burst of scientific activity, when he was about 40, he wrote his great treatise *Philosophiae Naturalis Principia Mathematica,* which sets forth his four major laws and uses them to account for the motions in the solar system.

Besides being one of the great mathematicians of all time, Newton was an ardent and skillful experimenter, working especially in optics and chemistry, including alchemy. His scientific achievements brought him fame, honors, and a lucrative office as Master of the Mint. He spent at least as much time on theology and biblical scholarship as on his scientific researches. In fact, he seems to have regarded science as little more than an amusement, of value only as a support to religion and an aid to navigation.

Engraved from a painting by Sir Godfrey Kneller

SIR ISAAC NEWTON
(1642–1727)

In short, Newton's Second Law can be stated in the alternative form

$$\text{Force} = \text{Mass} \times \text{Acceleration},$$

which is usually abbreviated with symbols to

$$F = ma,$$

a form that is easy to remember. Both ways of expressing the law will be useful to us.

5–4. Units for Acceleration. In the example in Article 4–4, a train was found to have an acceleration of 20 mi/hr/min. Since 20 mi/hr is the same as $\frac{1}{3}$ mi/min, the acceleration could have been written $\frac{1}{3}$ mi/min/min, which can be abbreviated $\frac{1}{3}$ mi/min^2. The minutes appear twice in the denominator because they occur in the velocity and they occur again when one calculates *how fast* the velocity is changing. Miles and minutes were used in the example because they are familiar units of length and time, but it will be appropriate now to start using the standard scientific units, meters and seconds. The unit of acceleration is of course meters/second/second, or m/sec^2. Using this unit, we can proceed to a sample calculation involving Newton's Second Law.

5–5. Illustrative Example. What force will give 70 kilograms an acceleration of 4 m/sec/sec?

$$\begin{aligned} F &= m \times a \\ &= 70 \text{ kg} \times 4 \text{ m/sec}^2 \\ &= 280 \frac{\text{kg m}}{\text{sec}^2}. \end{aligned}$$

5–6. The Newton, a Unit of Force. In the foregoing example, the answer is expressed in units that you may find quite meaningless, even though it is clear that they are correct. Just as multiplying feet by feet gives square feet, or ft^2, so multiplying kg by m/sec^2 must give kg m/sec^2. This situation illustrates something that is true for all physical equations: The units in which the quantities are expressed are to be multiplied or divided just like numbers.

Beginners in science often underestimate the importance and usefulness of the units in a quantitative statement. To say "the area is 6" is to say nothing; one must say whether the area is 6 ft^2, or 6 acres, or 6 mi^2, or 6 yd^2. If someone says "the area is 6 yards," you know he has made a mistake, because an area cannot be measured in yards. Hence the unit is actually more important than the number, because the unit alone tells what kind of quantity is being described, but the number alone tells nothing.

The unit kg m/sec² is the unit that must be used in order for $F = ma$ to be a correct equation when meters, kilograms, and seconds are used as units of length, mass, and time. For this reason, the unit is used so much that it has been given a name of its own: it is called the *newton.**

$$1 \text{ newton} \equiv 1 \text{ kg m/sec}^2.$$

A newton is the force that gives one kilogram an acceleration of one m/sec². It is about a quarter as large as the familiar commercial unit of force, the pound; in other words, a quarter pound of butter weighs about one newton.

Since a college sprinter might have a mass of 70 kilograms, and might have an acceleration of 4 m/sec² early in a 100-meter dash, the example in the last article shows that the force then accelerating him would be about 280 newtons.

5–7. Demonstrations of Newton's Laws. The various implications of Newton's Second Law can be illustrated, and also verified, by a simple set of experiments. Since the distance available for vertical motion indoors is likely to be limited to a couple of meters, measuring distances in meters would bring in decimal fractions that might becloud the issue. Therefore it will be expedient to measure distances in subsidiary units called "centimeters," there being 100 centimeters in a meter. (This is like using inches instead of feet.) For added convenience, time can be measured not in seconds but in ticks of a metronome adjusted so that the experiments give numerically simple results.

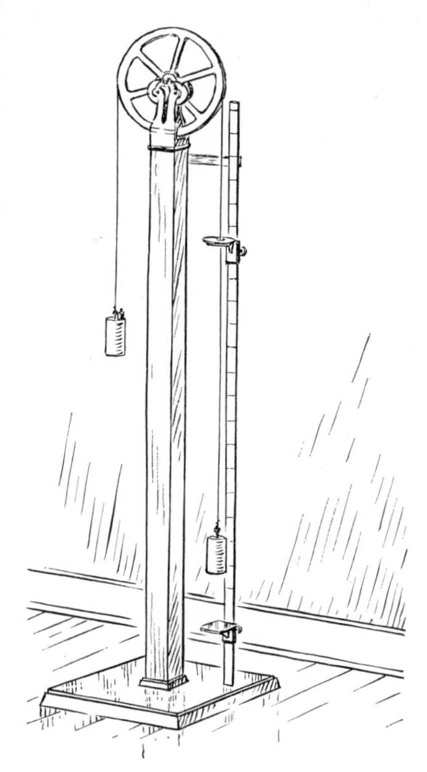

FIGURE 5–A. A device for making experiments on motion.

EXPERIMENTS. Identical metal cylinders, of known mass, hang on the ends of a string passed over a pulley which is carefully designed so as to be nearly frictionless (Figure 5–A). One cylinder starts from rest on a platform, and

* The situation is much the same as in navigation, where the common unit of velocity, a nautical mile per hour, is called a *knot.*

rises until it clicks against an adjustable bumper. The time interval during which the cylinder is in motion can be measured by the ticks of a metronome, and the distance covered can be measured with a scale calibrated in centimeters.

1. *Illustration of Newton's First Law.* A half-kilogram cylinder hangs on each end of the string. The cylinders are in balance and the friction in the pulley is very small, so the net force on each cylinder is very nearly zero. If set in motion, each cylinder moves very nearly uniformly until it strikes an obstacle. This motion very nearly demonstrates Newton's First Law.

2. *A Constant Force Produces Constant Acceleration.* A small weight * is placed on one of the cylinders, producing an unbalance. This unbalance causes an accelerated motion. Even though it is not free fall, the motion is related to falling, and we may suspect that it is uniformly accelerated, i.e., that the acceleration is constant. To see whether this is so, we can use Galileo's formula, $s = \frac{1}{2}at^2$, and see whether it fits the facts.

The metronome is adjusted so that each cylinder, starting from rest, travels 100 cm in 5 ticks. If it is true that

$$s = \tfrac{1}{2}at^2,$$

then

$$100 \text{ cm} = \frac{1}{2}\, a \times (5 \text{ ticks})^2$$

or

$$200 \text{ cm} = a \times 25 \text{ ticks}^2$$

whence

$$a = 8\,\frac{\text{cm}}{\text{tick}^2} \quad \text{or} \quad 8\,\frac{\text{cm}}{\text{tick}} \text{ per tick.}$$

The calculation shows that if the acceleration is constant, then its value is 8 cm/tick². Using this figure, we can calculate how far the cylinder will move in 6 ticks, starting from rest.

$$\begin{aligned} s &= \frac{1}{2}at^2 \\ &= \frac{1}{2} \times 8\,\frac{\text{cm}}{\text{tick}^2} \times (6 \text{ ticks})^2 \\ &= 4\,\frac{\text{cm}}{\text{tick}^2} \times 36 \text{ tick}^2 \\ &= 144 \text{ cm.} \end{aligned}$$

An experimental test shows that the cylinder actually does travel 144 cm in 6 ticks. Since Galileo's formula correctly predicts the distance traveled, we are justified in believing that the acceleration actually does have a constant value. We therefore conclude that *motion under constant force is uniformly accelerated.* Thus one aspect of Newton's equation $F = ma$ is verified.

3. *Doubling the Force Doubles the Acceleration.* To the little weight that produces the unbalancing force, add another just like it. The cylinder will now fall inconveniently far in 5 ticks, perhaps as far as the length of string will permit. Measuring the distance traveled in 4 ticks will do just as well, and it turns

* About a tenth of a newton works well.

out to be 128 cm. Application of Galileo's formula will show that the acceleration is now 16 cm/tick^2. *Doubling the force has doubled the acceleration.* This too is in accord with Newton's equation $F = ma$, which says the acceleration is proportional to the force.

4. *Doubling the Mass Halves the Acceleration.* Finally we examine the effect of using a cylinder with different mass. Of course, if one cylinder is changed then the other has to be changed too, so that their weights will cancel one another and only the little unbalancing weight acts to produce acceleration. Using one-kilogram cylinders instead of half-kilogram ones, we find that a single unbalancing weight produces a movement of 128 cm in 8 ticks. Application of Galileo's formula shows that the acceleration is now only 4 cm/tick^2, as compared with 8 cm/tick^2 when the same unbalancing weight was used with the half-kilogram cylinders. Therefore, *doubling the mass has halved the acceleration.* This verifies the remaining implication of Newton's equation, $F = ma$; namely that if the force stays the same, then the product of mass and acceleration is constant.

5-8. Remarks on the Experimental Method. In the set of experiments just discussed, each implication of Newton's Second Law was tested by a single trial. Of course one trial does not establish a law; in testing a new law the working scientist makes as many trials as possible, under varying conditions. No matter how many trials he makes, however, he labors under a difficulty that is nicely illustrated by our interpretation of Experiment 2. There, the reasoning was as follows:

> If the motion is uniformly accelerated, then Galileo's formula holds. Observation shows that Galileo's formula holds. Therefore the motion is uniformly accelerated.

The critical student will see a distressing similarity between this argument and the following one:

> If an animal is a lion, then it has a long tail. Observation shows that this animal has a long tail. Therefore this animal is a lion.

For all the experiment has told us, there may be motions-obeying-Galileo's-formula that are not uniformly accelerated, just as there are animals-having-long-tails that are not lions. The reasoning about the motion, a kind of argument often needed in science,* actually does have the same form as the reasoning about the animal. The scientist recognizes, of course, that his conclusion may have to be revised when more data are available. Successful scientific reasoning requires judgment and experience, and at best its conclusions are never absolutely reliable. These limitations are inevitable, because the business of a scientist is to draw very general conclusions from a small number of special experiences.

* The argument about the motion is untypical in one respect. It happens that a mathematician can prove that *only* uniformly accelerated motions can obey Galileo's formula. Such reassurance, from outside the experiment, is often not available.

Summary

An important property of a moving body is its momentum, which is defined by the equation

$$\text{Momentum} = \text{Mass} \times \text{Velocity}.$$

Newton's Second Law states that, if force is measured in units of the proper size, then

$$\text{Force} = \text{Rate of change of momentum}.$$

Alternatively, the law can be stated in the form

$$\text{Force} = \text{Mass} \times \text{Acceleration},$$

which is usually abbreviated to

$$F = ma.$$

In the system of units we are using, these equations hold when force is measured in kg m/sec^2, these units being called newtons. (Compare with nautical terminology, in which mi/hr are called knots.)

The implications of Newton's First and Second Laws can be illustrated by using a small unbalancing weight to accelerate a pair of cylinders suspended from a string running over a pulley. In particular, the following facts can be verified:

1. A moving body free from the action of unbalanced forces has no acceleration; its velocity is constant.
2. A body moving under constant force has constant acceleration, i.e., it is uniformly accelerated.
3. The acceleration of a body is proportional to the force applied to it.
4. If equal forces act on two different bodies, the bodies have accelerations that are inversely proportional to their masses. That is, doubling the mass will halve the acceleration, if the force stays the same.

Questions

1. What is the weight of a body?
2. What is momentum?
3. A sprinter has a mass of 70 kg and a velocity of 9 m/sec. What is his momentum? How does the sprinter's momentum compare with that of a 0.012-kg rifle bullet traveling at 700 m/sec?
4. State Newton's Second Law in terms of momentum, and again in terms of acceleration.
5. The text states that $\frac{1}{3}$ mi/min/min can be abbreviated $\frac{1}{3}$ mi/min^2. To show that the abbreviation is a sensible one, suppose that a velocity

changes by $\frac{1}{3}$ mi/min in 1 min. Applying the definition of acceleration and the ordinary arithmetical laws for working with fractions, show that the acceleration comes out in mi/min^2.

6. If you had trouble with the units of acceleration in the problems about falling stones in Chapters 3 and 4, review those problems now.
7. In Article 5–7 Galileo's formula is invoked in Experiment 4, but the details of the calculation are omitted. Work out the calculations to show that the acceleration is 4 cm/tick^2.

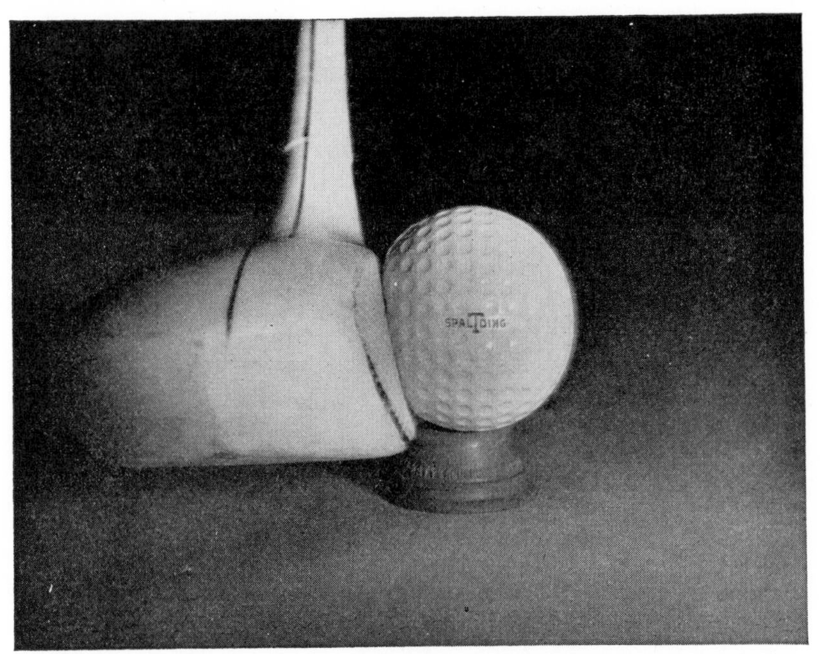

H. E. Edgerton, Massachusetts Institute of Technology

FIGURE 5–B. Imparting momentum to a golf ball.

8. Suppose two unbalancing weights were used instead of one in Experiment 4 of Article 5–7. What would the acceleration of the cylinders be? How far would they move in 5 ticks? Compare this situation with that in Experiment 1.
9. In Experiment 3, each cylinder started from rest and moved 128 cm in 4 ticks.
   (a) Find the average velocity of the cylinder.
   (b) Find the final velocity of the cylinder. (Use the answer to (a) and remember that the motion is uniformly accelerated.)
   (c) Find the acceleration of the cylinder, using the answer to (b).
   (d) Find the acceleration of the cylinder by using Galileo's formula.
10. What is a newton? What common object weighs about 1 newton?

11. The mass of a golf ball is 0.046 kg. When driven by a good player, as in Figure 5–B, it acquires a velocity of about 75 m/sec.
    (a) Find the momentum of the ball just after the impact.
    (b) The club is in contact with the ball for about a half of a thousandth of a second. What is the average force the club exerts on the ball?
    (c) What is the average acceleration of the ball?

6

VECTOR QUANTITIES

Nature and Nature's laws lay hid in night;
God said, *Let Newton be!* and all was light.
ALEXANDER POPE

The motions discussed in the last two chapters have been motions along some straight path. Much of our knowledge about atoms has come from experiments in which atoms or parts of atoms move along paths that are jagged or curved. Of particular importance in some of these experiments is motion along a circular path. It is therefore necessary for us to learn to deal with motions that change in direction.

6–1. Scalar Quantities. The amount of gasoline that a tank holds can be completely specified by a number and a statement about the unit of measure being used. If you know that a tank holds 17 gallons, then you know all there is to know about the volume of the tank. Similarly, a statement like "the temperature is 38 degrees Fahrenheit" gives complete information about a temperature. Quantities that can be specified completely by means of a number and a unit of measure are called *scalar quantities.* You already know all about them, although you may be just beginning to appreciate the importance of stating the unit of measure.

6–2. Vector Quantities. Motion involves *change of position,* which is often called *displacement.* A displacement cannot be specified by simply telling how big it is. A displacement of one block west may put you in a drug store, whereas a displacement of one block south might put you at a gas station. To specify a displacement, one must specify its *magnitude* and also its *direction*: 1 mile east, 2 feet upward, or the like. Quantities that have to be specified by a magnitude and a direction are called *vector quantities.*

Displacement has been used as an example because it is so easy to visualize, but there are many other important vector quantities. Walking east at 3 miles per hour certainly does not have the same effect as walking south at 3 miles per hour; velocity is therefore a vector quantity. Acceleration, which is the rate of change of velocity, is also a vector quantity. Force is another.

6–3. Vector Diagrams. A *vector* is a diagrammatic device for reckoning with vector quantities. It is a line segment whose length represents, on some suitably chosen scale, the magnitude of the vector quantity, and whose direction, as indicated by an arrowhead and the orientation of the line, represents the direction of the vector quantity. This device is useful because vector quantities must be added like displacements, not like numbers.

FIGURE 6–A. Adding vectors. C is the sum of A and B.

Let A and B in Figure 6–A represent displacements. If a body experiences a displacement A, and then another displacement B, the result is the same as if the body experienced the single displacement C. We call C "the vector sum of A and B," because C is the equivalent of A and B taken together. If we have vectors of magnitude 3 and 4, we can see as in Figure 6–B that their sum can have a magnitude equal to 5 (by the

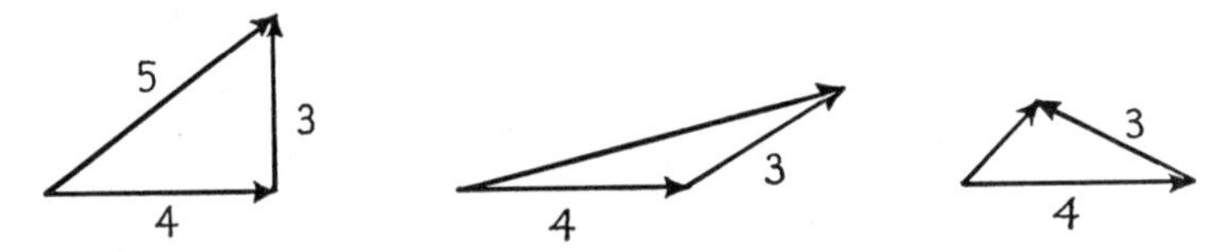

FIGURE 6–B. The sum of two vectors depends on their relative directions.

Pythagorean theorem), or greater than 5, or less than 5. Do you see that the magnitude of this sum can be anything between 1 and 7, depending on the angle between the vectors?

6–4. Uniform Circular Motion. The use of vector diagrams in connection with displacement is so obvious as to be almost trivial. The diagrams work equally well, however, for adding *any kind* of vector quantity. By way of illustration we shall consider the velocity and acceleration of a body moving uniformly around a circular path. Not only will this example complete the discussion of velocity and acceleration that was begun in Chapter 4, but also it will give information which is of prime importance in the study of planetary motion and of atomic affairs.

Suppose a point is moving around a circular path in such a way that the distance it travels along the path in 1 second is the same at one time as it is at any other time. Then the point is said to be in *uniform circular motion.* (The tip of a hand on an electric clock is in uniform circular motion.) The magnitude of the point's velocity does not change, but the direction of the motion is always changing. Therefore, as will be shown in detail in the next paragraph, the velocity of the point is always changing, which means that the point always has an acceleration. In order to apply Newton's Second Law to circular motion, as we shall need to do on several occasions, we must know about the acceleration in such motions. The remainder of this article will show that the acceleration depends in a very simple way on how big the circle is and on how fast the point is moving along the circumference.

The position of a point on a circle can be specified by stating the displacement of the point from some reference position. Any reference position will do; it will be convenient to use the center of the circle. In Figure 6–C, the position vector of the point at some instant will be S and at a later instant it will be S'. The displacement that occurs during the interval is s, and in the vector sense $S + s = S'$. Taking s and dividing it by the time interval gives the average velocity of the point during the time interval. Now clearly the orientation of s will depend on how big the time interval is, because for a larger time interval the particle will travel farther and S' will make a bigger angle with S. As was mentioned in Article 4–3, when the average velocity depends on our choice of time interval, then we must make the time interval extremely short, in fact "infinitely small." *

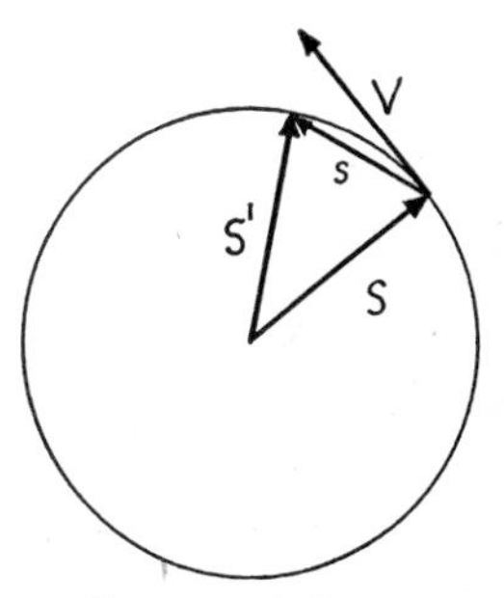

FIGURE 6–C. Displacement and velocity vectors for circular motion.

Reference to Figure 6–C shows that as the time interval is made smaller and smaller, the vector s will become tangent to the circle. When s is divided by the corresponding very small time interval, the quotient, which is the (instantaneous) velocity V, will also be directed along the tangent. The velocity is therefore perpendicular to the radius of the circle. Newton's First Law of Motion implies that, if a body is moving in a circular path and is suddenly freed from all forces, it will move with whatever velocity it had when it was released, and will therefore move along a tangent to the circular path. This conclusion, which nicely illustrates the meaning of Newton's First Law, can be verified by observing mud or water flying off a revolving tire, or by whirling an object on the end of a string and then letting the string hit a razor blade.

* The idea expressed here can be formulated more exactly, by means of a branch of mathematics called the calculus.

Consider next the acceleration. When we say that the body is in uniform circular motion, we mean that it moves in a circle, and that its velocity always has the same magnitude. The velocity is constantly changing in direction, and the body therefore has an acceleration. The velocities V and V' at two different instants are indicated in Figure 6–D.

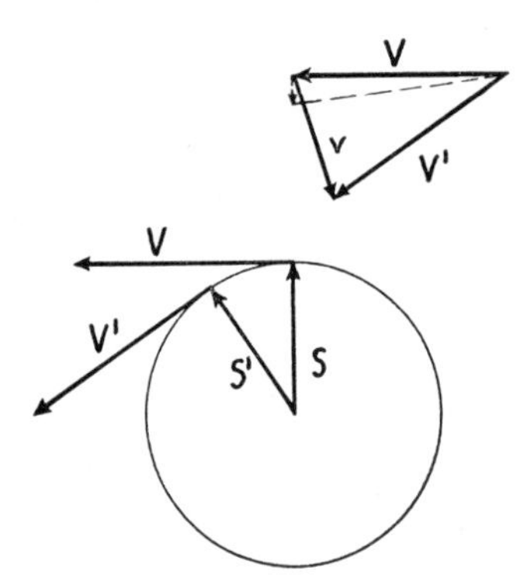

FIGURE 6–D. Velocity and velocity change in uniform circular motion.

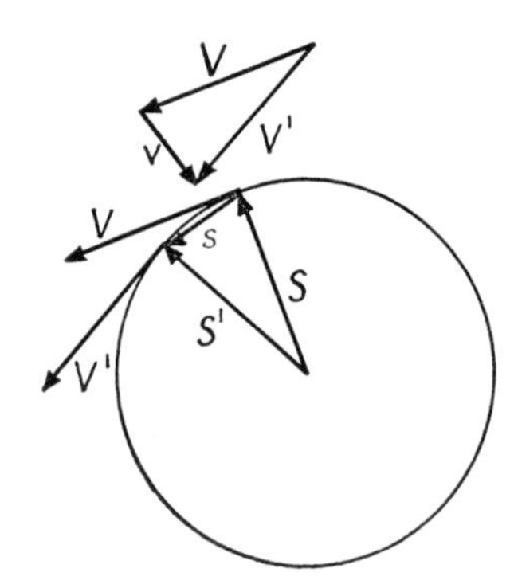

FIGURE 6–E. Relations among the vectors for uniform circular motion. Since the triangles are similar, their sides are proportional.

The velocity vectors are redrawn near the circle, and the difference between them is v, as can be seen by noting that in the vector sense $V' = V + v$. The acceleration, the rate of change of velocity, is found by dividing the velocity change v by the time required for the change to occur. Since the direction of v depends on how big the time interval is, we must again choose an "infinitely small" time interval in order to calculate the acceleration. As the time interval is made shorter and shorter, v becomes more and more nearly perpendicular to V, as shown by the dashed vectors in Figure 6–D. Therefore the acceleration is perpendicular to the velocity, which means that *the acceleration is directed exactly toward the center of the circle.*

Frequently we shall want to know the magnitude, as well as the direction, of the acceleration in uniform circular motion. Going back to the definition, we have

$$\text{Acceleration} = \frac{\text{Velocity change}}{\text{Time interval}}.$$

If the time interval is made smaller and smaller, the velocity change is smaller and smaller, so it is not obvious what value their quotient will have. A formula for the quotient can be derived, however, using a simple geometrical argument. Let the velocity of the particle be V at the beginning, and V' at the end, of a very small time interval. The displacement s and the velocity change v that occur in this time interval are shown in Figure 6–E. The triangles in the diagram are similar, because their sides are mutually perpendicular. Therefore

$$\frac{s}{S} = \frac{v}{V},$$

where the symbols represent only the *magnitudes* of the vectors shown in the diagram. In words, this equation says

$$\frac{\text{Displacement}}{\text{Radius}} = \frac{\text{Velocity change}}{\text{Velocity}}.$$

Since

$$\text{Displacement} = \text{Velocity} \times \text{Time interval},$$

we have

$$\frac{\text{Velocity} \times \text{Time interval}}{\text{Radius}} = \frac{\text{Velocity change}}{\text{Velocity}}.$$

This can be rearranged thus:

$$\frac{\text{Velocity change}}{\text{Time interval}} = \frac{\text{Velocity} \times \text{Velocity}}{\text{Radius}},$$

or

$$\text{Acceleration} = \frac{(\text{Velocity})^2}{\text{Radius}}.$$

This statement about the magnitude of the acceleration, together with our earlier statement that the acceleration is directed toward the center of the circle, gives a complete account of the acceleration in uniform circular motion. If your acquaintance with mathematics is very limited, you may have thought the argument difficult to follow; you can take comfort in the fact that the mathematics to be encountered in the rest of this book will in almost all cases be simpler.

6–5. Vector Components. The addition of two vectors is the process of finding one vector which is equivalent to the two given ones. This vector is called the sum of the two given ones. Another process that is useful is the finding of two vectors whose sum is equivalent to a given vector. They are called *components* of the given vector; in most cases the two vectors desired are perpendicular to one another. Suppose one wants to find a horizontal vector and a vertical vector whose sum is the given vector V. In a self-explanatory

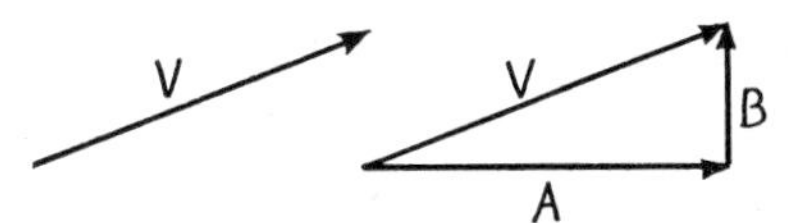

FIGURE 6–F. The given vector V has A and B as its horizontal and vertical components.

way, Figure 6–F shows how to do this. The vectors A and B, whose sum is V, are components of V.

6–6. Adding Forces. According to Newton's Second Law (Article 5–3), the rate of change of a body's momentum is equal to the force that acts on the body. What happens if several forces act on a body at the same time? This would have been a hard question if asked at the end of the last chapter, but it is easy now. Forces have direction as well as magnitude; hence they are vector quantities. Any set of forces acting on a particle is therefore equivalent to a single force, their vector sum.* This sum of the forces can readily be calculated by graphical means, and it is the force to be used in applying Newton's Second Law. A simple experiment will show that forces really are vector quantities; it will incidentally illustrate the addition of vector quantities in general.

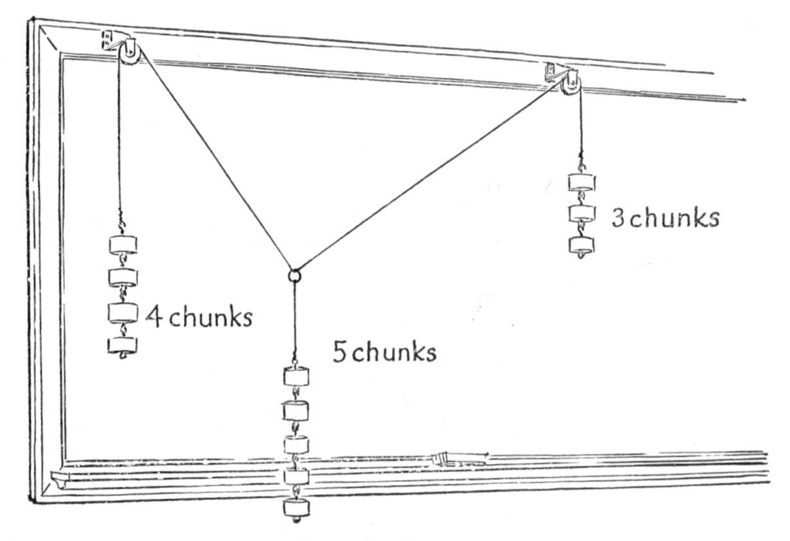

FIGURE 6–G. Verifying that forces are vector quantities.

EXPERIMENT. Take a dozen one-pound chunks of iron, to which hooks are attached. Fasten three strings to a little ring as shown in Figure 6–G, letting two of the free ends pass over a pair of pulleys mounted against a blackboard. If 3, 4, and 5 chunks of iron are fastened to the strings as shown, then the strings exert forces of 3, 4, and 5 pounds on the ring to which they are joined.

* If several forces act on a large body, rather than on a particle, then the situation is more complicated because the forces may act at different points, and possible rotation of the body must be taken into account. In these cases, there may be no single force that is equivalent to the set of forces. It is still true, however, that the rate of change of momentum of the body will be equal to the vector sum of all the forces that act on it.

The ring adjusts itself to some position and stays there, with no acceleration. Therefore, according to Newton's First Law, the (net) force on the ring is zero. That is, the vector sum of the three forces is zero. This can be verified by drawing lines on the blackboard parallel to the strings, and constructing vectors on the lines to represent the forces in the strings. (Do not confuse the length of the vector with the length of the string. Note, in fact, that the shortest vector, representing 3 pounds, lies in this case along the longest string.) A black-

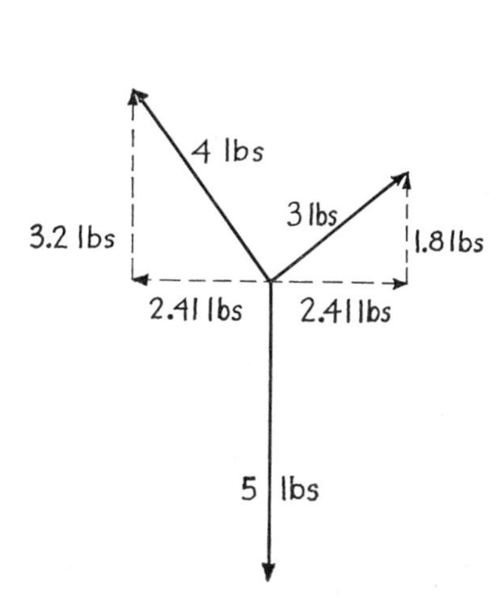

FIGURE 6–H. When treated as vectors, the 4-pound force and the 3-pound force just balance the 5-pound force.

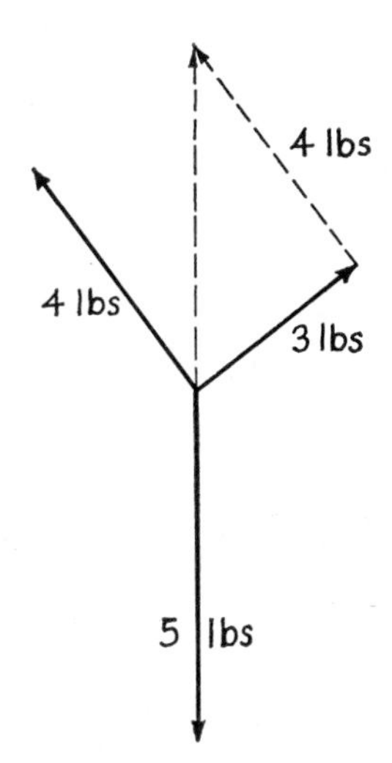

FIGURE 6–I. When added vectorially, the 4-pound force and the 3-pound force have a sum that is directed vertically upward. Its magnitude is 5 pounds.

board construction, as in Figure 6--H, will show that the ring has assumed a position such that the 4-pound force and the 3-pound force have equal but opposite horizontal components, so their horizontal pulls cancel. Their vertical components are found by measurement to be 3.2 pounds and 1.8 pounds, respectively. The sum of these vertical components is 5.0 pounds, which is just right to balance the 5-pound pull of the vertical string.

Instead of working with components, one can simply add the 4-pound vector and the 3-pound vector by placing them end to end, as in Figure 6–I. Their sum turns out to represent 5 pounds directed upward. Together, therefore, they just cancel the effect of the 5-pound downward pull of the third string.

This experiment not only illustrates the meaning of vector components and vector addition, but it also shows that forces actually are vector quantities, as alleged.

Summary

Scalar quantities have magnitude only, but vector quantities have magnitude and direction. Displacement is a vector quantity, and other vector quantities (for example, forces) are added like displacements. They can be represented graphically by vectors, which are arrows drawn to some scale.

A body in uniform circular motion has a velocity directed along the tangent to the circle, and an acceleration directed toward the center of the circle. The acceleration arises from the fact that the velocity, although it is constant in magnitude, is continuously changing in direction. The magnitude of the acceleration is V^2/r, where V is the magnitude of the body's velocity and r is the radius of the circle.

The components of a vector are mutually perpendicular vectors whose sum is equal to the given vector.

Questions

1. Distinguish between a scalar quantity and a vector quantity.
2. Should momentum be classified as a scalar quantity or as a vector quantity?
3. What is a vector? What is a vector component?
4. What is uniform circular motion? Explain why this motion involves an acceleration.
5. The halfback who excels in broken-field running is seldom a heavy man. How is this fact correlated with Newton's Second Law of Motion?
6. The moon travels about the earth in an orbit which is approximately a circle with a 240,000-mile radius, and it goes once around the orbit in about 28 days. The moon therefore has a velocity of about 38 mi/min. Find the magnitude and direction of the moon's acceleration.
7. During the time it is in a turn, a plane usually approximates uniform circular motion. Point out some of the difficulties confronting a designer who wants to make a fast and maneuverable fighter plane.
8. By reference to the text, devise a formal definition of the term "vector sum."

7

NEWTON'S THIRD LAW OF MOTION

> Where the statue stood
> Of Newton with his prism and silent face,
> The marble index of a mind for ever
> Voyaging through strange seas of Thought, alone.
>
> WORDSWORTH

Newton's first two Laws of Motion are closely related; in fact, the First is merely a special case of the Second. They correlate the acceleration of a body with the force that acts on the body. The Third Law deals with the forces that two bodies exert on one another. Considered by many to be Newton's subtlest achievement, it is one of the cornerstones of mechanics. Since our concern with mechanics is only incidental, we shall not need the Third Law very often, but it will play a vital role in our discussion of the solar system (which atoms to some extent resemble) and of gas pressure (which gave some of the first scientific evidence that matter is composed of invisibly small particles).

7–1. Newton's Third Law of Motion. The third and last of Newton's Laws of Motion can be stated thus: *When one body exerts a force on a second body, then the second body always exerts an equal and opposite force on the first.*

This law, when first encountered, is likely to seem contrary to experience. Actually, of course, it is in accord with experience. The law says that if a tennis racquet pushes on a ball, then the ball pushes equally and oppositely on the racquet. This does not mean that nothing happens; it means that *two things happen.* The ball changes its motion (bounces off), because a force acts on the ball. Also, the racquet changes its motion (slows down), because the other force acts on the racquet. (Remember that Newton's Second Law says that the acceleration of a body is proportional to the force that acts *on that body.*) One force is sometimes designated arbitrarily as the "action"; the other force is then called the "reaction."

Newton's Third Law explains how locomotion is possible. To make himself accelerate, a runner leans forward and pushes back against the ground with his feet. The ground therefore pushes forward on the runner, giving him an acceleration. The reality of the backward force exerted by the runner can readily be seen if the ground is soft; each footprint shows that the earth has been pressed backward. In walking, the same procedure is followed, but the forces are not usually large enough to deform the ground.

FIGURE 7–A. When the train starts one way, the track starts the other way, because each exerts a force on the other.

Another common illustration of Newton's Third Law is the backward motion of a boat when someone steps or jumps out of it.

Consider a train. The train accelerates because the wheels push backward on the track, and therefore the track pushes forward on the wheels. If the track is fastened to the earth, the backward push of the train on the track modifies the spinning of the earth, by an amount that is not detectable. If, however, the track is free to move, then the force that the train exerts is easily observable.

EXPERIMENT. A toy train runs on a horizontal circular track that is free to rotate about its center (Figure 7–A). The train moves one way and the track moves the other way. Again we see that the two forces do not cancel; they produce two motions because they act on different bodies.

7–2. Conservation of Momentum. In spite of all that has been said, one may perhaps still feel that *in some respect* the two equal and opposite forces must nullify one another. This feeling is correct. The fact is that when two bodies that are free to move exert forces on one another, then each experiences a change in its motion, but the changes occur in such a way that if the momentum of one body *increases,* then the momentum of the other *decreases by the same amount.* That this is true is easily seen from Newton's Second Law, which says that the rate of change of momentum is equal to the force that acts on the body. The forces act oppositely, and equally, and for the same length of time. Therefore they produce equal and opposite changes of momentum, and the net change in momentum of the *pair* of bodies is zero.

Clearly, if we have a collection of bodies that interact with one another but experience no forces from other agencies, then the changes in momentum will cancel out in pairs, so that the total momentum of the collection of bodies remains unchanged. We say "the momentum of a collection of bodies, on which no forces act from outside, remains constant," or "in an isolated system, momentum is conserved." This generalization is called the Law of Conservation of Momentum.

7–3. Examples Involving Conservation of Momentum. Consider a cannon of the Revolutionary period. When it was shot off horizontally, the ball went forward and the cannon went backward. Assuming level ground and no friction in the axles of the wheels, we have a pair of bodies on which no horizontal force acts from outside. Therefore at the instant of firing, before the ball has acquired downward velocity because of its weight, the cannon and the ball will have equal and opposite momenta. As far as magnitudes are concerned,

$$\text{Mass of cannon} \times \text{Velocity of cannon} = \text{Mass of ball} \times \text{Velocity of ball.}$$

The mass of the cannon is relatively large; therefore its velocity is relatively small.

Actually, of course, friction in the wheels and roughness of the ground would provide an external force that would reduce the momentum acquired by the cannon. Therefore the earth would have to take up some of the momentum. In modern artillery, the gun is attached to the ground by a system of springs and brakes, so that the gun and the projectile do not constitute an "isolated system."

Summary

Newton's Third Law of Motion: When one body exerts a force on a second body, then the second body always exerts an equal and opposite force on the first.

The two forces mentioned in Newton's Third Law do not cancel one another, because they act on different bodies.

The two forces do, however, produce equal and opposite changes in momentum. Therefore the total momentum of an isolated set of bodies cannot change. This last statement is called the Law of Conservation of Momentum.

Questions

1. Explain the statement, "Newton's First Law is merely a special case of his Second Law."
2. Students sometimes argue this way: Newton's Third Law is absurd, because if for each force there is an equal and opposite force, then the forces must cancel and they can have no effect. Expose the fallacy in this argument.
3. Rewrite Article 7–3, eliminating the use of the concept of momentum and invoking Newton's Third Law instead.
4. In sailing races, it is illegal to throw anything overboard. Why is such a rule desirable?
5. If two teams are having a tug-of-war, Newton's Third Law says that they must always pull equally hard on one another. Show that the team that wins is the one that can push harder against the ground.
6. What must a swimmer's kick do in order to impel him forward?

8

GRAVITATION

If I have seen farther than others, it is because I have stood on the shoulders of Giants.

NEWTON

In order to see how Newton's laws of motion apply to actual mechanical problems, it is instructive as well as interesting to see how Newton himself used his laws to study the solar system. This study ushered in the idea that the universe is a machine, an idea which had a profound influence on the thought of the succeeding (eighteenth) century, especially in France.

8–1. Weight. In our discussion of falling bodies, no attempt has been made to explain why bodies do fall. In Aristotelian physics, bodies fell because the material of which they were constituted sought the center of the earth. In the Newtonian view, bodies fall because the earth exerts a downward force on them, called weight, or force of gravity. If this force is not counteracted by some other force acting upward, then the body accelerates downward. The acceleration of the body is constant because the force acting on it, its weight, is constant.

When any body near the earth's surface falls freely from rest, under the action of its weight alone, it falls almost exactly 16 feet, or 4.90 m, in the first second. Galileo's formula $s = \frac{1}{2}at^2$ therefore gives 32 ft/sec², or 9.80 m/sec², as the acceleration of the body. This acceleration, 9.80 m/sec², produced by the weight of the body, is referred to so frequently that it is designated by the special symbol g instead of a. If we designate the weight by W, then Newton's equation $F = ma$ becomes $W = mg$.

The fact that all freely falling bodies experience the same acceleration g leads to a startling conclusion. It implies that the weight of a body is proportional to its mass! (If one body has twice the mass of another, but they both have the same acceleration, then the first must be subject to twice as much force as the second.) When we realize that weight is the force of attraction exerted by the earth, while mass is the measure of inertia, it seems very strange that there should be a relationship of proportionality between them. Einstein (1916) was the first to give any hint as to the reason for the connection between weight and mass, and even now the problem is not settled.

Although the connection between weight and mass is mysterious, it is useful. To see whether a body has the same mass as the standard kilogram in Paris, we can simply put them both on a set of scales and see whether they have the same weight. If they do, then their masses are identical. This is of course simpler than making direct measurement of their inertias.

Example. Find the mass of a body that weighs 1.96 newtons.

$$W = mg$$

$$1.96\,\frac{\text{kg m}}{\text{sec}^2} = m \times 9.80\,\frac{\text{m}}{\text{sec}^2}$$

$$\frac{1.96\text{ kg}}{9.80} = m$$

$$m = 0.200\text{ kg.}$$

8–2. Newton's Work on Gravitation (about 1670). Recall from Chapter 2 that Kepler, about 1600, found the orbits of the planets to be ellipses with the sun at one focus. If a body describing an ellipse has a velocity that is constant in magnitude, then it is clear from Figure 8–A that the change in velocity, and consequently the acceleration, are directed toward the interior of the ellipse. Now recall also that Kepler discovered the Law of Equal Areas, which states that the line from the sun to a planet sweeps out equal areas in equal times. This means that the speed of the planet must increase as the planet approaches the sun, and decrease as the planet recedes from the sun. Newton showed that, for such a motion, the acceleration vector of the planet points exactly at the focus where the sun is. The acceleration must, according to Newton's Second Law of Motion, be caused by a force acting on the planet, and the force must be *toward the sun.**

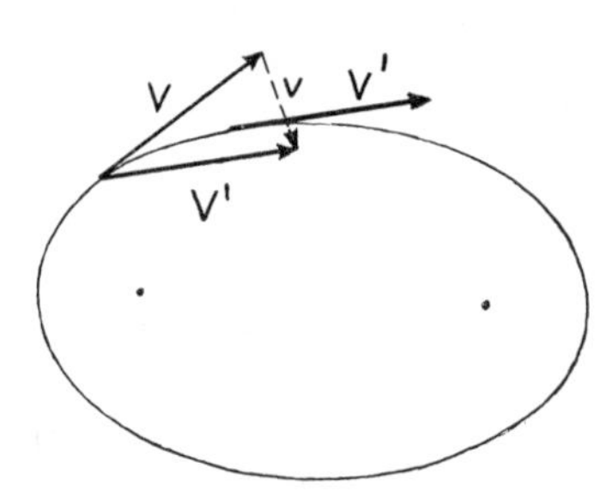

Figure 8–A. The velocity change v, and consequently the acceleration, are directed toward the interior of the ellipse.

* Kepler, not knowing the principle stated in Newton's First Law, thought something had to push on the planets in the direction of their motion, in order to keep them moving. He conjectured (wrongly) that the sun supplies this push somehow by means of magnetism.

An exactly similar argument shows that the moon experiences a force toward the earth. But how can the earth exert a force on the moon? Newton jumped to the conclusion that the influence of gravity extends all the way to the moon. Newton further assumed that the planets are attracted toward the sun in the same way that an apple or the moon is attracted to the earth. If this bold guess be correct, then the force on the planet should be proportional to the mass of the planet, just as the weight of the apple is proportional to the mass of the apple.

According to Newton's Third Law of Motion, forces occur in pairs. When one body exerts a force on a second, then the second exerts an equal and opposite force on the first. Since the sun exerts a force on the planet, the planet must exert a force on the sun.* Just as the pull of the earth on an apple is proportional to the mass of the apple, so also we should expect the pull of the planet on the sun to be proportional to the mass of the sun. The sun and planet therefore attract one another with a force that is proportional to the mass of the sun as well as to the mass of the planet.

Finally, from Kepler's third law (about the mean radii and the times of revolution) and some fairly simple mathematics, Newton deduced that the force experienced by the planet must vary as the inverse square of its distance from the sun.

Collecting these results in an algebraic formula, we have

$$F = G\frac{Mm}{d^2}$$

where F = force of gravitational attraction
M = mass of sun
m = mass of planet
d = distance from sun to planet
G = a constant.

Newton again generalized beyond all experience, and made the hypothesis that this formula *holds for all bodies in the universe,* and that G is the same for all bodies in the universe, that is, G is a "universal constant." He put forward no hypothesis about the *cause* of gravitation, which is still not understood at all well. Newton's Law of Universal Gravitation may be stated as follows: *Every body in the universe attracts every other body with a force proportional to the product of their masses, and inversely proportional to the square of the distance between them.*

* One may ask, "If the planets pull on the sun, why does the sun not move?" The answer is that the pull of the planets does make the sun move, but the sun is so massive that its motion is very small and has to be taken into account only in the most refined work.

Newton checked his law by comparing the acceleration of the moon toward the earth with the acceleration of a body falling at the earth's surface. Since the orbit of the moon about the earth is not very different from a circle, the acceleration of the moon toward the earth is given very closely by the formula (Article 6–4)

$$\text{Acceleration} = \frac{(\text{Velocity})^2}{\text{Radius}}.$$

One of the problems at the end of this chapter gives the data for proving that the acceleration of the moon compares with the gravitational acceleration at the surface of the earth in just the way required by the Law of Gravitation. It was by means of just this calculation that Newton satisfied himself of the correctness of his law.

8–3. The Mass of the Earth. The constant G can be measured in the laboratory, by measuring the force with which two ordinary spheres of metal, of known mass and at a known distance apart, attract one another. As might be expected from the fact that we are not ordinarily conscious of it, this force is very weak, and G turns out to be a very small number.

$$G = 0.0000000000667\,\frac{\text{newtons m}^2}{\text{kg}^2}.$$

Only when one or both bodies have very large masses does this gravitational attraction amount to very much.

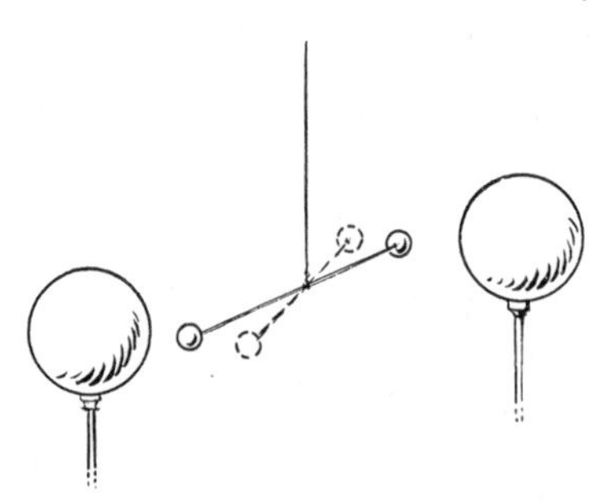

FIGURE 8–B. Measuring the force of attraction between metal spheres, to determine the gravitational constant, G.

As usually carried out, the experiment for measuring G involves two pairs of metal spheres. Figure 8–B shows the general scheme. Two small spheres form the ends of a dumbbell which is suspended on a very fine supporting fiber. When two larger spheres are brought into the neighborhood, their attraction for the smaller ones causes the dumbbell to turn a little, twisting the fiber. By measuring the angle of twist, and knowing the properties of the fiber, one can calculate the forces of attraction between the spheres. Then in the equation for the Law of Gravitation all the quantities are known except G, which can therefore be calculated.

When G is known, many fascinating results follow at once. For a body on the surface of the earth,

$$W = G\frac{M_{\text{earth}} m_{\text{body}}}{R^2},$$

where R is the radius of the earth and W is the weight of the body, which is mg. Hence,

$$M_{\text{earth}} = \frac{gR^2}{G}.$$

Knowing G, therefore, we can compute the mass of the earth. It is

5,980,000,000,000,000,000,000,000 kg.

8-4. The Masses of Celestial Bodies. We can go even further, and calculate the mass of the sun. For an approximate calculation, the elliptical orbit of the earth can be considered as a circle, with radius R. If the velocity of the earth in its orbit has a magnitude v, then the acceleration of the earth toward the sun is v^2/R. Combining Newton's Second Law with his Law of Gravitation, we have the equation

$$M_{\text{earth}}\frac{v^2}{R} = G\frac{M_{\text{earth}} m_{\text{sun}}}{R^2}.$$

In this equation, everything is known except the mass of the sun, which therefore can be calculated! As a matter of fact, the mass of the earth cancels out, and need not be known; the mass of the sun could be calculated by using any other planet instead of the earth, since all that has to be known is the radius of the planetary orbit and the velocity of the planet. The mass of any planet that has a moon can be found in an exactly similar way, using the orbital radius and velocity of its moon.

Many stars consist of two parts, revolving with respect to one another. The same method can be used to determine the masses of these double stars. The mass is found to be related to the type of light given out by the star. On the very plausible assumption that the same relationship between mass and type of light holds for stars that are not double, the masses of single stars can be determined by observing the type of light that they emit. Therefore the amazing task of finding the mass of a star is now a routine operation.

The foregoing method of determining masses cannot be applied to the few planets that do not have moons, but these masses can be found by a different method. Not only does each planet experience attraction to the sun, but it is also attracted by the other planets. These attractions cause the orbits to depart a little bit from truly elliptical shapes. The deviations from the elliptical orbits are small, but measurable, and from them one can determine the masses of the perturbing planets. On two occasions, data on the perturbations of planetary orbits have led to the prediction that, if a telescope were turned toward a designated region in the heavens, a new planet would be found. On both occasions, the new planet has been there (Neptune, 1846; and Pluto, 1930).

8–5. Gravitation and Kepler's Laws. As we have already described, Newton arrived at the Law of Gravitation by applying his laws of motion to the motion of the planets, as that motion is described by Kepler's laws. He showed that a planet traveling in an ellipse (Kepler's first law) and obeying the law of equal areas (Kepler's second law) has an acceleration toward the sun. According to the Second Law of Motion, then, the sun must exert an attractive force on the planet. By using Kepler's third law, Newton found how the gravitational force varies with the distance between the gravitating objects, and he checked this conclusion by comparing the motion of the moon with the motion of falling objects on the earth. In this chain of reasoning, he was using the available knowledge about particular bodies to lead him to a universal generalization.

Having discovered the Law of Gravitation, Newton to a certain extent turned his earlier argument end for end. He showed that any body moving under the gravitational influence of one other body must move in a conic section, which may be an ellipse, and that if the orbit is an ellipse, then Kepler's laws must hold. Until then, Kepler's laws had been simply unexplained facts of nature. After Newton's work, Kepler's laws were "understood," in the sense of being a consequence of the Law of Universal Gravitation. This change in the status of Kepler's laws is a fine example of what "understanding" and "explanation" mean in science. A fact is counted as understood if it is shown to be a consequence of some law, or proposition, that also accounts for other facts. Even today, we count gravitation as unexplained, since we cannot deduce it from a more general law which accounts for other things as well.

The meaning of explanation in science governs the meaning of the scientist's "why?" When he asks why a phenomenon occurs, the scientist is not asking anyone to read the mind of God. He is merely asking that the phenomenon be accounted for in terms of some general principle. If, for instance, he asks why an unsupported stone will fall, he is likely to be satisfied if we tell him that the stone falls because of the gravitational force exerted on it by the earth. Further examples occur in the "why?" questions that will turn up from time to time in the exercises at the ends of these chapters.

8–6. Fruits of the Law of Universal Gravitation. Even such an apparently abstract subject as gravitation has its application to commerce, since it explains the tides. The attraction of the moon and the sun makes the water of the oceans pile up in a mound that moves along the earth's surface. A knowledge of the laws of gravitation permits the governments of maritime nations to predict, years in advance, what time high tide will occur at the various ports, and how high it will be.

The chief significance of Newton's work, however, was that it constituted a mental conquest of the entire physical universe. All matter, however remote, was successfully alleged to behave in the same way as terrestrial matter, and to be amenable to mathematical prediction. These findings caused an intellectual revolution, by enhancing immeasurably the degree to which educated men were willing to rely on rational thought.

Summary

The weight of a body is the force exerted on it by the earth. When the body is at the surface of the earth, this force is just sufficient to give the body an acceleration of about 9.8 m/sec^2. This is called the acceleration of gravity; it is always designated by the symbol g. From Newton's Second Law, we get the relation $W = mg$, where W is the weight, and m the mass, of the body. Since g is the same for all bodies, the masses of two bodies are in the same ratio as their weights. This relation provides a simple, though indirect, way of comparing masses.

Using Kepler's laws of planetary motion, and his own general laws of motion, Newton discovered that the sun attracts the planets by gravitation, and that the magnitude of the force is given by the equation

$$F = G\frac{Mm}{d^2}.$$

He assumed that all bodies in the universe attract each other with forces governed by the same equation. The constant G can be determined in the laboratory, and when it is known, the mass of any celestial body that has a satellite can be computed. With this procedure as a beginning, means have been found for estimating the masses of other celestial bodies.

The mechanistic view of the universe, which Newton's work promoted, had a profound effect on the intellectual life of the succeeding generations.

Questions

1. Name three of the "Giants" to whom Newton refers in the quotation at the head of this chapter.
2. Draw a vector diagram to show the acceleration of a planet that moves in an ellipse according to Kepler's Law of Equal Areas. (The construction of

ellipses is described in Article 2–5, and the law is stated in Article 2–6.) Show, for several different positions of the planet, that the acceleration vector points at least approximately in the direction of the sun. Remember that the planet slows down when it gets farther from the sun, and speeds up when it gets closer. A diagram drawn without calculation can of course not be exact.

3. The acceleration of the moon, in familiar units, is treated in a problem at the end of Chapter 6. The moon's orbital velocity of 38 mi/min is almost exactly 1000 m/sec, and the orbital radius of 240,000 miles is equal to 385,000,000 meters. From these data, show that the moon's acceleration is 0.0026 m/sec^2.

   Now test Newton's Law of Gravitation, in exactly the way that Newton himself did. If the moon is held in its orbit by gravitational attraction to the earth, the ratio of the moon's acceleration to the acceleration of a freely falling body at the earth's surface must be equal to the ratio of the earth's gravitational pull at these two places. We know the two accelerations (0.0026 m/sec^2 and 9.8 m/sec^2); it remains to calculate the ratio of the earth's gravitational pulls at the orbit of the moon and at the surface of the earth.

   Accept the fact, which Newton proved mathematically, that if his law is true, then the gravitational pull of a sphere can be calculated correctly by considering the sphere to be concentrated at its center. That is, the d in the equation for gravitational attraction to the earth is the distance from the attracted object to the center of the earth; for a body on the earth's surface, d is the radius of the earth, about 4000 miles or 6,400,000 meters. The distance from the center of the earth to the center of the moon is given above.

   Combining the equation $F = G\frac{Mm}{d^2}$ with $F = ma$, we see that the acceleration produced by gravitational pull is $a = \frac{Gm}{d^2}$. From this the *ratio* of accelerations at the surface of the earth and the orbit of the moon can be worked out without knowledge of G or M. Show that the ratio demanded by the equation is equal to the ratio of the actual accelerations, so that the motion of the moon confirms Newton's Law of Gravitation.

   To which of the steps in Article 3–4 does this problem correspond?

4. What is a scientific explanation?

> That very law which moulds a tear
> And bids it trickle from its source,—
> That law preserves the earth a sphere,
> And guides the planets in their course.
>
> SAMUEL ROGERS (*ca.* 1800)

9

CALCULATION IN PHYSICAL SCIENCE

Mathematical reasoning and deductions are a fine preparation for investigating the abstruse speculations of the law.

THOMAS JEFFERSON

The mathematics encountered so far in this book is a fair sample of what will come later. Perhaps most of what comes later is a little easier. This being true, one may wonder why a chapter on mathematics appears now instead of at the beginning of the book. The reason is that the material in this chapter can be better appreciated now that one has had a little experience with what is needed. The first three articles in this chapter will simply review some topics that have already been introduced. The last article will present an arithmetical procedure that is particularly useful in dealing with the extremely large and extremely small numbers that arise in scientific work.

9–1. Constants. A *constant* is a number or quantity that does not change during the discussion. For example, when a ball rolls down a straight inclined track, its acceleration is constant. This means: The acceleration of the ball is the same, no matter where it is on the track or how fast it is moving.

If the ball in the example above is shifted to a steeper track, it will then have a larger acceleration. The acceleration will be constant in this case, as in the previous one, but the constants will be different because the conditions are different.

There is another type of constants, called *universal constants*. These are constants that have the same value under all conceivable conditions. One familiar example is π, the ratio of the circumference of a circle to its diameter. This has the value $3.14159\cdots$ for all circles. We have met one other universal constant, the quantity designated by G in the equation for the Law of Gravitation. This constant always has the value 0.0000000000667 nt m/kg^2, for all gravitational attractions in the universe.

9–2. Proportionality. To say that one number is *proportional* to another is to say that their quotient is a constant. Therefore, if one of them is doubled, then the other must be doubled also. Again the circle provides an example: The ratio of the circumference to the diameter is constant, and if one circle has twice the diameter of another, it also has twice the circumference. We write

$$\text{Circumference}/\text{Diameter} = \pi.$$

Very often the idea is expressed with a different symbol. We sometimes write

$$\text{Circumference} \propto \text{Diameter},$$

which is read "the circumference is proportional to the diameter."

In buying rope, one finds that

$$\text{Cost} \propto \text{Length},$$

provided, of course, that there is no discount for quantity. An equivalent statement is

$$\text{Cost} = \text{Constant} \times \text{Length}.$$

Here the constant is called the *constant of proportionality*. Its value will depend on what kind of rope is being bought.

If an airplane flies at a steady rate, the distance traveled is proportional to the time of flight:

$$\text{Distance} \propto \text{Time of flight},$$

or

$$\text{Distance} = \text{Constant} \times \text{Time of flight}.$$

Here the constant is of course the velocity; or, to be precise, the magnitude of the velocity.

Another relationship frequently met with is *inverse proportionality*. Two quantities are inversely proportional when their product is always the same. For example, the number of slices of bread that can be cut from a loaf is inversely proportional to the thickness of one slice. This situation fits the definition just given, because

$$\text{Number of slices} \times \text{Thickness of slice} = \text{Length of loaf}.$$

A relationship of this kind is often written in quotient form:

$$\text{Number of slices} = \frac{\text{Length of loaf}}{\text{Thickness of slice}}.$$

For another example, suppose one has a certain sum to spend on the hotel bill for a vacation. Then the number of days he can stay is inversely proportional to the cost per day of the room he selects.

$$\text{Number of days available} = \frac{\text{Money available}}{\text{Cost per day}}.$$

9–3. Units in Equations. It has already been pointed out that in stating physical quantities, one must specify the unit of measure being used. To say that the magnitude of velocity is 5, or the length of a rope is 8, gives no information at all. One has to say, for example, that the magnitude of the velocity is 5 ft/sec, or that the length of the rope is 8 yards.

The need for stating units is sometimes considered by beginners to be a source of confusion, or at best a nuisance. Actually, it is an aid and convenience, for it affords a check on the correctness of an equation and on its fitness for the problem at hand. When substituting into an equation, put in the units as well as the numbers and perform whatever algebraic operations are called for by the equation. The answer will then come out expressed in the proper units.

EXAMPLE. A stone falls freely for 4 seconds under the action of gravity. How far does it fall?

The acceleration of a freely falling body is 9.80 m/sec^2, as mentioned in Article 8–1. Using Galileo's formula, we have

$$s = \tfrac{1}{2}at^2,$$

$$s = \frac{1}{2} \times 9.80 \frac{\text{m}}{\text{sec}^2} \times (4 \text{ sec})^2$$

$$= 4.90 \frac{\text{m}}{\text{sec}^2} \times 16 \text{ sec}^2$$

$$= 4.90 \times 16 \text{ m}$$

$$= 78.4 \text{ m}.$$

Here there is no doubt whatever that the answer is expressed in meters. The fact that the answer purports to be a distance, and is expressed in units of length, affords a check on the calculation. If one is seeking a distance and the answer comes out in m/sec, then there is a mistake in the calculations, or perhaps one has used a formula that does not apply to the problem.

Keeping an eye on the units that appear in the equations in the text will make the meaning of the equations easier to follow.

9–4. Calculating with Decimals. The constant G in Newton's Law of Gravitation has the value $0.0000000000667 \frac{\text{newtons m}^2}{\text{kg}^2}$. Another important physical constant is the velocity of light, 299,800,000 m/sec. In dealing with numbers such as these, the zeros that are put in merely to fill up decimal places are a great nuisance. A much better method for writing large or small numbers is in common use.

Suppose we have the number 7290. This can be written 7.29×1000. But $1000 = 10^3$, so the number can be written 7.29×10^3.

Now consider the number 0.00729. It can be written 7.29/1000, or $7.29/10^3$. By convention, $1/10^3$ is abbreviated 10^{-3}. Therefore the second number can be written 7.29×10^{-3}.

From these examples, a very simple rule can be evolved. From the equalities $7290 = 7.29 \times 10^3$ and $0.00729 = 7.29 \times 10^{-3}$, one sees that the power of 10 in the new notation shows *how far the decimal point would have to be shifted* in order to put the number into the more usual form.

10^3 means "shift the decimal point three places to the right."
10^{-3} means "shift the decimal point three places to the left."

The rule works equally well for all other powers of 10. For example,

$$\begin{aligned} 299{,}800{,}000 &= 29.980 \times 1000 \times 1000 \times 10 \\ &= 29.980 \times 10^3 \times 10^3 \times 10 \\ &= 29.980 \times 10^7, \end{aligned}$$

because $10^3 \times 10^3 = 10^6$, and $10^6 \times 10 = 10^7$.

Two more comments must be made. First, the zero in 29.980 got there as a space filler, and is no longer needed. (It would be kept if it were the result of actual measurement. Zeros that are not the result of measurement are dropped in order to avoid giving a false impression of accuracy.) Dropping the superfluous zero, we have 29.98×10^7.

Finally, it is convenient to adopt the uniform practice of putting the decimal point after the first digit, and adjusting the power of 10 as may be necessary: $29.98 \times 10^7 = 2.998 \times 10^8$. The velocity of light is therefore expressed in the form 2.998×10^8 m/sec.

It is left to you to show that $G = 6.67 \times 10^{-11}$ nt m²/kg².

Summary

A constant is a quantity that does not change during the discussion. A universal constant is a quantity that has the same value under all conditions.

The statement "A is proportional to B" means "A/B is a constant," or "$A = \text{Constant} \times B$." A frequent abbreviation is $A \propto B$.

The statement "A is inversely proportional to B" means "$A \times B = \text{Constant}$," or "$A = \text{Constant}/B$."

In stating a physical quantity, one must specify the unit of measure. In substituting into an equation, it is good procedure to put the units in along with the numbers, and then to perform on the units the operation demanded by the equation. This procedure gives the units for the answer and also acts as a check on the calculation.

Zeros to fill up decimal places can be avoided by using a scheme based on powers of 10. The exponent on the 10 tells how many places to shift the decimal point. If the power is positive, the shift is to the right; if negative, to the left. For example, $7.29 \times 10^3 = 7290$, and $7.29 \times 10^{-3} = 0.00729$.

Questions

1. What is a constant?
2. What is meant when we say that one quantity is proportional to another?
3. In terms that your mother could understand, explain the meaning of the statement: The gravitational attraction between two bodies is inversely proportional to the square of the distance between them.
4. Put the following numbers in more convenient form:

   6670000
   0.0000000000667
   0.0000000667
   0.06
   2574×10^4
   0.59×10^{-5}
   the mass of the earth (Article 8–3).

5. Repeat the calculations for Question 6, Chapter 6, using the more convenient way of expressing large and small numbers.
6. Repeat the calculations for Question 3, Chapter 8, using the more convenient way of expressing large and small numbers.

10

WORK AND ENERGY

> I do not know what I may appear to the world, but to myself I seem to have been only like a boy playing on the seashore, and diverting myself in now and then finding a smoother pebble or a prettier shell than ordinary, whilst the great ocean of truth lay all undiscovered before me.
>
> NEWTON

The concepts of velocity, acceleration, force, and momentum discussed heretofore are familiar to all who live in our culture, although not everyone understands them with the precision that is necessary for scientific purposes. We now introduce two concepts on a higher level of abstraction; they are derived from the simpler ones already discussed, and in the strict sense they are superfluous. Nevertheless, they are such powerful intellectual tools that they greatly facilitate the construction of theories, and it would be foolish to avoid using them. They are called *work* and *energy*, names imported from ordinary English vocabulary and given a specialized meaning. Of the two, energy is the more general. In fact, it pervades all science to such an extent that it is no serious exaggeration to say that science is the study of energy. (Such a statement, of course, must not obscure the fact that energy is a mental invention used merely in the description of events.) Work is so closely related to energy that they must be discussed together. The kindred concept of *power* is mentioned briefly for the sake of its general interest.

10–1. Work. Work, in the technical sense, is done when a force acts on a body that moves, unless the motion is at right angles to the force. Quantitatively, *work* is the product of the displacement of the body and the component of force acting in the direction of the motion.

$$\text{Work} = \text{Distance moved} \times \text{Component of force along the motion.}$$

We say that work is done *on* the body *by* the force. Since work is the product of a force and a distance, the metric unit of work is the newton meter. This unit is so important that it is given a name of its own; it is called the *joule*, in honor of a British scientist whose experiments will be discussed in the next section.

$$1 \text{ joule} \equiv 1 \text{ newton meter}.$$

EXAMPLE. If a steady force of 80 newtons is directed along a lawn mower shaft inclined at 60° to the ground as in Figure 10–A, then the component of

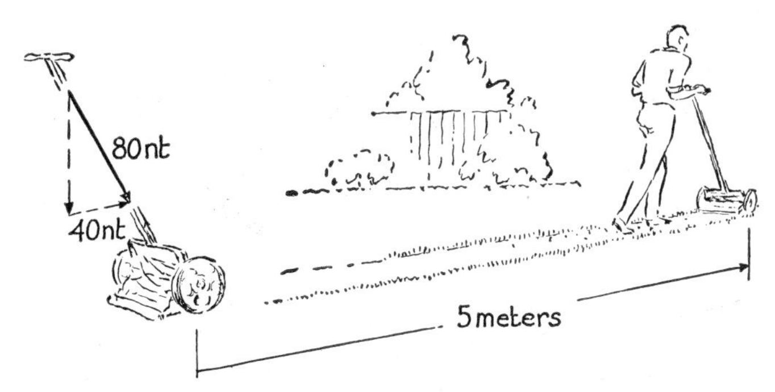

FIGURE 10–A. Doing work on a lawn mower.

force along the direction of motion is 40 newtons. If the mower is pushed 5 meters in this way, then the work done on the lawnmower by the force is

$$\begin{aligned} \text{Work} &= 40 \text{ newtons} \times 5 \text{ meters} \\ &= 200 \text{ newton meters} \\ &= 200 \text{ joules}. \end{aligned}$$

The usefulness of the idea of work will become apparent as our studies proceed. It can be summarized loosely by saying that work is a measure of the effect of a force, and that in very many situations it is enough to know how much work was done, without bothering about the details of how the force acted.

10–2. Power. Suppose a small boy toils upstairs with a suitcase, a step at a time. It may take him 3 minutes. A strong man might be able to take the same suitcase and rush it upstairs in 10 seconds. The same amount of work is done on the luggage in either case, but the *rate of doing work* is much greater in the second case. We say that the man applies more *power*, power being the rate of doing work. Our fundamental unit of power is obviously the joule/sec; this unit is also given its own name, *watt*, after the man whose development of the steam engine did so much to increase the power available for man's pursuits. The power of engines is usually rated in *horsepower*, because the early purchasers of engines were interested in knowing how many horses an engine would replace. Somewhat arbitrarily, one horsepower is taken to be the equivalent of 745.7 watts.

10–3. Kinetic Energy. After Newton had put forward a set of general laws concerning mechanical systems, mechanics became to a great extent a branch of mathematics, like geometry. In effect, Newton's laws were used as postulates and their implications were expressed as theorems. This deductive activity, which flourished for about two hundred years (1670–1870), fell into two categories: The first (which was supplemented by experimental work) dealt with the behavior of particular kinds of bodies, for example vibrating strings, moving liquids, spinning tops, or gyroscopes; the second category dealt with general truths deduced from Newton's laws and applicable to a wide variety of mechanical situations. We examine now one of these general truths that are implicit in, but not obvious from, Newton's laws. The mathematics is simple, but otherwise the argument is a typical example of the deductive argument in theoretical mechanics. It leads to conclusions of capital importance.

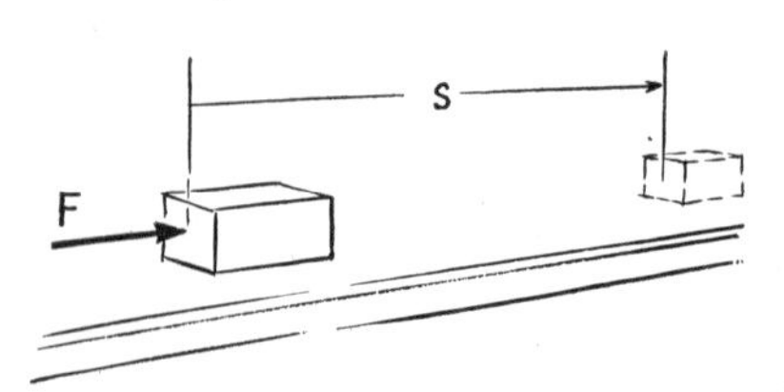

FIGURE 10–B. Doing work to accelerate a body. The vector F represents the sum of whatever forces may be acting on the body.

Suppose that a constant force F acts on a body which is initially at rest, and moves it a distance s in the direction of the force, as depicted in Figure 10–B. Then

$$\begin{aligned} \text{Work done} &= \text{Force} \times \text{Distance} \\ &= F \times s \\ &= ma \times s \end{aligned}$$

because $F = ma$ (Newton's Second Law). Since the force is constant, the acceleration is constant, and Galileo's formula $s = \frac{1}{2}at^2$ is valid. Therefore

$$\begin{aligned} \text{Work done} &= ma \times \tfrac{1}{2}at^2 \\ &= \tfrac{1}{2}m \times (at)^2. \end{aligned}$$

But the velocity v acquired by a body that starts from rest and has a steady acceleration a for a time t is given by $v = at$, because a is the rate at which the velocity increases. Hence

$$(at)^2 = v^2$$

and therefore

$$\text{Work done} = \tfrac{1}{2}mv^2.$$

This is a remarkable result. The quantity $\frac{1}{2}mv^2$, which is computable from the attributes of the *body*, tells us how much work has been done on the body by *some external agent.* We have assumed the work to be done in a particularly simple way, but with more elaborate mathematics it can be shown that the same result follows even when F does not act along the direction of motion, and even when F is not constant. Therefore, by making simple measurements on the body to determine its velocity and mass, we can tell how much work was done on it, regardless of whether we know anything about *how* the work was done. The quantity $\frac{1}{2}mv^2$ is called the *kinetic* * *energy* of the moving body. Our result can therefore be stated as follows:

$$\text{Work done on body} = \text{Kinetic energy acquired by body.}$$

(If several forces act at once on the body, then their sum should be used in computing the work done.)

The equation in the form last written can be shown to hold even when the body does not start from rest. If it is initially in motion, the body has some kinetic energy, but it experiences a *gain in kinetic energy* equal to the work done on it.

Notice that since kinetic energy is $\frac{1}{2}mv^2$, its units are $\frac{\text{kg m}^2}{\text{sec}^2}$ or $\frac{\text{kg m}}{\text{sec}^2}$ m, or newton-meters. Kinetic energy is therefore to be measured in joules. If this were not true, then of course work and kinetic energy could not be equal.

Kinetic energy is acquired by a body on which work is done. Conversely, a body with kinetic energy to *lose* can *do work* on something else. In a first study of work, it is useful to consider a specific device, the pile driver. A pile driver is a kind of hammer, used to drive timbers into the bottom of a river or a harbor. It is a very simple machine, consisting essentially of a heavy iron block that can be raised to a height of several meters and then dropped onto the pile that is to be driven into the mud. The working model shown in Figure 10–C consists of a wooden block, protected by an iron plate on the bottom, and sliding freely in a vertical frame. The block serves as the hammer, and a nail in a piece of soft wood plays the part of the pile. If the block simply rests on the head of the nail, the nail does not move. Therefore,

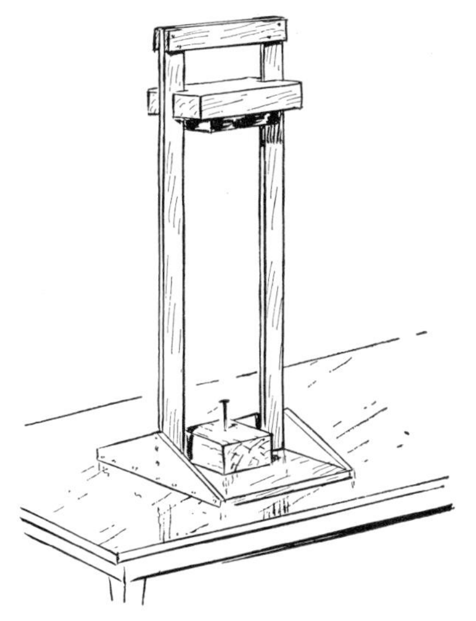

FIGURE 10–C. A model of a pile driver. The block acquires kinetic energy as it falls, and it loses this kinetic energy when it does work on the nail, which represents the pile.

* "Kinetic" means having to do with motion.

although the block applies a force to the nail, no work is being done. (Actually the wood gripping the nail also applies a force to it, and the net force on the nail is zero.) Suppose now that the block is allowed to fall on the nail from some height. When the *moving* block strikes the nail, the nail moves; work is done on it. Kinetic energy is converted into work.

Kinetic energy can be regarded, in a loose sense, as work that is stored up in a body by reason of its motion. A Roman soldier, operating against a foeman's torso, could do work on it directly by means of forces exerted with a short sword, or he could operate indirectly with a thrown javelin. He did work on the javelin to set it into motion, and the javelin did work on the foeman when it was stopped by his body.

10–4. Potential Energy. Returning to the pile driver, it is very instructive to inquire "Where did the kinetic energy of the falling block come from?" Before the block fell, it was at rest and had no kinetic energy. While it was falling, the only force acting on it was its weight. The block was moving in the direction of this force, so work was being done on the block. If m is the mass of the block and g its acceleration under gravity, then, by Newton's Second Law, its weight is mg (Article 8–1). If it fell through a height h, then the work done (Force $\times$ Distance) was $mg \times h$.

$$\begin{aligned}\text{Kinetic energy acquired by block} &= \text{Work done on block by its weight,}\\ &= \text{Weight of block} \times \text{Distance fallen,}\\ &= mgh.\end{aligned}$$

The raised block does not have kinetic energy, but it is capable of acquiring kinetic energy and therefore of doing work. We say that the block has *potential energy* when it is raised, and that this potential energy is converted into kinetic energy when the block falls. Then

$$\text{Kinetic energy acquired} = \text{Potential energy lost}$$

$$\tfrac{1}{2}mv^2 = mgh.$$

Furthermore, we think of the potential energy as being stored in the body when work is done to raise the body.

Hereafter, the abbreviations K.E. and P.E. will be used for kinetic energy and potential energy.

To review and clarify the situation, suppose a block, of mass $\frac{1}{2}$ kilogram, falls 0.51 meter from rest and then strikes a nail.

$$\begin{aligned}\text{Weight of block} &= mg\\ &= \tfrac{1}{2}\text{ kg} \times 9.8\text{ m/sec}^2\\ &= 4.9\text{ kg m/sec}^2\\ &= 4.9\text{ newtons.}\end{aligned}$$

$$\begin{aligned}\text{P.E. of raised block} &= \text{Weight} \times \text{Height}\\ &= 4.9 \text{ newtons} \times 0.51 \text{ meter}\\ &= 2.5 \text{ newton meters}\\ &= 2.5 \text{ joules.}\end{aligned}$$

The P.E. stored in the raised block is 2.5 joules. The work done by gravity when the block falls is therefore 2.5 joules, and the K.E. acquired by the block is 2.5 joules.

10–5. Energy. Early in the nineteenth century, scientists began to have clear ideas about a concept called *energy*. This concept, which can be defined in the simplest terms, is one of the most fruitful that has ever been introduced into science.

Energy is the capacity for doing work. The energy of a body is the amount of work that the body can be made to do.

In the preceding article, P.E. was discussed, and a quantitative statement about the P.E. was made in the special case of a raised block, but no general definition of P.E. was given. It is now possible to give one: *Potential energy is the energy a body has by reason of its position.* This definition of P.E. differentiates it clearly from K.E., which is energy that a body has by reason of its motion. Some bodies have P.E. even though they are not placed so that they can fall. Examples: a body attached to a compressed spring; a magnet alongside another magnet.

10–6. Transformations of Energy. Let a man hold a body down against a compressed spring, and then release it. When it is held down, the body has P.E.; when released it acquires K.E. and travels upward. As it rises, it gains P.E. because of its increasing height, but loses K.E. as it slows down. Eventually it stops rising, when all of its energy of motion (K.E.) has been converted into energy of position (P.E.). This situation does not last, of course. The body falls, and its P.E. is converted back into K.E.

In later chapters, we shall encounter many other transformations of energy.

10–7. The Production of Heat from Work. One further point can be illustrated by the pile driver. After gravity does work on the falling block, giving it K.E., the block hits the nail. It does work on the nail, but the nail moves only a little and then comes to rest. This is because the force exerted by the impinging block is not the only one that acts on the nail. The wood in which the nail moves exerts on the nail a force which *opposes* the motion, doing *negative* work on the nail and thereby causing it to *lose* K.E. Since the nail experiences no permanent gain in K.E., we know that the total work done on the nail must have been zero. It is natural to raise the question "What happened to the K.E. of the block, which seems to have disappeared?" For a clue to what happens to the

K.E. that disappears, remember that when friction brings a body to rest by doing negative work on it, or when a moving object is brought to rest by striking a relatively unmovable obstacle, a *rise in temperature* is often observable. Examples: brakes get warm when bringing a car to rest; a bullet gets hot from the effect of air resistance; skidding across a basketball floor after a fall, one is likely to feel a sensation of warmth.

In order to learn more about energy, therefore, we are led to a study of temperature changes. Such a study lies outside of the realm of mechanics, but our study of mechanics has now been carried far enough for the purpose of introducing us to atomic science, and we are free to take up a new subject.

Summary

The work done when a force acts on a body is the product of the displacement of the body and the component of force acting in the direction of the motion. In our system of units, the fundamental unit of work is the joule.

Power is the rate of doing work. It can be measured in joules/sec. The joule/sec is given the name of watt.

If a body has mass m and velocity v, then the quantity $\frac{1}{2}mv^2$ is called the kinetic energy of the body. Its units turn out to be joules, and it can be shown that the gain in K.E. that a body experiences is equal to the work that is done on it. Conversely, a moving body can do work at the expense of its K.E.

Energy is the capacity for doing work. Potential energy is energy due to position. Kinetic energy is energy due to motion. Under suitable conditions, P.E. can be converted into K.E., or vice versa.

Questions

1. Define work.
2. What is a joule?
3. Name three common objects that have
   (a) kinetic energy
   (b) potential energy.
4. The hammer of a real pile driver may weigh about a ton; if so, it will have a mass of about 1000 kg. Suppose such a hammer is raised 67 feet (20.4 meters).
   (a) How much work is required to raise it?
   (b) How much power would be required to raise the hammer in 10 seconds? In 1000 seconds (about 17 minutes)?
   (c) How much potential energy does the raised hammer have?
   (d) How much kinetic energy does the hammer acquire when it falls?

(e) How much work is done on the pile by the hammer?
(f) If the work done on the pile drives it 1 meter farther into the bed of the river, what is the (average) force exerted on it by the hammer? How does this compare with the weight of the hammer?

5. Verify that the block in Article 10–4 will fall for about 0.322 sec before striking the nail. From this time, find the velocity of the block at the end of its fall. Then calculate the K.E. of the block, and compare it with the P.E. found in the example. State the general proposition which this example illustrates.
6. On body *A*, a force of 20 nt acts through 1 m; on body *B*, a force of 2 nt acts through 10 m. How will the motions of the two bodies differ? How will the motions be alike? Use the answers to justify the statement "Work is a measure of the effect of a force."
7. Describe the energy interchanges that occur as a pendulum swings.
8. What is a watt?

GENERAL VIEW OF SECTION I

The chapters on Mechanics are now at an end, although the concepts they have introduced will reappear throughout the coming pages. A discussion of mechanics for its own sake would indeed have proceeded somewhat differently; the discussion here has been restricted to topics that will be useful in what follows. Our aim has been twofold: to show by example the kind of thinking used in physical science, and to introduce some of the fundamental concepts used in such science.

A summary of the scientific procedure has already been given (Article 3–4) and need not be repeated here. The section as a whole, however, affords a basis for some general remarks about scientific activity. In the first place, the material presented here illustrates very clearly that science is cumulative. The great pioneers of modern physical science were Copernicus, Kepler, Galileo, and Newton, but Copernicus consciously drew on the work of Aristarchus and Ptolemy, Kepler on that of Apollonius and Brahe, Galileo on that of Apollonius, and Newton on that of Galileo and Kepler. If these pioneering giants depended strongly on their predecessors, how much more must the ordinary scientist do so!

One sees also, however, the importance of individual genius. No rules of thumb or rules of logic could have led Kepler to his ellipses, or Galileo to his concept of acceleration, or Newton to his laws of motion. These contributions were all based on brilliant imagination, supplemented in Kepler's case by an astonishing amount of tedious labor. Logic, after all, is capable of leading only to clarification of that which is already known.

Finally, it should be evident that all of the progress made by these men depended on quantitative observation and quantitative calculation. Perhaps the most telling reason that physical science has advanced so rapidly is that it has been based on concepts that can be made quantitative.

Since mechanical concepts form the basis for much that follows, you should review at this time the meaning of velocity, acceleration, mass, force, momentum, work, and energy. Note that these and other terms are listed in the index, where the page number in italics will enable you to find quickly the definition of a term that needs to be recalled.

II

Heat

The rise in temperature that is often observed when mechanical energy disappears shows that there is a connection between mechanics and heat. An investigation of this connection not only led to an understanding of heat, but it also gave some of the first real evidence that matter consists of minute particles.

The first part of this section deals with the problem of measuring temperature, and with measuring the related but different quantity called "heat." Then, there is a brief account of the first scientific theory of heat, a theory that was simple and that succeeded in accounting for most of the then-known phenomena of heat. This theory nevertheless proved to be entirely unsatisfactory, because there are heat phenomena that it utterly fails to account for. The formation and abandonment of inadequate theories is a continuing process in science; the example given here is typical and should be kept in mind as illustrative of the many false leads that science follows until it has proved, by its own efforts, that they are false.

The modern theory of heat, the subject of the closing chapters, gained acceptance about a century ago and has been satisfactory ever since. It is therefore of interest not only because of its role in the development of knowledge about the constitution of matter, but also because it is a fine example of a mature physical theory, in contrast with the theories we shall discuss later about nuclear physics, where all is tentative and much is frankly makeshift.

The subject of heat originally constituted a separate branch of study, based on concepts that were not related to mechanics. It is instructive to observe how experimental information was used to establish a set of scientific concepts (notably "temperature" and "heat"), and how these concepts were finally merged with those of mechanics.

11

THERMOMETERS

Changes in temperature have become an object of study for us because they are often noticed when kinetic energy disappears. The first step in the study of any new phenomenon is to set up, if possible, a scheme for making quantitative measurements. Devices for the quantitative measurement of temperature are called thermometers; their familiar form is so common that few people ever think much about them. They are much simpler, yet depend much more on arbitrary conventions, than one might suppose.

11–1. Simple Thermometers. Temperature changes were naturally studied long before the idea of kinetic energy was invented. Primitive notions of "hot" and "cold" are induced by sensory equipment in our skins. This equipment, of course, does not give any quantitative information.

The concept of temperature can be made quantitative by defining temperature in terms of some measurable property of a body, if that property changes when our senses tell us that the body has become warmer. Under this definition, temperature is that which is measured by a thermometer. Starting with this definition, we may hope to arrive, by means of experiments and theory, at an *interpretation* of temperature that relates it to other quantities.

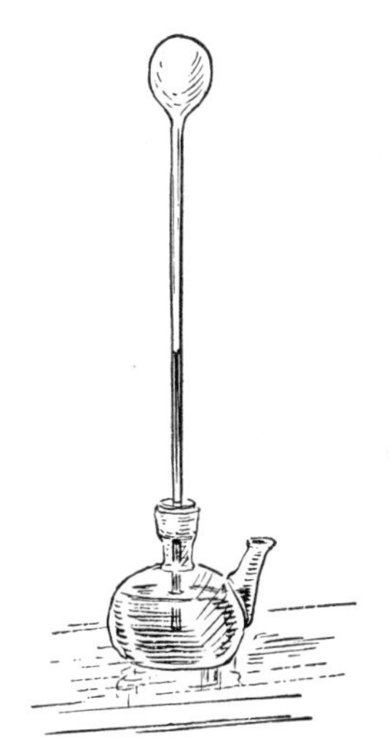

FIGURE 11–A. Galileo's thermometer.

Galileo is credited with making the first thermometer, about the year 1600. He set up the simple apparatus shown in Figure 11–A: a vertical tube partly filled with colored water, resting in a reservoir and terminating at the top in a bulb full of air. If the bulb becomes hotter (as judged by one's skin), the air expands and displaces some of the water from the tube. By putting a scale alongside the stem, Galileo was able to set up a crude scheme for associating numbers with different degrees of hotness.* This device is not very satisfactory, however, because it responds not only to changes in hotness but also to changes in the pressure exerted on the water by the atmosphere, an effect unknown to Galileo until many years later (see Chapter 12).

The familiar mercury-in-glass thermometer works on the same principle, but it is much better than Galileo's thermometer. It is sealed at both ends so that the liquid cannot spill or evaporate or be affected mechanically by the atmosphere. In the seventeenth and eighteenth centuries, different instrument makers used different scales on their thermometers. One in Holland, named Fahrenheit, made thermometers that were particularly reliable, and so many scientists used his instruments that his scale became standard in England and, later, in the United States.

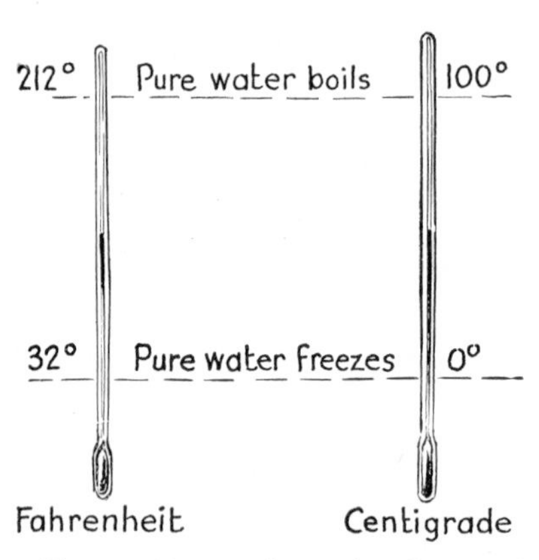

FIGURE 11–B. The Fahrenheit and Centigrade scales of temperature.

Fahrenheit's scale is set up as follows. The temperature of water boiling at normal atmospheric pressure is arbitrarily taken to be 212°, and the temperature of melting ice is taken to be 32°. These points are marked on the scale, and intermediate temperatures are indicated by dividing the interval between the two primary marks into 180 equal parts ($212 - 32 = 180$). Temperatures lower than 32° and higher than 212° are indicated by continuing the scale in both directions, using degree intervals of equal length. Note that the use of water and the numbers 212 and 32 are both entirely arbitrary. What is important is the assignment of definite numbers to two temperatures that are easily reproducible.

The Fahrenheit scale is not in general use in Europe. In ordinary life in large sections of Europe and in scientific work everywhere, the Centigrade scale is used. This scale is established on the same principle as that of Fahrenheit, but the numbers are different, as shown in Figure 11–B. The reading when the thermometer is in boiling water is taken to be 100°, and the reading in melting ice is taken to be 0°. The interval between these levels is divided into 100 equal parts to establish the size

* The displacement of water by expansion of heated air was utilized in devices described by Hero of Alexandria, a late Greek scientist or engineer, with whose recently translated writings Galileo was familiar. Hero applied the idea to temple fakery, such as the opening of a door when a fire was built on an altar.

of the degree, and then the scale is extended above 100° and below 0°. The Centigrade scale has no real advantage over the Fahrenheit scale; it is just as arbitrary, but we shall use it because on it is based the familiar unit of heat, the calorie (Article 14–2).

11–2. Other Thermometers. The expansion of a liquid in a glass tube is not the only phenomenon that can be used to measure temperatures. (In fact, it is not even a very convenient phenomenon, because at low temperatures the liquid freezes, and at high temperatures the glass melts.) Any property of any body can be used as an indicator of temperature, provided the property changes when the body gets hotter or colder. It is well known that a metal bar is longer when it is hot than when it is cold; the length of a metal bar could therefore be used as a measure of temperature.

A thermometer that can be read by a large audience is often needed. The need is filled nicely by what is called the *thermocouple* thermometer (Fig. 11–C). If the ends of a piece of iron wire are joined to the ends of

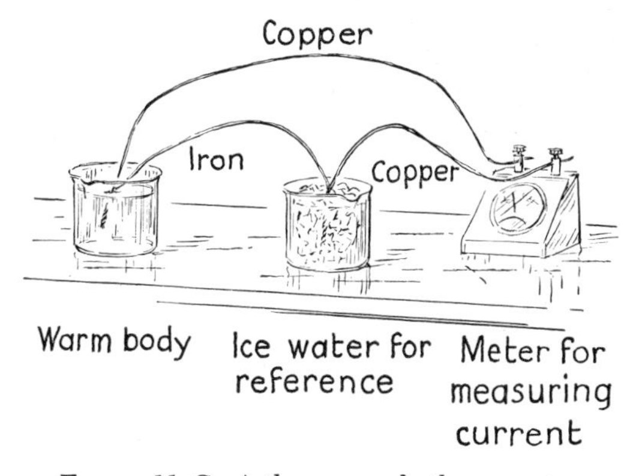

FIGURE 11–C. A thermocouple thermometer.

a piece of copper wire, then, in the metallic loop so created, an electric current will flow if one junction is hotter than the other. Without bothering about the details of the operation, we can measure the current with an appropriate instrument. The instrument will read 0 when both junctions are at the same temperature. The junctions can be made to differ in temperature by 100 Centigrade degrees by placing one of them in ice water and the other in boiling water. Let the corresponding reading of the instrument be called 100°, and divide the interval from zero to this point on the scale into a hundred even divisions. If one junction is kept in ice water, the temperature of the other junction will be indicated on the scale.

11–3. A Difficulty in the Measurement of Temperature. Suppose now that we have a mercury-in-glass thermometer and a thermocouple thermometer, both calibrated by use of melting ice at 0° and boiling water at 100°. Suppose further that we have put the mercury thermometer in some hot coffee and that the mercury level stands halfway between the 0° and 100° marks. Then, according to the mercury thermometer, the temperature of the coffee is 50° C. If we now put the thermocouple junction in the coffee, what guarantee do we have that the detector will read just halfway between the marks for 0° and 100°? Obviously, there is no such guarantee; the mercury and thermocouple thermometers operate so differently that it would be very surprising if one of them read halfway between the 0° and 100° marks under just the same conditions that the other one does. Actually, according to the thermocouple thermometer, the temperature will be a little different from 50° C.

There is one thermometer in common use that is very much like the mercury-in-glass thermometer. It is made in the same way, except that alcohol is used instead of mercury. Careful measurement shows that when alcohol-in-glass and mercury-in-glass thermometers are immersed in the same coffee, they do not read quite alike.

Here are three equally respectable instruments for measuring temperature, yet they agree only at 0° and 100°, where they are arbitrarily set to do so. Other kinds of thermometers establish still other scales of temperature. In most practical cases, the differences are not large, but in principle this is still a very unsatisfactory state of affairs. We could fix on one kind of thermometer, say the mercury-in-glass one, and arbitrarily agree to measure temperatures always on that scale and rule off the divisions on other kinds of thermometers so that they agree with it. To avoid the troubles that mercury-in-glass thermometers experience at low and high temperatures, some different type of thermometer would be preferable as a standard. This scheme is essentially the one that is actually adopted, but one very important further stipulation must be added. If we are to discover any simple and general relationships involving temperature, we should try to define temperature in a way that does not depend on the properties of a particular substance. It will be seen in Chapter 13 that this can be done, but first we must digress to consider a special topic in mechanics that will be needed as background.

Summary

Organs responding to changes of temperature are present in our skins. In order to study temperature changes by the methods of physical science, however, it is necessary to devise a scheme for making quantitative statements about temperature changes. A device for associating a number with a temperature is called a thermometer. Many kinds of thermometers are possible; one simply needs a way of measuring some property of the material that varies according to whether the material is hot or cold. Measuring the property at the temperatures of melting ice and boiling water gives the thermometer readings called 0° and 100° on the Centigrade scale. Intermediate temperatures are fixed by the postulate that the change in temperature shall be proportional to the change in the property. Naturally, thermometer scales that do not depend on the same property of the same material do not generally agree with one another. This state of affairs can be rendered less painful by agreeing always to use a scale based on some specific property of some specific material, for example the length of a rod of pure platinum. Other more convenient kinds of thermometers could then have their scales ruled off with divisions of unequal size so that they agree with the established scale. This scheme is sound, but it has one limitation: If we are to discover any simple and general relationships involving temperature, then we should try to define temperature in such a way that it does not depend on the properties of a particular substance.

Questions

1. Describe the construction of a mercury-in-glass thermometer with a Centigrade scale.
2. Devise some thermometer that is different from those discussed in the text.

12

PRESSURE

In order to understand how a satisfactory temperature scale can be established, it is necessary to know something about pressure.

12–1. Pressure. A man on skis can walk over soft snow without sinking in nearly as far as he would if he had no skis. The force with which he bears on the snow is about the same in the two cases. Actually, it is a little greater when he has skis on, because they weigh something. How is it that the snow is disturbed more by the smaller force exerted by the man without skis? Clearly, the force applied to the snow does not tell the whole story; not much insight is required to see that the area over which the force is applied is also an important consideration. In this and in many other situations, the governing factor turns out to be the force divided by the area over which the force acts. This quotient is called *pressure*. Pressure is force per unit area; that is, force applied divided by the area over which it acts. In our system of units, pressure is naturally measured in newtons/meter^2, but more convenient for our use is another, rather irregular, unit introduced below.

If the force is distributed unevenly over the area on which it acts, the pressure is calculated for each portion of the area. This is done, of course, by taking the force that acts on a small piece of the surface and dividing by the area of that piece. By taking ideally small pieces of surface, we can associate pressure with a point rather than with a whole area. For example, we say that the pressure exerted on the ground by a man's foot varies from point to point; if he is standing still, the pressure is usually greatest under his heel.

12–2. Atmospheric Pressure. We live at the bottom of an ocean of air. This air is attracted gravitationally to the earth; that is, it has weight. Therefore it exerts pressure. Since much information about the world of atoms depends on measurements of gas pressure, it is worth while to discuss the simplest means of measuring the pressure exerted by the atmosphere. Any instrument for measuring atmospheric pressure is called a *barometer*; an instrument for measuring gas pressures in general is called a *manometer*.

When iced tea is sipped through a straw, air is sucked out of the straw, and tea rushes up to take its place. Why does the tea run uphill? The reason is that the atmosphere pushes it up. That this is true can be simply demonstrated, using mercury instead of tea.

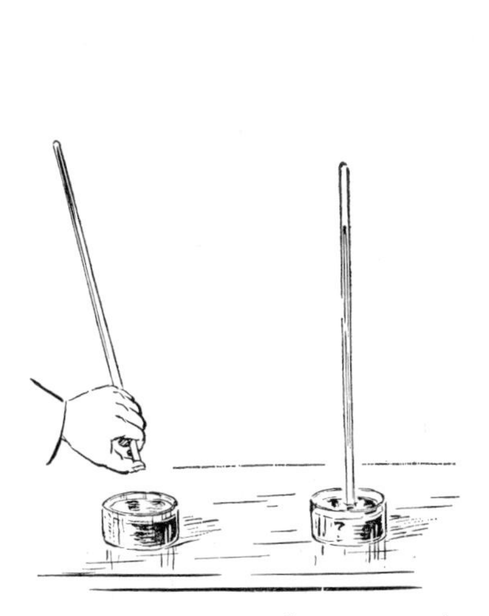

FIGURE 12–A. Making a simple barometer.

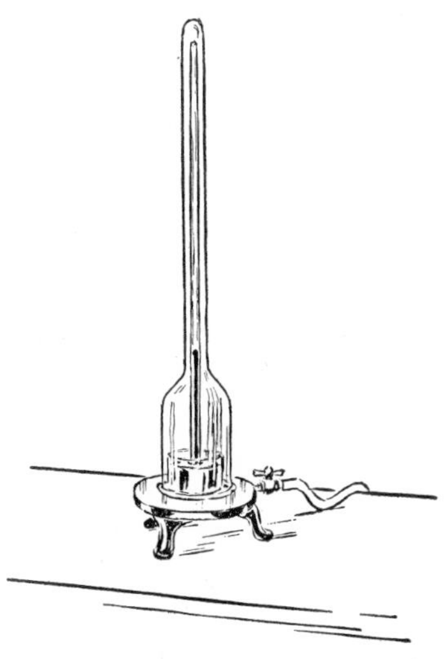

FIGURE 12–B. Proving that the mercury column in a barometer is held up by atmospheric pressure.

EXPERIMENT. A glass tube, about a meter long and closed at one end, is filled with mercury as in Figure 12–A. With his finger covering the open end to prevent the mercury from spilling out, the experimenter inverts the tube and places the open end beneath the surface of a pool of mercury. When the finger is withdrawn, the mercury in the tube drains out until the top surface stands about three-quarters of a meter above the level of the pool. To show that the pressure exerted by the atmosphere is really responsible for holding up the mercury in the tube, the experimenter can enclose the equipment with a glass cover (Figure 12–B) and pump out the air under the cover. The top of the mercury column falls still farther down the tube, dropping to the level of the pool if all of the air is removed from around the pool. When air is readmitted to the surface of the pool, the air pushes mercury up into the tube again.

The top of the tube above the mercury contains nothing but a little mercury vapor. In an approximate sense, it is a vacuum.

The device illustrated in the experiment is a barometer, because it gives a way of measuring atmospheric pressure, as well as demonstrating its existence. The pressure exerted on the mercury in the dish by the elevated column of mercury is equal to the pressure exerted on the mercury in the dish by the atmosphere; if this were not so, the unbalanced pressure would make mercury move into or out of the tube. Therefore the height of the mercury column is a measure of the atmospheric pressure. On a normal day at sea level, the atmosphere pushes the mercury up to a height of 0.760 meter. By weighing a known volume of mercury and doing some simple algebra in which the cross-sectional area of the tube would cancel out, we could find out how many newtons/meter^2 is the pressure exerted by 0.760 m of mercury. However, it is quite customary to describe a pressure by saying how tall a column of mercury it would support. Following this custom, we shall simply say that normal atmospheric pressure at sea level is 0.760 meter-of-mercury. This of course is only a colloquialism; the 0.760 m is not a pressure, but only a height, from which the pressure in nt/m^2 (or lb/in.^{2}) can be computed if desired.*

In the experiment described above (Figure 12–B), the air is gradually removed from above the mercury pool. When some of the air has been removed from the chamber, the pressure in the chamber is less than atmospheric, and it will only hold up a column of mercury less than 0.760 m high. Just how big the pressure is can be determined by measuring the height of the mercury column.

12–3. The U-tube Manometer. One more device has to be explained before we go on with our study of temperature. Suppose we want to measure the pressure exerted by a sample of gas in a bottle, or in an automobile tire. Let the vessel containing the gas be connected to a U-shaped tube containing mercury, as in Figure 12–C. In one arm of the tube, the mercury is subject to atmospheric pressure; in the other arm, it is subject to the pressure we want to measure. If these two pressures are the same, the mercury will stand at the same level in both arms of the U-tube, just as if both sides were open to the atmosphere. If the atmospheric pressure exceeds the pressure in the closed vessel, then it will push mercury up into the arm connecting with the vessel. If, on the other hand, the pressure in the vessel is greater than atmospheric pressure, it will force mercury into the arm communicating with the atmosphere; this is the situation depicted in Figure 12–C. In any case, the difference in the level of the mercury in the two arms is a measure

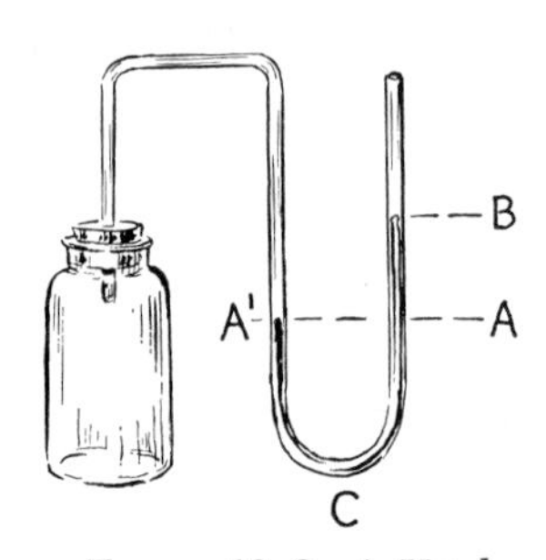

FIGURE 12–C. A U-tube manometer.

* A pressure of 0.760 meter-of-mercury works out to be 10^5 nt/m^2, or about 15 lb/in^2.

of the difference in the pressures.* For example, if AB is 0.10 m on a day when atmospheric pressure is 0.75 meter-of-mercury, then the pressure in the closed vessel is 0.85 meter-of-mercury.

Summary

Pressure is force per unit area.

A mercury barometer is a vertical glass tube about a meter long, containing mercury and standing in a pool of mercury. The atmospheric pressure on the pool can be measured by noting how high it pushes the mercury up the tube.

The U-tube manometer is a U-shaped tube filled with some liquid, usually mercury. One side of the tube is open to the atmosphere, and the other is connected to a chamber of gas whose pressure is to be measured. The difference in level of the mercury in the two sides gives a measure of the difference between the pressure in the chamber and atmospheric pressure. The pressure in the chamber can therefore be computed if the atmospheric pressure is known.

Columns of mercury are so much used for pressure measurements that pressures are often expressed in terms of the height to which they will thrust a column of mercury.

A device for measuring the pressure exerted by the atmosphere is called a barometer; a device for measuring gas pressures in general is called a manometer.

Questions

1. Distinguish between force and pressure.
2. The atmospheric pressure at sea level normally averages about 0.76 meter-of-mercury, but at the altitude of Denver, Colorado, atmospheric pressure is normally only about 0.63 meter-of-mercury. What accounts for this difference?
3. One cubic meter of mercury weighs 1.34×10^5 newtons. Show that the pressure exerted by a column of mercury is proportional to the height of the column, and is independent of the cross-sectional area of the column. Find the pressure exerted by a mercury column 0.760 meter high.

* If this statement is not obvious, it can be proved as follows. The pressure at A' is the same as at A, since, if these pressures were not equal, the column ACA' would not stay motionless. But the pressure at A is greater than that at B by just the pressure exerted by the mercury column AB, and the pressure at B is atmospheric. Therefore the pressure at A', which is the pressure in the vessel, is greater than atmospheric by an amount just sufficient to support AB.

13

ABSOLUTE TEMPERATURE

In the study of the structure of matter, there is a curious paradox: Our senses give us much direct information about solids and liquids and very little about gases; nevertheless, it is through the study of gases that we have arrived at an understanding of liquids and solids. This paradox is no freak of history. Gases at rest very often cannot be seen or felt or heard or smelled or tasted, but they can exert pressure and occupy volume and experience temperature changes. Gases are therefore knowable through instruments, and their nature is simple enough to be understood on the basis of only a few experiments. Later, we can figure out what happens to a gas when it is chilled to form a liquid or a solid. Therefore much of this section and the next will deal with the study of gases.

13–1. The Liter, a Unit of Volume. Because we are expressing lengths in terms of the meter, our regular unit of volume is the cubic meter, abbreviated to m^3. Expressing all volumes in cubic meters is a good way to avoid confusion about units when working with complicated equations. On the other hand, a volume as large as a cubic meter is rarely met in

---

ROBERT BOYLE had a career in science which, like the century he lived in, was one of transition between the Renaissance and the modern age. His father, the Earl of Cork, was a lusty Elizabethan, the richest Englishman of his time. Robert, being a youngest son, had no grave worldly obligations, and he dedicated his life to the promotion of religion, especially to "the theological uses of natural philosophy." First at Oxford and then in London, with hired assistants, he ran a laboratory on what was then a grand scale. His learning and character won him many friends, among them John Locke, Samuel Pepys, and Christopher Wren.

Although remembered as the discoverer of the law that bears his name, Boyle served science chiefly with his pen, using it with vigor and effect in support of the new experimental philosophy. After devoting years to the pursuit of alchemy, he wrote a critique, *The Sceptical Chymist,* which earned for him the cognomen Father of Chemistry.

ROBERT BOYLE
(1627–1691)

the laboratory. Except in a few calculations, therefore, we shall express measurements of volume in terms of a smaller unit called the *liter*. A liter is defined as the volume occupied by a kilogram of water at a certain temperature. A liter is almost exactly 1/1000 of a cubic meter, and it is not very much different from a quart.

Laboratory vessels are frequently marked off in *milliliters* (ml), a milliliter being a thousandth part of a liter.

13–2. Boyle's Law. One of Newton's contemporaries, Robert Boyle, discovered a simple but very important fact about the pressure exerted by a gas. It is a matter of common knowledge that if the volume of a sample of gas is *decreased*, then the pressure exerted by the gas *increases*. For instance, if you squeeze a tennis ball, the pressure in the ball gets so high that your hands are unable to effect any further decrease in the volume. Using a U-tube manometer, Boyle measured the pressure of a sample of air when it was confined in various volumes. He discovered that *if the temperature of the gas is kept fixed*, then the product of the volume of a given sample and its pressure is always the same.

Pressure × Volume = Constant (if temperature does not change).

In symbols: $pV = \text{Constant}.$

This statement is called Boyle's Law. In homely language, it says that, if you halve the volume of a sample of gas, then you double its pressure, provided there is no change in its temperature.

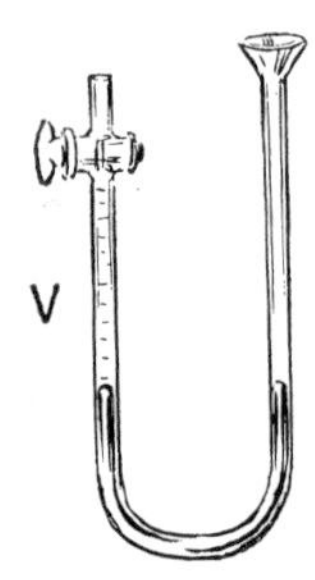

FIGURE 13–A. First part of an experiment to verify Boyle's Law. The gas in the left-hand column is at atmospheric pressure.

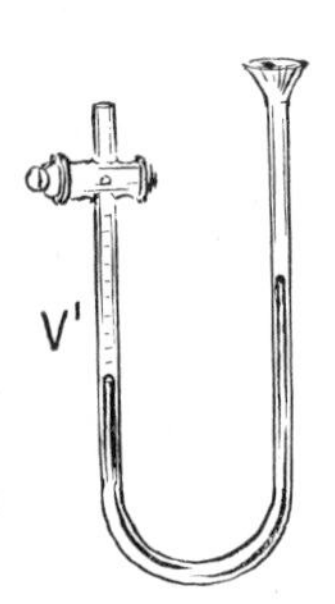

FIGURE 13–B. Second part of the experiment. The gas in the left-hand column is at a pressure greater than atmospheric.

EXPERIMENT. Boyle used a simple apparatus, similar to that in Figures 13–A and 13–B. It is a U-tube manometer, the left arm of which can be closed at the top by means of a stopcock.

In the left figure, the pressure p in the closed arm is equal to atmospheric pressure, since the mercury is at the same level in both sides of the manometer. (This condition can be achieved by opening the stopcock for a short time.)

With the stopcock closed, let more mercury be poured into the right side of the manometer. The mercury rises on the left side, decreasing the volume of the enclosed gas and increasing its pressure. Because of the increase in pressure, the mercury rises even higher on the right side. This condition is shown in Figure 13–B. Here the pressure is p', greater than atmospheric by enough to support a column of mercury of height h. If the atmospheric pressure is 0.76 meter-of-mercury, and h is 0.04 m, then $p' = 0.80$ meter-of-mercury.

It is possible to measure the volumes V and V' by means of a scale etched on the glass of the chamber. Suppose $V = 20$ ml. Then Boyle's Law predicts that

$$p'V' = pV,$$

specifically that

$$0.80 \text{ meter-of-mercury} \times V' = 0.76 \text{ meter-of-mercury} \times 20 \text{ ml},$$

or

$$V' = \frac{0.76 \times 20}{0.80} \text{ ml}$$

$$= 19 \text{ ml}.$$

The observed volume is found to be in accord with this prediction, provided of course that the temperature of the gas does not change during the experiment.

13–3. The Gas Thermometer. As one might guess from the statement of Boyle's Law, if the temperature of the gas does change, then the product pV changes also. *The change in the product of pressure and volume can therefore be used to establish a temperature scale.* Take a sample of gas and measure its volume and pressure at the temperatures of melting ice and of boiling water.* A device for making this sort of measurement is called a *gas thermometer.* The gas is usually enclosed in a glass bulb (or, for high temperatures, a metal or porcelain bulb) connected with a mercury manometer, as in Figure 13–C. The manometer measures the pressure of the gas. The volume of the gas is measured by knowing the volume of the bulb and noting how much additional gas is in the manometer tube. Since the temperature is determined by the product of pressure and volume, the thermometer scale is not usually ruled on the instrument itself. Instead, one can lay out a graph with temperature plotted horizontally and the pressure-volume product plotted vertically. The pres-

* The temperature of boiling water, as judged by any kind of thermometer, is found to depend on the pressure at the surface of the water. The same is true of other liquids. Also, the temperature at which a substance melts is influenced by the pressure on the substance. A liquid boiling in an open vessel is subject simply to the pressure of the atmosphere. By general agreement, boiling temperatures are measured with the surface of the liquid under a pressure of 0.760 meter-of-mercury, the "normal" atmospheric pressure at sea level. Melting temperatures (also called freezing points) are measured with the melting substance under a pressure of 0.760 meter-of-mercury. Throughout this book, it is to be understood that melting and boiling temperatures are to be measured at this standard pressure.

sure-volume product corresponding to the melting point of water and the boiling point of water can be marked on the graph and a straight line drawn to connect them (Figure 13–D). Using this graph to assign a temperature to each intermediate value of the product pV, we can establish a temperature scale. For example, if the bulb is immersed in coffee and the pV product takes on the value indicated by the black dot on the graph, then the coffee is at about 75° C on the gas-thermometer scale.

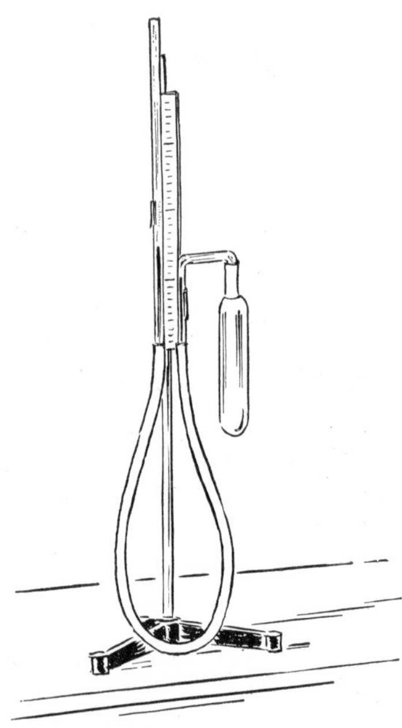

FIGURE 13–C. A gas thermometer. The gas, perhaps air, is in the bulb at the right. The two vertical glass tubes, together with the rubber tubing that connects them, serve as a U-tube manometer for measuring the pressure of the gas.

The temperature scale thus established turns out to agree pretty well with the mercury-in-glass scale and others in common use, but it is found to differ from them in a very attractive way. Provided the pressure of the gas never gets too high, *all thermometers of this kind agree with one another, no matter what gas is used in them.* We have therefore found a temperature scale which does not depend on the properties of a particular substance.

As with other thermometers, we can extend the scale above 100° C and below 0° C. There are two differences, however. Gas thermometers will function at much lower and much higher temperatures than will, for example, the mercury-

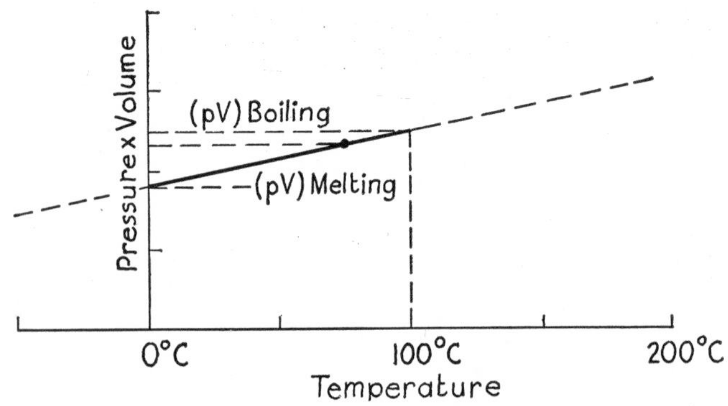

FIGURE 13–D. A graph for determining temperature by means of a gas thermometer.

in-glass thermometer. Furthermore, the gas thermometers retain their advantage of agreeing with one another all along the extended scale, provided the pressure is kept low enough.

13–4. The Absolute Scale of Temperature. No matter what gas is used, the line on the gas-thermometer graph will, if extended toward lower temperatures, indicate that $pV = 0$ when the temperature is $-273°$ C. Since this is true for *all* gases, there must be something special about the temperature $-273°$ C. Neither the pressure nor the volume can ever be less than zero, so we surmise that no lower temperature than $-273°$ C can ever be attained.

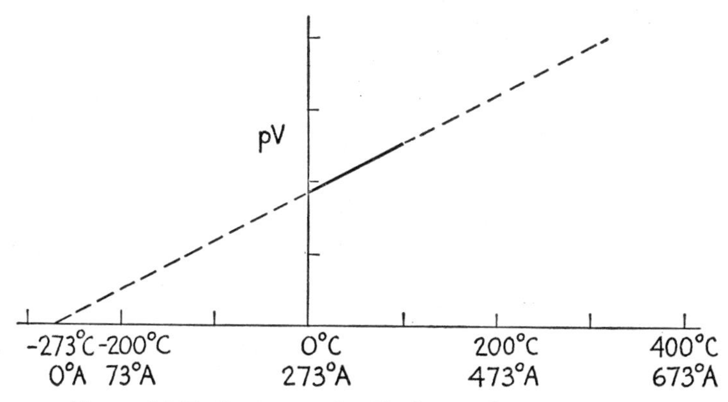

FIGURE 13–E. Setting up the Absolute scale of temperature.

Recall that we took the zero point of the Centigrade scale quite arbitrarily, in accord with the usage of some of the early makers of thermometers. We now have a temperature that can more rationally be taken as a zero point; Figure 13–E shows how the new zero comes into use. A new temperature scale, called the *Absolute scale,* is set up by using a gas thermometer and taking the temperature of melting ice to be 273° A and the temperature of boiling water to be 373° A, so that the lowest temperature that appears to be possible can be called 0° A, or *Absolute Zero.* The size of the degree is the same on the Absolute scale as on the Centigrade gas scale, but the zero point is different for the two scales. The letter T is usually used to represent temperature measured on the Absolute scale.

13–5. The General Gas Law. Boyle's Law gives the relation between pressure and volume when the temperature does not change. It is now possible to state a much more general law, which describes the behavior of pressure and volume when the temperature does change. The graph showing the relation of pV to T is a straight line passing through the

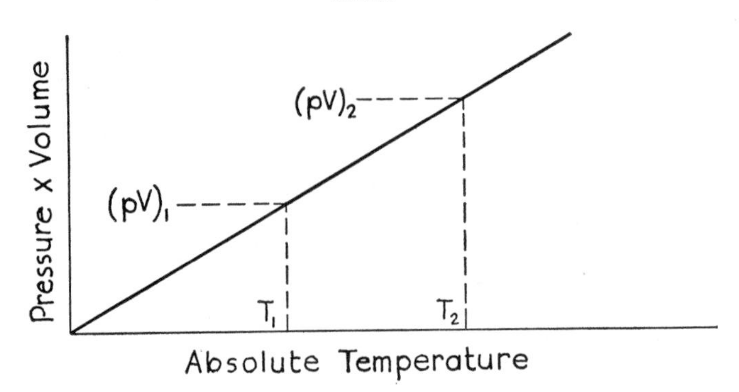

FIGURE 13–F. On the Absolute scale of temperature, T and pV are proportional.

origin of coordinates (Figure 13–F). The graph shows that we have defined T in such a way that pV is proportional to T, for we can see by similar triangles that

$$\frac{(pV)_2}{T_2} = \frac{(pV)_1}{T_1}$$

for all values of T_1 and T_2. In other words, the quotient pV/T does not change, so we can write

$$\frac{pV}{T} = \text{Constant.}$$

Representing the constant by c, we have

$$pV = cT.$$

This equation is called the *General Gas Law*. It holds for all gases when the pressure is not too high.

SUMMARY

Boyle's Law: If the temperature of a sample of gas is kept fixed, then the product of its pressure and volume stays fixed. $pV = \text{Constant}$.

If the temperature of a sample of gas does change, then the product pV changes also. The product pV can therefore be used to define a temperature scale; this scale has the special merit that, as long as the pressure of the gas does not get too high, the scale is the same no matter what gas is used. It is called the gas scale of temperature.

No matter what gas is used, the extension of the gas scale toward lower temperatures indicates that the product of pressure and volume vanishes at $-273°$ C. Since no lower temperature is believed to be possible, this temperature is called Absolute Zero. The Absolute scale of temperature starts at Absolute Zero and has degrees of the same size as the degrees on the Centigrade gas scale. Since its zero point is independent of the properties of any particular substance, and since the scale is the same for all gases, temperatures measured on the Absolute scale can be expected to have some fundamental significance.

From the way the Absolute scale of temperature is set up, it follows that

$$pV = cT.$$

This relation is called the General Gas Law.

Questions

1. What is a liter?
2. State Boyle's Law in terms of proportionality (Chapter 9).
3. On a day when the barometer stands at 0.70 meter-of-mercury, an experimenter attempts to verify Boyle's Law with apparatus like that in Figures 13–A, 13–B.
   (a) When the mercury level is at the same height in both tubes, the experimenter notes that the volume of the entrapped gas is 40 ml. What is the pressure?
   (b) The experimenter adds mercury to the apparatus until the entrapped gas is compressed to a volume of 35 ml. One mercury column is then 0.10 meter higher than the other. What is the pressure exerted by the compressed gas?
   (c) Do the observations substantiate Boyle's Law?
4. A student measures the melting point of tin, using a gas thermometer (Figure 13–C). He collects the following data:
   Bulb in melting ice, $p = 0.81$ meter-of-mercury, $V = 280$ ml;
   Bulb in boiling water, $p = 1.10$ meters of mercury, $V = 282$ ml;
   Bulb in melting tin, $p = 1.47$ meters-of-mercury, $V = 285$ ml.
   Construct a temperature scale for this thermometer and use it to find the melting point of tin.
5. State the General Gas Law in words, without writing an equation.
6. Show that Boyle's Law is a special case of the General Gas Law.

Suggestion for Further Reading

J. B. Conant, *Robert Boyle's Experiments in Pneumatics* (Cambridge: Harvard University Press, 1950). Case 1 of the *Harvard Case Histories in Experimental Science.* Describes and evaluates Boyle's experiments on air pressure and his discovery of the law that bears his name. Contains extensive quotations from Boyle's writings.

14

HEAT

Having analyzed what we mean by temperature, we can proceed to an investigation of temperature changes. As long as we are dealing only with temperature *differences,* it does not matter whether temperatures are expressed in terms of the Absolute scale or the Centigrade scale. Ideally, one should use a gas thermometer, or some other kind of thermometer that is graduated in accord with the gas scale. Actually, temperature measurements made for demonstration purposes are usually rather crude, and any of the usual thermometers will be good enough to demonstrate the essential facts.

14–1. Heat. Let two small metal cylinders of the same size, one made of copper and the other made of lead, be placed in boiling water for a while so that they attain a temperature of 100° C. Then let them be placed quickly in two beakers each containing the same amount of cool water at known temperature. Now measure the temperature change of each sample of water (Figure 14–A). The water warmed by the copper cylinder will rise to a higher temperature than will the water warmed by the lead cylinder.

FIGURE 14–A. Two heated cylinders, made of different metals but otherwise alike, produce different changes in the temperature of a given amount of water.

Initially, the two pieces of metal were at the same temperature (that of boiling water), but they produced different temperature changes in the cool water. To explain this effect, and many others, we adopt the concept of quantity of heat. Although the two samples of water were identical, one was warmed to a higher temperature than the other. We account for this by saying that more *heat* was transferred to the water by the copper than by the lead. To be of maximum scientific utility, the idea of quantity of heat must be made susceptible of measurement.

Anyone given the job of defining heat would probably feel that the amount of heat in a body should depend on the temperature of the body and on the amount of body that is present. Surely one burns himself worse on a hot potato than on a warm one, and he can burn himself worse with a large one than with a small one. In the matter of "amount of body," however, a difficulty crops up. One's first impulse might be to use the volume of the body to determine how much of the body was present. But the volume of the body changes when the temperature changes. To say that we are dealing with 10 ml of copper does not specify how much copper is present, because copper, like most other substances, shrinks when it cools. If we start with 10 ml of copper and cool it, we wind up with less than 10 ml of copper, although no copper has left the scene. To avoid this difficulty, we must measure the "amount" of the body by some property of the body that does not change with temperature. Mass is such a quantity. Therefore, as a first attempt, it is reasonable to say that the quantity of heat transferred to a body shall be *proportional* to the *temperature change* it produces in the body, and shall be proportional also to the *mass* of the body. This approach, which is justified by the fact that it gives useful results, is used to define a unit of heat.

14–2. The Calorie, a Unit of Heat. Because water is readily available in very pure form, the unit of heat is defined in terms of the behavior of water: A *calorie* is the amount of heat that will raise 1 kilogram of water through 1 Centigrade degree.

This definition, coupled with the meaning assigned to "heat" in the previous paragraph, implies that when water gets warmer,

$$\underset{\text{(calories)}}{\text{Heat gained by water}} = \underset{\text{(kg)}}{\text{Mass of sample}} \times \underset{\text{(C degrees)}}{\text{Temperature rise.}}$$

Also, when water cools,

$$\text{Heat lost by water} = \text{Mass of sample} \times \text{Temperature drop.}$$

The usefulness of the concept of heat can be demonstrated as follows. When a warm (100° C) slug of copper is dropped into a cool (20° C) sample of water of the same mass, the temperature of the water is found to rise to about 26.5° C, and the copper of course cools to 26.5° C. The drop in temperature of the copper is much greater than the rise in temperature of the water: 73.5° as against 6.5°. One has the feeling that something passed from the copper to the water. The "something" clearly was *not temperature,* because the copper lost more temperature than the water gained. We assume that the "something" transferred from the copper to the water was heat, and that the heat gained by the water was equal to the heat lost by the copper:

$$\text{Heat gained by water} = \text{Heat lost by copper.}$$

In order to acquire some experience with the ideas involved, you should work through the details of the following calculations.

Suppose that in the experiment just described, ⅒ kg of copper and ⅒ kg of water were used. Then the temperature measurements show that the *water gained* 0.65 calorie of heat. Therefore we believe the *copper lost* 0.65 calorie. Now the temperature change of the copper was 73.5 degrees. If only about 0.009 kg of water dropped 73.5 degrees, it would give up 0.65 calorie. We therefore say that the water equivalent of ⅒ kg of copper is about 0.009 kg, or the water equivalent of 1 kg of copper is about 0.09 kg.*

14–3. Change of State. There are many occasions when heat is delivered to a body without raising its temperature. For example, experience shows that bodies are warmed by stoves or sunshine, which therefore must be sources of heat, but boiling water on the stove stays at 100° C, and ice melting in the sun stays at 0° C. The concept of heat was developed through a study of temperature changes, but it must be broadened to permit the notion of heat transfer *without* change in temperature. Experience shows that when heat leaves one body, but produces no rise in temperature in another body, then it produces another kind of change called "change of state." (By the *state* of a substance, we mean simply its condition of being solid, liquid, or gaseous.) Conversely, when there is a change of state, then heat is absorbed or liberated in order to produce that change. For example, heat is absorbed when ice turns to water.

EXPERIMENT. Let two beakers each contain about ½ kg of water at room temperature. Into one, put a lump of ice of known mass, say ⅒ kg, and at 0° C. Into the other, put the same mass of ice water at 0° C. Observe the amount of cooling produced by the ice water and by the ice. The beaker cooled by the ice water will, for the masses named, drop in temperature by about 3 Centigrade degrees. The beaker cooled by ice will drop by about 15 degrees.

The experiment shows that in the second beaker, heat had to be given to the ice in order to change its state.

Careful measurements show that if a kilogram of ice at 0° C is put into 80 kg of water at 1° C, the ice melts and brings the whole mixture to 0° C. The water gives up 80 calories when it cools, and these 80 calories of heat are required to melt the ice without raising its temperature. It is for

* The ratio of the water equivalent of a sample to its actual mass is called its *specific heat.* Each substance has its own specific heat. The specific heat of water is of course 1.00; practically all other substances have specific heats less than 1.

this reason that an old-fashioned ice box is effective. Each kilogram of ice that melts in the box takes up 80 calories of heat from its surroundings, thus lowering the temperature of the food in the box.

The fact that 80 calories of heat are required to melt a single kilogram of ice shows that the heat transfer involved in a change of state is by no means trivial. Even more striking is the fact that 540 calories are required to convert a kilogram of water at 100° C into steam at 100° C. About this same amount of heat is required to vaporize a kilogram of water at body temperature. Perspiration therefore enables the body to regulate its temperature very effectively. Conversely, when a kilogram of steam at 100° C condenses to water at 100° C, it gives up 540 calories. This heat liberated in the change of state explains why steam produces worse burns than does hot water of the same temperature.

14–4. Another Experiment Involving Change of State. Some liquids, if carefully handled, can be cooled below their freezing points without actually freezing. One such liquid is molten thymol, a substance that is used in some patent medicines. Thymol melts at a little over 50° C, but if not jarred, it will stay liquid when cooled to room temperature, say 20° C. If a crystal of solid thymol is then placed in the liquid, the liquid freezes into a crystalline solid. The heat liberated in this change of state cannot escape as rapidly as it is liberated, and therefore the temperature of the thymol rises, going almost as high as the melting point (Figure 14–B). The fact that heat is liberated in the freezing process can easily be demonstrated in this case, merely by putting a thermometer into the material. A thermocouple thermometer is particularly suitable.

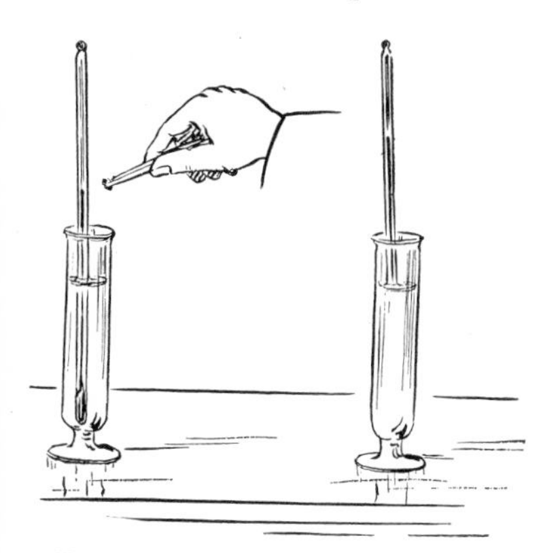

Figure 14–B. Demonstrating that heat is liberated when a liquid freezes.

Ordinarily, freezing occurs slowly, at a rate determined by how rapidly heat is removed by the surroundings. The heat given off in freezing is therefore not usually so apparent as it is in this experiment.

Summary

When a hot body warms a cool one, their temperature changes are not usually equal. Therefore it is not temperature that passes from one to the other. We suppose that something called heat does pass from one to the other, and this idea turns out to be profitable if the heat gained or lost by a body is taken to be proportional to the mass of the body and to the temperature change it experiences. Quite arbitrarily, the heat lost by

1 kilogram of water when it cools through 1 Centigrade degree is taken to be the unit of heat. It is called the calorie. The heat lost by 1 kilogram of any other substance cooling through 1 Centigrade degree is usually less than 1 calorie. (Just how much less depends on the substance; tables giving this information have been compiled.)

In order to retain the idea that the heat given up by one body is transferred to another body, the concept of heat must be extended to include cases where a body absorbs or liberates heat even though its temperature does not change. It does this when its state changes; i.e., when it melts, freezes, vaporizes, or condenses. The heat required to change the state of a body is just as important as the heat required to change the temperature of the body.

Questions

1. In Article 14–1, it is recorded that equal volumes of copper and lead cause different temperature rises when they are heated to 100° C and then plunged into equal volumes of cool water. Later in the same article, it is pointed out that mass is more suitable than volume as a criterion of the amount of material in a body. Given the fact that a cubic inch of lead is more massive than a cubic inch of copper, show that if equal masses of lead and copper had been used in the experiment, then an even larger temperature difference in the heating of the water would have been observed.
2. Work through the details of the calculation in the last paragraph of Article 14–2.
3. How much heat is needed to change 3 kg of ice at 0° C into steam at 100° C?

15

THE CALORIC THEORY

Because of the essential relativity and incompleteness of science, we cannot fully understand it unless we see it flow and develop.

SARTON, *The New Humanism* (1924)

You are now acquainted with the most important phenomena involving heat and temperature. So far nothing has been said to correlate or explain them. If we regard the theory of heat as a jigsaw puzzle, we can say that perhaps we have enough pieces to try to fit the puzzle together. Of course, there is no guarantee that all of the pieces are available; such a guarantee never exists for any of the puzzles of science. It will be useful to inspect our pieces by tabulating the facts that have been presented in the recent chapters—facts that any theory of heat must account for.

15–1. Raw Material for a Theory of Heat. Devices called thermometers are available for measuring *temperature*, and gains or losses of *heat* can be measured with a thermometer and a suitable known mass of water. To be acceptable, a theory of heat must account for the following facts:

1. When work is done without producing mechanical energy, then something usually gets warmer.
2. For a sample of gas, pressure × volume is proportional to temperature ($pV = cT$), provided the temperature is measured on the Absolute scale and the pressure is not too big.
3. Most liquids and solids expand when their temperature rises. (A few do not. A satisfactory theory must account for the common case and for the exceptions.)
4. When solids turn to liquids, or liquids to gases, heat is taken in but there is no rise in temperature. When gases turn to liquids, or liquids to solids, heat is given up with no drop in temperature.

These facts were all known, at least in a general way, before 1800, and a theory had been devised which accounted for most of them. It was not a quantitative theory, but one could hope that further work would make it quantitative. The whole theory, however, was soon upset by the discovery of a fact that was inconsistent with the theory. Nevertheless the theory is of some interest to the student of science, as an example of a theory that appeals to common sense, explains a large variety of phenomena in terms of a simple hypothesis, and yet is entirely unsatisfactory. Its shortcomings were uncovered by the self-correcting procedure which is a distinguishing feature of scientific activity.

15–2. The Caloric Theory of Heat. The theory in question can be summarized as follows. Heat is a fluid, called "caloric," which can soak into any substance. Caloric can flow from one body to another if the bodies are placed in contact, and it always flows from the hotter to the colder because it repels itself. This self-repulsion of caloric accounts for the expansion a body experiences when heated: The body is distended by the caloric. The fact that heat has to be added to a substance in order to melt it means that the liquid is a compound of the solid and caloric. For example,

$$\begin{aligned} \text{Ice} \quad &+ \text{Caloric} = \text{Water} \\ \text{Water} &+ \text{Caloric} = \text{Steam.} \end{aligned}$$

Rough mechanical treatment like rubbing or pounding will squeeze caloric out of a body, so that it becomes readily observable.

15–3. The Failure of the Caloric Theory. Clearly the caloric theory goes far in explaining the phenomena listed on page 113. One could hope to elaborate it to explain the exceptional contractions in (3) and to make it quantitative. Unfortunately, the theory is as wrong as a theory can be. Just when it seemed that all the pieces of the puzzle were fitting together nicely, a new piece was discovered, and this new piece simply would not fit into the pattern that had been put together.

Benjamin Thompson, born on a small farm near Lexington, Massachusetts, was apprenticed at 13 to a Salem merchant. Nevertheless he studied under private teachers and attended Harvard for a short time. At 19, he closed a brief career as a schoolmaster by marrying a wealthy New Hampshire widow, thereby becoming a landed proprietor. When the Revolution broke out, he went to England, where he served in the colonial office; later he commanded a regiment on Long Island. On a tour of the Continent after the war, he brought himself to the attention of the Elector of Bavaria, under whom he served in the highest offices for about fifteen years. In 1791, he became a Count of the Holy Roman Empire. After a few years of scientific and philanthropic activity in London at the turn of the century, he went into retirement in France.

From a painting by Thomas Gainsborough,
by courtesy of the Fogg Art Museum, Harvard University

BENJAMIN THOMPSON, COUNT RUMFORD
(1753–1814)

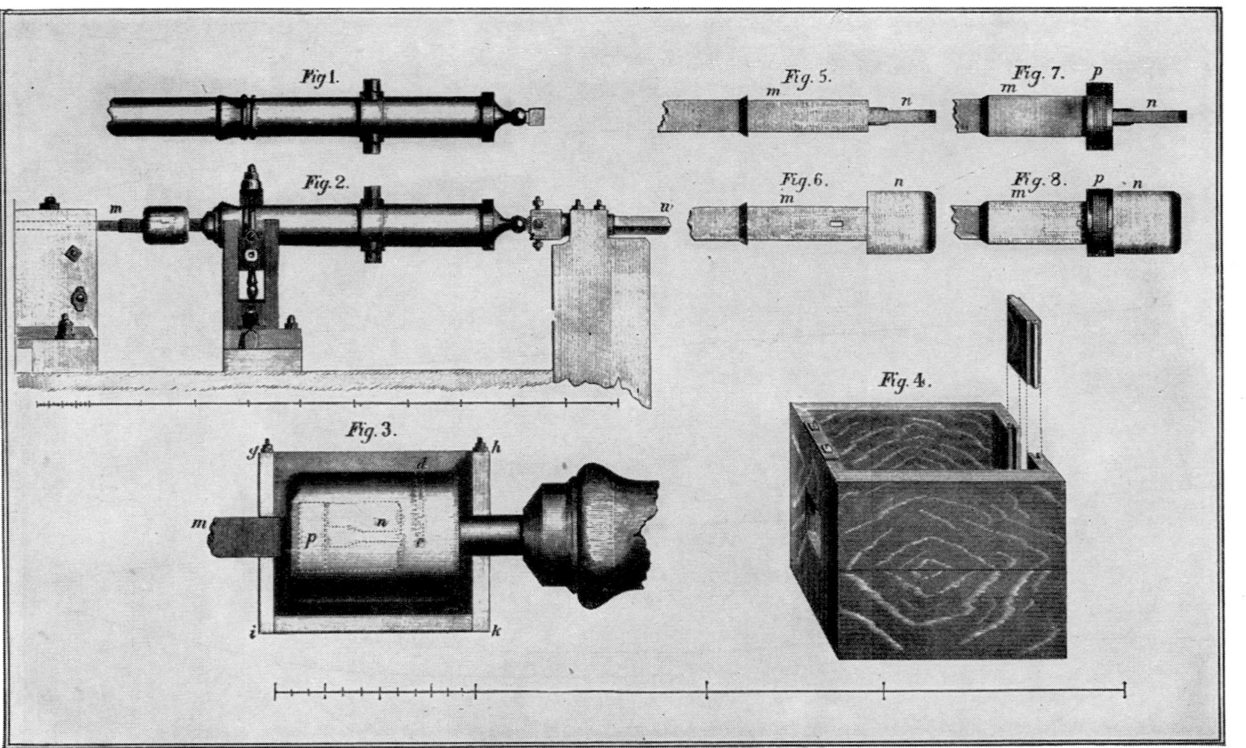

FIGURE 15–A. Rumford's picture of his apparatus. In the lathe (*Fig. 2*) for finishing and boring the rough casting (*Fig. 1*), Rumford had a cylindrical appendage, about 10 inches long, fashioned from the waste metal beyond the cannon's mouth. He then turned the cannon against a blunt boring tool (n), sometimes with the cylinder enclosed in a water-filled box (*Figs. 3* and *4*) in order to estimate the amount of heat that was generated.

The new piece of the puzzle was discovered in 1798 by one of the most colorful men in the history of science, Benjamin Thompson, who started out in life as a barefoot farm boy and became in succession a school teacher, the squire of a New Hampshire village, a British colonel and knight, a Bavarian major general, a Count of the Holy Roman Empire, and a Parisian philanthropist. He chose the title of Count Rumford, after the New Hampshire town where he had taught school, and he is usually referred to by that name.

Along with all his other activities, Rumford had an abiding interest in physics, and had already published several researches before making the discovery for which he is most noted. While supervising the arsenal in Munich, he was impressed by the large amount of heat that was produced when a cannon was bored. Measuring the heat that was produced when a blunt tool was used (Figure 15–A), he found that heat kept coming out at an undiminished rate as long as the horses operated the boring machine. The supply of caloric in a small cannon was apparently inexhaustible! This experiment convinced him that heat cannot be a substance. He concluded that heat must be motion, since he could imagine nothing else that the horses could produce in unlimited amounts.

From very early Greek times, many philosophers and scientists had had a notion that all matter is made up of small indivisible particles. This notion had not had a scientific basis; it was a mere speculation, but by the eighteenth century it had gained wide acceptance. Rumford suggested that the change in a substance when it is heated is a change in the motion of the tiny particles of which the substance is composed. This is close to the modern view, and we shall see how it came to be accepted and elaborated.

Summary

In the eighteenth century, the facts that were known about heat and temperature were interpreted as meaning that heat is a fluid substance, called caloric, and that the presence of caloric in a body was made manifest by the temperature of the body.

The caloric theory was called into question by Rumford, whose experiments showed that the supply of heat in a small cannon appeared to be inexhaustible. Since he could not imagine how any substance could be inexhaustible, he suggested that heat was connected in some way with the motion of the small particles of which bodies were thought to be composed.

Questions

1. In Article 3–4 there is a discussion of scientific method. Analyze the rise and fall of the caloric theory in terms of that article. (Suggestion: for each of the steps listed in the article, write one or possibly two sentences stating its counterpart in the progress of the caloric theory.)
2. State concisely the contradiction between the caloric theory of heat and Rumford's experiment in the Munich arsenal.

Suggestions for Further Reading

Rumford's paper is in the *Philosophical Transactions of the Royal Society* (London), vol. 88 (1798). It is also in *The Complete Works of Count Rumford* (Boston: American Academy of Arts and Sciences, 1870–75). An abridgment appears in W. F. Magie's *A Source Book of Physics* (New York: McGraw-Hill Book Co., Inc., 1935), pp. 151–61.

S. C. Brown, "The Caloric Theory of Heat," *American Journal of Physics,* vol. 18, 367–73 (1950). Outlines the caloric theory and quotes some contemporary objections to Rumford's conclusion.

D. Roller, *The Early Development of the Concepts of Temperature and Heat* (Cambridge: Harvard University Press, 1950). Case 3 of the *Harvard Case Histories in Experimental Science.*

16

THE CONSERVATION OF ENERGY

> However significant a single experiment may seem in retrospect, no important step forward in experimental science rests solely on the record of any single investigator's observations.
>
> J. B. Conant (1950)

One might expect that after Rumford's work (1798), the caloric theory would have been immediately abandoned. This did not happen; in fact, Rumford's work does not seem to have attracted much attention, although it was published in one of the principal scientific journals. That scientists went happily on, using the caloric theory, can be ascribed to two causes. First, Rumford did not really have a theory of his own. He only had a general hypothesis, and said so.* Scientists could scarcely be blamed for using an old theory until someone had suggested a better one. Second, and probably more important, the work of Rumford was not quantitative. He did make an estimate of the amount of heat produced by a given amount of work in boring a gun, but he apparently made no attempt to find out how much work was required to produce the same amount of heat by means of a different mechanical device.

Someone has said that facts are stubborn things. Granting this, we may say that the most stubborn of all facts are those that can be expressed numerically. As a cannon was the final argument of kings, so a number is the final argument of scientists. It was a number that finally killed the caloric theory of heat, fifty years after Rumford's experiment.

16–1. The Conservation of Energy (about 1847). The number just referred to was the result of many measurements made by a young Englishman, James Joule, whose name is commemorated in our unit of work. Joule, provided amply with funds, and occasionally with apparatus, by his father's brewery, devised many ways of doing work on bodies without

* In the light of contemporary knowledge, it was easy to find fault with the hypothesis. For example, critics asked: If heat is the motion of the particles of matter, how does it come to us from the sun, through millions of miles of space?

giving them kinetic energy. For example, he allowed falling weights to turn a paddle wheel and do work on water, the motion of the water being impeded by a set of fixed vanes, as shown in Figure 16–A. He found that the water not merely got warmer, but that it gained 1 calorie of heat when about 4000 joules * of work were expended on it, 2 calories when about 8000 joules were expended, and so on. He also tried churning oil and mercury, and heating cast iron by friction, always with the same numeri-

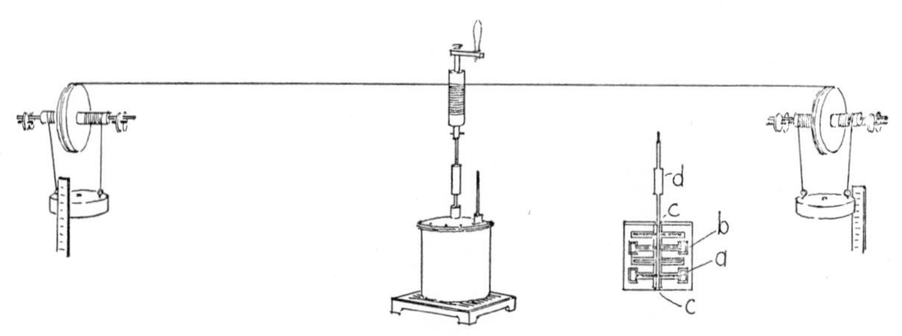

FIGURE 16–A. Joule's apparatus, as depicted by him. The inset shows the interior of the churn. The parts are: *a,* rotating vanes; *b,* fixed vanes; *c,* bearings; *d,* a wooden block to keep heat from escaping along the shaft.

cal result. When Joule reached the age of 30, he had spent a decade in making ever more varied and more refined measurements of the heat produced when work is expended in different ways. His experiments showed conclusively that when a given amount of mechanical energy is lost, a perfectly definite amount of heat is generated. In other words, mechanical energy that disappears is converted into heat. *We are therefore justified in regarding heat as a form of energy* and are encouraged to believe that *the amount of energy in the universe is fixed.* This is the famous Law of the Conservation of Energy.

* Joule actually used British units in his calculations, but the figures given here are their equivalents in the metric system we have been using.

JAMES PRESCOTT JOULE, growing up in a suburb of Manchester, was educated by private tutors. After an athletic boyhood, he set up a laboratory in his father's house, and published his first research papers when he was 20. Motivated, no doubt, by the Industrial Revolution that was converting Manchester into a great manufacturing city, Joule made and studied an electric motor. On finding the operation of this device a very expensive way to produce mechanical work, he began to investigate the relation between work and heat. He soon convinced himself of the Conservation of Energy; in the course of time, his exquisite skill in measurement enabled him to marshal enough data to convince the rest of the world. His later years were brightened by the fame and honors befitting the discoverer of one of the great laws of nature.

James Prescott Joule
(1818–1889)

The same idea is expressed in slightly different form in the First Law of Thermodynamics:

> Work and heat are interchangeable, at the rate of 4180 joules to the calorie.

An analogous statement is that British and American money are interchangeable, at the rate of so many shillings to the dollar.

Knowing that heat is a form of energy, we could now measure it in joules instead of in calories. Actually this is sometimes done, but the calorie is more widely used, partly because of tradition and partly because it is convenient in the laboratory, where heat is measured by the temperature rise it will produce in a known mass of water.

The discovery of the Conservation of Energy illustrates a phenomenon that is fairly common in the development of science. Rumford came very close to discovering the law in 1798, but his work was not sufficiently conclusive to win acceptance for its implications. After another fifty years of general advance in science, not only Joule but also at least three other men, all working independently, hit on the idea of conservation of energy at about the same time, by very different approaches.* Joule is usually given credit for discovering the fact that heat is a form of energy, because he made the most conclusive experiments.

16–2. A Specific Example of Conservation of Energy. On his honeymoon in the Alps, Joule took along his bride and a large, sensitive thermometer. The thermometer was for measuring the temperature of a certain stream before and after it passed over a high waterfall.

When water goes over a fall, its P.E. is converted into K.E., and then at the bottom the K.E. is converted into heat. It will be an instructive exercise to calculate the temperature rise that one would find at the Upper Yosemite Falls, where the water drops 1430 feet.

The first thing to do is convert the given height of 1430 feet into meters. Since

$$1 \text{ ft} = 0.3050 \text{ m},$$
$$1430 \text{ ft} = 1430 \times 0.3050 \text{ m} = 436 \text{ m}.$$

Consider a definite amount, say 1 kg, of water at the top of the fall. Its P.E. is

$$\text{P.E.} = mgh = 1 \text{ kg} \times 9.80 \text{ m/sec}^2 \times 436 \text{ m} = 4270 \text{ joules}.$$

Now 4270 joules is the same as 4270/4180 calories, or 1.02 calories, and 1.02 calories will warm 1 kg of water by 1.02 Centigrade degrees, which is a little less than 2 Fahrenheit degrees.

16–3. Steam Engines. Until now, this chapter has dealt explicitly only with the conversion of work into heat. The converse process, the conver-

* The average age of these four men was 27 years.

sion of heat into work, is also both possible and important, although it requires somewhat elaborate equipment. Of the many devices for converting heat into work, we shall consider only the steam engine, shown diagrammatically in Figure 16-B. In this engine, fuel is burned to boil water, thereby converting water into steam and storing energy in it in the form of heat. Some of the energy stored in the steam is removed by letting the steam push a piston (a movable plug in a cylindrical chamber).

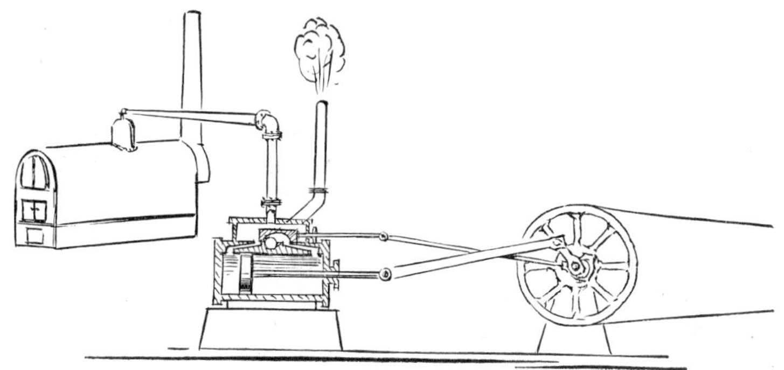

FIGURE 16-B. A steam engine with its furnace and boiler.

This action cools the steam, because some of the heat in the steam is being converted into work. Then the steam is permitted to escape through a valve. By means of a crank arm, the moving piston turns a shaft which is connected to a pump, a buzz saw, or some other useful machine. The inertia of a flywheel, together with a system of automatic valves for admitting steam and letting it out again, permits the engine to run continuously.

The fact that the steam still has some heat in it when it is ejected means that not all of the heat supplied by the boiler can be converted into work. This turns out to be true for any kind of engine; it is simply a consequence of the fact that heat will not of itself run from a cold body to a hot one. Considerations of this sort led to the formulation of the Second Law of Thermodynamics:

> Although mechanical energy can be converted entirely into heat, heat can be converted into work only if other heat is discarded.

The *efficiency* of an engine is the ratio of the work put out to the energy taken in. Because it is necessary to discard some heat in order for the engine to operate, heat engines are necessarily inefficient. In practice, an efficiency as high as 25 percent can be obtained only with very large and expensive engines.

16-4. Refrigerators. In a heat engine, heat flows from a hot place (the boiler) to a cool one (the condenser or the atmosphere), and heat is converted into work. A refrigerator uses work (from an electric motor) to make heat flow from a cool place (inside the box) to a warm one (the surrounding air). In function, therefore, a refrigerator is just the reverse of a steam engine. Actually the two mechanisms are much the same, except that the arrangement of valves is somewhat different, and in a refrigerator some other gas than steam is much more convenient.

Summary

In what amounted to a continuation of Rumford's work, Joule found by careful measurement that whenever heat is produced by the expenditure of mechanical energy, 1 calorie of heat is produced for each 4180 joules of mechanical energy expended. This relationship holds regardless of the mechanism involved. It is therefore agreed that heat is a form of energy.

The work of Joule led him to the Law of Conservation of Energy: The amount of energy in the universe is fixed.

What amounts to the same thing is expressed in the First Law of Thermodynamics: Work and heat are interchangeable, at the rate of 4180 joules to the calorie. Joules and calories are therefore different units for measuring the same kind of physical quantity.

A steam engine is a device for converting heat into work. Its efficiency is inevitably far from high, because in order to convert some heat into work, other heat has to be discarded (the Second Law of Thermodynamics).

A refrigerator is a device for using work to move heat from a cool place to a hot one. It is, in principle, a steam engine run backwards.

Questions

1. Describe the experiments that led Joule to the Law of Conservation of Energy. What do the experiments indicate about heat?
2. A 60-watt bulb converts electrical energy (which we shall study later) into heat and light, at the rate of 60 watts, or 60 joules/sec. Suppose that such a bulb is immersed in 0.300 kg of water (about a tumblerful) and that 90 percent of the power dissipated in the bulb goes into heating the water. If the bulb is turned on for 100 sec, calculate:
   (a) The energy converted into heat and light.
   (b) The heat gained by the water.
   (c) The temperature rise of the water.

17

THE DYNAMICAL THEORY OF HEAT

I remember distinctly at the Royal Society, I think it was either —— or —— saying he simply did not believe Joule, because he had nothing but hundredths of a degree to prove his case by.

LORD KELVIN

The work of Joule proved that heat is a form of energy, and not a substance. It will be recalled that Rumford, led by his discovery that heat can be generated indefinitely by doing work, suggested that heat is motion—motion of the little particles of which matter is composed. Fifty years later, Joule and others, elaborating on this idea, worked out a theory of heat that has now been accepted for nearly a century. Before examining this theory, let us digress long enough to consider the first direct evidence that matter actually is composed of tiny particles.

17–1. The Brownian Motion (1827). Tobacco smoke consists of fairly small solid particles suspended in air. When observed individually under a microscope, these particles are seen to undergo a very irregular motion. This motion affords direct evidence that air consists of very small particles (much too small to be made visible by a microscope), and that these particles are in constant motion. The particles of air collide with the smoke particles on all sides, in a random manner. Sometimes a few more air particles hit one side of the smoke particle than the other, and the smoke particle is small enough so that a slight difference in the number of particles striking opposite sides will give it a visible displacement.

The motion of the microscopic particles is called *Brownian motion,* in honor of a British botanist named Brown, who discovered it in 1827 while examining pollen granules suspended in water.

17–2. The Influence of the Particles on One Another. Accept, as a hypothesis to be tested by its results, the view that all matter consists of submicroscopic particles. Then the fact that solids resist deformation, and usually do not evaporate noticeably, leads one to suppose that the particles of a solid exert attractive forces on one another. Gases, on the other hand, will swell to fill any container, however large. From this, one infers that the particles of a gas do not attract one another very strongly. Liquids are an intermediate case; they do not necessarily fill the vessel that holds them, as a gas does, but on the whole they evaporate more readily than solids do.

If a paint brush is wet with any liquid, the hairs will adhere to one another, because of the attraction that the particles of the liquid exert on one another. On the other hand, the hairs in a dry brush that is surrounded by air, or any other gas, do not stick together.

It is a matter of common knowledge that water, and watery things like milk, expand when they freeze. Most substances behave differently, however: they expand when they *melt.* Therefore when these are in the liquid state, their particles are on the average farther apart than in the solid state, so it is not surprising that they exert smaller forces on one another. Similarly, when a liquid changes to a gas, as when water changes to steam, there is another expansion. (Steam at atmospheric pressure and 100° C occupies over 1000 times as much volume as the water from which it came.) Therefore the particles of gas must be relatively far apart, and we should expect that they would not exert much force on one another.

17–3. The Dynamical Theory of Gases (about 1850). Joule's experimental work convinced him that Rumford was right in associating heat with the motion of the submicroscopic particles of matter. He then set out to develop from this hypothesis a quantitative theory of heat. The obvious way to commence is by applying Newton's laws to the motions of the particles. This procedure will correlate the motions of the particles with the forces that act on them. The fewer the forces, the simpler the problem. It is therefore best to begin by studying gases and ignoring whatever small forces the gas particles may exert on one another. It was in this way that Joule attacked the problem, and the treatment that follows resembles his in many respects. But to simplify matters we shall ignore the remaining, and less interesting, history of the development, and simply state the theory in its present form.

If we try to apply Newton's laws to a sample of gas enclosed in a balloon, the situation is confused because the particles are traveling in all directions and the walls are curved. To get started on the problem, we resort to a standard technique used by all workers who apply mathematics to science. We devise an artificial situation that resembles the real one in many physical respects, but that differs from the real one in such a way as to eliminate many mathematical difficulties. Fortified by his experience with the artificial problem, one can often devise a way of solving the real one. (By solving a succession of artificial problems, each a little closer to reality, one can cope with the mathematical difficulties one at a time.)

Imagine a rectangular box full of flying particles. Suppose for simplicity that one-third of the particles are traveling perpendicularly to each pair of faces, as in Figure 17–A. That is, if n is the number of particles in the box, then $n/3$ particles are traveling straight up and down, making "head-on" collisions with the top and bottom. Another $n/3$ particles are traveling between back and front, and the remaining $n/3$ are migrating between the left and right walls. Suppose further that the magnitude of the velocity is the same for all particles. It would be unreasonable to expect that the particles in a box of gas really behave in this way, but after having made calculations for this artificial problem, we shall have a better idea of how to solve a more realistic one.

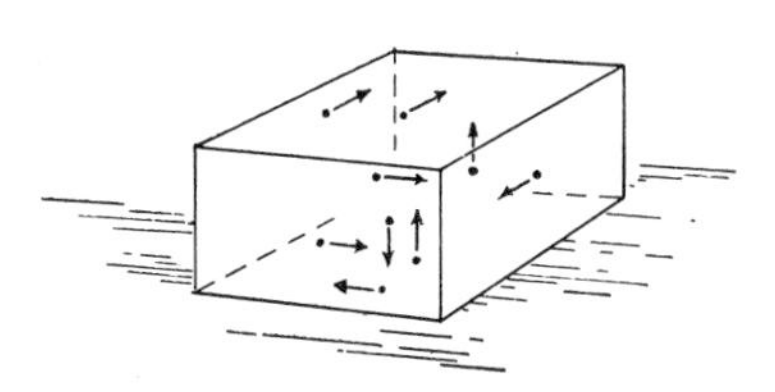

FIGURE 17–A. A model of a box of gas.

When a particle bounces against one of the walls, its direction of motion changes, so its velocity changes. The change in velocity implies a change in the particle's momentum, which can occur only if the particle experiences a force (Newton's Second Law). The force in this case is exerted by the wall. We shall calculate the force exerted by the wall on the particles; Newton's Third Law (Article 7–1) states that the particles exert an equal and opposite force on the wall. Taking this force and dividing it by the area of the wall gives the pressure that the flying particles exert on their container. We calculate this pressure because pressure is one of the easily observed properties of a real gas. We find a striking similarity between the result *calculated* for an artificially behaving collection of ideal particles and the result *observed* in experiments on real gases.

The calculation runs as follows. Referring to Figure 17–B, let

n = number of particles in box
m = mass of each particle
v = velocity of each particle
L = width of box
A = area of right-hand wall
V = volume of box.

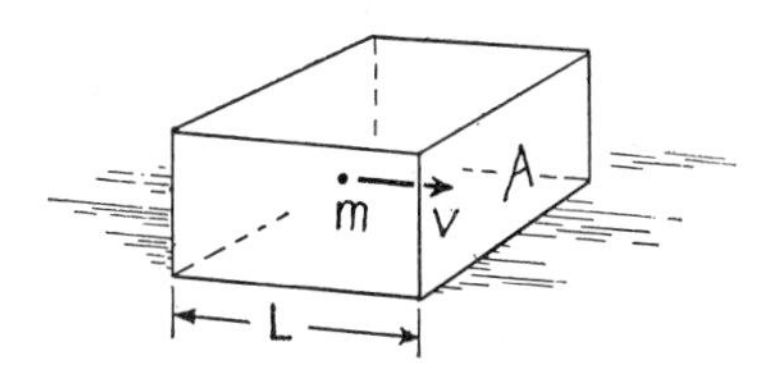

FIGURE 17–B. A gas particle in a box.

Take the direction from left to right to be positive, and consider the collisions that a single particle makes with the right-hand wall. At each such collision, the momentum of the particle changes from mv to $-mv$, because its direction of travel is reversed. The change in momentum is

$$(\text{Final momentum}) - (\text{Initial momentum}) = (-mv) - (mv) = -2mv.$$

To calculate the average force exerted on the particle, what we need of course is not simply the change in momentum, but the average *rate* of change of momentum. We must therefore find the average time associated with the change in momentum just calculated. There is one collision with the right-hand wall every time the particle makes a round trip across the box. The time required for a trip is the distance divided by the magnitude of the velocity, in this case, $2L/v$.

The average rate of change of momentum of our particle in its collisions with the right-hand wall is

$$\frac{\text{Change of momentum at each collision}}{\text{Time interval between collisions}} = \frac{-2mv}{\dfrac{2L}{v}} = -\frac{mv^2}{L}.$$

By Newton's Second Law (Article 5–3), the average force exerted *on the particle by the wall* is therefore $-mv^2/L$, and by Newton's Third Law (Article 7–1), the force exerted *on the wall by the particle* is mv^2/L. (The fact that this quantity is positive indicates that the force on the wall is in the positive direction, which is toward the right. This is certainly to be expected.) The average force exerted on the wall by all of the $n/3$ particles that make collisions with it is

$$F = \frac{n}{3} \times \frac{mv^2}{L} = \frac{nmv^2}{3L}.$$

This is only the average force, because of course each particle exerts a force on the wall only when it is actually making a collision. But when we consider a very large number of particles, all pattering against the wall independently, we see that the total force due to *all* of the particles must be very nearly a *steady* one. (Fluctuations in the average force on a smoke particle, in a real gas, are made apparent by the Brownian motion mentioned above. The fluctuations in the force exerted by a real gas on anything as large as the wall of a box are too small to be detected by anything but the most refined apparatus.)

To calculate the pressure p exerted on the wall by the particles, take the force computed above and divide it by the area of the right wall, which is A.

$$p = \frac{\text{Force}}{\text{Area}} = \frac{\dfrac{nmv^2}{3L}}{A} = \frac{nmv^2}{3LA} = \frac{nmv^2}{3V},$$

because $LA = V$, the volume of the box. We have, then,

$$pV = \tfrac{1}{3}nmv^2,$$

an equation that contains two familiar products. The quantity pV enters into laws that describe the results of *experiments* on real gases, and mv^2 is twice the kinetic energy of each particle. We have therefore established a relationship between the experimentally observable properties of a real gas and the K.E. of the particles that constitute our artificial "gas." This result is lovely and encouraging. The equation can be put in a nicer form by writing

$$pV = \tfrac{2}{3}n \times \tfrac{1}{2}mv^2$$

$$pV = \tfrac{2}{3}n \times (\text{K.E. of each particle}).$$

Stimulated by this success, one can go through the same kind of reasoning for the more difficult, but more realistic, case of a box of arbitrary shape, full of particles that are bounding about in all directions at random, making collisions with each other as well as with the walls, and not all having the same K.E. The result is

$$pV = \tfrac{2}{3}n \times (\text{Average K.E. of a particle}).$$

Comparing this with Boyle's Law (Article 13–2), we see that keeping the temperature of a gas constant means keeping constant the average K.E. of the gas particles. Comparing it with the General Gas Law, $pV = cT$, shows that the *Absolute temperature* of a gas is proportional to the *average K.E. of the gas particles.*

17–4. The Nature of Heat. If a hot gas surrounds a cool solid, the temperature of the solid is known to rise. We conjecture that the bombardment of the particles of the solid by the highly energetic particles of the gas will agitate the particles of the solid, setting them into more violent motion than before. Therefore, in the case of solids also, a rise in temperature is to be correlated with an increase in K.E. of the particles. One can readily suppose, then, that even in the case of solids (or, equally well, of liquids) *the Absolute temperature is a measure of the average K.E. of the particles of the substance.* The consequences of this assumption can be examined mathematically. Although the analysis is more difficult than it is for gases, the theory leads to predictions that are verified by experiment.

We now, at last, have a definite interpretation of the meaning of temperature, and we see why the Absolute scale of temperatures has a special significance. Each kind of thermometer scale defines temperature in a somewhat different way. Temperature defined in any one of these ways is a guide to the average K.E. of the particles of the body whose temperature is being measured. The Absolute scale is a particularly clear and simple guide, because this scale makes the average K.E. and the temperature just proportional to one another.

The connection between heat and work is also apparent now. We started to study heat because we observed that when K.E. seems to disappear, there is often a rise in temperature. The dynamical theory of heat explains this rise: The K.E. of some large moving body is simply converted into K.E. of the submicroscopic particles. The more material we have, the more particles we have, and the more work must be supplied in order to raise the average K.E. of the particles by a given amount. Comparing this theory with the fact that the more material we have, the more heat we have to put into it to raise its temperature by a given amount, we might get the notion that heat is the *total* K.E. of *all* the particles. When changes of state are taken into account, however, we see that this notion has to be extended. When a liquid changes to a gas, heat energy enters the substance, but no change in temperature results. Now the change from a liquid to a gaseous state does produce an increase in volume, and therefore it must produce a separation of the particles of the liquid in spite of their attraction for one another. This separation of the attracting particles results in an increase of P.E., just as does the stretching of a spring or the lifting of a weight. Therefore, heat energy put into a substance can increase either the K.E. or the P.E. of the particles, and heat energy must be the total energy of the particles.

The difference between temperature and heat is now very clear: The Absolute temperature of a body is a measure of the *average K.E.* of the *individual* particles of the body; the heat in a body is the *total energy* (both K.E. and P.E.) of *all* the particles of which the body is composed.

During the past century the implications of this theory of heat have been thoroughly worked out and found to be in complete accord with very detailed quantitative experiments. The theory is therefore regarded as thoroughly satisfactory; it affords perhaps the finest example of a mature theory that science has to offer. The next chapter will be devoted to some of its implications.

Summary

The Brownian motion, a random jiggling of microscopic particles suspended in a fluid, provides direct evidence that matter consists of very tiny particles, too small to be visible even in the most powerful microscope.

By comparing the properties of solids, liquids, and gases, one can infer that in a solid the particles of matter must be close to, and exert considerable attraction on, one another. In a gas the particles are farther apart and do not attract one another strongly. Liquids form an intermediate case.

The dynamical theory of gases is based on the application of the laws of mechanics to the motion of the gaseous particles. A simple mechanical "model" of a gas, consisting of particles flying about independently of one another in a box of volume V, can be shown to produce on the walls of the box a pressure p such that

$$pV \propto \text{Average K.E. of a particle.}$$

Comparing this with the experimental fact that for a real gas

$$pV \propto T,$$

one concludes that the Absolute temperature of a gas is a measure of the average K.E. of the individual gas particles.

Interpreting heat is a trifle more complicated. When we raise the temperature of a body by putting heat into it, we raise the average K.E. of its particles, and therefore the total K.E. of its particles is increased. Heat is energy, and one might jump to the conclusion that the heat in a body is simply the total K.E. of its particles. There are times, however, when a body takes in heat without any change in its temperature. That is, the body takes in energy, but its particles do not gain K.E. On these occasions, the state of the body changes in such a way that its particles gain P.E. We conclude, therefore, that the heat put into a body to raise its temperature goes into an increase in the K.E. of its particles, while heat put into a body to melt or vaporize it goes into an increase in the P.E. of the particles. The total heat in a body is the sum of the K.E. and the P.E. of the particles.

Questions

1. What is Brownian motion?
2. What is the implication of Brownian motion?
3. Cite evidence to support the belief that the particles of matter exert attractive forces on one another, and that these attractions are stronger when the particles are closer together.
4. How does the existence of Brownian motion bear on the work of Rumford?
5. In formulating a theory of how the particles of matter behave, why is it best to start with matter in the gaseous state?
6. Explain the connection between Newton's Third Law of Motion and the pressure exerted by a gas.
7. Describe and explain the behavior of a gas as the temperature decreases.
8. Explain the significance of the Absolute scale of temperature, and of Absolute Zero.
9. What facts demand that, when considering the amount of heat in a body, we must include both the K.E. and the P.E. of its particles?
10. The pressure exerted by a gas depends on the *square* of the velocity of its particles. Show that it does so because the pressure depends on the momentum of the particles and on the frequency of the collisions.

18

IMPLICATIONS OF THE THEORY OF HEAT

We have reached an important milestone in our study of molecules and atoms. Although the distinction between molecules and atoms will have to be deferred until we begin a study of chemistry, you probably know already, at least in a hazy way, that molecules and atoms are the tiny units from which matter-in-bulk is assembled. The dynamical theory of heat is based on the existence of such units, and its success is one of the most convincing proofs that they actually do exist. Further proof is afforded by the facts of chemistry, which will be taken up in the next section. It is appropriate now to consider some of the information about the particles that can be deduced from the theory of heat.

18–1. The Size of the Gas Particles. In the last chapter, we discussed an artificial model of a gas, consisting of particles that are ideally small, exert no forces on one another, move in paths perpendicular to the walls, and all have the same velocity as far as magnitude is concerned. We found that such a gas would produce a pressure on the walls which is given by the equation

$$pV = \tfrac{1}{3}nmv^2,$$

or

$$pV = \tfrac{2}{3}n \times (\text{K.E. of each particle}).$$

It was stated without proof that by using somewhat more complicated mathematics, one can treat the case of particles moving at random, the result being almost the same:

$$pV = \tfrac{2}{3}n \times (\text{Average K.E. of a particle}).$$

One can also make calculations on a still more realistic model of a gas, a model composed of particles that occupy space (rather than being "infinitely small") and that exert slight attractive forces on one another. The result is a relationship between pressure and volume that differs from the General Gas Law, but is in accord with the actual behavior of gases, which you will remember is not satisfactorily described by the General Gas Law, nor by Boyle's Law, when the pressure is high. This gratifying result enhances our faith that real gases are made up of small flying particles, and it also gives information about the size of the particles. Although the details of the calculation are a little sophisticated, it is very easy to see in a general way how this information about size is obtained. In making the calculation of the pressure–volume relationship for gases whose particles are not ideally small, the physicist has to make some assumption as to the volume of each particle. The assumption that makes the resulting gas law agree best with experimental measurements is easily found by trial. By this means it is found that the diameter of the gas particles is of the order of a hundred-millionth of an inch, or about 10^{-10} m.

18–2. The Velocity of the Gas Particles. Suppose one has two boxes with the same volume, one containing air and the other containing some other gas, say hydrogen. Suppose further that both gases are at the same temperature, and that just enough hydrogen is put in the one box to produce a pressure equal to that of the air in the other box. Then we have two dissimilar gases at the same pressure and temperature, occupying equal volumes. Look again at the equation

$$pV = \tfrac{2}{3}n \times (\text{Average K.E. of a particle}).$$

Because the two boxes of gas are at the same temperature, the average K.E. of a particle is the same for both. The equation says that then n is proportional to pV. But p is the same for both boxes, and so is V. Therefore n must be the same for both boxes, or in other words the theory implies that *equal volumes of gas at the same temperature and pressure contain the same number of particles.* This proposition will be encountered again later in connection with the foundations of chemistry, but at present it permits qualitative support for the dynamical theory to be drawn from a simple experiment.

EXPERIMENT. Let hydrogen be put into two test tubes, one right side up and the other inverted. A lighted match applied to the mouth of the inverted tube will cause a small explosion, indicating the presence of hydrogen; no such result is produced in the other tube. The immediate conclusion is that hydrogen rises in air and is therefore lighter than air. A less direct conclusion can also be drawn. The first step, of which the details are left to you, is the realization that if hydrogen is lighter than air of the same volume, temperature, and pressure, then the italicized proposition in the last paragraph implies that the particles of hydrogen gas are less massive than the particles of air. Now at a given temperature, the particles of hydrogen have the same average K.E. as the particles of air. Then mv^2 is the same for the hydrogen and for the air, but m, the mass of a particle, is less for hydrogen than for air; therefore v^2 must be greater for hydrogen. The dynamical theory asserts, then, that at any given temperature the particles of hydrogen move, on the average, more rapidly than those of air. This assertion can be verified as follows.

An unglazed earthenware vessel holds in its stopper a glass tube that dips into a small beaker of water. A large inverted beaker surrounds the earthenware vessel, as in Figure 18–A. Fill the inverted beaker with hydrogen. The air trapped in the earthenware vessel will diffuse out through the walls, but the hydrogen, by reason of the more rapid motion of its particles, will diffuse into

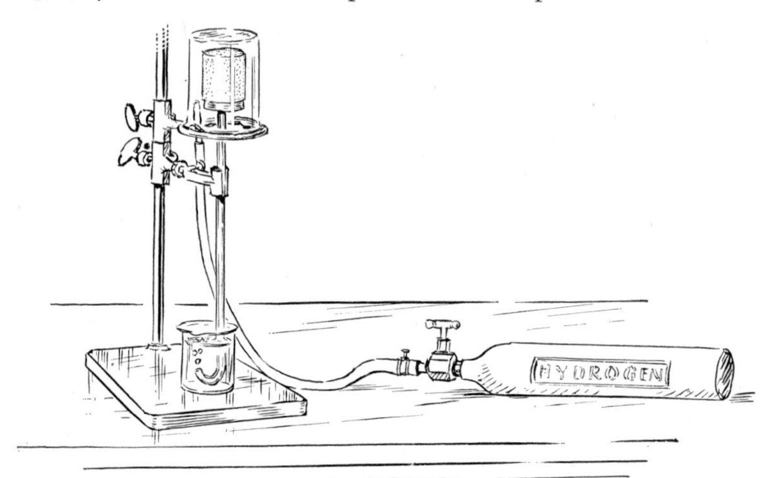

FIGURE 18–A. An experiment to verify that the particles of hydrogen, at room temperature, move more swiftly than those of air.

the vessel faster than the air diffuses out. Therefore an excess of gas accumulates in the vessel, and it is detected by the bubbles it makes in the water as it emerges from the tube. The dynamical theory of heat is therefore correct in its prediction that at a given temperature the particles of a lighter gas move more swiftly than those of a heavier one.

Return now to the equation for the simple artificial model,

$$pV = \tfrac{1}{3}nmv^2.$$

Notice that nm is the mass of "gas" in the box, because m is the mass of one particle and n is the number of particles in the box. If the mass, volume, and pressure of such a "gas" were measured, one could solve for v^2 and take the square root to find the magnitude of the velocity of the particles. The result is

$$v = \sqrt{\frac{3pV}{nm}}.$$

Using a more realistic model leads to nearly the same result, so we are justified in using this simple result to get an *estimate* of the average velocities of the particles in *real* gases. To use the equation, simply measure the pressure, volume, and mass of a sample of the gas. If this is done for air, the equation shows that the average velocity of the particles is about a quarter of a mile per second if the air is at room temperature. Of course, the particles go faster if the air is hotter.

18–3. Evaporation. In a liquid, the particles are moving about, some of them having a little more than the average K.E., some a little less. Suppose that one of the particles moves to the surface of the liquid in Figure 18–B. The attractive forces exerted by its neighbors will urge it back into the body of the liquid. If it is one of the more energetic particles, however, it may be going fast enough to escape from its neighbors. In this case it will pass through the surface and leave the liquid, becoming a "free" particle. (An accumulation of such free particles is a gas.) The higher the temperature, the more particles will have energy enough to break through the surface. This explains why a liquid evaporates more rapidly when it is warm.

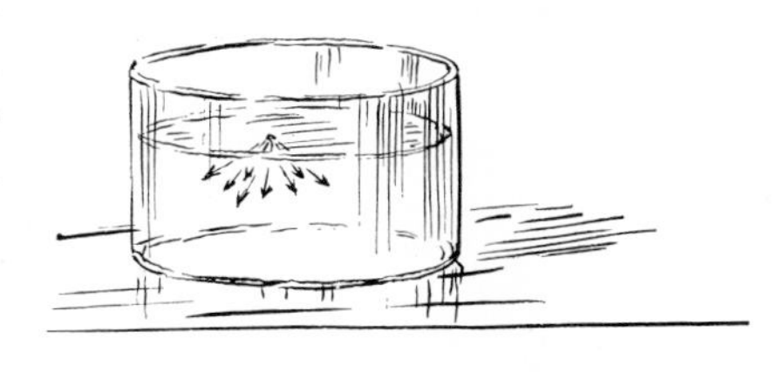

FIGURE 18–B. Evaporation: the escape of a particle is hindered by the attractions of the neighboring particles.

18–4. The Structure of Solids. Perhaps the most interesting application of the dynamical theory is to solids. In contrast to liquids and gases, which resist only changes in volume, a solid resists deformation of any kind. If one believes a solid to be composed of small particles, then one must think of the particles as each belonging in a definite position with respect to its neighbors, and as resisting displacement from this position. Such a view is strengthened by the fact that many solids occur in the form of *crystals,* that is, in aggregates that have certain definite geometrical properties. Snow crystals are a familiar example. They occur in enormous variety, but in all of them an angle of 60 degrees plays a fundamental part, giving them six sides or six prongs. A few are shown in Figure 18–C. Other crystals are shown in Figures 18–D to 18–F.

Although each particle in a crystal must have an appointed position, it must also have some freedom of local motion near that position. Otherwise a solid could not be distorted at all, neither could it change temperature and still remain a solid. Warming a crystal increases the K.E. that its particles attain as they vibrate about in their places. If the temperature gets high enough, the particles will jiggle right out of their regular locations. (Crude analogy: coffee sloshing out of a cup in a dining car on a rough track.) Of course energy must be supplied to move the particles out of the allotted places to which they are attracted. This

By permission from Snow Crystals, *by W. A. Bentley and W. J. Humphreys. Copyright, 1931. McGraw-Hill Book Co., Inc.*

FIGURE 18–C. Crystals of snow.

energy, which goes into P.E. of the particles, is the heat that has to be put in to melt the crystal.

There are some solids, for example glass, that are not crystalline, and they might seem to invalidate this explanation of melting. Actually, however, they confirm it; when they melt, they go imperceptibly from solid to liquid, the temperature rising all the time. All the heat that is put into them goes into an increase in the K.E. of the particles, because they do not have the preferred locations that exist in crystals, and in a strict sense there is no change of state.

18–5. Freezing. As a final application of the dynamical theory of heat, consider the process of freezing. Suppose that a crystalline solid is melted and then cools. The particles slow down in their motions, and have a tendency to regroup themselves to form a crystal. Usually they will do so spontaneously. Sometimes they need a "seed" crystal to establish a pattern on which they can build. In either case, the particles lose

FIGURE 18-D. Crystals of quartz.

FIGURE 18-E. A crystal of garnet.

FIGURE 18–F. Crystals imbedded in dolomite rock. The large cubic ones are galena; the small dark pyramids are calcopyrite.

P.E. when they "drop" into their preferred locations, and this energy is usually given off to the surroundings as the crystallization proceeds. If the substance can be cooled well below its freezing temperature before freezing actually sets in, then a seed crystal, or often just a shake, will make the substance crystallize more rapidly than it can transfer heat to its surroundings. In such cases the P.E. of the particles of the freezing substance goes suddenly into K.E. of the same particles, and the material gets warm before the heat is passed off to the surrounding air. The dynamical theory of heat therefore explains in detail the delayed freezing of thymol, which was described in Article 14–4.

SUMMARY

The success of the dynamical theory of heat is strong evidence in support of the view that matter is composed of small particles, even though it may seem "continuous" to our senses. One can combine the results of the theory with measurements on gases to obtain estimates of the sizes and velocities of the particles. The particles turn out to have diameters of the order of 10^{-10} m, and velocities of the order of 10^3 m/sec, or a kilometer per second, at room temperature.

Evaporation, melting, and freezing can be explained by the dynamical theory. It appears that in a crystalline solid, the particles are grouped in geometrically regular arrays.

The dynamical theory successfully explains the observed facts associated with evaporation, melting, and freezing.

The external appearance of crystals, and their thermal behavior, both support the hypothesis that the particles comprising a crystal are arranged in some regular manner.

Questions

1. What is the approximate size of a gas particle? How is it known?
2. What is the approximate velocity of a gas particle, if the gas is air at room temperature? How can this velocity be found?
3. Hydrogen has about one-sixteenth as much mass as does a sample of air that has the same temperature, pressure, and volume. At room temperature, what is the approximate velocity of the particles of hydrogen gas?
4. In terms of the dynamical theory of heat, explain the absorption or liberation of heat during a change in state.
5. The text argues that the particles in a solid must have freedom to move locally, for "otherwise a solid could not be distorted at all, neither could it change temperature and still remain a solid." Fill in the details of the reasoning.
6. It is shown in the experiment of Article 18–2, that hydrogen gas in bulk is lighter than a similar sample of air; then the text states that the particles of hydrogen gas are less massive than the particles of air. Give the full line of reasoning involved.
7. (a) A kilogram of steam at 100° C occupies 1.67 cubic meters at a pressure of 10^5 newtons per square meter. Using the appropriate equation in Article 18–2, find the magnitude of the velocity of the particles of the steam.

   (b) The equation makes no mention of temperature. How is it to be reconciled with the statement that if the gas is hotter, then the particles move faster?

GENERAL VIEW OF SECTION II

Temperature can be defined in terms of some property of a body that changes when the body gets warmer (as judged by sense of touch). Each kind of thermometer can be made to establish a scale of temperature. These scales will be different for different types of thermometers; the scales will usually depend on the properties of the thermometric substance. The gas thermometer, however, gives the same scale no matter what gas is used, as long as the pressure is kept low. Temperatures as defined by this thermometer can therefore be expected to have some kind of fundamental significance. If the temperature corresponding to zero pressure or zero volume is taken as zero temperature (Absolute Zero), then the pressure, volume, and Absolute temperature of a gas are related by the equation $pV = cT$.

Heat is a concept that is introduced in order to explain changes in temperature. It is not the same as temperature or change in temperature, because if the same amount of heat is removed from different bodies, they usually experience different changes in temperature. Heat is measured by observing the temperature change of a known mass of water. The unit of heat is the calorie, which is the amount of heat that will produce in 1 kg of water a temperature change of 1 Centigrade degree. (It is an experimental fact that this same amount of heat will produce a temperature change of about 33 Centigrade degrees in 1 kg of lead, or 11 degrees in 1 kg of copper. These figures are not important in themselves, but they may help to distinguish the concept of heat from the concept of temperature.)

There are times when heat can be given to or taken from a body without producing any change in the temperature of the body. When this happens, there is a change in the state of the body; i.e., it melts or freezes, or vaporizes or condenses.

In the eighteenth century these facts were explained in terms of the caloric theory, which considered heat to be a substance. The substance, called caloric, was supposed to seep into bodies, and to pass from warm ones to cooler ones when they were placed in contact. This theory was undermined by Rumford, who showed that an ordinary piece of metal could be made to give off heat as long as work was done on it. The theory did not finally collapse, however, until Joule showed that 1 calorie of heat is liberated when 4180 joules of mechanical energy is expended, regardless of the process by which one expends the work. This indicates that heat is energy. (Except for reasons of tradition and convenience, one could just as well measure heat in joules, instead of calories.) Devices called heat engines—steam, gasoline, diesel, jet—are able to convert heat into mechanical energy. Mechanical energy can be converted into heat by friction, pounding, etc.

Joule suggested that a gas exerts pressure because it is composed of tiny particles which bombard the walls of the containing vessel. A quantitative investigation of the consequences of this assumption shows that if it is true, then

$$pV \propto \text{Average K.E. of a particle.}$$

But we know, from the definition of Absolute temperature, that

$$pV \propto T.$$

Therefore T, the Absolute temperature, is proportional to the average K.E. of a particle.

To raise the temperature of a gas, we must increase the average K.E. of the particles; that means we must put energy into the gas. We must also put energy into a substance to separate its particles against their mutual attraction for one another. Energy put in to raise temperature increases the K.E. of the particles. Energy put in to melt or to vaporize the substance increases the P.E. of the particles. The total energy of the particles, K.E. and P.E., is the heat the body possesses.

The fact that the foregoing set of assumptions explains heat phenomena is strong evidence that matter is composed of tiny particles. Additional evidence for such belief is afforded by the Brownian motion of smoke or pollen particles (due to their bombardment by the invisibly small particles of air) and also by the regular geometry of crystals.

Still further evidence was brought out in the same period (early nineteenth century) by the study of chemical phenomena, to which the next section will be devoted.

III

Foundations of Chemistry

It is time to turn to another path of exploration which confirmed scientifically the ancient surmise that matter consists of invisibly small particles. Here we shall find one of the most impressive examples of the power of quantitative study. Although the individual particles are far too small to affect even the most sensitive modern balance, strong evidence for their existence was found by the use of very mediocre balances, bulk samples of matter, and clear thinking.

The first few chapters of this section describe the scientific discovery of atoms. The later chapters introduce a few of the simpler techniques for describing the interactions of atoms with one another. To avoid confusion of the rather exacting logic, the variety of chemical experiments discussed is kept small. In some of the ensuing sections, the abstractions introduced here will be applied to a host of concrete situations.

19

THE ELEMENTS

> And, to prevent mistakes, I must advertize You, that I now mean by Elements, as those Chymists that speak plainest do by their Principles, certain Primitive and simple, or perfectly unmingled bodies; which not being made of any other bodies, or of one another, are the Ingredients of which all those call'd perfectly mixt Bodies are immediately compounded, and into which they are ultimately resolved.
>
> BOYLE

It has already been mentioned that Thales, pondering the nature of matter about 580 B.C., came to the conclusion that water is the primal stuff from which all matter is made. His successors among the Greek philosophers disagreed with this view. One thought that fire is fundamental; another that air is. By the time of Aristotle, it was widely held that there are actually four different kinds of terrestrial matter, namely fire, air, water, and earth. These were called "elements"; a curious survival of this conception is encountered in such phrases as "the raging of the elements." Substances were supposed to differ from one another because they contained the elements in varying proportions. Green wood "clearly" contained all four elements, for when it burned the fire could be seen coming out of it, the water could be heard hissing, the smoke ascended and turned into air, while the ashes showed by their heaviness and dryness that they were earthy.

Along with the *constitution* of matter, the Greeks were concerned about its *structure.* Is matter continuous, so that it can be subdivided indefinitely, or is it composed of indivisible particles too small to affect the human senses? Both views had their supporters. The belief in indivisible particles is associated with the name of Democritus and was part of the Epicurean tradition. Aristotle, however, rejected the belief in particles and taught that matter is continuous and capable of infinite subdivision.

19–1. The Origins of Chemistry. It is neither possible nor desirable for us to trace here the highly confused history of chemistry before 1800.

Engraved from a painting by David Teniers the Younger
By courtesy of the Fisher Collection of Alchemical and Historical Pictures

A LABORATORY AT THE TIME OF BOYLE AND NEWTON

Partly to supply cheap imitations of materials (for example, fine dyes) that were too expensive for general use, partly to further the practice of medicine, and partly in an attempt to improve base metals so that they became gold, chemical experimentation flourished in Alexandria, in the Moslem world, and in medieval Europe. By the early sixteenth century, at the time, say, of Copernicus, Martin Luther, and Henry VIII, European learning had inherited from the past an awareness of the two fundamental questions about matter. It also inherited for each of these questions a set of conflicting answers. To the question as to the primal substances, or elements, the answer handed down in the works of Aristotle was that the elements are fire, air, water, and earth, and a fifth element called quintessence, of which the heavenly bodies are made. From the Arabs in Spain, however, came the view that the elements are mercury, sulfur, and salt. As to the structure of matter, the great Aristotle said that matter is continuous, but the dissenting opinion of Democritus found expression in the works of other authors.

In the sixteenth and seventeenth centuries, chemical investigation was carried on by two groups, the physicians and the alchemists. The alchemists had three major objectives: to turn cheap metals into gold, to discover an elixir of life that would confer immortality, and to discover a universal solvent that would dissolve all materials. Neither the physicians nor the alchemists discovered any important generalizations, but their activities did result not only in the accumulation of considerable lore about the chemical behavior of specific substances, but also in a background of laboratory techniques. Real progress was of course delayed until chemical investigation could be put on a quantitative basis. Aided by improvements in balances or scales, quantitative experimentation was off to a good start by 1700. By 1800, some tottering steps had been taken along the road to a valid identification of the chemical elements, and the groundwork had been laid for a scientific decision about the structure of matter. Our study of chemistry will commence with an outline of the attack on these two problems.

19–2. Chemical Reactions. Any change in matter which leads to the formation of a substance not previously present is called a *chemical reaction.* Without some knowledge of chemistry, it is often hard to be sure whether a new substance is formed or not, and in fact the early chemists themselves sometimes went astray in particular cases. A time-honored illustration of chemical reaction will make the idea clear enough for present use.

EXPERIMENT. Let equal volumes of powdered iron and powdered sulfur be stirred together on a paper, forming a gray-green mixture. Particles of iron and sulfur are easily distinguishable in the mixture, and the iron can be removed by a magnet, leaving the sulfur behind (Figure 19–A). No new substance has been formed.

Let the two powders now be mixed again, put in a test tube, and strongly heated. A red glow starts at the bottom of the material and may be seen to work upward, even after the test tube is removed from the flame. (*Caution:* The test tube should be aimed in such a way that no injury will result if its hot contents shoot out, as occasionally happens.)

After cooling, the material in the tube is found to be black and to be unaffected by a magnet. It no longer shows the properties of iron or of sulfur, but shows a new set of properties of its own. It is a new substance, created by the chemical union of sulfur and iron.

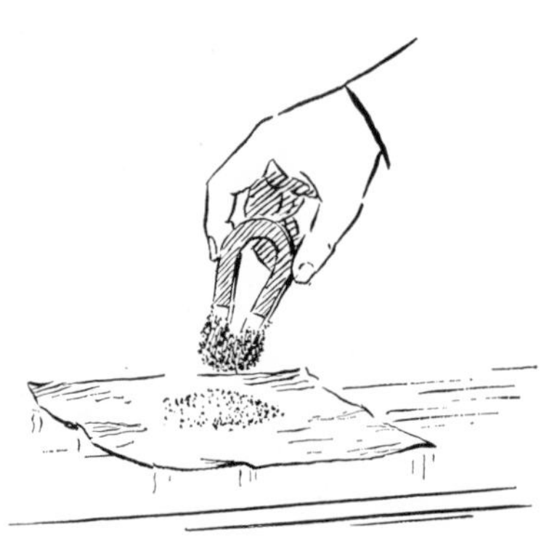

FIGURE 19–A. Before finely powdered iron and sulfur have entered into chemical union, they can easily be separated, because each retains its own properties.

The experiment not only illustrates chemical reaction, but also it shows the need for distinguishing between *substances* and *mechanical mixtures.* A substance has a set of characteristic properties and is the same throughout, so that any small part of it is like any other small part. Water and iron are substances, and so is sulfur. A mechanical mixture consists of two or more substances, and some small parts of it are different from other small parts. From the iron-sulfur mixture, you could select with tweezers, or with your eye and a microscope, some small parts that were iron and other small parts that were sulfur. Another mechanical mixture is granite, whose light and dark parts are clearly visible to the naked eye.

In the reaction of iron and sulfur, two substances combined to form one new one. Another variety of chemical reaction is the decomposition of a single substance into two new substances.

EXPERIMENT. About half a teaspoonful of mercuric oxide, an orange powder, is placed in the test tube in Figure 19–B. When the powder is heated, bubbles of gas emerge from the end of the delivery tube and are collected in the inverted bottle, which is initially full of water. Several bottles of gas may be collected; the first should be discarded because it consists largely of the air that was in the test tube before the heating began. The other bottles clearly contain something else than air, because an ignited wooden splint, that in air only glows quietly, bursts into a bright flame when thrust into a bottle of the gas. The gas is called "oxygen."

After the production of gas has ceased, the flame and stopper should be removed from the test tube, which will be found to contain droplets of a

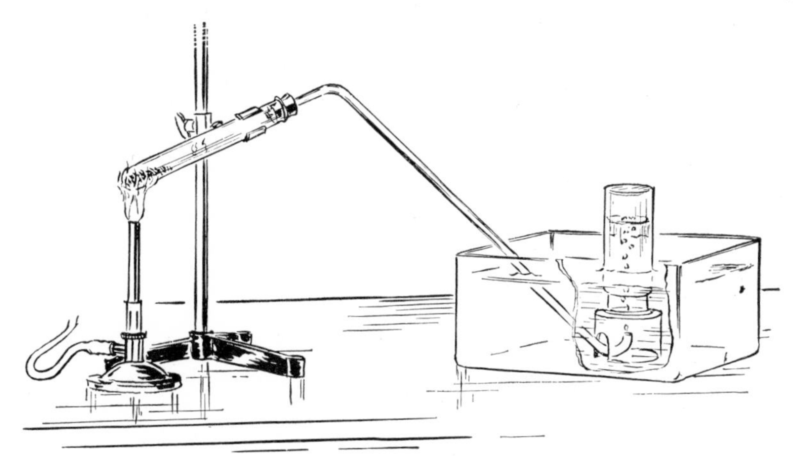

FIGURE 19–B. Decomposing mercuric oxide.

shining metal recognizable as mercury. The orange powder has therefore undergone a chemical reaction; it has decomposed into oxygen and mercury.

19–3. Energy in Chemical Reactions. One important fact about chemical reactions is that they all entail transformations of energy. Some reactions, for example the union of iron and sulfur, liberate energy in the form of heat. (This explains why the material glowed during that reaction, even though the flame had been removed.) On the other hand, some reactions absorb energy. An example is the decomposition of mercuric oxide, for which heat had to be supplied continuously in order for the reaction to proceed. Our original, purely mechanical, conception of energy had to be extended (Article 16–1) to include heat. Since energy can be released or absorbed by chemical reactions, we again extend the idea of energy so that it includes chemical energy, energy that is stored in a substance by reason of its chemical composition. Reactions that liberate energy are called *exothermic reactions* (reactions that give out heat), and those that absorb energy are called *endothermic reactions* (reactions that take in heat).

EXPERIMENT. By letting the escaping gas bubble through water, one can adjust separate sources of oxygen and hydrogen so that the hydrogen escapes twice as fast as the oxygen does. When these sources feed the arms of a Y-tube, the mixed gases that flow from the stem of the Y can be used to fill soap bubbles. When freed, the bubbles float upward, where they may be ignited by a glowing taper on a long stick. The amount of gas in a 3-inch bubble is small, but the noise of the explosion is impressive; the reaction is highly exothermic.

It will be recalled that an energy transfer also occurs when a substance changes its state (Articles 14–3, 17–4). One must realize, however, that changes of state are not chemical reactions, because no new substance is formed.

19–4. Solutions. It is well known that when some solids are placed in water, the result is a *solution.* A solution is an intimate mingling of two or more substances, each dispersed throughout the other.

EXAMPLE. A small blue crystal of copper sulfate, if placed in a beaker of water, will soon disappear. The result is a solution. The process of solution may be hastened by stirring, which will soon distribute the blueness uniformly throughout the liquid.

Some early chemists considered the process of solution to be a chemical reaction. This view no longer prevails. One objection to it is that a solution can too easily be made and unmade. For example, if copper sulfate solution is sufficiently chilled, some of the water separates and forms pure ice. Or if the solution is simply left uncovered, then the water evaporates and leaves copper sulfate crystals behind.

A solution may or may not have the same properties throughout, but it cannot be classified as a substance because it does not have a set of characteristic properties. For example, the color of a copper sulfate solution, and likewise the temperature at which it freezes, can be varied over a wide range by changing the amount of water it contains. Nor can a solution be regarded as a mechanical mixture, because by sufficient stirring it may be made uniform throughout. We must therefore distinguish three kinds of matter: substances, mechanical mixtures, and solutions.

Solutions can be formed not only by a liquid and a solid, but also by a liquid and a gas, by two liquids, or by two gases. Moreover, a gas can dissolve in a solid, and it is even possible to have a solid dissolve in another solid, but these situations are less common. A simple experiment with the solution of two liquids points plainly to the conclusion that a solution is such an intimate mixture that the particles of one substance are dispersed among those of the other substance.

EXPERIMENT. If 50 ml of pure ethyl alcohol and 50 ml of water are mixed, they dissolve in one another. The volume of the solution is about 95 ml, noticeably less than the sum of the constituents' volumes.

ANTOINE LAURENT LAVOISIER was by vocation a financier. His scientific work, carried on as an intensely cultivated hobby, led to government appointments on technical matters. For many years, he was in charge of France's national supply of gunpowder. During the French Revolution, he was a member of the National Treasury Commission, but in the Reign of Terror he went to the guillotine on account of his earlier membership in the firm that had collected the royal taxes.

Mme. Lavoisier, who was an active aide to her husband in his scientific work, was later married, very unhappily, to Count Rumford.

Painting by Jacques Louis David
By courtesy of the Rockefeller Institute for Medical Research
Photo, courtesy of the Metropolitan Museum of Art

ANTOINE LAVOISIER AND HIS WIFE
(1743–1794) (1758–1836)

The experiment actually points to two conclusions. The first is that apparently continuous matter has empty spaces in it; in other words, the experiment gives support to the view that matter does consist of small particles. The result shows furthermore that in a solution, the particles of the two substances are so intimately mingled that one kind enters the spaces between the other kind.

19–5. Elements and Compounds. Our modern conception of an element stems from Robert Boyle, Newton's contemporary whose name we have met in the study of gas pressure (Article 13–2). Boyle's definition, quoted at the head of this chapter, can be rephrased as follows: The elements are those substances that are not made of other substances; substances that are not elements are compounded from elements and can be decomposed into elements.

It will be profitable to pause here for a comment on the role of definitions in science. Before Boyle's time, the word "element" had been much used without any specific agreement as to what it meant. Such a procedure is certain to produce much controversy and little progress. By insisting on a definition, Boyle was making a long step in the right direction. Moreover, Boyle's definition is in accord with our present knowledge of chemistry. Nevertheless, from the point of view of a modern scientist, Boyle's definition is entirely unsatisfactory. The trouble with it is that Boyle had no way of telling which substances satisfied his definition and which did not. In the modern view, a definition should be "operational"; that is, the definition should prescribe some operation for detecting, and preferably for measuring, the thing that is being defined. By thinking back, you will see that our discussions of temperature and of heat fulfilled this requirement. Keep the requirement in mind as we proceed to define new concepts in later chapters.

Boyle recognized the difficulty of finding out which substances are elements according to his definition, but a century elapsed before anyone saw what to do about it. Then Lavoisier, a French chemist, proposed that any substance not known to be decomposable should be regarded as an element. This definition, which today we should call operational, brought the term "element" out of the realm of metaphysics and into the realm of the laboratory. At first the resulting list of elements had to be frequently revised, but in the course of one generation the list took very much the form it has today.

In the light of modern knowledge, Lavoisier's definition of an element can be replaced by a more positive one: an *element* is a substance that cannot be broken down, by chemical means, into two or more other substances. This definition, which says "cannot be" where Lavoisier's said "has not been," is an acceptable one in terms of modern operations, by which it is possible to determine in advance whether a substance can be decomposed or not. The modern definition implies a greater certainty in identifying the elements, but we do well to remember that Lavoisier's definition broke an impasse that had lasted for centuries.

Before we go further with the question of identifying elements, it will be useful to point out how the experiments on page 148 illustrate the concept of *compound.* A compound is a substance formed by the chemical union of two or more elements. Forming a compound by combining simpler compounds, or by combining elements, is called *synthesis.* The opposite process of separating a compound into its constituents is called *analysis.* The iron and sulfur used in the first experiment are known to be elements, and they combined to form a compound called iron sulfide. In the second experiment, the mercuric oxide decomposed into oxygen and mercury. Mercuric oxide is therefore a compound. Neither oxygen nor mercury has ever been chemically decomposed in several centuries of experimentation; for this reason, as well as for more positive reasons that will appear later, we are sure that they are elements.

It was Lavoisier himself who put forward the idea that oxygen is an element. Although he had experimented with it extensively, he had never found it to break up into two or more components. On the basis of his definition, therefore, it should be tentatively regarded as an element. Moreover, he found that oxygen not only combines with mercury to form the familiar red powder, but it also combines with carbon to form another gas, and with many metals to form other compounds. This presence of oxygen in many compounds was interpreted by Lavoisier as an indication that oxygen would maintain permanently its position on the list of elements.

By 1800, some twenty-five or thirty substances had been recognized as elements. At present the list has increased to about a hundred. Many are substances such as gold, silver, iron, mercury, and sulfur that have been familiar through the ages; a few are so rare that most chemists have never seen them. Fortunately one can proceed with the study of chemistry without learning how each element was originally recognized, and without even knowing the names of many of them. It is necessary, however, to know the names of a few.

19–6. Metals and Nonmetals. It is very convenient to place the elements in two general categories, *metals* and *nonmetals,* although this division is sometimes indistinct. Metals are usually characterized by a luster that serves to distinguish them from nonmetals. Further distinctions are that metals are good conductors of heat and electricity, and are tough; nonmetals are poor conductors of heat and electricity, and when they are in the solid state, they are brittle.

Familiar metallic elements are *gold, silver, zinc, mercury, lead, copper, tin, iron,* and *aluminum. Sodium* and *potassium* are also metallic elements, but they react so quickly with air that they are seldom seen outside the laboratory. Although they look much like silver or tin, they are soft enough to cut with a knife. *Calcium* and *magnesium* are of interest because of their common occurrence in compounds.

Nonmetallic elements are less commonly encountered in the uncombined condition than are the metals, and moreover, they are not so numerous; consequently, they are less familiar. *Carbon* and *sulfur* have probably been seen by nearly everyone. We live in an atmosphere consisting mainly of *oxygen* and *nitrogen,* not chemically combined. *Chlorine,* a heavy greenish gas, is one of the elements in common salt.

Hydrogen, the lightest of all substances, is a gas at ordinary temperatures and might therefore be classed as a nonmetal. In its chemical behavior, however, it often resembles the metals. Actually, hydrogen is unique and does not fit well in either category.

Metals have little tendency to react with one another, but they have a strong tendency to react with nonmetals. Nonmetals often react with other nonmetals.

19–7. Chemical Symbols. For over a hundred years, each element has been given a symbol, so that substances and reactions can be written in an international shorthand which is a distinct aid to thought. The symbol is simply the first letter of the element's name, followed by a second letter when it is needed to avoid ambiguity, but sometimes the name in question is Latin rather than English. The list of symbols in Table 19–I will serve as a beginning; others will be introduced later as they are needed. A complete list appears in the Appendix.

TABLE 19–I

SOME COMMON ELEMENTS AND THEIR SYMBOLS

Metals		Nonmetals	
Hydrogen	H		
Aluminum	Al	Carbon	C
Magnesium	Mg	Oxygen	O
Zinc	Zn	Nitrogen	N
Lead (Plumbum)	Pb	Chlorine	Cl
Copper (Cuprum)	Cu	Iodine	I
Iron (Ferrum)	Fe	Sulfur	S
Sodium (Natrium)	Na		
Potassium (Kalium)	K		
Calcium	Ca		

19–8. Nomenclature. There are conventions for naming chemical compounds in terms of their constituent elements. There is no need to learn these rules all at once; they will be introduced as need arises. Only two will be immediately useful:

1. The metallic part (there usually is one) is always mentioned first.
2. A binary compound, one composed of only two elements, always has a name ending in "ide."

For example, ordinary table salt is a compound of sodium and chlorine. Its chemical name is "sodium chloride."

Summary

A chemical reaction is any change in matter that leads to the formation of a substance not previously present.

Chemical reactions entail transformation of energy, most often in the form of heat. Those that liberate energy are called exothermic; those that absorb energy are called endothermic. Chemical energy is energy that a substance has by reason of its chemical composition.

Elements are substances incapable of chemical decomposition. Elements can combine to form compounds. It is useful to classify elements as metals and nonmetals, because the two classes have a strong tendency to react with one another. Hydrogen does not fit well in either category, but acts in many respects like a metal.

A rough classification of matter may be summarized in a diagram:

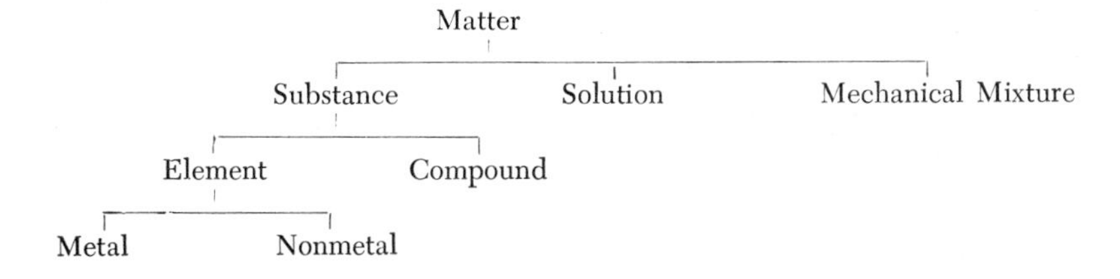

Questions

1. What is a chemical reaction?
2. Distinguish between exothermic and endothermic reactions.
3. The text states that the atmosphere consists mainly of oxygen and nitrogen, not chemically combined. Would you say that the oxygen and nitrogen form a mechanical mixture, a solution, or a substance?
4. Give the modern term for what Boyle, in the quotation at the head of the chapter, called "perfectly mixt bodies."
5. What is an element?
6. Name the binary compounds formed by the chemical union of the following pairs of elements: Zn and O, Al and Cl, Na and I, N and Mg, S and Pb.

7. Suppose salt and sand were ground up together to make a uniform white powder. How could you prove the powder to be a mechanical mixture and not a substance?
8. Distinguish between analysis and synthesis in the chemical sense. Give one example of each.

Si . . . nous attachons au nom d'éléments ou de principes des corps l'idée du dernier terme auquel parvient l'analyse, toutes les substances que nous n'avons encore pu décomposer par aucun moyen sont pour nous des éléments, . . . et nous ne devons les supposer composées qu'au moment où l'expérience et l'observation nous en auront fourni la preuve.

LAVOISIER (1789)

20

THE BIRTH OF SCIENTIFIC ATOMISM

> We have no knowledge, that is general principles drawn from the contemplation of particular facts, but what has been built up by pleasure, and by pleasure alone. The Man of science, the Chemist and Mathematician, whatever difficulties and disgusts they may have had to struggle with, know and feel this.
>
> WORDSWORTH (1800)

By the middle of the eighteenth century, the study of chemistry was no longer being pursued primarily by artisans, physicians, and charlatans; it was also attracting scientists, men who were interested in understanding for its own sake. What they knew about chemistry was really very little. They had a feeling for the significance of elements, but had not yet forsaken Aristotle's earth, air, water, and fire. They had an acquaintance with a fairly large number of reactions, but they had little in the way of unifying principles, and what they had was mostly wrong. For example, they recognized many reactions that they correctly grouped together as "burning," but burning was supposed to be the liberation of a substance called "phlogiston." This phlogiston was essentially the same as Aristotle's "fire"; it is now known to be nonexistent. In its conception and its shortcomings, the phlogiston theory of combustion is much like the caloric theory of heat. Having studied caloric (Chapter 15) we should not gain much new insight into science by studying phlogiston. It was abandoned toward the end of the century, after Lavoisier's experiments had shown that combustion is combination with oxygen.

The chief reason for the lack of sound chemical theory was the lack of quantitative data. Chemistry, one can see now, needed a man to play a role like that of Galileo in mechanics and that of Joule in heat.

20–1. Lavoisier. The man chiefly responsible for putting chemistry on a quantitative basis was Lavoisier, the Frenchman whose recognition of oxygen as an element has already been mentioned (Article 19–5). Like many other scientists of his time, Lavoisier was a man of means who devoted himself to science as a hobby. He began experimenting as a young man, a few years before the American Revolution, and soon won a place of leadership in chemistry. His work has two notable qualities: he had his eye on general principles as well as on individual facts, and he emphasized the quantitative method. He painstakingly weighed every substance that went into a chemical reaction, and every product that came out.

20–2. The Conservation of Matter. Lavoisier's work with mercuric oxide (Article 19–5) led not only to the recognition of oxygen as an element, but also to the knowledge that in a chemical reaction, matter is neither created nor destroyed. By heating, he converted 41½ grains of

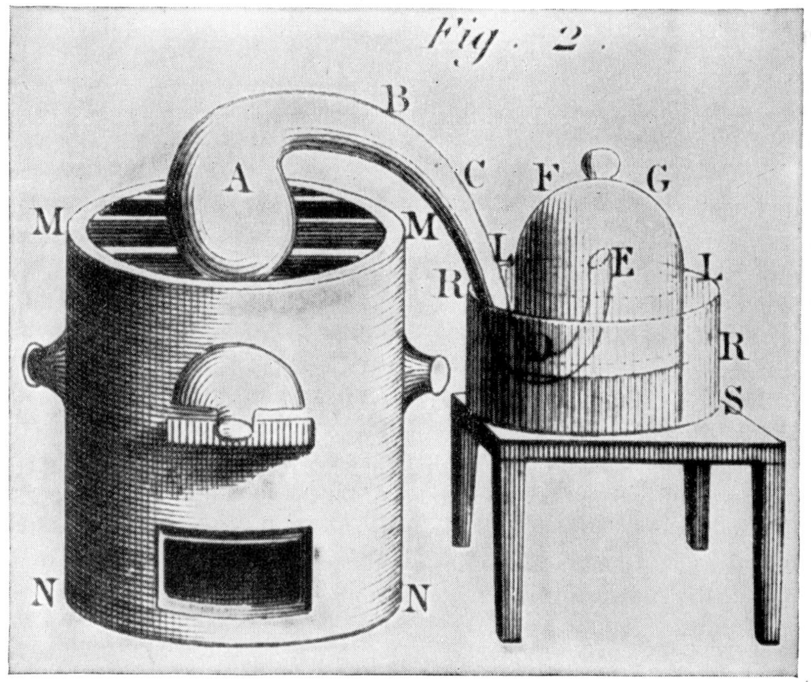

FIGURE 20–A. Lavoisier's apparatus for producing and decomposing mercuric oxide.

JOHN DALTON was born in the Lake District of England, the son of a weaver. Except for a few years in rural schools, in which he himself began to teach while still in his early teens, Dalton was self-taught. In 1793 he moved to Manchester, where he devoted the rest of his life to scientific investigations, gaining a livelihood by teaching. Among his pupils was a lad named Joule, himself destined for scientific fame. Dalton was a Quaker and a bachelor; his life, a model of plain living and high thinking, was centered entirely on his work.

John Dalton
(1766–1844)

mercury, in a vessel containing a known amount of air, into what was then called a "calx" (now called an oxide). In his *Elementary Treatise on Chemistry*, he depicts the apparatus that he used in this experiment; the drawing is reproduced in Figure 20–A. He determined the loss in weight suffered by the air during the reaction, finding it to be $3\frac{1}{2}$ grains. The amount of matter entering into the reaction was therefore $41\frac{1}{2} + 3\frac{1}{2} = 45$ grains. Then he weighed the calx, and found the weight to be just 45 grains. Therefore no matter was lost or created in the formation of the calx.

$$41\tfrac{1}{2} \text{ grains mercury} + 3\tfrac{1}{2} \text{ grains from the air} \rightarrow 45 \text{ grains calx.}$$

On further heating to decompose the calx, he recovered $41\frac{1}{2}$ grains of mercury and $3\frac{1}{2}$ grains of a gas (oxygen), the same weights that were consumed in the original formation of the calx. Therefore nothing was lost and nothing gained in the reactions.

Similar experiments on the burning of hydrogen, charcoal, sulfur, phosphorus, and several metals all led to the same conclusion: *In a chemical reaction, matter is neither created nor destroyed.* This statement is called the Law of Conservation of Matter.

20–3. The Law of Constant Composition. Although Lavoisier had not been the first investigator to pay attention to the weights of reacting substances, his outstanding successes led to a greatly increased emphasis on weight relations. A controversy soon arose between two schools, one holding that a compound always contains its elements in the same proportion by weight, and the other holding that the composition of a compound can vary. Both sides presented data to support their claims, and the conflict was not resolved until about 1800, when the Frenchman Proust showed, by a brilliant series of analyses of metallic oxides and sulfides, that the combining proportions of the elements are indeed fixed.* For example, one finds that the black oxide of copper always consists of 79.87 percent copper and 20.13 percent oxygen. From Proust's work emerged the Law of Constant Composition: *Every sample of each pure compound is composed of the same elements combined in a particular proportion by weight.* At first sight, such a law might strike the uninitiated as a useless and not very interesting piece of pedantry. Actually, it is one of the fundamental clues to the existence of atoms.

20–4. Dalton's Atomic Hypotheses (1805). The hypothesis that matter consists of atoms had been accepted by most of the English pioneers of

* Proust showed that the proponents of the opposite view had been analyzing impure compounds, a situation which is not surprising in view of the undeveloped condition of chemistry.

science, including the great Newton. No actual knowledge about atoms was achieved, however, until the opening years of the nineteenth century. Soon after the Law of Constant Composition was discovered, the Englishman John Dalton realized that the relative weights of atoms should be accessible through experiment. His interest in meteorology had bent his attention to gases, and he proceeded to experiment on their chemical composition. The outcome was the foundation on which modern chemistry rests.

Trying to retrace the train of thought that has led to a great advance in science is usually a speculative business at best. Sometimes, as in the case of Galileo, the scientist in question has left an account of his experience. Unfortunately, Dalton gave his contemporaries several different accounts, and they are all inconsistent with the entries in his laboratory notebooks. We shall therefore simply state Dalton's hypotheses about the atomic structure of matter, without trying to guess how he arrived at them. In modern wording, they are as follows:

1. A sample of an element consists of tiny particles called atoms.
2. Atoms may not be divided, nor destroyed, nor created.
3. Atoms of the same element are alike in all respects; in particular, they are alike in weight.
4. Atoms of different elements combine chemically in definite simple ratios.
5. Atoms of different elements may combine in more than one ratio to form different compounds.
6. When two elements form only one compound, their atoms combine one-to-one; if there are two compounds of the same elements, one is one-to-one and the other two-to-one; and so on.

The last hypothesis, probably evoked by a belief in the simplicity of nature (Article 3-1), has turned out to be false. The other hypotheses, of which only two have needed some revision in the light of modern discoveries, were the guideposts for the superb march of chemistry during the past century and a half.

The first two hypotheses, of course, were nothing new. Taken together they account for the conservation of matter: matter can certainly not be created or destroyed in a chemical reaction if the reaction is only a reshuffling of indestructible atoms. In the third hypothesis, Dalton fits the elements into the atomic scheme; he puts emphasis on the weights of atoms, because weight was so important in the mechanics and the chemistry of his time.

The fourth hypothesis accounts for the Law of Constant Composition. Indeed, it is made almost inevitable by that law, for unless the linkage of the atoms themselves occurs in definite proportions, it is hard to see, for example, how bits of mercury ore from all over the world should contain, if they are pure, always just the same proportion of mercury. It is surely no accident that Dalton's scheme occurred to him almost as soon as the Law of Constant Composition was found to hold. The fifth hypothesis, a simple extension of the fourth, was necessary to account for the fact that sometimes two elements can combine in more than one way, to form different compounds. The next article will enlarge on this point.

In spite of the uncertainty as to how Dalton arrived at them, these foundations of chemical theory offer a brilliantly clear example of an important aspect of scientific method. After much groping, certain experimental laws are discovered—in this case the Law of Conservation of Matter and the Law of Constant Composition. Arriving at such laws from the limited experimental evidence is a matter that requires skill and is subject to error. It involves the risky process, called *induction,* of reasoning from the particular to the general (Article 5–8). Then sometimes, as in this case, the laws or generalizations about observable events can be subjected to further induction to form a set of hypotheses about some broader aspect of nature. Newton's work on motion and on gravitation are examples; Dalton's hypotheses are another. This second induction, also subject to error, requires more than skill; it often requires genius. Once the grand hypotheses have been laid down, the experimental laws can be "predicted" as consequences of the hypotheses. The kind of reasoning needed here is relatively easy and familiar, being finely exemplified in elementary geometry. It is reasoning from the general to the particular. We call it "logical" reasoning, or *deduction.* The contrast between induction and deduction is apparent in regard to the Law of Constant Composition. Given this law, not everyone would see that it points vigorously to the first four hypotheses that Dalton adopted. Even given the hypotheses, nobody could be sure that these, and not some other set, correspond to reality. Actually some excellent chemists doubted it, even a hundred years later. Once given Dalton's first four hypotheses, however, any intelligent freshman can see that the Law of Constant Composition inevitably follows.

20–5. The Law of Multiple Proportions. Having arrived at a hypothesis, the thing to do is base on it a theory, and then test the theory by an experiment (Article 3–4). Dalton did this almost immediately. During the recent controversy about constant composition, many compounds had been analyzed. Some turned out to consist of the same pair of elements combined in different proportions. For example there is a black oxide of copper, mentioned on page 160, and there is also a red oxide of copper. Analysis shows that oxygen makes up a larger fraction of the black oxide than of the red. Dalton's hypotheses demand that the atoms of copper and of oxygen be combined in a simple ratio in each oxide; his faith in simplicity would lead him to picture the red and black oxides either thus:

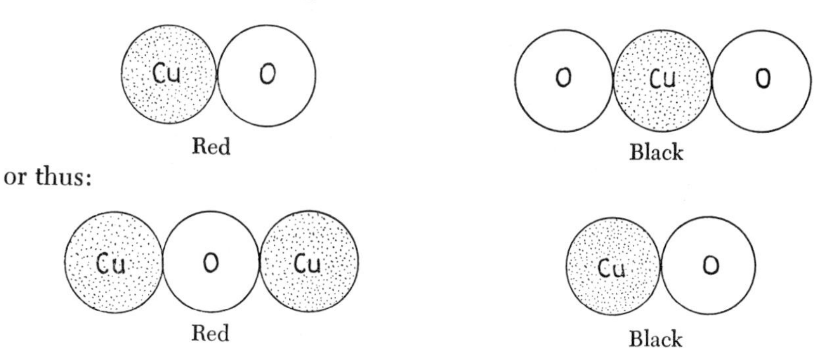

or thus:

In the first case, for each atom of copper there is one atom of oxygen in the red oxide, and two atoms in the black. In the second case, for every two atoms of copper there is one atom of oxygen in the red oxide and two in the black. In either case (and Dalton could not tell which represented reality), a given amount of copper is accompanied by exactly half as much oxygen in the red oxide as in the black.

The argument can be generalized to any case of two compounds formed from the same elements. It is easy to see that if Dalton's hypothesis about atoms combining in simple ratios is correct, then *a simple ratio must exist between the two weights of one element that can combine with a given weight of the other element.** This conclusion is called the Law of Multiple Proportions. Note that it deals with the relative weights of *one* element combined with a given weight of another element in *two* compounds, while the Law of Constant Composition refers to the relative weights of *two* (or more) elements in *one* compound. Both laws deal with matter in bulk and can be tested directly. Dalton's hypotheses have these laws as simple consequences, but the hypotheses deal with individual atoms and cannot be tested directly by chemical experimentation.

20-6. A Test of the Law of Multiple Proportions. By analyzing many pairs of compounds, Dalton showed that his theory about multiple proportions is in accord with experiment. Consider, for example, the oxides of copper. One newton of red copper oxide contains approximately 0.11 nt of oxygen, combined of course with 0.89 nt of copper. On the other hand, 1 nt of black copper oxide contains 0.20 nt of oxygen and

* A formal proof can be given. Suppose the ratio of atoms in one compound is p/q, and in the other it is m/n, where p, q, m, and n are small whole numbers. These ratios can be written pn/qn and qm/qn, to get a common denominator. With qn atoms of the second element, one can therefore combine either pn or qm atoms of the first. The allowed amounts of the first element have the ratio pn/qm, which will be fairly simple (and can usually be made simpler by cancellation).

0.80 nt of copper. Note that these figures are not very edifying in themselves; if there were no theory to test, they would attract no attention. The theory says, however, that a simple ratio can be expected between the weights of oxygen that combine with a given amount of copper. The two amounts of copper mentioned above are not equal, but knowing the composition of the black oxide (0.20:0.80), we can find out how much oxygen would be present if we had 0.89 nt of copper in it. Let this amount be x. We have

$$\frac{x}{0.89\ \text{nt}} = \frac{0.20}{0.80}$$

$$x = \frac{0.89\ \text{nt}}{4} = 0.22^{+}\ \text{nt}.$$

Note that this is almost exactly *double* the 0.11 nt of oxygen found with the same amount of copper (0.89 nt) in the red oxide. If more accurate figures for the compositions had been used, the agreement between the theory and the calculation would become exact, but the arithmetic would be less easy to follow.

One of the hurdles confronting any physical scientist is illustrated by this last calculation. The data on the compositions of the copper oxides can be obtained by purifying the oxides, decomposing them, and weighing. In each of these processes, imperfections in technique can cause errors, which will in turn cause a discrepancy between the answer calculated from theory and the answer calculated from experimental data. In a young science where techniques are not yet refined, such discrepancies may be large. The scientist has to decide whether the disagreement between the theoretical prediction and the experimental check is serious enough to invalidate the theory. This he does by learning to estimate limits of error for his experiment. The actual techniques for so doing need not detain us here, but one must keep in mind that absolute accuracy is not experimentally obtainable, so that the testing of a theory against laboratory data is a job calling for disciplined imagination.

Summary

By studying the weights of substances undergoing chemical reaction, two experimental laws were discovered late in the eighteenth century.

1. The Law of Conservation of Matter: In a chemical reaction, matter is neither created nor destroyed.
2. The Law of Constant Composition: Every sample of a pure compound is composed of the same elements combined in a fixed proportion by weight.

Dalton laid down a set of hypotheses which correlate these laws, and the concept of elements, with the idea that matter is composed of atoms. Omitting one which has since proved incorrect, these hypotheses are:

1. A sample of an element consists of tiny particles called atoms.
2. Atoms may not be divided, nor destroyed, nor created.
3. Atoms of the same element are alike in all respects; in particular they are alike in weight.
4. Atoms combine chemically in definite simple ratios.
5. Atoms of different elements may combine in more than one ratio, to form different compounds.

From these hypotheses, the Law of Conservation of Matter and the Law of Constant Composition can be derived by deduction. There also follows the Law of Multiple Proportions, which states that when two elements can combine in more than one way, then a simple ratio exists between the weights of one element that can combine with a given weight of another element. Dalton's experimental verification of this law lent support to his hypotheses.*

Questions

1. State the Law of Conservation of Matter. Describe an experiment by Lavoisier that illustrates the law.
2. State the Law of Constant Composition.
3. State three of Dalton's hypotheses.
4. Show how the Law of Constant Composition can be deduced from Dalton's hypotheses.
5. Differentiate between induction and deduction. In the scientific study of a particular subject, which must come first: induction or deduction?
6. Derive the Law of Multiple Proportions from Dalton's hypotheses.
7. To what extent did Galileo, Joule, and Lavoisier play similar roles in their respective branches of science?
8. Different chemists analyzed three samples of pure table salt (sodium chloride) from different sources. They obtained the following data for the relative weights of sodium and chlorine in their respective samples:

Chemist A	Na, 11.5	Cl, 17.7
Chemist B	Na, 27.5	Cl, 42.4
Chemist C	Na, 4.35	Cl, 6.70

   Show that these data support the Law of Constant Composition.
9. Two different compounds of nitrogen and hydrogen have the following composition, by weight:

Compound A	N, 82.35 percent	H, 17.65 percent
Compound B	N, 87.5 percent	H, 12.5 percent

   Show that these data conform to the Law of Multiple Proportions.

* Recent discoveries show that the second and third hypotheses can no longer be retained without change, but these changes have no bearing on the work of the next few sections.

10. Assume that the lower picture on page 163 is correct, i.e., that the black oxide of copper contains one atom of oxygen for each atom of copper. Using the data in Article 20–6, find how many times heavier a copper atom is than an oxygen atom.
11. The compositions of several oxides of nitrogen appear below, in percentage by weight. Show that these experimental data are in accord with the Law of Multiple Proportions.

Compound	Percent Oxygen	Percent Nitrogen
A	36.35	63.65
B	53.32	46.68
C	63.18	36.82

Hint: Find how many newtons of oxygen would be combined, in each case, with 1.000 newton of nitrogen.

Suggestions for Further Reading

L. K. Nash, *The Atomic-Molecular Theory* (Cambridge: Harvard University Press, 1950). Case 4 of the *Harvard Case Histories in Experimental Science.*

J. H. Plumb, *England in the Eighteenth Century* (Harmondsworth, England: Pelican Books, 1950). This pleasant little book contains a few pages that show Lavoisier and Dalton in the setting of their times.

21

MOLECULES

> The discovery of Gay-Lussac, that gaseous bodies combine in equal or in multiple volumes, and that the resulting compounds stand in a simple relation to their constituents, is one of the most important discoveries ever made in physical science.
>
> JOULE (1845)

Dalton's success in predicting and explaining the Law of Multiple Proportions won favorable consideration for his atomic hypotheses. Difficulties soon arose, however. Understandably enough in view of their past successes and his Newtonian background, Dalton had put primary emphasis on weight relationships. It occurred to a French experimenter, Gay-Lussac, that since the volumes of all gases respond in the same way to changes in pressure (Boyle's Law, Article 13–2) or to changes in temperature (Article 13–3), it might be instructive to examine the volume relationships of gases in chemical reactions.

21–1. The Law of Combining Volumes. Availing himself of the refined techniques that had by that time (1808) been developed for handling gases, Gay-Lussac performed analyses and syntheses of several gaseous compounds. He found that, if all the volumes are measured at the same pressure and temperature, 1 volume of oxygen will unite with just 2 volumes of hydrogen. Furthermore, 1 volume of chlorine will unite with exactly 1 volume of hydrogen, and the union produces 2 volumes of hydrogen chloride.

The simplicity of these relationships suggests that they must have some fundamental significance. Experiments on other gases yielded results of a similar character, from which Gay-Lussac formulated the Law of Combining Volumes: *When two or more gases take part in a chemical reaction* (whether as reactants or products), *their volumes are in the ratio of small whole numbers* when the gases are at the same temperature and pressure. Figure 21–A depicts some examples.

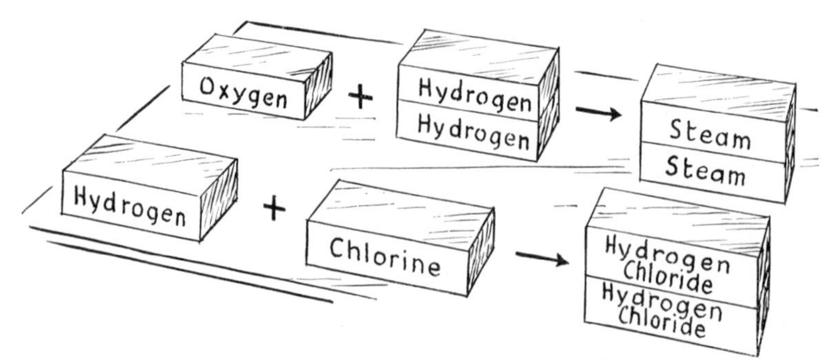

FIGURE 21–A. A pictorial representation of the combining volumes in two reactions studied by Gay-Lussac.

21–2. Avogadro's Hypothesis. Although England and France were bitterly embroiled in the Napoleonic war, Dalton was quickly informed of Gay-Lussac's discovery. Dalton did not believe it. He had studied the weight relations that prevail among hydrogen, oxygen, nitrogen, and the gaseous compounds that they form with one another. Applying his atomic theory to these weight relations, he had deduced the relative weights of the atoms of the elemental gases involved, assuming as an axiom that the particles of the elemental gases are individual atoms. Being unable to bring his findings into harmony with Gay-Lussac's report, Dalton concluded that Gay-Lussac was mistaken, and quoted some earlier and inaccurate experiments to refute him.

A short time later, a young Italian physicist named Avogadro showed that Dalton's hypotheses and the Law of Combining Volumes can easily be reconciled. His argument ran as follows. He accepted Gay-Lussac's discovery that the volumes of reacting gases are simply related. He also accepted Dalton's idea that the numbers of the various reacting particles are simply related. He concluded that the volume of a gas and the number of particles in it must be simply related. The simplest relation of all is proportionality, and Avogadro saw that proportionality was just what he needed in order to explain the facts. He therefore postulated that the volume of a gas depends simply on the number of particles in it—what

---

COUNT LORENZO ROMANO AMADEO CARLO AVOGADRO di QUAREGNA e di CERRETO was born in Turin. He took degrees in philosophy and jurisprudence, and the doctorate in ecclesiastic law. For a while he practiced law, but his interest in mathematics and physics led him into the teaching of physics, and he was for many years professor of that subject at the University of Turin. Having filled many public offices related to science, technology, and education, he died a few years before his hypothesis about molecules was accepted by the world of science.

AMADEO AVOGADRO
(1776–1856)

kind of gas it is does not matter. In other words, equal volumes of different gases contain the same number of particles. Of course, the volumes being compared must be measured at the same temperature and the same pressure. Avogadro called the particles *molecules,* and he saw that they are not necessarily the same as atoms. Avogadro's hypothesis is therefore usually stated thus: *At any given temperature and pressure, equal volumes of gases contain the same number of molecules.*

21–3. The Structure of Molecules. To see how Avogadro's ideas work, apply them to the reaction of hydrogen with chlorine, using Figure 21–B as an aid. On the right is the product, two volumes of hydrogen chloride. Suppose each of these volumes contains 1 million molecules. In order to be hydrogen chloride, each molecule of the gas must contain at least one atom of hydrogen and at least one of chlorine. We therefore must be dealing with at least 1 million hydrogen atoms in each of the two boxes on the right, or 2 million hydrogen atoms altogether. According to Avogadro's hypothesis, each box, including those on the left, must contain the same number of molecules, namely 1 million. If the box of hydrogen con-

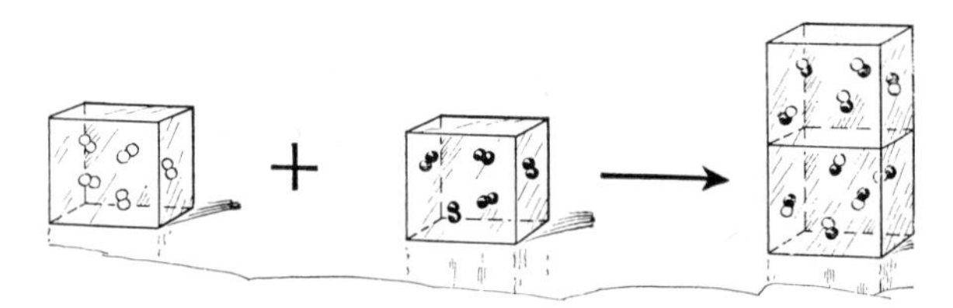

FIGURE 21–B. An illustration of Avogadro's hypothesis.

tains only 1 million molecules and yet contains at least 2 million atoms, it is clear that *each hydrogen molecule must contain at least two hydrogen atoms.* An exactly similar argument shows that each chlorine molecule must contain at least two chlorine atoms. Figure 21–B makes it clear that without Avogadro's hypothesis, we should have a hard time explaining why equal volumes of hydrogen and chlorine contain just the right number of atoms to produce two volumes of hydrogen chloride with no atoms left over.

As yet, we have only been able to argue that a hydrogen molecule contains at least two atoms, nothing in the argument rules out the possibility of four or six atoms to the molecule. If there were more than two atoms in a hydrogen molecule, however, we should expect to find some reaction in which one volume of hydrogen would yield more than two volumes of product. No such reaction is known. We shall therefore assume that the hydrogen molecule consists of two atoms; confirming evidence will appear later.

The reaction of hydrogen with chlorine could be represented by the diagram

(H-H) + (Cl-Cl) ⟶ (H-Cl) + (H-Cl)

The chemical shorthand (Article 19–7) gives us a way of presenting the same information in more compact form. We write

$$H_2 + Cl_2 \rightarrow 2HCl.$$

Here the symbol H_2 means "a molecule of hydrogen, containing 2 atoms," and the symbol 2HCl means "2 molecules of hydrogen chloride."

From the volume relationships observed when hydrogen combines with oxygen to form steam (Figure 21–A), it is easy to show that the reaction can be represented by the diagram

(H-H) + (H-H) + (O-O) ⟶ (H H O) + (H H O)

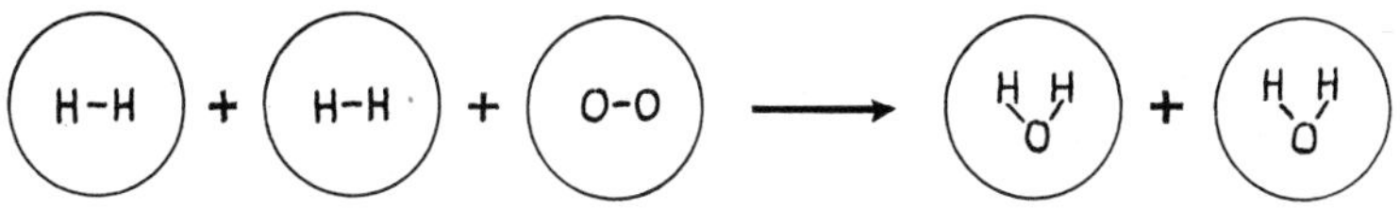

The compact symbolism is

$$2H_2 + O_2 \rightarrow 2H_2O.$$

21–4. The Gradual Acceptance of Avogadro's Hypothesis. Avogadro's ideas are accepted today as being among the foundations of atomic science, but when they were published in 1811 (in the leading French journal of physics), they attracted little or no attention. Actually they ran counter to a very generally accepted hypothesis about atoms, namely that atoms of the same kind repel one another. It therefore seemed absurd to suppose that two hydrogen atoms, for example, could attract one another to form a two-atom molecule. On the other hand, if hydrogen atoms did attract one another, why should hydrogen gas resist compression? For nearly fifty years chemists tried various alternative notions about atomic behavior, and worked up such a series of contradictions that the very existence of atoms seemed to many to be in doubt. At last, at an international conference in 1860, the acceptance of Avogadro's ideas was urged afresh by one of his countrymen, and some of the leading chemists gave Avogadro's hypothesis a trial. In the words of one of them, "It was as though scales fell from my eyes; doubt vanished, and was replaced by the feeling of calm assurance."

21–5. Interactions Among the Sciences. It is worth a moment's pause to consider why a valuable idea like Avogadro's should be almost ignored for half a century, and then accepted. The chief reason lies in the advances in physics that were made during the half century. When Avogadro published his hypothesis (1811), gas pressure was attributed to mutual repulsion of the gas particles, either because of their intrinsic properties or because of the self-repulsion of the caloric in which they were thought to be imbedded. It must therefore have seemed simply unreasonable to suppose that like atoms could attract one another in pairs to form molecules. After Joule and others had shown that gas pressure comes from the pattering of swiftly moving particles against the containing walls (Article 17–3), there was no need to assume that like particles repel one another, so Avogadro's two-atom molecules were much easier to believe in. Progress in chemistry therefore followed from an advance in physics. Soon the dynamical theory of gases was able to *deduce* that equal volumes of gas at the same temperature and pressure contain equal numbers of particles (Article 18–2). By its arguments pointing to this same conclusion, chemistry then gave support to the dynamical theory of heat.

This example of interplay between physics and chemistry is typical of numberless others in all the sciences.

21–6. Molecules and Atoms. Both of Avogadro's ideas, now tested by a century of use, have turned out to be correct. His name is chiefly associated with the hypothesis about equal numbers of molecules in equal volumes of gases, a relationship which will be important in some of the following chapters. No less important, however, was his service in distinguishing between *atoms,* which are the units in which an element enters into chemical reactions, and *molecules,* which are the smallest particles in which a compound or element can exist as an independent substance.

In a gas, the flying particles are molecules. In a few gases, notably mercury vapor and neon, the molecules are atoms; in other gases the molecules consist of two or more atoms connected together. In liquids, the molecules are much closer together and are likely to link together in groups. In a solid, each atom has so many close neighbors that the formation of distinct molecules is often impossible. The evidence on which these statements depends will come forth in its proper place, as part of the story of why atoms group together at all. For the present it is sufficient to note that molecules exist in their integrity in gases, but that in speaking of liquids and solids we shall often be on safer ground if we merely speak of "particles," which may be individual atoms or groups of atoms.

Molecules consisting of one atom are called "monatomic." Those composed of two atoms each (such as H_2, Cl_2, or HCl) are called "diatomic" molecules. Molecules, such as H_2O, containing three atoms each, are called "triatomic." In the gaseous state, many elements are diatomic, although most of the metallic ones are monatomic.

SUMMARY

Gay-Lussac's Law of Combining Volumes states that when two or more gases are involved in a chemical reaction, their volumes (under like conditions of temperature and pressure) are in a simple ratio.

To account for the Law of Combining Volumes, Avogadro suggested that the particles of gases, which he called "molecules," can consist of more than one atom even when the gas is an element. In addition he put forward the hypothesis known by his name: Equal volumes of different gases, at the same temperature and pressure, contain the same number of molecules.

After a delay of about fifty years, Avogadro's ideas won general acceptance. Applying them to definite reactions, we find that hydrogen, chlorine, oxygen, and some other elemental gases are diatomic; we also learn in what ratio these atoms combine when they form certain compounds.

QUESTIONS

1. State the Law of Combining Volumes.
2. State Avogadro's hypothesis.
3. What is the difference between an atom and a molecule of hydrogen? of mercury?
4. By applying Avogadro's hypothesis to the volume relations that hold when hydrogen combines with oxygen to form steam (Figure 21–A), prove that oxygen has at least two atoms to the molecule.
5. Assuming that oxygen is diatomic, prove that water is H_2O. (Repeat the arguments of Article 21–3 and Figure 21–B, with appropriate changes.)
6. Using diagrams like those in Article 21–3, represent the reaction of three molecules of hydrogen with one of nitrogen (which is also diatomic) to form two molecules of ammonia. Show that the ammonia molecule should be designated by the symbol NH_3.
7. Under like conditions of temperature and pressure, how many liters of ammonia can be formed from 45 liters of hydrogen? What volume of nitrogen would be required? Give your reasoning.
8. The gas ozone has molecules consisting of three oxygen atoms. It is an unstable substance that changes of its own accord to ordinary oxygen, O_2. When it does so, what is the ratio of the volumes of the two gases? Represent this reaction by a diagram and by the symbolism introduced in Article 21–3.

9. In considering the dynamical theory of heat (Article 17–3), we derived the expression $pV = \frac{1}{3}nmv^2$. Show that if this expression is correct, then Avogadro's hypothesis is also correct.

Suggestion for Further Reading

Foundations of the Molecular Theory, Alembic Club Reprint Number 4 (Edinburgh: Oliver & Boyd, Ltd., 1923). Selections from the writings of Dalton, Gay-Lussac, and Avogadro.

Es fiel mir wie Schuppen von den Augen, die Zweifel schwanden, und das Gefühl ruhigsten Sicherheit trat an ihre Stelle.

Lothar Meyer (1862), speaking of his conversion to Avogadro's view.

22

MOLECULAR AND ATOMIC WEIGHTS

> Want of time prevents me from saying anything at present respecting other points on which we differ. Those which are purely speculative will long afford room for discussion. Respecting a matter of fact, which can easily come under the test of experiment, we cannot long be at variance.
>
> A fellow-scientist in a letter to Dalton (1804)

One of Dalton's primary concerns was finding the relative weights of different kinds of atoms. Because his sixth hypothesis (Article 20–4) was a bad guess, his conclusions about the relative weights of atoms were not valid. After the acceptance of Avogadro's ideas, Dalton's approach to atomic weights yielded correct results.

In presenting the fundamental ideas of chemistry, we have described in some detail how these ideas came to be accepted. Knowing where the ideas came from makes them easier to understand, and some acquaintance with the evolution of scientific thought is an essential part of any real understanding of science. Once the fundamental concepts have been established, however, the history of a science is much less rewarding. Following all the twists and turns by which progress has been made is likely to confuse rather than to clarify. The next chapters, therefore, will present today's view of the information that has been won by applying the ideas of Dalton and Avogadro to weights and volumes in chemical reactions. This information is one of the basic tools of the modern chemist.

22–1. A New Unit of Force. From time immemorial, merchants have bought and sold many materials by weight, and governments have long undertaken to establish standards of weight for use in commerce. In Europe the standard commercial unit of weight is the kilogram-weight, which is the weight, at a specified place, of the lump of metal called the kilogram (Article 4–6). This lump of metal therefore serves two purposes: its mass is the standard of mass, and its weight is the standard of weight in European commerce. The kilogram-weight, which is equal to about 9.8 newtons, is mentioned now because chemists almost never express weight in newtons. Instead they use the gram-weight, often called simply a "gram," which is 1/1000 of a kilogram-weight. A penny weighs about 3 grams. In dealing with chemical experiments, we shall follow custom and use grams instead of newtons.*

22–2. Atomic Weights. By use of Avogadro's hypothesis, the relative weights of the molecules in different gases can be found by simply weighing equal volumes of the gases (at the same temperature and pressure). At 0° C and atmospheric pressure, experiment gives the following weights for one liter of various gases:

Hydrogen	0.089944 g
Nitrogen	1.2499
Oxygen	1.4277
Chlorine	3.1638

Each one-liter sample of the gases contains the same number of molecules (Avogadro's hypothesis). The weights of the samples are therefore in proportion to the weights of the molecules:

$$\frac{\text{Weight of one liter of gas A}}{\text{Weight of one liter of gas B}} = \frac{\text{Weight of one molecule of gas A}}{\text{Weight of one molecule of gas B}}.$$

Moreover, from the kind of experiment discussed in Chapter 21, each of the gases in the table is known to have diatomic molecules. The two samples of gas therefore contain the same number of atoms. Hence the weights of the atoms have the same ratio as the weights of the samples. For example, the atoms of nitrogen and of hydrogen must have weights in the ratio 1.2499:0.089944, or 13.897:1. Similarly, the atoms of oxygen and of hydrogen have weights in the ratio 1.4277:0.089944, or 15.873:1. The last ratio can also be put in the form 16.000:1.0080.

It is clear that no amount of weighing of gases can give us the weight of one atom, unless we can find out how many atoms there are in the sample of gas. How many there are has been discovered in the fairly recent past, but of nearly equal value for practical work is a knowledge of the *relative* weights of the various atoms. As shown above, if we take the relative weight of a hydrogen atom to be 1, then the relative weight of a nitrogen atom is 13.897, and that of an oxygen atom is 15.873. Instead, it has been found better to take the relative weight of an oxygen atom to be exactly 16. This choice makes the relative weight of a hydrogen atom

*Nowhere in this book will a weight or other force be expressed in kilogram-weight, nor will the word "gram" ever refer to anything except weight. Therefore "20 g" will always refer to a weight, and "5 kg" will always refer to a mass. In this way, confusion can be entirely avoided.

come out 1.008, but it makes the relative weights of many other atoms come out very close to integers. For example, that of nitrogen comes out to be 14.008. The *atomic weight* of any element is the relative weight of one of its atoms, on a scale such that the relative weight of an oxygen atom is exactly 16.

Note that an atomic weight is not an actual weight, expressible in force units; it is only a ratio, so it is simply a number.

The atomic weights of only a few elements can be determined by the simple method just described, because only a few elements exist in gaseous form at temperatures suitable for weighing. The atomic weights of other elements have to be obtained indirectly.

22–3. Molecular Weights. Avogadro's hypothesis holds for all gases, whether elements or compounds. It can therefore be used to find the relative weights of the molecules of all materials obtainable in the gaseous state. The oxygen molecule, known to be composed of two oxygen atoms (Article 21–3), is used to establish the scale. The scale is the same as for atomic weights: The relative weight of an oxygen atom is taken to be 16, so the relative weight of the oxygen molecule is 32. The *molecular weight* of any substance is the relative weight of one of its molecules, on a scale such that the relative weight of an oxygen molecule is 32.

From Avogadro's hypothesis, we see as before that

$$\frac{\text{Weight of a given volume of gas X}}{\text{Weight of the same volume of oxygen}} = \frac{\text{Weight of one molecule of gas X}}{\text{Weight of one molecule of oxygen}}.$$

From this equation and the definition of molecular weight, it follows that

$$\frac{\text{Weight of a given volume of gas X}}{\text{Weight of the same volume of oxygen}} = \frac{\text{Molecular weight of gas X}}{32}.$$

Hence

$$\text{Molecular weight of gas X} = 32 \times \frac{\text{Weight of a given volume of gas X}}{\text{Weight of the same volume of oxygen}}.$$

Therefore we can find the molecular weight of any substance that can be weighed in the gaseous state.

22–4. Finding Atomic Weights from Molecular Weights. There are only a few elements whose atomic weights can be found by weighing the element in the gaseous state, because few elements are gaseous at temperatures where weighing is practical. Carbon, for example, is a solid at all ordinary temperatures. The atomic weight of carbon, however, is a clue to the composition of many important compounds. It can be found indirectly, from the molecular weights of some compounds of carbon.

TABLE 22–I

APPROXIMATE ATOMIC WEIGHTS OF SOME ELEMENTS

Element	Symbol	Atomic Weight
Aluminum	Al	27.0
Antimony	Sb	121.8
Arsenic	As	74.9
Barium	Ba	137.4
Bismuth	Bi	209.0
Boron	B	10.8
Bromine	Br	79.9
Cadmium	Cd	112.4
Calcium	Ca	40.1
Carbon	C	12.0
Chlorine	Cl	35.5
Chromium	Cr	52.0
Cobalt	Co	58.9
Copper	Cu	63.5
Fluorine	F	19.0
Hydrogen	H	1.0
Iodine	I	126.9
Iron	Fe	55.9
Lead	Pb	207.2
Magnesium	Mg	24.3
Manganese	Mn	54.9
Mercury	Hg	200.6
Nickel	Ni	58.7
Nitrogen	N	14.0
Oxygen	O	16.0
Phosphorus	P	31.0
Potassium	K	39.1
Silicon	Si	28.1
Silver	Ag	107.9
Sodium	Na	23.0
Strontium	Sr	87.6
Sulfur	S	32.1
Tin	Sn	118.7
Zinc	Zn	65.4

Many compounds of carbon are gases when at room temperature. Among them may be mentioned methane, found in natural fuel gas; carbon monoxide, found in exhaust fumes from automobiles; and carbon dioxide, seen commonly in soda water and less commonly in champagne. By weighing these gases and comparing with oxygen, it is found that they have molecular weights as follows: methane 16; carbon monoxide 28; carbon dioxide 44. By analyzing the gases, one finds that methane is (by weight) 75 percent carbon. If carbon contributes 75 percent to a molecular weight of 16, then it contributes 12. We can apply experimental analysis and the same reasoning to the other compounds, with results as follows:

Substance	Molecular Weight	Fraction That Is Carbon	Contribution of Carbon to Molecular Weight
Methane	16	0.75	12
Carbon monoxide	28	0.43	12
Carbon dioxide	44	0.27	12

In each of the molecules under discussion, carbon contributes 12 to the molecular weight. There are other molecules in which carbon makes a contribution of 12 to the molecular weight, and still others where it contributes 24, 36, or some other multiple of 12, but none where it contributes less than 12. We conclude, then, that the atomic weight of carbon is 12,* and that carbon contributes 12, 24, or 36 to a molecular weight, depending on whether the molecule in question contains 1, 2, or 3 atoms of carbon.

Table 22-I shows the atomic weights of the more common elements. An immediately striking feature of the table is that very many of the atomic weights are quite close to being whole numbers. This makes one surmise that perhaps the atoms themselves are compound structures built up from more fundamental entities that have a relative weight near 1. On the other hand, exceptions like chlorine (at. wt. 35.5) make difficulty for such a view. Relatively recent work in physics has shown that the weights of atoms actually are compounded of the weights of smaller entities, and surprisingly enough the studies which led to this conclusion led on to discoveries that profoundly affect the whole world. Before pursuing this thought further, however, we must see what can be learned by simply exploiting a knowledge of atomic weights.

Summary

The unit of force generally used in chemical laboratories is the gram-weight, or gram for short. It is 1/1000 of the weight of the kilogram, when the kilogram is in a specified place.

The atomic weight of an element is the relative weight of one of its atoms, on a scale such that the relative weight of an oxygen atom is exactly 16.

The molecular weight of a substance is the relative weight of one of its molecules, on a scale such that the relative weight of an oxygen molecule is exactly 32.

The scales of atomic and molecular weights agree, because an oxygen molecule contains two oxygen atoms.

The molecular weight of a gas can be found by comparing the weight of some volume of the gas with the weight of the same volume of oxygen, and applying Avogadro's hypothesis. The gases must, of course, be compared at the same temperature and pressure.

* Precise weighings and analyses give the result 12.010.

The atomic weight of a gaseous element can be found from the molecular weight of the gas, if one knows how many atoms there are in one of the molecules.

The atomic weight of an element that is not obtainable as a gas can often be worked out by finding the molecular weights, and the composition by weight, of several of its compounds. The atomic weight of the element is the smallest contribution that the element can make to the molecular weight of any of its compounds.

Questions

1. Define atomic weight.
2. Define molecular weight.
3. One liter of a certain gas was found to weigh 0.715 g. Under the same conditions, a liter of oxygen weighs 1.430 g. Calculate the molecular weight of the gas.
4. Suppose you had a large number of apples, all alike, and another large number of potatoes, also all alike. You also have a hay-scales, which is insensitive to the weight of one apple or one potato. How could you determine the relative weight of *one* potato with respect to *one* apple? How is this procedure related to the determination of molecular weights of gases?
5. Calculate the best value you can for the atomic weight of carbon, using the following experimental data:

Compound	Molecular Weight	Percent Carbon
Methane	16.0	75.0
Propane	44.1	81.8
Ethane	30.0	80.0
Hydrogen cyanide	27.0	44.5
Carbon dioxide	44.0	27.3
Pentane	72.2	83.2

6. How many atoms of carbon does each of the compounds in Question 5 contain? To what extent is your answer uncertain?
7. Calculate the best value you can for the atomic weight of chlorine, using the following experimental data:

Compound	Molecular Weight	Percent Chlorine
Hydrogen chloride	36.5	97.3
Compound B	137.5	77.5
Compound C	208.5	85.0
Compound D	154.0	92.2

8. How many atoms of chlorine are there in one molecule of each of the compounds in Question 7? To what extent is your answer uncertain?
9. From the data in Article 22–2, calculate the atomic weight of chlorine.

23

FORMULAS AND VALENCE

Once the atomic weights became known, the analysis of compounds took on an added power. It was now possible to find out how many atoms of each kind there are in a molecule, without depending on the Law of Combining Volumes. This knowledge in turn divulged certain regularities about the way atoms combine with one another. Such information has led ultimately to industrial processes for manufacturing molecules of substances that are rare or nonexistent in nature, but valuable in commerce or medicine. Our present chemical industry therefore has a fundamental debt to Dalton and others like him who were curious about such seemingly useless information as the relative weights of atoms.

This chapter will show how the atomic constitution of a molecule can be worked out, and will introduce the concept of "valence" which systematizes the linking together of atoms.

23–1. Chemical Formulas. The atomic composition of a molecule is designated by a shorthand notation called a *chemical formula.* It employs the symbols introduced in Article 19–7; the list in Table 19–I should now be memorized. The formula for a molecule contains the symbol for each element that is present in the molecule, and each symbol is given a subscript to show how many atoms of that kind are present. For example, the molecule NH_3 contains one nitrogen atom and three hydrogen atoms; C_4H_{10} contains four atoms of carbon and ten of hydrogen. A substance is commonly designated by the formula its molecules have when it is a gas; for example sodium chloride is NaCl, even though, as we shall see later, its atoms are not grouped in pairs when it is a solid. Even in a solid, however, the *proportions* in which the atoms combine are shown correctly by the formula.

The order in which the symbols are written is prescribed by custom, metallic elements usually being mentioned first.

23–2. The Determination of Formulas by Experiment. If the molecular weight of a substance can be determined directly, by weighing it in the gaseous state (Article 22–3), and if the elements in it are known, then its formula is often easy to determine by using a table of atomic weights. For example, steam has a molecular weight of 18, and it is known to consist of oxygen, at. wt. 16, and hydrogen, at. wt. 1. The O must contribute at least 16 to the molecular weight, and it cannot contribute more because the total is only 18. This leaves 2 to be contributed by the H, which takes two atoms of H. The formula is therefore H_2O.

Even without knowing the molecular weight of a substance, one can find its formula by knowing the atomic weights and by determining the composition of the substance in bulk. Suppose a compound contains two elements, X and Y. Its formula will be of the type X_mY_n. This formula represents a group of atoms (often a molecule). The number of such groups in any sample of the substance is related in a simple way to the amount of element X in the sample:

$$\text{Weight of X in the sample} = \text{Number of groups} \times \text{Weight of X in a group.}$$

Therefore

$$\text{Number of groups in any sample} = \frac{\text{Weight of X in the sample}}{\text{Weight of X in a group}}.$$

A simple substitution gives

$$\text{Number of groups in any sample} = \frac{\text{Weight of X in the sample}}{m \times \text{Weight of one X atom}}.$$

The number of groups can also be expressed in terms of element Y instead of X, and the result must be the same. Hence

$$\frac{\text{Wt. of X in the sample}}{m \times \text{Wt. of one X atom}} = \frac{\text{Wt. of Y in the sample}}{n \times \text{Wt. of one Y atom}}.$$

Since the weight of one atom is proportional to the atomic weight of the element in question, we can substitute atomic weights for the actual weights in the equation of proportion. The result is

$$\frac{\text{Wt. of X in the sample}}{m \times \text{At. wt. of X}} = \frac{\text{Wt. of Y in the sample}}{n \times \text{At. wt. of Y}}.$$

The numerators can be determined in a laboratory, by analyzing a sample and weighing its constituents. The atomic weights are known from the kinds of experiments discussed in Chapter 22. Therefore only m and n are unknown, and they have to be small integers. The formula is constructed by using the smallest values of m and n that will fit the equation.*

Example. In our earlier encounter with the oxides of copper (Article 20–5), we were unable to say whether the red oxide contains two atoms of copper or only one. By analysis, one finds that the red oxide is about 89 percent Cu and

* The numbers of atoms in one molecule are either m and n, or some multiple of them. The actual numbers cannot be determined without measuring the molecular weight.

11 per cent O, by weight. To find the formula, assume it has the form Cu_mO_n, and use the last equation, in the form

$$\frac{\text{Wt. of Cu in Sample}}{m \times \text{At. wt. of Cu}} = \frac{\text{Wt. of O in sample}}{n \times \text{At. wt. of O}}$$

$$\frac{89}{m \times 63.6} = \frac{11}{n \times 16.0}$$

$$\frac{m}{n} = \frac{89}{11} \times \frac{16.0}{63.6} = 2.0.$$

The simplest possibility that gives $m/n = 2$ is $m = 2$, $n = 1$. Therefore the formula of red copper oxide is Cu_2O; the lower figure on page 163 is the correct one.

The method is easy to extend to compounds containing more than two elements. If a compound contains three elements, X, Y, and Z, its formula will be of the type $X_mY_nZ_p$. The number of atomic groups in any sample may in this case be expressed in three different ways, and all three ways must give the same result. An argument exactly like the previous one leads to the conclusion:

$$\frac{\text{Wt. of X in the sample}}{m \times \text{At. wt. of X}} = \frac{\text{Wt. of Y in the sample}}{n \times \text{At. wt. of Y}} = \frac{\text{Wt. of Z in the sample}}{p \times \text{At. wt. of Z}}.$$

Example. An experiment shows that dehydrated Epsom salt contains approximately 20 percent Mg, 27 percent S, and 53 percent O. To find its formula, write $Mg_mS_nO_p$, and use

$$\frac{\text{Wt. of Mg in sample}}{m \times \text{At. wt. of Mg}} = \frac{\text{Wt. of S in sample}}{n \times \text{At. wt. of S}} = \frac{\text{Wt. of O in sample}}{p \times \text{At. wt. of O}}.$$

We have

$$\frac{20}{m \times 24} = \frac{27}{n \times 32} = \frac{53}{p \times 16}.$$

Taking these ratios in pairs for convenience, we have

$$\frac{20}{m \times 24} = \frac{27}{n \times 32}$$

or

$$\frac{m}{n} = \frac{20 \times 32}{27 \times 24} = \frac{80}{81}, \text{ or approximately } 1{:}1;$$

and

$$\frac{20}{m \times 24} = \frac{53}{p \times 16}$$

or

$$\frac{m}{p} = \frac{20 \times 16}{24 \times 53} = \frac{40}{159}, \text{ or approximately } 1{:}4.$$

The simplest possibility is $m = 1$, $n = 1$, and $p = 4$. Hence the formula for dehydrated Epsom salt is $MgSO_4$.

23–3. Valence. Formulas, determined by the methods just discussed, reveal certain regularities in the combining tendencies of atoms. There is no compound known in which one H atom is attached to two or more other atoms; each H atom can combine with only one other atom. The H atom therefore can serve as a standard of comparison for combining ability. The measure of combining ability is called *valence*; it is the number of H atoms that the atom in question can combine with, or the number of H atoms whose place it can take in a compound. Some elements have different valences in different compounds; a given element does not commonly exhibit more than two valences, however, and one usually predominates. The array of compounds in Table 23–I shows how the concept of valence coordinates the behavior of the elements.

TABLE 23–I

A Set of Compounds That Illustrates the Idea of Valence

HCl	H_2O	H_3N	H_4C
$NaCl$	Na_2O		
$CaCl_2$	CaO	Ca_3N_2	
$AlCl_3$	Al_2O_3	AlN	Al_4C_3
CCl_4	CO_2		

In HCl, Cl combines one-to-one with H, so Cl has a valence of 1. In H_4C, C exhibits a valence of 4. If Cl has a valence of 1, it should take 4 atoms of Cl to stand in the place of 4 atoms of H; we see in Table 23–I that the compound of C and Cl is indeed CCl_4.

In H_2O, O shows a valence of 2. If it has a combining ability of 2, and C has a combining ability of 4, we expect carbon oxide to be CO_2. Actually there are two oxides of carbon, but CO_2 is the more common.

If Cl has a valence of 1, then from the existence of $CaCl_2$ we see that Ca has a valence of 2, so that it can be expected to combine one-to-one with O. Calcium oxide actually is CaO.

Work out for yourself what Table 23–I says about the valence of Al and of N.

Chemistry is vastly simplified by the fact that each element has one characteristic valence, or at most a few. When a metallic element has two common valences, the smaller is indicated by using the suffix "–ous," and the larger by the suffix "–ic," usually on its Latin name. For example iron (ferrum) in compounds is called "ferrous" if it has valence 2 as in FeO, and "ferric" if it has valence 3 as in Fe_2O_3. Tin (stannum) is called "stannous" if it has valence 2, and "stannic" if it has valence 4. The red and black oxides of copper (cuprum) are called cuprous oxide, Cu_2O, and cupric oxide, CuO, respectively.

Table 23–II shows the characteristic valences of the most common elements.

TABLE 23-II

SOME ELEMENTS AND THEIR VALENCES

Metallic		Nonmetallic		Valence
Sodium	Na			1
Potassium	K	Chlorine	Cl	1
Silver	Ag	Bromine	Br	1
Mercury (-ous)	Hg	Iodine	I	1
Copper (cuprous)	Cu			1
Barium	Ba			2
Calcium	Ca			2
Copper (cupric)	Cu			2
Iron (ferrous)	Fe			2
Lead	Pb	Oxygen	O	2
Magnesium	Mg	Sulfur	S	2
Mercury (-ic)	Hg			2
Tin (stannous)	Sn			2
Zinc	Zn			2
Aluminum	Al			3
Iron (ferric)	Fe	Nitrogen	N	3
Chromium	Cr			3
Tin (stannic)	Sn	Carbon	C	4
		Silicon	Si	4

23-4. Radicals. There are some atomic groupings that have a strong tendency to enter into chemical reactions without breaking up. Such groups of atoms are called *radicals,* and to some extent they behave like single atoms. Radicals are not substances; they are found in compounds, but they themselves cannot be isolated and poured into bottles.

The commonest radicals and their valences are shown in Table 23-III.

TABLE 23-III

SOME RADICALS AND THEIR VALENCES

Metallic		Nonmetallic		Valence
Ammonium	NH_4	Hydroxide	OH	1
		Nitrate	NO_3	1
		Carbonate	CO_3	2
		Sulfate	SO_4	2
		Sulfite	SO_3	2
		Phosphate	PO_4	3
		Silicate	SiO_4	4

In formulas the atomic symbols representing a radical are always kept together, as in $CaCO_3$ (calcium carbonate, the chief constituent of limestone) or NH_4OH (ammonium hydroxide, or "household ammonia"). If several radicals of the same kind enter into the combination designated by the formula, the radical is enclosed in parentheses and given the appropriate subscript, as in $Zn(NO_3)_2$ (zinc nitrate).

23–5. Writing Chemical Formulas by Using Valence. Knowing valences permits us to work out the formulas for most simple compounds from a knowledge of their constituents. The cardinal rule is that the valence of the metallic part must balance the valence of the nonmetallic part. The scheme can be made clear by a few illustrations. In hydrogen bromide, each atom (H and Br) has a valence of 1, so the formula is HBr. In hydrogen sulfate, the sulfate radical with its valence of 2 will have to be balanced by two hydrogen atoms; the formula is H_2SO_4. Aluminum sulfate takes more thought; of Al (valence 3) we need two atoms (total, six valences), and of SO_4 (valence 2) three radicals (total, six valences), to achieve balance. The formula is $Al_2(SO_4)_3$.

Building a formula on the basis of valence is often complicated by the fact that some atoms exhibit more than one valence. For example, a compound of copper and oxygen may be either Cu_2O or CuO, depending on whether the copper is playing its cuprous role or its cupric one. Auxiliary information on such questions is often available—when it is not, the formula has to be found by a weight analysis in the laboratory.

Facility in writing correct formulas comes only with practice. There is a simple graphical approach that may be an aid in the beginning. Pretend that valence represents the number of arms that an atom stretches out to other atoms. No compound contains any atoms with unjoined arms. A few examples follow.

Atoms	Diagram	Formula
H— =O	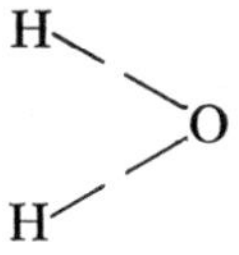 H╲ O H╱	H_2O
Ca= =S	Ca= =S	CaS
Al≡ =O	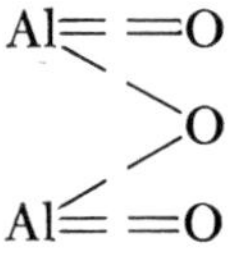 Al≡ =O O Al≡ =O	Al_2O_3
Fe≡ ≡SiO_4	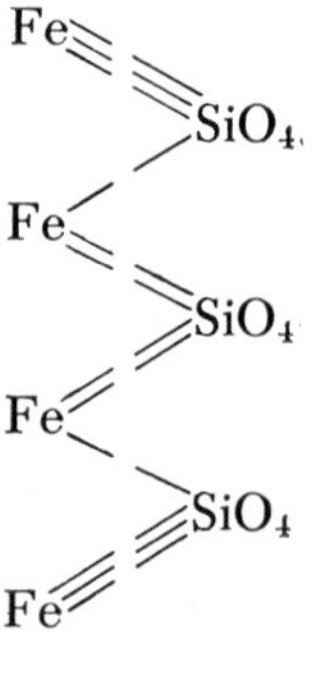 Fe≡ SiO_4 Fe≡ SiO_4 Fe≡ SiO_4 Fe≡	$Fe_4(SiO_4)_3$

Summary

A chemical formula is a shorthand notation for describing molecules or other groups of atoms. Each atom in the group is represented by the symbol of its element, and a subscript on the symbol shows how many such atoms there are in the group. Usually the metallic elements are written first.

If the molecular weight and the constituent elements of a compound have been determined in the laboratory, we can often figure out its formula by consulting a table of atomic weights. If the molecular weight is unknown, then the formula can be calculated, using (1) a table of atomic weights and (2) a laboratory analysis that gives the weight of each element in a sample of the compound. The simplest formula consistent with the analysis is used, until such time as the molecular weight can be measured.

The valence of an atom is the number of hydrogen atoms that the atom in question can combine with, or the number of hydrogen atoms that it can take the place of. Some atoms exhibit different valences under different conditions. The valence of an atom is judged by examining formulas to see how it combines with other atoms, the ultimate test being how it combines with, or takes the place of, hydrogen.

Radicals are atomic groupings that have a strong tendency to enter into chemical reactions without breaking up. Among the most important are ammonium, NH_4; hydroxide, OH; nitrate, NO_3; carbonate, CO_3; sulfate, SO_4.

If the constituents of a reasonably simple compound are known, its formula can be worked out from a knowledge of valences. The valence of the metallic part must balance the valence of the nonmetallic part. Beginners find it helpful to make diagrams in which the symbol for each atom has arms that must each be attached to the arms of another atom, the number of arms representing in each case the valence of the atom.

Questions

1. Sulfur dioxide, a gas much used in industry, has molecular weight 64.0. Analysis shows that, by weight, it is 50 percent sulfur and 50 percent oxygen. Calculate its formula.
2. Benzene is a compound of hydrogen and carbon. It has a molecular weight of 78.1, and it is 92.3 percent carbon. What is its formula?
3. A certain compound of iron and oxygen is found by analysis to be 70 percent iron, by weight, and 30 percent oxygen. Using the principles in Article 23–2, find the simplest formula the compound can have. What valence does the iron have? What is the name of the compound?

4. The "arsenic" used in crime and rat poison is usually an oxide of arsenic. It is approximately 75 percent arsenic and 25 percent oxygen by weight. What is its formula? What is the valence of arsenic, at least in this compound?
5. Using Tables 23–II and 23–III, write the formulas for the following compounds:

   (a) Zinc oxide
   (b) Lead chloride
   (c) Mercurous sulfate
   (d) Aluminum hydroxide
   (e) Magnesium carbonate
   (f) Stannic phosphate
   (g) Ammonium carbonate

6. Show which of the following formulas is incorrect: Mg_3N_2, $CaSO_4$, $Al_2(PO_4)_3$, K_2SO_4, HNO_3.
7. State the valence of the first element in each of the following formulas, which are all correct: $GaCl_3$, GeO_2, Sc_2O_3, $Th(OH)_4$, Cs_2SO_4, $Bi_2(CO_3)_3$.
8. A weight of 4.24 g of a certain compound of potassium, phosphorus, and oxygen was found to comprise: K, 2.34 g; P, 0.62 g; O, 1.28 g. What was the formula for the compound? What was its name?

24

CHEMICAL EQUATIONS

L'art de raisonner se réduit à une langue bien faite.

LAVOISIER, quoting CONDILLAC

The chemical formulas, as described in the last chapter, give compact descriptions of molecules, and they help in the determination of valence. They also have a further use, because they make possible a concise algebra of chemical reactions. Using formulas, we can usually write in a single line all the essential information about a reaction. This one-line description is called a "chemical equation." For us, the chief use of chemical equations will be simply as direct and vivid descriptions of reactions. For the working chemist, equations have a further use. They enable him to figure out very quickly how much of any substance will react with a given amount of another substance, and also how much product will result. Such calculations are much used in quantitative experimentation; they also afford a basis for efficient operation in chemical industry.

24–1. Writing and Balancing Chemical Equations. Chemical equations are symbolic descriptions of chemical reactions; they give both qualitative and quantitative information. If they are to represent a reaction correctly, they must comply with the laws of chemical combination. In particular, all the atoms that enter into the reaction must be present in the products, and no others must be present there.

As a beginning, recall Avogadro's explanation (Article 21–3) of how the reaction of chlorine with hydrogen fits the Law of Combining Volumes. The experimental fact is:

$$\begin{matrix}\text{1 Volume} \\ \text{of hydrogen}\end{matrix} + \begin{matrix}\text{1 Volume} \\ \text{of chlorine}\end{matrix} \rightarrow \begin{matrix}\text{2 Volumes of} \\ \text{hydrogen chloride.}\end{matrix}$$

From the fact, Avogadro inferred that

$$\begin{matrix}\text{1 Molecule} \\ \text{of hydrogen}\end{matrix} + \begin{matrix}\text{1 Molecule} \\ \text{of chlorine}\end{matrix} \rightarrow \begin{matrix}\text{2 Molecules of} \\ \text{hydrogen chloride.}\end{matrix}$$

We can abbreviate this statement by using the formulas for the molecules, as was done in Article 21–3. The result is a simple example of a chemical equation:

$$H_2 + Cl_2 \rightarrow 2HCl.$$

Note that each kind of atom appears the same number of times on each side of the equation, in recognition that atoms are not created or destroyed in a chemical reaction. An equation that satisfies this condition is said to be "balanced."

For quick comprehension of chemical situations, one must learn to write a balanced chemical equation from a verbal description of a reaction. The following procedure will always work.

Step 1: (This may be omitted after a little practice.) Write, in words, the reaction that the equation is to represent.

Step 2: Write the correct formula (Article 23–5) for each substance beneath its name. For substances that are elements, write the formula for a molecule if the element is in the gaseous state. Put in the necessary + signs and the arrow.

Step 3: In front of each formula, insert whatever number is needed in order to make a balanced equation.

Step 4: For each element in the reaction, check to make sure the same number of atoms appears on each side of the equation. If this is not the case, at least one of the multipliers is incorrect and must be changed. (Do not change the subscripts in any formulas, since such a change would make the formula represent a different substance.)

EXAMPLE 1. To write an equation for the reaction when a strip of the metal magnesium burns in air to form magnesium oxide.

Step 1: Magnesium combines with oxygen to form magnesium oxide.

Step 2: $Mg \quad + \quad O_2 \quad \rightarrow \quad MgO.$

(We know the formula for magnesium oxide is MgO because Mg and O each have valence 2.)

Step 3: Since there are two oxygen atoms in O_2, there must be enough MgO formed to employ two O atoms. Therefore we put the coefficient 2 in front of MgO. This requires two Mg atoms, so we need a coefficient 2 on the Mg. The result is

$$2Mg + O_2 \rightarrow 2MgO.$$

Step 4: On each side there are the same number of Mg atoms (two) and the same number of O atoms (two). Therefore the equation balances.

EXAMPLE 2. To write an equation for the reaction of barium chloride with cupric sulfate, which forms barium sulfate and cupric chloride.

Step 1: Barium chloride + Cupric sulfate → Barium sulfate + Cupric chloride.
Step 2: $BaCl_2 + CuSO_4 \rightarrow BaSO_4 + CuCl_2$.
Step 3: The equation balances as it stands; no coefficients are needed.
Step 4: On each side there are the same number of Ba atoms (one), Cl atoms (two), Cu atoms (one), and SO_4 radicals (one). The equation balances.

EXAMPLE 3. To write an equation for the reaction of barium chloride with aluminum sulfate, to form barium sulfate and aluminum chloride.

Step 1: Barium chloride + Aluminum sulfate → Barium sulfate + Aluminum chloride.
Step 2: $BaCl_2 + Al_2(SO_4)_3 \rightarrow BaSO_4 + AlCl_3$.
Step 3: The equation as it stands is not balanced, for since we start with two Al atoms in $Al_2(SO_4)_3$, we must try $2AlCl_3$. This involves six Cl atoms, so we put a 3 in front of $BaCl_2$. The tentative result is

$$3BaCl_2 + Al_2(SO_4)_3 \rightarrow BaSO_4 + 2AlCl_3.$$

Notice now that we have three Ba atoms on the left and only one on the right; to make a balance we need $3BaSO_4$, which incidentally uses up the three SO_4 radicals from $Al_2(SO_4)_3$. The equation becomes

$$3BaCl_2 + Al_2(SO_4)_3 \rightarrow 3BaSO_4 + 2AlCl_3.$$

Step 4: On each side, there are the same number of Ba atoms (three), Cl atoms (six), Al atoms (two), and SO_4 radicals (three).

Chemical equations will be very useful to us in the discussion of reactions. An equation, of course, is not a reaction; it is only a description of a reaction. To avoid tedious repetition, however, the text will frequently say "The reaction is: ." and display an equation, instead of saying "The reaction is described by the equation: ." The usage is the same as that which permits us to point to a photograph and say "This is my sister."

24–2. Molecular Weights from Formulas. A measurement of molecular weight is often the basis for our knowledge of the formula and chemical name for a substance (Article 23–2). Once the name is known, however, the formula can usually be written down by simply using a knowledge of valence (Article 23–5). From the formula, in turn, one can deduce the molecular weight by consulting a table of atomic weights. When the molecular weight of a common substance is needed in a calculation, therefore, it is usually easier to get the molecular weight from the formula than from the records of previous experimenters.

To find the molecular weight of a substance when the formula is known, refer to a table of atomic weights. The molecular weight implied by the formula is found by adding up the atomic weights of all the atoms in the formula. Write down the atomic weight of each element that appears in the formula, and multiply it by the number of atoms that each element contributes to the formula. The sum of these numbers is the molecular weight.

EXAMPLE. To find the molecular weight of carbon dioxide, CO_2:

Carbon contributes one atom whose atomic weight is 12.0. The atomic weight of oxygen is 16.0, and this element contributes two atoms to the formula; oxygen contributes 2×16.0 to the molecular weight. The molecular weight of CO_2 is therefore

$$12.0 + 2 \times 16.0 = 44.0.$$

24–3. Weights in Reactions. A balanced chemical equation not only shows what substances enter into a reaction, but also it opens the way for us to calculate *how much* of one substance is needed to react with a given amount of some other substance. We shall have little occasion to exploit this use of chemical equations, but some idea of what can be done may be of interest. An essential feature of the procedure is its dependence on molecular weights.

Consider the equation for the reaction of hydrogen with oxygen to form water. It provides a qualitative description of the reaction, and it makes a quantitative statement of the relative numbers of molecules that take part. From the relative numbers of molecules, we can infer the relative weights of the substances that enter into the reaction.

	$2H_2$	+	O_2	→	$2H_2O$
Qualitative:	Hydrogen		Oxygen		Water
Quantitative:	2 molecules		1 molecule		2 molecules
Relative weights:	(2×2.0)		(1×32)		(2×18)

Suppose that for some reason we want to know how much oxygen is needed to react with 5.0 g of hydrogen. Each molecule that takes part in the reaction has a weight that is proportional to the molecular weight of that substance. Therefore, the needed weight of each substance is proportional to the molecular weight of the substance times the relative number of molecules that it contributes to the reaction. To find the relative weight that each substance contributes, multiply its molecular weight by the number in front of its formula in the equation. It is convenient to write the result under the equation, thus:

$$\begin{array}{ccccc} 2H_2 & + & O_2 & \rightarrow & 2H_2O \\ 2 \times 2.0 = 4.0 & & 1 \times 32 = 32 & & 2 \times 18 = 36 \end{array}$$

The weights of hydrogen and oxygen in this reaction are in the proportion 4.0:32. To find how many grams of oxygen are needed to react with 5.0 g of hydrogen, use the proportion

$$\frac{5.0 \text{ g}}{4.0} = \frac{x}{32}$$

The result is $x = 40$ g. Therefore 40 grams of oxygen will react completely with the 5.0 grams of hydrogen. If more than 40 g of oxygen is supplied, then 40 g will be used in the reaction and the rest will be left over; if less than 40 g of oxygen is supplied, then not all of the hydrogen will be used up. It is easy to see that calculations of this sort are vital to the industrial chemist, who may be ordering his materials by the ton.

As a more complicated example, consider the reaction in Example 3 on page 191. Suppose one needs to prepare 35 g of the white pigment $BaSO_4$, by means of the reaction

$$3BaCl_2 + Al_2(SO_4)_3 \rightarrow 3BaSO_4 + 2AlCl_3.$$

How much $BaCl_2$ and $Al_2(SO_4)_3$ are needed to start with? First calculate the molecular weights of $BaCl_2$, $Al_2(SO_4)_3$, and $BaSO_4$ from their formulas and the table of atomic weights. Under the equation, enter the molecular weights and multiply them by the appropriate coefficients.

$$\begin{array}{ccccccc} 3BaCl_2 & + & Al_2(SO_4)_3 & \rightarrow & 3BaSO_4 & + & 2AlCl_3 \\ 3 \times 208.4 = 625.2 & & 1 \times 342.3 = 342.3 & & 3 \times 233.5 = 700.5. & & \end{array}$$

The resulting numbers are the relative weights that enter into the reaction. To get the actual weights needed in a given case, use the information about that case to set up a proportion. In particular, the amount of $BaCl_2$ needed to produce 35.0 g of $BaSO_4$ is given by

$$\frac{x}{625.2} = \frac{35.0 \text{ g}}{700.5} \quad \text{whence} \quad x = 31.3 \text{ g}.$$

The amount of $Al_2(SO_4)_3$ required can be found by the same method.

Summary

Chemical equations are symbolic descriptions of chemical reactions. A correctly written equation has the same number of atoms of each kind on both sides, in accord with the Law of Conservation of Matter.

After the formula of a substance has been found, anyone who knows it can calculate the molecular weight of the substance. To do so, one simply adds up the atomic weights of all the atoms appearing in the formula, with proper regard for the subscripts that show how many atoms of each element are present.

A knowledge of weight relations in chemical reactions is important for fruitful experimentation and for industrial operations. Weight relations can be calculated by using molecular weights and the equation for the reaction.

Questions

1. Write balanced equations for the following:
   (a) Zinc reacts with oxygen to form zinc oxide.
   (b) Aluminum hydroxide decomposes, forming water and aluminum oxide.

(c) Barium chloride reacts with silver nitrate to form silver chloride and barium nitrate.

2. Write balanced equations for the following:
   (a) Zinc added to copper sulfate forms copper and zinc sulfate.
   (b) Sodium hydroxide reacts with hydrogen sulfate to form water and sodium sulfate.
   (c) Sodium reacts with sodium nitrate to form sodium oxide and nitrogen.
3. Balance the following:
   (a) $CH_4 + O_2 \rightarrow CO_2 + H_2O$
   (b) $KClO_3 \rightarrow KCl + O_2$
   (c) $Al + O_2 \rightarrow Al_2O_3$
   (d) $H_2S + O_2 \rightarrow H_2O + SO_2$
   (e) $KMnO_4 \rightarrow K_2O + MnO_2 + O_2$
4. For each of the following compounds, calculate the molecular weight from the formula: barium chloride, lead nitrate, sodium hydroxide, carbon tetrachloride, hydrogen sulfate, potassium carbonate.
5. A dime weighing 3.12 g was dissolved in nitric acid, and the silver nitrate so formed was then converted into silver chloride, which could easily be separated from the other substances present. The silver chloride weighed 3.73 g. Assuming that all of the silver in the coin was converted into silver chloride, what percentage of the coin was silver?
6. Find the weight of hydrogen that will be formed when 13.8 g of zinc all reacts with hydrogen chloride. (The products are zinc chloride and hydrogen.)
7. What weight of hydrogen chloride will just react completely with 340 g of ammonia to form ammonium chloride? The equation for the reaction is $HCl + NH_3 \rightarrow NH_4Cl$.
8. An example in the text calculates how much barium chloride must be used in order to produce 35 g of barium sulfate by reacting with aluminum sulfate. How much aluminum sulfate would have to be used?
9. How much ferrous sulfide (FeS) can be formed from 10 g of sulfur and an ample supply of iron powder? How much can be formed from 10 g of iron powder and an ample supply of sulfur? Suppose that in the demonstration in Article 19–2, exactly 10 g of iron powder had been mixed with exactly 10 g of sulfur. How much FeS could be formed in the resulting reaction?

GENERAL VIEW OF SECTION III

The section falls into two closely related parts. The first presents evidence in support of the idea that matter is composed of small particles called atoms; the second demonstrates some general methods of analyzing the behavior of the atoms.

Aside from some preliminary gropings, of interest only to scholars, the development of chemistry dates from about the time of the American Revolution. By 1800, experimenters had properly identified an assortment of elements and had discovered the Conservation of Matter and the Law of Constant Composition. To correlate the new experimental knowledge with the long-standing belief that matter is composed of small particles, Dalton proposed his atomic hypotheses. From them he deduced the Law of Multiple Proportions; the experimental verification of the law provided strong support for the belief in atoms.

By experimenting on reactions involving gases, Gay-Lussac discovered the Law of Combining Volumes. Avogadro, learning of this discovery, saw that it could be accounted for by assuming that the particles of a gas are generally not individual atoms, but rather they are groups of atoms called "molecules," even when the gas is an element. In addition, Avogadro had to assume that under like conditions of temperature and pressure, equal volumes of all gases contain the same number of molecules (Avogadro's hypothesis).

Using Avogadro's hypothesis, it is easy to determine the relative weights of the molecules of different gases. If samples of two gases have the same temperature, pressure, and volume, then they contain the same number of molecules. The weights of the samples will then be in the same ratio as the weights of the individual molecules, so the relative weights of the molecules can be found by simply weighing the gases in bulk.

If the number of atoms in one molecule of an elemental gas can be found by an experiment of the Gay-Lussac type, then the atomic weight of that element can be calculated from its molecular weight. If an element is not obtainable in the gaseous state, its atomic weight can be determined by analyzing many of its gaseous compounds and finding out how much the element contributes to their molecular weights.

The formulas for a few gaseous compounds can be found by applying Avogadro's hypothesis to the volumes of reactants and products. In general, however, formulas must be found by performing a weight analysis of the compound and knowing the atomic weights of its constituents.

When formulas for a large number of compounds had been worked out, it became possible to classify elements according to their combining ability, or valence. The valence of an atom is the number of hydrogen atoms it will combine with or take the place of. A knowledge of valences is helpful in remembering old formulas and forming conjectures about new ones.

Looking back, we see that the experiments and reasoning discussed in this section give strong grounds for believing in atoms. They also give much information about the behavior of atoms, but the information is not of a richly satisfying kind. We know the relative weights of atoms, but not their real weights, nor their sizes; we know their combining abilities, but do not know why they combine. The missing details will be worked out in later sections. The next section, however, is devoted to further study of the chemical behavior of matter in bulk. It will provide concrete illustrations of some things that we have heretofore discussed in a rather abstract way.

IV

Some Chemical Reactions

Now that we have considered the fundamental laws of chemistry and recognized the difference between atoms and molecules, it will serve our purpose to consider some details of the chemistry of oxygen and hydrogen. In doing so, we shall introduce numerous concepts and terms that will be useful later on. Of nearly equal value will be the opportunity to use in concrete cases some of the ideas that have been introduced in the past few chapters. This section will therefore improve your command of the language of chemistry, and it will also enlarge the background of facts against which we may later view any theory of chemical behavior.

25

OXYGEN

The recognition of oxygen as an element was one of the fruits of Lavoisier's experiments (Article 19–5). Lavoisier also found that oxygen is necessary for the support both of animal life and of combustion. He named it "oxygen" from Greek roots meaning "acid-former."

25–1. Occurrence of Oxygen. The natural occurrence of oxygen as a "free," or uncombined, element is limited to the atmosphere, which is about one-fifth oxygen. In the combined form, however, the occurrence of oxygen is very widespread; in fact, oxygen is the most abundant element on the earth's surface. It represents 88 percent, by weight, of water. It is present in all plant and animal tissue. Most rocks contain oxygen as a constituent of silicates, carbonates, or oxides; sand, for example, is mostly silicon dioxide, SiO_2. By weight, nearly half of the accessible portion of the earth's crust is oxygen.

25–2. Preparation of Oxygen. Most of the oxygen of commerce comes from the air. First the air is compressed and cooled until it becomes a liquid. Nitrogen, the chief component of the air, boils at a lower temperature than oxygen does. In the liquid mixture, therefore, the nitrogen evaporates more rapidly than the oxygen. By letting the liquid air evaporate in a suitable apparatus, it is possible to make the nitrogen boil away first. Then the oxygen evaporates and is collected, compressed, and shipped in strong steel containers. Most of the oxygen sold commercially is used in oxygen-acetylene or oxygen-hydrogen torches for cutting or welding steel. The gas also has important medical uses, in the treatment of pneumonia and other cases of restricted respiration.

Small quantities of oxygen, suitable for small-scale experiments, are usually obtained from compounds of oxygen that decompose when heated. We have in fact already seen oxygen prepared in this way from mercuric oxide, in Article 19–2. Potassium chlorate, $KClO_3$, decomposes very conveniently. The reaction is

$$2KClO_3 \rightarrow 2KCl + 3O_2.$$

Experiment. Let about 10 grams of potassium chlorate be put in a test tube (Figure 25–A) and gently heated until it melts. With stronger heating, bubbles appear in the molten material and collect in the inverted bottle. The glowing-splint test (Article 19–2) shows that the gas is oxygen. Three or four bottles of it may be collected.

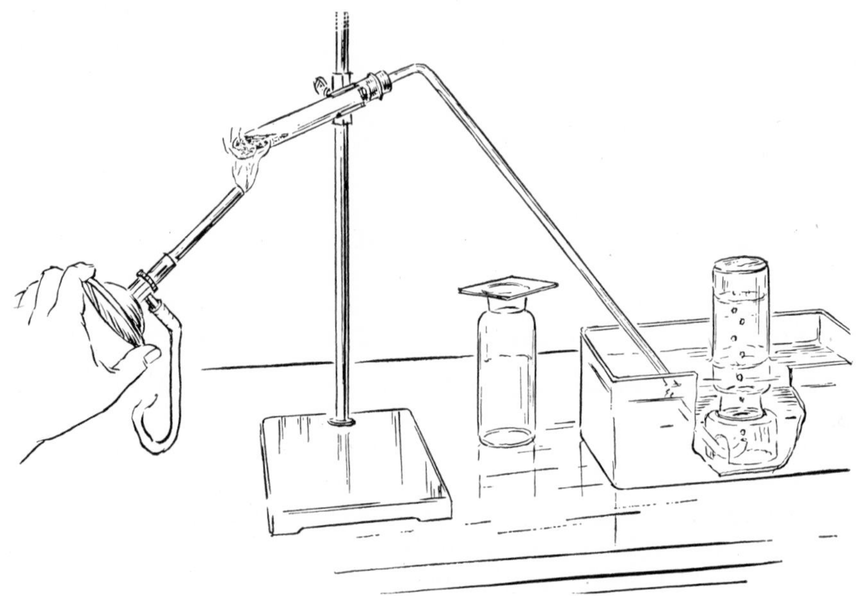

Figure 25–A. Obtaining oxygen through the decomposition of potassium chlorate.

25–3. Catalysts. Pure potassium chlorate does not decompose noticeably when it is just hot enough to melt. The presence of manganese dioxide, however, will make the decomposition occur rapidly at that temperature, or even at a lower one.

Experiment. A couple of grams of potassium chlorate, $KClO_3$, in a vertical test tube, is just melted by careful heating. The glowing-splint test shows that little if any oxygen is set free. Then the flame is removed, and into the test tube is thrown as much manganese dioxide, MnO_2, as will cover the head of a pin. A glowing splint will show that there is a prompt and copious evolution of oxygen.

The experiment shows that the manganese dioxide did something to increase the speed of liberation of oxygen. One might think that the oxygen came, at least in part, from the manganese dioxide. It is a fact, however, that all of the manganese dioxide can be recovered, unchanged, after the experiment. All of the oxygen must therefore have come from the decomposition of potassium chlorate. The manganese dioxide merely hastens the action.

A substance that changes the speed of a chemical reaction is called a *catalyst*. Catalysts undergo no permanent chemical change through the part they play in the reaction. Catalysts are called "positive" if they increase the speed of a reaction. "Negative" catalysts, often called "inhibitors," slow down a reaction. For example, an inhibitor is added to rubber to retard the reaction of oxygen with the rubber. The inhibitor thereby lengthens the useful life of the rubber.

25-4. Physical Properties of Oxygen. In the gaseous state, oxygen is colorless, tasteless, odorless, and slightly heavier than air. Oxygen boils at $-183°$ C ($-297°$ F) and freezes at $-218°$ C ($-368°$ F). In its liquid and solid states, it is blue and is attracted by a magnet.

Oxygen dissolves in water only to a very limited extent, but the small amount that will dissolve is sufficient to support the life of fish.

25-5. Chemical Properties of Oxygen. Chemically, oxygen is a typical nonmetal, forming compounds with the metals and hydrogen, as well as with most of the nonmetals.

(a) *Reactions With Metals.* Except for a very few (notably silver, gold, and platinum), the metals combine directly with oxygen to form oxides. The oxygen in the air is sufficiently concentrated to support some of the reactions at an observable rate. Some of the reactions, however, occur rapidly only when there is a higher concentration of oxygen.

EXPERIMENTS. (1) A piece of magnesium ribbon can easily be heated until it burns in air. The dazzling flame shows that the reaction is highly exothermic. The reaction forms magnesium oxide:

$$2Mg + O_2 \rightarrow 2MgO.$$

(2) Iron in contact with the atmosphere combines more or less slowly with oxygen, to produce rust. Rust is mostly ferric oxide, Fe_2O_3, formed in the reaction

$$4Fe + 3O_2 \rightarrow 2Fe_2O_3.$$

A more spectacular reaction takes place when steel wool is quickly heated and thrust into a bottle of oxygen. The steel burns with scintillating sparks, forming another of the oxides of iron:

$$3Fe + 2O_2 \rightarrow Fe_3O_4.$$

The product is called ferroso-ferric oxide.*

(3) Let a little aluminum powder be put in a glass tube about a meter long, and 2 or 3 cm in diameter, supported at a slight angle to the horizontal.

* The formula Fe_3O_4 might lead one to wonder whether the oxide is ferric or ferrous. Actually, it is a combination of both, and it is called ferroso-ferric to indicate this dual character. The formula might be written $FeO \cdot Fe_2O_3$. This particular oxide is always formed when iron combines with oxygen at high temperatures.

The lower end should be connected to a cylinder of oxygen. If a flame is placed near the upper end of the tube, and the powder is blown into the flame with a puff of oxygen, the aluminum burns with a brilliant flash when it hits the flame. The product is aluminum oxide:

$$4Al + 3O_2 \rightarrow 2Al_2O_3.$$

(b) *Reactions With Nonmetals.* Oxygen combines not only with metals but also with most of the nonmetals. The glowing-splint test depends upon the fact that carbon reacts faster with oxygen when the oxygen is more concentrated. In pure or nearly pure oxygen, the reaction

$$C + O_2 \rightarrow CO_2$$

is so rapid that the liberated heat causes the glowing wood to burst into flame.

Sulfur and phosphorus both burn in air if they are heated to start the reaction. The burning of phosphorus produces a white smoke, because the product is a finely divided white solid. The reactions are:

$$S + O_2 \rightarrow SO_2 \quad \text{(sulfur dioxide)}$$

$$4P + 5O_2 \rightarrow 2P_2O_5 \quad \text{(phosphorus pentoxide).}$$

To prove that the burning really is combination with oxygen, one can see whether the burning occurs in pure oxygen. In fact, on experimenting, we find that the burning not only occurs, but even that it occurs at an enhanced rate.

Experiments. A piece of sulfur about the size of a pea is ignited in a long-handled metal spoon and lowered into a jar of pure oxygen. The flame is pale blue in air, but bright blue in oxygen. Red phosphorus, similarly treated, also burns more vigorously in oxygen than in air. Both reactions are plainly exothermic.

(c) *Reaction With Hydrogen.* The combination of oxygen with hydrogen to form water has already merited some attention (Articles 19–3, 21–3, 23–2, 24–3). We mention it here simply for the sake of completeness.

(d) *Reactions With Carbon-Hydrogen Compounds.* Since oxygen combines both with carbon and with hydrogen, it is not surprising that it also reacts with carbon-hydrogen compounds, of which there are many.

In conjunction with deposits of petroleum, there are large amounts of what is called "natural gas." The gas, of which the chief constituent is methane (CH_4), is widely used for fuel. During its combustion, methane combines with oxygen to form carbon dioxide and water.

$$CH_4 + 2O_2 \rightarrow CO_2 + 2H_2O.$$

A very similar reaction takes place when gasoline burns with a copious * supply of oxygen. Although gasoline is a mixture of many carbon-hydrogen compounds, it may fairly be represented by a sort of average formula, C_7H_{16}. When it burns,

$$C_7H_{16} + 11O_2 \rightarrow 7CO_2 + 8H_2O.$$

Coal is a very complex mixture of carbon and carbon-hydrogen compounds. The chief products of its combustion are carbon dioxide and water. In fact, these same products are to be expected whenever a carbon-hydrogen compound burns in an unrestricted supply of oxygen.

25–6. Oxidation and Combustion. We have now seen a variety of reactions in which oxygen combines with some element or compound. For the time being, the term *oxidation* will be taken to mean the union of a substance with oxygen. For example, when iron combines with oxygen, then the iron is said to be "oxidized." Oxidation is often exothermic. Heat is liberated when iron rusts, but the reaction is so slow that the heat leaks away unnoticed. When iron burns in pure oxygen, however, the energy of the reaction is liberated quickly, and some of the energy goes into light. An oxidation that takes place with the evolution of heat and light is called *combustion.*

25–7. Oxygen in Human Affairs. Our interest in oxygen will lie mainly in the chemical behavior of its compounds. We can afford a moment's pause, however, to comment on the role of oxygen in everyday matters. Although the oxygen in the air causes some troubles like rusting, oxygen is essential to human life and comfort. The energy required for body heat and movement comes from oxidation of our food. One example is the complete oxidation of sugar, $C_{12}H_{22}O_{11}$:

$$C_{12}H_{22}O_{11} + 12O_2 \rightarrow 12CO_2 + 11H_2O.$$

Furthermore, it is energy from the oxidation of fuels—wood, coal, oil, or gas—that keeps our buildings warm, cooks our food, and drives our engines. As fuels become scarcer, other energy sources will become more important. At present, however, most of the energy we use comes from the combination of some other substance with oxygen.

* When the supply of oxygen is meager, some or all of the carbon is transformed into the very poisonous carbon monoxide, CO, which is particularly dangerous because it is odorless. In the cylinders of an automobile engine, only a limited amount of air is mixed with the gasoline vapor. There is never enough oxygen present for complete combustion. The exhaust gases therefore contain carbon monoxide, and there is serious danger of carbon monoxide poisoning when an automobile runs in a poorly ventilated space.

Summary

Oxygen is the most abundant element on the earth's surface. Of the materials available to man, about 50 percent by weight is oxygen, either free or in compounds.

The chief source of oxygen is air, from which the oxygen is obtained by liquefaction and subsequent evaporation. It is convenient to prepare small amounts of oxygen by thermal decomposition of certain of its compounds, notably potassium chlorate.

Although it is not very active at room temperature, at higher temperatures oxygen readily combines with most other elements.

Combustion, or burning, normally is an act of union of some substance with oxygen. The process of combining with oxygen is called oxidation.

Oxygen is necessary for the support of animal life, which depends on the oxidation of food. The energy we employ for our work and convenience comes largely from the reaction of oxygen with various fuels.

Questions

1. Why do fish not live in rivers that carry large amounts of oxidizable material, such as sewage?
2. Why does a forced draft make a fire burn more vigorously?
3. Point out several disadvantages that we should experience if a larger fraction of the air were oxygen.
4. When acetylene (C_2H_2) burns in the oxy-acetylene welding torch, the products are CO_2 and H_2O. Write the balanced equation for the reaction.
5. Wood and paper consist largely of cellulose, which has the formula $C_{6x}H_{10x}O_{5x}$, where x is some large integer. Write the balanced equation for the burning of cellulose to form CO_2 and H_2O.
6. Do you see any fundamental difference between the burning of oil to warm a house and the oxidation of sugar to warm a man? Explain.
7. What is the melting point of oxygen on the Absolute scale? What is its boiling point on this scale?

26

BASES, ACIDS, AND SALTS

The distinction between metals and nonmetals rests most simply on their physical properties (Article 19–6). There are important differences, however, in the chemical aspects of metals and nonmetals. This chapter will show that there is a deep-seated difference between metallic and nonmetallic oxides, a difference which is reflected in three important classes of compounds—bases, acids, and salts.

26–1. The Metallic Oxides; Bases. The metallic oxides have high melting points; at room temperatures they are all solids. A few of them dissolve in water. If the water is then allowed to evaporate, the substance that remains behind has properties that are different from those of the oxide we started with. (For example, it may have a lower melting point than the oxide did.) This is clear evidence that the oxide not only dissolved, but also took part in a chemical reaction with the water.

One of the oxides that reacts with water is sodium oxide, Na_2O. By weighing the water that is used up in the reaction, and also weighing the sodium oxide that is used, we find that the reaction uses one molecule of water for each molecule of sodium oxide that reacts. Moreover, the product of the reaction is a single substance. The equation for the reaction must therefore be

$$Na_2O + H_2O \rightarrow 2NaOH.$$

Notice the presence of the OH radical, which was introduced in Article 23–4.

All metallic oxides that dissolve in water react to form metallic hydroxides. These substances have certain properties in common. In solution, they have a soapy feel and a bitter taste, and they have the ability to make certain vegetable dyes, notably one called *litmus,* change from pink to blue.

Experiment. A small piece of calcium is ignited in air and allowed to burn until it has become calcium oxide. Then the oxide is allowed to react with water. The resulting solution may be cloudy, but filtering will make it clear. Paper dyed with pink litmus turns blue on contact with the solution.

The oxides of some metals scarcely dissolve at all in water, and they do not react with water at any appreciable rate. Hydroxides of these metals clearly cannot be obtained by the method just discussed. Nevertheless, these hydroxides can be obtained in other ways, and they do exhibit kinship with the oxides.

EXPERIMENT. Adding sodium hydroxide (NaOH) solution to a solution of copper sulfate ($CuSO_4$) gives rise to a pale-blue gelatinous substance that separates from the solution. This substance is copper hydroxide. The equation for the reaction is

$$CuSO_4 + 2NaOH \rightarrow Na_2SO_4 + Cu(OH)_2.$$

The same method will produce hydroxides of the other metals whose oxides do not dissolve in water.

Although the conversion of oxides to hydroxides works only when the oxides are soluble, the reverse process always works. The relation of the hydroxides to the oxides is therefore apparent in all cases.

EXPERIMENT. Copper hydroxide, made in the last experiment or bought ready-made, turns to copper oxide and water when it is heated. The dry hydroxide can be put in a test tube and heated with the tube held horizontal so that its mouth remains cool. The blue copper hydroxide decomposes, leaving in its place black copper oxide, such as forms when air acts on hot copper. Furthermore, drops of water collect in the cooler part of the tube.

The reaction in the experiment is

$$Cu(OH)_2 \rightarrow CuO + H_2O.$$

A similar reaction occurs whenever any metallic hydroxide is heated. Clearly this reaction is, in type, just the reverse of the reaction that takes place spontaneously between water and the metallic oxides that dissolve in it. The experiment gives evidence that the kinship of the metallic oxides and hydroxides is not limited to the ones that dissolve in water.

Because the metallic hydroxides have in common the properties that have been mentioned, and have also some properties that will appear later, it is convenient to place them in a category with a simple name. They are called *bases*.

26–2. The Nonmetallic Oxides; Acids. In contrast to the metallic oxides, the nonmetallic oxides usually have low melting points. In fact, many of them are gaseous at room temperature. The two classes of oxides differ also in the products that ensue when they react with water. Instead of being bitter, the products formed from nonmetallic oxides are sour. In solution, they do not feel soapy, and they change the color of litmus from blue to pink. When they react with other substances, these products readily give up hydrogen, which may escape as the free element or may enter into a new compound. Their common characteristics suggest that these products belong in one class, but not to the class of bases. Compounds that taste sour, turn litmus from blue to pink, and readily contribute hydrogen to a reaction, are called *acids.**

Experiment. A piece of sulfur is ignited in an iron spoon and burned in a bottle of air, with a little water in the bottom. When the sulfur stops burning, the bottle is stoppered and shaken to dissolve the sulfur dioxide (Article 25–5) that formed during the combustion. The solution will turn litmus paper from blue to pink.

When SO_2 and H_2O react, no hydrogen or oxygen is given off, and no sulfur appears. (Sulfur does not dissolve in water, so its presence would be easy to detect.) The reaction must therefore be one of simple combination, such as

$$SO_2 + H_2O \rightarrow H_2SO_3.$$

By determining the weights of SO_2 and H_2O that react with one another, it can be shown that the left side should contain one molecule of SO_2 for each molecule of H_2O. The product H_2SO_3 is the only one that will fit these facts. By its behavior, H_2SO_3 shows that it is an acid; it is called "sulfurous acid."

It will be convenient to introduce here the names and formulas of several common acids, along with the nonmetallic oxides to which the acids are related:

Oxide		Acid	
SO_2	Sulfur dioxide	H_2SO_3	Sulfurous acid
SO_3	Sulfur trioxide	H_2SO_4	Sulfuric acid
N_2O_5	Nitrogen pentoxide	HNO_3	Nitric acid
P_2O_5	Phosphorus pentoxide	H_3PO_4	Phosphoric acid
CO_2	Carbon dioxide	H_2CO_3	Carbonic acid

Notice that all these acids contain hydrogen, and that they all contain oxygen as well.

26–3. Oxyacids and Hydracids. There are some substances that have the acid characteristics but contain no oxygen. Since they have the character of acids, they are classified as acids. Examples are hydrochloric acid, HCl; hydrobromic acid, HBr; and hydrocyanic acid, HCN. Note that all these have hydrogen for one constituent. All the acids in Article 26–2 also contain hydrogen, and in fact hydrogen is the one constituent that all acids have in common.

Acids that contain oxygen as well as hydrogen are called *oxyacids.*

* The word comes from the Latin *acidus,* meaning "sour."

Acids that contain no oxygen are called *hydracids*; their names all begin with "hydro," as in hydrochloric, hydrocyanic, and so on.

26–4. Base Versus Acid; Neutralization. Chemists recognized very early that bases and acids are in some sense opposing classes. The simplest illustration is their effect on litmus and certain other dyes. A base in solution turns litmus from pink to blue—an acid in solution will turn it back to pink again. If they are mixed in just the right proportions, the resulting solution does not affect litmus at all.

EXPERIMENT. The continued slow addition of a calcium hydroxide solution to one of sulfurous acid eliminates the acidic property of turning litmus pink. Likewise, adding acid to the base will eliminate the basic property of turning litmus blue.

The annulment of acid properties by the addition of a base, or of basic properties by the addition of an acid, is called *neutralization.*

It is not hard to see why a base and an acid will neutralize one another. The constituent that bases have in common is the hydroxyl radical, OH. The common constituent of acids is hydrogen, H. These two sets of atoms can combine to form water, H_2O. Water does not meet our criteria for being an acid or for being a base, and therefore the basic and acidic properties both disappear. The condition for neutralization is simply to have the acid and the base present in just such quantities that there is one H from the acid for each OH from the base.*

26–5. Salts. In the last experiment, calcium hydroxide and sulfurous acid neutralized one another by forming water. The reaction must therefore have been

$$Ca(OH)_2 + H_2SO_3 \rightarrow 2H_2O + CaSO_3.$$

One of the products of neutralization is always water; the other product is called a *salt.* In this case, the salt is $CaSO_3$, calcium sulfite. It dissolves in water to such a small extent that most of it is *precipitated,* i.e., thrown down in solid form to the bottom of the vessel. The throwing down must not be taken literally; if the solid, called the precipitate, is a finely divided powder, it may take a long time to settle to the bottom.

Salts, by definition, are compounds in which a metal (or a metallic radical) stands in place of the hydrogen of an acid.† Not all salts have

* When water decomposes in a reaction, it often breaks up into an H part and an OH part. Then its behavior sometimes resembles that of an acid or of a base, depending on what else is present.

† Not *all* of the hydrogen has to be supplanted by a metal. In ordinary salts, no hydrogen is present. If the acid contains two atoms of hydrogen, however, the replacement of one of them by a metal will form what is called an "acid salt." An example is $NaHCO_3$, sodium acid carbonate, also known as sodium bicarbonate. The prefix "bi" indicates that a metal has taken the place of one out of two hydrogens in the acid.

to be made by starting with an acid. In fact, many salts are found in nature, and the acids are commonly manufactured from them. What distinguishes a salt is its chemical constitution, not its history.

Several salts were known to the ancients, common table salt ($NaCl$) being of course the principal one. Some of the others were sodium carbonate, used as a cleanser, and iron sulfate, used in dyeing. Since the salts at room temperature are strongly inclined to form transparent crystals, they were very early classified as a family. (Some mistakes were made, of course. On the basis of its appearance, sugar was once incorrectly classified as a salt.) The fact that salts are related to acids and bases was beginning to be perceived even as early as the time of Lavoisier. From then until the present, the study of salts has played a very important part in the advance of atomic science.

Summary

All metallic oxides that dissolve in water react with the water to form metallic hydroxides. Some metals have oxides that do not dissolve in water, but these metals, too, can be made to unite with the hydroxide radical. The metallic hydroxides are called bases. If a base dissolves in water, its solution has a soapy feel, a bitter taste, and the ability to turn litmus from pink to blue. Representative bases are $NaOH$, $Ca(OH)_2$, and $Cu(OH)_2$.

When the oxides of nonmetals react with water, the resulting solution does not feel soapy. It tastes sour, it will turn litmus from blue to pink, and it will readily contribute hydrogen in reactions. Compounds with these properties are called acids. Not all acids come from the oxides of nonmetals. Some acids, in fact, do not contain any oxygen. All acids do have one element in common; it is hydrogen. Acids that contain oxygen are called oxyacids, and those that do not contain oxygen are called hydracids. Representative acids are H_2SO_4, HNO_3, H_2CO_3, HCl.

Bases and acids react with one another, and the reactions all have the same form. One of the products is always water. The other product, called a salt, is what arises when the metallic part of the base takes the place of the hydrogen of the acid. An example is

$$Ca(OH)_2 + H_2SO_3 \rightarrow 2H_2O + CaSO_3.$$

Such a reaction is called a neutralization, because the basic properties and the acid properties both vanish.

Questions

1. Write balanced equations for the reactions that occur in the first experiment in Article 26–1. They are the oxidation of calcium and the reaction of calcium oxide with water.

2. Aluminum oxide does not dissolve in water. Describe a method for making aluminum hydroxide. Include an equation for the reaction.
3. Write balanced equations for:
   (a) The neutralization of hydrochloric acid (HCl) by sodium hydroxide (NaOH)
   (b) The neutralization of potassium hydroxide by carbonic acid (H_2CO_3)
   (c) The neutralization of sulfuric acid (H_2SO_4) by ammonium hydroxide (NH_4OH).
4. Make balanced equations for the reactions of the following substances:
   (a) $Al(OH)_3 + H_3PO_4$
   (b) $Zn(OH)_2 + HCl$
   (c) $Pb(OH)_2 + HNO_3$.
5. What is a salt? Arguing from the definition, show why it is that one of the products of neutralization is always a salt.
6. Write the formulas for the "parent" acid and "parent" base of each of the following salts: NaCl, K_2CO_3, $CaSO_4$, $Mg(NO_3)_2$, $Fe_4(SiO_4)_3$.
7. Are all hydroxides bases? Explain your answer.
8. In the experiments in the text that concern copper sulfate, copper hydroxide, and copper oxide, is the copper cuprous or cupric?

27

HYDROGEN

Hydrogen is a gas which was recognized as a distinct substance about the time Lavoisier took up chemistry. He gave it its name, which means "water-former."

27–1. Occurrence of Hydrogen. The earth has very little free hydrogen. In the atmosphere less than one part in a million is free hydrogen. There is a great deal of combined hydrogen on the earth, however. Besides being present in water, hydrogen is a constituent of natural gas, petroleum, and coal. It occurs also in most compounds found in plant and animal material.

Later chapters will describe ways of identifying the elements that are present in stars. The observations show that the sun and other stars consist largely of hydrogen. Taking the universe as a whole, hydrogen is by far the most abundant element.

A thoughtful person might wonder why the earth has so little free hydrogen. The answer is related to our earlier work on the dynamical theory of gases (Article 18–2). There we saw that, since hydrogen is such a light gas (its molecular weight is only 2.016), the hydrogen molecules move faster, on the average, than do those of the other gases. Putting observable data into the last equation in Article 18–2, we can find that, at room temperature, the average velocity of the hydrogen molecules is over a mile per second. Using Newton's Law of Gravitation, it is not hard to show that a body going more than about 7 miles per second can escape from the earth. Now although the *average* velocity of the hydrogen molecules at room temperature is about 1 mile per second, a molecule will occasionally be going much faster. Even in the topmost part of the atmosphere, a hydrogen molecule has a definite chance of getting up to 7 miles per second. Unless it then hits another molecule, it escapes into outer space and is irretrievably lost to the earth. The stars, being much more massive than the earth, have enough gravitational attraction to retain their hydrogen.

27–2. Preparation of Hydrogen. Commercial hydrogen usually comes from water, which can be decomposed by any of several processes that lend themselves to use on an industrial scale. One widely used process depends on passing steam over hot iron. The oxygen of the steam combines with the iron, setting the hydrogen free:

$$3Fe + 4H_2O \rightarrow Fe_3O_4 + 4H_2.$$

For preparing hydrogen on a small scale, acids form a convenient source. Many metals will react with acids and liberate the hydrogen.

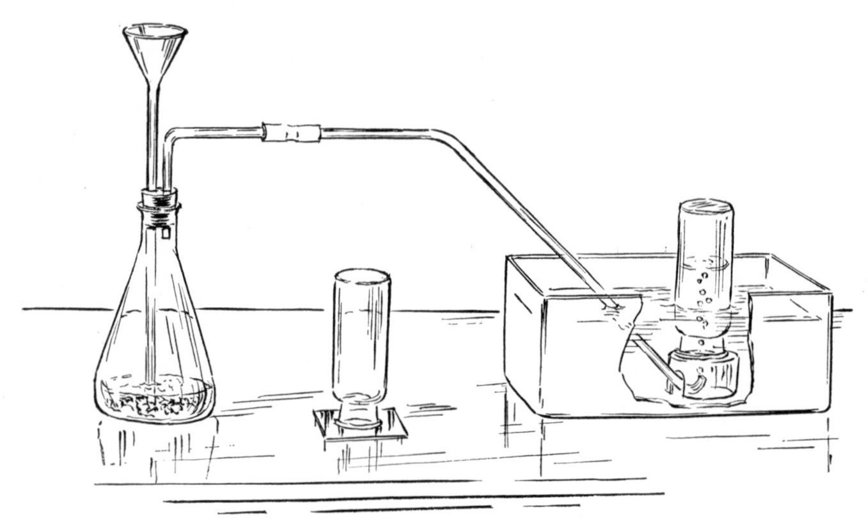

FIGURE 27–A. Generating hydrogen by the reaction of sulfuric acid with chips of zinc.

EXPERIMENT. In an apparatus like the one in Figure 27–A, let there be about 10 grams of zinc. When enough dilute sulfuric acid to cover the zinc chips is poured down the funnel, hydrogen comes bubbling out of the liquid, passes through the side tube, and collects in the inverted bottle. The reaction liberates hydrogen and produces a salt:

$$Zn + H_2SO_4 \rightarrow H_2 + ZnSO_4.$$

The experiment exhibits an important property of acids, which has already been mentioned in Article 26–2. Acids, far more than other hydrogen compounds, are notable for their ability to furnish hydrogen in a reaction. In some reactions, as in this one, the hydrogen is liberated as a gas. In other reactions, as in neutralization, the hydrogen enters into the formation of a new compound. The tendency of acids to give up their hydrogen is especially marked when the acids are in solution. These facts will contribute toward our understanding of the nature of acids.

27–3. A Test for Hydrogen. In order to get experimental checks on his interpretation of reactions, the working chemist needs a test that will show whether a particular element is present or not. He should have a test for each element, and ideally the test should respond to that element alone. He also needs tests for the various radicals. For the general understanding that this book aims at, it is unnecessary to learn many of these tests, but it is important to realize that they exist.

One of the tests for hydrogen is very simple, and we shall sometimes have occasion to use it. In the first place, its small molecular weight makes hydrogen gas lighter than air. Hydrogen will therefore stay in a vessel that is open only at the bottom, although it escapes from a vessel that is open at the top. Furthermore, hydrogen burns very quickly, in fact explosively, when enough oxygen is available. The standard test for hydrogen makes use of these two facts. If you suspect a gas of being hydrogen, put some of it in a small inverted test tube and apply a flame to the mouth of the tube. If there is a sharp, explosive "pop," the gas is pretty certainly hydrogen.

EXPERIMENT. The gas evolved in the last experiment gives an affirmative response to the test for hydrogen.

27–4. Physical Properties of Hydrogen. Hydrogen is a gas at all ordinary temperatures. It boils at −253° C and freezes at −259° C. As a gas, hydrogen is colorless, odorless, tasteless, and not poisonous. Being the lightest of all known substances, hydrogen has been used extensively for filling balloons and dirigibles.

27–5. Chemical Properties of Hydrogen. At ordinary temperatures, hydrogen is relatively inert. At higher temperatures, however, hydrogen becomes very active, combining with most of the nonmetals and with some of the metals.

The combination of hydrogen with the nonmetal oxygen is already familiar (Article 25–5). Large quantities of hydrogen are used in the welding trade, in oxygen-hydrogen, or "oxyhydrogen," torches. In these torches, the exothermic reaction of hydrogen with oxygen produces flame temperatures in excess of 2500° C. Iron melts at about 1500° C.

Other important compounds of hydrogen result from the direct union of hydrogen with nitrogen, with sulfur, and with chlorine:

$$3H_2 + N_2 \rightarrow 2NH_3 \quad \text{(ammonia)}$$

$$H_2 + S \rightarrow H_2S \quad \text{(hydrogen sulfide)}$$

$$H_2 + Cl_2 \rightarrow 2HCl \quad \text{(hydrochloric acid)}$$

EXPERIMENT. A small wide-mouthed bottle of hydrogen is mixed with a similar volume of chlorine by placing the bottles mouth-to-mouth and turning them over a few times in subdued light. The gas mixture in each bottle explodes with a whitish flame if the mouth of the bottle is held near a lighted burner.

Hydrogen will also react directly with some metals. For example,

$$2Na + H_2 \rightarrow 2NaH.$$

Such reactions are of interest because they show hydrogen acting like a nonmetal. In many reactions, however, hydrogen plays the role of a metal in the sense that it can exchange places with a metal. The experiment on page 212 affords an example. From physical considerations (Article 19–6), it is obvious that hydrogen is not actually a metal.

27–6. The Replacement Series. Laboratory experience shows that some metals will spontaneously replace hydrogen in acids or water, but other metals will not. Moreover, the metals can be ordered into a hierarchy based on the vigor with which replacement proceeds. This hierarchy of metals, called the *replacement series,* turns out to be a guide to how the metals will behave in a wide variety of situations.

As a first step in ordering the metals into a series, consider the reactions between metals and water.

EXPERIMENTS. (1) A small bit of sodium is placed in a metal cartridge * and sunk in a beaker of water. The rapidly liberated gas can be collected in a test tube filled with water and held inverted over the rising bubbles. The collected gas is hydrogen, as one finds by applying the standard test (page 213). One might surmise that the reaction has been

$$2Na + 2H_2O \rightarrow H_2 + 2NaOH.$$

Testing the solution with litmus shows that the reaction really has produced a base. Since the reaction produces hydrogen and a base from sodium and water, the proposed equation seems plausible. Actual analysis of the products would show that the equation represents the reaction correctly.

(2) A small piece of calcium is put in a fresh beaker of water. Testing the products shows that again they are hydrogen and a base, although this time the reaction is less vigorous.

(3a) When the experiment is repeated with a small piece of magnesium, no gas is liberated and no base is formed.

(3b) A piece of magnesium is put in a test tube of boiling water. Hydrogen is produced, as can be shown by collecting and testing it. The formation of magnesium hydroxide, which does not dissolve in water, makes the water milky.

The experiments show that the reaction of sodium with cold water is very rapid, that of calcium is slow, and that of magnesium is so slow as to

* The cartridge is needed as a sinker. Sodium by itself would float on the water, and it would be ignited by the heat of the reaction. Then the hydrogen might explode and scatter bits of burning sodium. The experiment therefore demands extreme caution.

be unapparent. We thus have evidence that some of the metals may fairly be called more "active" than others. Using the sign > to mean "greater than," we can say that the order of activity of these metals is Na > Ca > Mg. Of course, we have jumped to the conclusion that the rate of reaction of the metals with water is a guide to their activity in all kinds of situations. This assumption demands experimental test by observations on many different kinds of reactions. We shall not pause here to test the assumption. If you will keep it in mind, however, you will find the assumption supported by many reactions that will come up in later chapters.

Zinc and iron also react with water to give hydrogen, but they do so even less readily than magnesium. They must be nearly red hot, and the water must be steam. Zinc reacts a little more readily than iron. Copper, on the other hand, will not liberate hydrogen from water under any conditions. Including these metals, the order of activity is

Na > Ca > Mg > Zn > Fe > Cu.

So far, we have been dealing only with the question of how metals replace hydrogen. Is there some regularity about the way metals will replace other metals? We can make some trials, not on water, but on solutions of salts.

EXPERIMENTS. (1) Two tall beakers contain solutions of lead nitrate and zinc nitrate, respectively. A piece of zinc is suspended upright in the lead nitrate solution. A similar piece of lead is immersed in the zinc nitrate. In half an hour or so, the zinc becomes coated with lead, because zinc goes into the solution and replaces the lead. In the other beaker, nothing happens; lead will not replace zinc.

(2) A similar experiment will show that copper replaces silver in solutions.

Experiments like these show that the metals we have been calling "more active" will replace the ones that we have been calling "less active." Such experiments lead to the ranking called the replacement series. Table 27–I shows where the commoner metals and hydrogen stand in this series. In solutions, each element in the series will replace the ones below it, but not the ones above it. Moreover, as our experiments on the replacement of hydrogen suggest, the rapidity of the reaction can be judged from the separation of the elements in the series. Thus, under like conditions, zinc replaces copper more vigorously than lead does.

For the particular purpose of liberating hydrogen, it is well to use a fairly active metal like sodium or calcium if the hydrogen is to be obtained from water. On the other hand, if the hydrogen is to be released from an acid, then it is wise to use a less active metal like zinc, because acids give up their hydrogen more readily than water does. It is dangerous to use sodium with an acid, because the reaction is too violent.

TABLE 27–I

THE REPLACEMENT SERIES OF METALS

Cesium
Potassium
Sodium
Barium
Calcium
Magnesium
Aluminum
Zinc
Iron
Tin
Lead
Hydrogen
Copper
Mercury
Silver
Gold

These experiments on replacement have advanced our study of metals from the stage of observation to the stage of classification. We have put forward no theory of replacement. Without further data on metals, it would be rash even to make a hypothesis. Nevertheless, the classification represents progress, because we now have a systematic order for some theory to explain.

27–7. Reduction. We have seen (page 214) that the most active metals will replace hydrogen in its oxide, which is water. The least active metals can, in turn, be replaced in their oxides by hydrogen, with the consequent formation of water.

EXPERIMENT. The test tube in Figure 27–B contains a couple of grams of copper oxide (CuO). Hydrogen, generated by zinc and sulfuric acid in the flask, is allowed to sweep through the apparatus. The U-shaped tube contains calcium chloride or some other substance that absorbs water, to ensure that no water travels to the test tube from the flask. (*Caution:* At this stage, all flames are kept at least 4 feet from the exit tube.) Samples of the flowing gas are collected at the exit tube, by downward displacement of air in a test tube, until a sample burns quietly when touched to a flame some distance from the apparatus. When such a sample comes forth, the hydrogen issuing from the exit tube is sufficiently pure to be ignited safely from the flame of burning hydrogen in the test tube. This is the only safe way to ignite the hydrogen at the jet. If the hydrogen were ignited before all the air was swept out of the apparatus, there might be an explosion.

When the hydrogen is burning at the exit tube, the copper oxide can safely be heated, whereupon its color soon changes. The color turns from the black of the oxide to the pink that characterizes pure copper metal. At the same time, drops of water appear on the cooler parts of the test tube. These effects show that the oxygen of the copper oxide has combined with the hydrogen:

$$CuO + H_2 \rightarrow Cu + H_2O.$$

As far as the copper oxide is concerned, the reaction in the experiment is the reverse of oxidation. The process of deoxidation is called *reduction.* The copper oxide is said to be "reduced" to copper by the hydrogen, which is therefore called a "reducing agent."

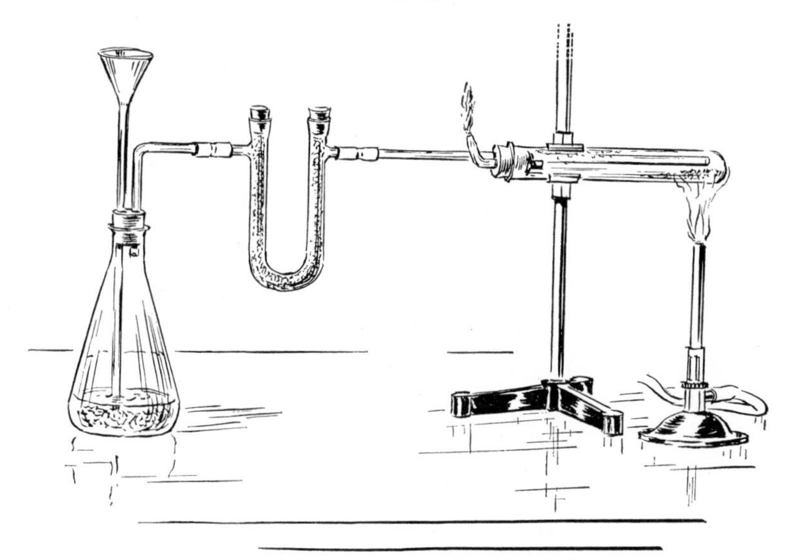

FIGURE 27–B. Reducing copper oxide with hydrogen.

In the experiment, hydrogen replaced copper, which lies below it in the replacement series. Under the action of a suitable stimulus, for instance heat, hydrogen can replace metals that lie above it in the series. For example, hydrogen passed over hot ferroso-ferric oxide (Fe_3O_4) will reduce the iron oxide and form water.

$$Fe_3O_4 + 4H_2 \rightarrow 3Fe + 4H_2O.$$

On the other hand, we know (page 215) that iron will replace hydrogen if steam is passed over hot iron:

$$3Fe + 4H_2O \rightarrow Fe_3O_4 + 4H_2.$$

One reaction is just the reverse of the other. Such a set of reactions is called a *reversible reaction*; the pair is described symbolically by the single equation

$$3Fe + 4H_2O \rightleftharpoons Fe_3O_4 + 4H_2.$$

The net result of a reversible reaction is governed by the conditions under which the reaction takes place. Here it is sufficient to state that the more active the metal, the more does its oxide resist reduction.

27–8. The Dissociation of Molecules. One of the experiments in this chapter shows the union of hydrogen with chlorine (page 213). The reaction is clearly exothermic—explosively so. Why, then, must heat be used to start it? Why does it not start of its own accord, like a ball rolling downhill? Such a question may have occurred to you even in earlier chapters, because there, too, we have seen examples of exothermic reactions that do not start spontaneously. Not all reactions are alike in this respect, but we can give here an explanation for the behavior of hydrogen with chlorine, and this explanation holds also for other cases that involve molecules of elemental gases.

Chlorine and hydrogen both have molecules that contain two atoms. The atoms in each molecule attract one another; to separate them requires energy. Chlorine and hydrogen do not react unless energy is supplied, in heat or in some other form. From these facts, we infer that the energy needed to start the reaction is used to break apart, or "dissociate," hydrogen molecules and chlorine molecules. When some of these molecules are broken apart, hydrogen and chlorine atoms are free to combine with one another. When they do so, they liberate energy, and this energy can dissociate more molecules of hydrogen and chlorine. Such a reaction, which itself maintains the conditions under which it can continue, is called a *chain reaction.*

The effects of dissociation are vividly illustrated by the atomic-hydrogen torch, Figure 27–C. A jet of hydrogen passes through an electric arc, in which the intense heat dissociates the hydrogen molecules. The free hydrogen atoms then combine again to form molecules, and in doing so they release the energy

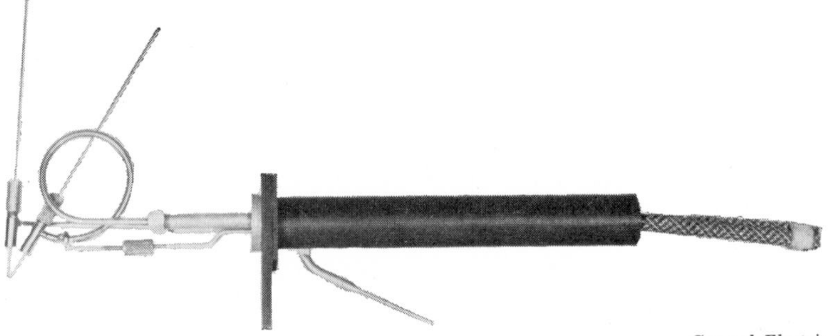

General Electric Co.

FIGURE 27–C. An atomic-hydrogen torch.

that they took from the arc. The result is an intensely hot flame in which oxygen plays no part. The hydrogen torch will melt the most refractory metals. It has the great advantage of surrounding the metal with a "reducing atmosphere" of hot hydrogen, so that oxygen from the air cannot oxidize the hot metal.

SUMMARY

Little free hydrogen is found on the earth, but hydrogen is a constituent of many common materials, among which are water, petroleum, and coal. Commercial hydrogen usually comes from water, from which hydrogen can be liberated by a variety of processes. Hydrogen for laboratory use is often made by letting zinc react with sulfuric acid. It is a gas at all ordinary temperatures.

The common laboratory test for hydrogen depends on its lightness and its explosively rapid combination with oxygen. Hydrogen will remain in an inverted test tube and will ignite with a characteristic "pop" when held to a flame.

In many of its reactions, hydrogen replaces, or is replaced by, a metal. The metals and hydrogen can be ordered into a list, called the replacement series. As a first rough classification, one can list the metals in the order of the vigor with which they displace hydrogen from water or from acids. Metals that will not displace hydrogen from acids are listed below hydrogen. The ordering in the series can be made exact by finding the order in which metals will replace one another in solutions of salts in water. One finds that the metals at the top of the list have a high degree of chemical activity, and those at the bottom of the list are the chemically sluggish metals.

The process of deoxidation is called reduction. Hydrogen is a good reducing agent. It readily reduces the oxides of metals that lie below it in the replacement series. Hydrogen can also be made to reduce oxides of metals that lie somewhat above it in the series. The possibility of replacement contrary to the series shows that some reactions are reversible.

Molecules of hydrogen and other diatomic elemental gases have to be dissociated into atoms before the gas can enter into a reaction. The energy needed for the dissociation often has to come from an initial application of heat. After an exothermic reaction has started, it generates enough heat to produce the dissociations needed for continuing the reaction.

QUESTIONS

1. When zinc and sulfuric acid react, the products are hydrogen and another substance. Name and classify this other substance.
2. In the test for hydrogen, what product is formed if the gas under test is actually hydrogen?
3. At what Absolute temperature does hydrogen boil?
4. Name one way in which hydrogen behaves like a metal. Why is it obvious that hydrogen is not a metal?

5. Write equations for the reaction of calcium with water. Do the same for magnesium with water. How do the two reactions differ?
6. Describe the replacement series of metals.
7. Keeping in mind the widespread occurrence of water, comment on the probability of finding various metals free in nature.
8. We have discussed the replacement, by metals, of other metals in their salts and of hydrogen in acids. Wherein lies the similarity between these two kinds of situations?
9. Why is there some basis for likening (page 218) an exothermic reaction to a ball rolling downhill?

Wer sie nicht kennte
Die Elemente
Ihre Kraft
Und Eigenschaft
Wäre kein Meister
Über die Geister.

GOETHE, *Faust*

GENERAL VIEW OF SECTION IV

From observations on the chemistry of two common elements, oxygen and hydrogen, we have become more familiar with some typical kinds of chemical phenomena. We have done much more, however. From the observations, we have built up a considerable amount of classification. Instead of treating each compound as a disconnected unit, we can now classify many compounds as bases, acids, or salts. Likewise, many reactions can be grouped together as neutralizations, or as oxidations, or as reductions. The behavior of metals is predictable on the basis of the replacement series. An understanding of principles can now begin to take the place of feats of memory. Chemistry is thus becoming for us an ordered body of knowledge.

V

Electricity

You are now in possession of an abundance of evidence, both physical and chemical, for the belief that matter consists of submicroscopic particles.

Chemical experiments tell us what kinds of atoms enter into the construction of the various kinds of molecules, but they really give little information about the atoms. These experiments do enable us to distinguish between different kinds of atoms, to determine the relative weights of the atoms, and to investigate the combining abilities, or valences, of the atoms. Chemistry in the nineteenth century developed into a great science without much knowledge of the atoms it dealt with, but in the twentieth century further information, derived from experiments that are partly or wholly physical, has greatly enlarged our understanding of chemical phenomena. This is not surprising, for the difference between physics and chemistry is not really a difference in subject matter—it is a difference in experimental techniques, and even this difference is rapidly vanishing.

Much of the new information about atoms has been obtained from experiments that depend on electrical phenomena. Before proceeding further with the study of atoms, therefore, we must develop some acquaintance with electricity.

Electricity is of course a subject with wide ramifications, many of which are extremely interesting examples of applied science. The subject is so large that it cannot all be covered in a text of this sort; we shall discuss only those ideas that bear directly on atomic investigations.

28

FUNDAMENTAL ASPECTS OF ELECTRICITY

It is no longer a cause for wonder that electric devices will carry a message around the world, or make a moving picture talk, or milk a cow, or train a battery of guns on an unseen airplane. In this sophisticated age, it is perhaps more a cause for wonder that all these devices had their origin in the painstaking study of a few childishly simple experiments, which in a different culture might well have been deemed a waste of time.

28–1. Electric Charge. It has been known since very ancient times that when amber is rubbed with cloth, it acquires the property of attracting bits of straw, hair, or the like. Amber is not the only substance that shows this effect—glass, hard rubber, and many other substances behave in much the same way. The effect is called *electrification,** and bodies that exhibit it are said to be electrified, or electrically *charged.*

Hard rubber shows very pronounced electrification after it has been in contact with fur or wool. The fur or wool also becomes electrified.

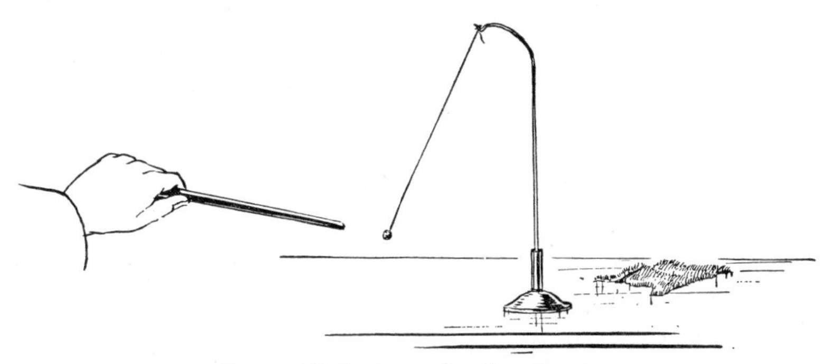

FIGURE 28–A. A test for electrification.

EXPERIMENT. A hard-rubber rod, after contact with fur, attracts a pith ball hung on a string (Figure 28–A), showing that the rod has an electric charge.

* "Electric" derives from the Greek word for "amber."

The pith ball also experiences a noticeable force when the fur, instead of the rod, is brought near. The fur, therefore, also has a charge.

The study of electric charges began to attract serious attention about 1700. It was soon discovered that there are actually two kinds of electric charge.

EXPERIMENT. Let a rubber rod be charged by contact with fur and then hung in a sling so that it is free to turn, as in Figure 28–B. If another rubber rod, charged by contact with fur, is brought near the suspended one, then the motion of the suspended one shows that the rods repel one another. On the other hand, if the piece of fur is brought near the suspended rod, the motion of the rod shows that it is attracted to the fur. Since the charges on the fur and on the second rod have a different influence on the first rod, these charges must be different.

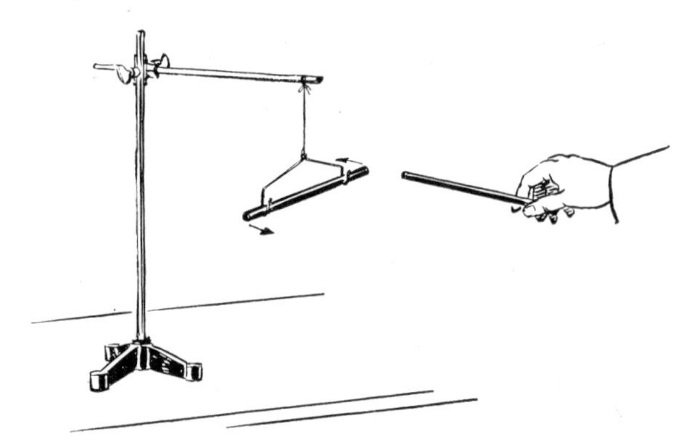

FIGURE 28–B. Like charges repel one another.

This last experiment actually implies more than the mere existence of two kinds of charge. Since the rubber rods received the same treatment, they must have the same kind of charge, and the charge on the fur is of another kind. The fact that the rods repel one another, though the fur attracts a rod, shows that *like charges repel one another* and *unlike charges attract one another*.

Not knowing how else to christen the two kinds of charge, we call them simply "positive" and "negative." The designation "negative" is assigned, quite arbitrarily, to the kind of charge acquired by a rubber rod, and the charge on the fur is called "positive."

To find out whether a charge is positive or negative, one merely has to find out whether it attracts or repels a rubber rod that has been in contact with fur. Experiment shows that a glass rod becomes positively charged from contact with silk. This is sometimes useful to know, because a glass rod is easier to handle than a piece of fur.

28–2. The Gold-Leaf Electroscope. Picking up bits of paper, or observing the motion of a suspended rubber rod, does not afford a very sensitive test for electrification. A convenient instrument for detecting small charges is the gold-leaf electroscope, Figure 28–C. It consists of a very thin (therefore light and flexible) leaf of gold fastened at its upper end to a vertical metal rod, or stem. To exclude drafts, the leaf and stem are enclosed in a box with glass windows. When the electroscope stem is put in contact with fur or wool, the stem and leaf acquire a charge and repel one another. The leaf, being light and flexible, stands out at an angle to the stem.

FIGURE 28–C. A gold-leaf electroscope.

28–3. Conductors and Insulators. If a charged electroscope is touched with one's finger, or with a metal wire held in the hand, the charge leaves

FIGURE 28–D. Charge leaves an electroscope touched by a metal rod held in the hand.

the electroscope (Figure 28–D). Charge will not leave the electroscope, however, through a rubber rod or a glass one (Figure 28–E). This illustrates the fact that, according to whether or not they will conduct charge away from a charged body, materials can be divided into two categories: *conductors,* and *nonconductors* or *insulators.* As examples, metals and some solutions are conductors, whereas rubber, sulfur, glass, and porcelain are insulators. Some materials, for in-

FIGURE 28–E. Charge does not leave an electroscope touched by a rubber rod held in the hand.

stance wood, do not fit very well in either category; they are usually called "poor conductors."

In an electroscope, the stem sits in an insulating collar so that a charge placed on the stem will stay there.

28–4. The Displacement of Charge in Conductors. Although electric charge cannot be seen, the effects of its displacement are sometimes vividly apparent.

EXPERIMENT. If the stem of an electroscope is touched with a slightly charged rubber rod, the electroscope will acquire some of the negative charge from the rod; when the rod is removed, the leaf will stand out, as in Figure 28–Fa. Then, when a more strongly charged rubber rod is simply brought

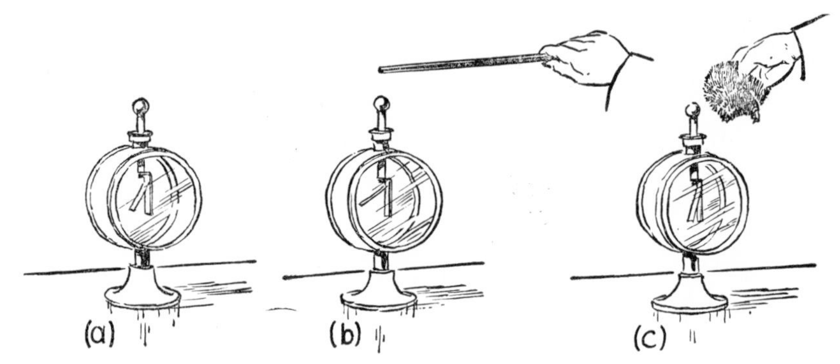

FIGURE 28–F. An experiment on the movement of charge in a conductor.

into the neighborhood of the charged electroscope, the leaf will stand out farther. The reason is that the negative charge on the electroscope is repelled by the negative charge on the rod. Being free to move because it is on a conductor, the charge on the electroscope becomes more concentrated on the leaf and the lower parts of the stem. The repulsion of the leaf by the stem therefore increases (Figure 28–Fb). On the other hand, bringing a positive charge near the negative electroscope, by means of an electrified glass rod or piece of fur, causes the leaf to fall. It falls because the negative charge on the electroscope is attracted to the positive charge that is nearby, and charge migrates to the top of the electroscope stem. The removal of charge from the leaf causes the leaf to drop back under the action of gravity (Figure 28–Fc).

The facts of the experiment provide an easy way of determining whether a charge is positive or negative. Charge the electroscope in any way, and then bring a negatively charged rubber rod near it to see whether the leaf rises or falls. Any other charge that affects the electroscope as the rubber rod does is negative; a charge that has the reverse effect is positive.

28–5. An "Uncharged" Body Contains Both Kinds of Charge. The displacement of charge can be exploited to demonstrate a fact of great importance.

EXPERIMENT. Let a metal sphere, on an insulating stand, be charged by rubbing it with fur. Bringing it near a charged electroscope shows the sphere to be negatively charged. Place it near one end of an insulated and uncharged metal cylinder, as shown in Figure 28–G. If a little metal plate on an insulating handle is put in contact with the end of the cylinder and then tested with the electroscope, it will show that each end of the cylinder is charged. The end near the negative sphere turns out to have a positive charge, while the opposite end has a negative charge.

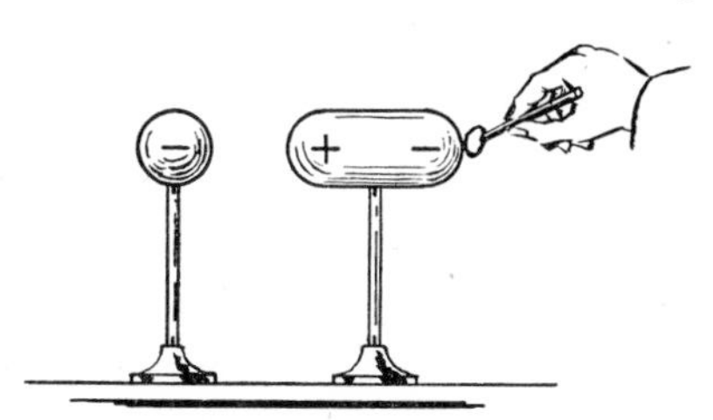

FIGURE 28–G. The uncharged conductor on the right actually contains both kinds of charge.

The experiment shows that *an "uncharged" body actually contains both kinds of charge.* In a conductor, the two kinds of charge can be (to some extent) separated by bringing a charged body into the neighborhood. Since the charges in the conductor are free to move, the charge that is repelled by the charged body accumulates at the far end of the conductor, and the charge that is attracted by the charged body accumulates at the near end.

28–6. Charging by Induction. The process of charging "by induction" affords an instructive and useful illustration of the ideas discussed thus far. The process can be broken down into four steps, pictured in Figure 28–H.

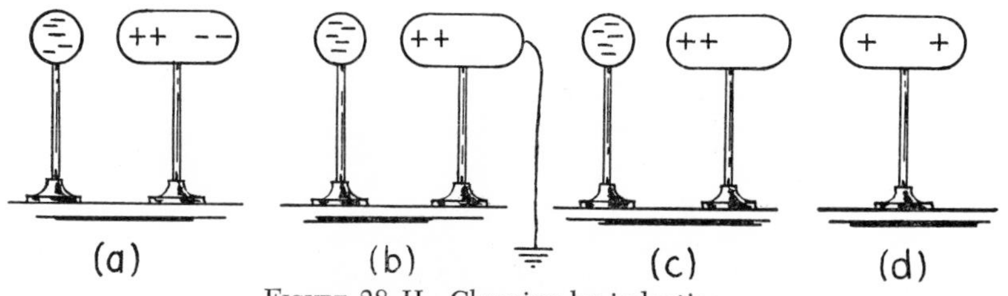

FIGURE 28–H. Charging by induction.

(a) A sphere that the electroscope shows to be negatively charged is placed near an uncharged conductor mounted on an insulating stand.

(b) The uncharged conductor is placed in electrical contact with the earth, through a conducting wire or the experimenter's body. Negative charge flows through this path to the earth, because it is repelled by the negative charge on the sphere. The second body has lost negative charge, so it now has an excess of positive charge.

(c) The conducting path to the earth is removed. The second body is now in an insulated condition, and the excess of positive charge cannot escape.

(d) The sphere can now be removed. The second body, being insulated, retains its charge.

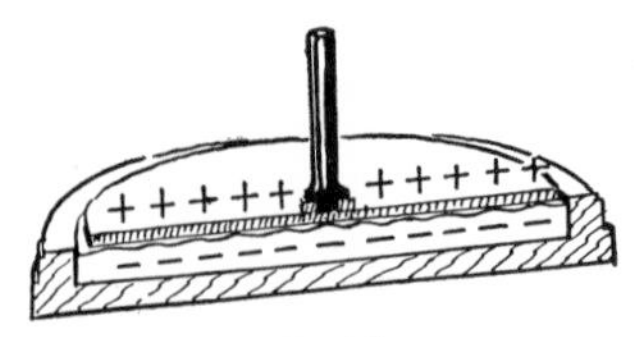

FIGURE 28–I. The cross section of an electrophorus.

28–7. Applications of Charging by Induction. The "electrophorus," Figure 28–I, consists of two parts: a flat bed of sealing wax, Lucite, or some other good insulator; and a metal disk on an insulating handle. If the bed is charged by rubbing it with fur, then the metal disk can be charged by induction by placing it on the wax bed and

FIGURE 28–J. An electric machine.

connecting it momentarily to the earth. Since the metal disk is very close to the charge on the bed, the charge acquired by the disk is rather large.

An "electric machine," Figure 28–J, is a device that uses induction to charge a set of conductors mounted on a glass wheel. When the wheel is turned, these charges are transferred to a pair of collecting terminals. By this means, enough charge can be placed on the terminals so that sparks pass between them, as in Figure 28–K.

Both of these devices are useful for producing large charges for simple experiments.

FIGURE 28–K. An electric machine in action.

Summary

Some substances, after contact with certain other substances, become electrified, or electrically charged. A primitive criterion for electrification is the ability to attract bits of paper or a ball of pith; a more delicate criterion is the ability to affect an electroscope.

There are two kinds of charge. The kind acquired by a rubber rod through contact with fur is arbitrarily called "negative," and the other kind is called "positive." Like charges repel one another, but unlike charges attract one another. If two charges are too small for their repulsion or attraction to be easily detectable, whether they are alike or not can be determined by seeing whether they have the same effect on a charged electroscope.

According as they will or will not conduct charge away from a charged body, materials are divided into two categories: conductors and insulators. Charges migrate freely in conductors, but do not migrate in insulators. These categories are idealizations; no actual substance insulates or conducts perfectly.

By experimenting with the displacement of charge in conductors, it is found that uncharged bodies really contain both kinds of charge.*

Questions

1. How can it be proved that there are two kinds of electric charge?
2. How would you find out whether a body is charged? If it were, how would you determine the kind of charge?
3. Describe a gold-leaf electroscope and tell how it works.
4. Give evidence for the belief that an "uncharged" body contains both kinds of charge.
5. If you had a positively charged glass rod, and also an uncharged conductor on an insulating stand, how would you put a negative charge on the conductor?
6. If a highly charged negative rod is brought near a positively charged electroscope, the leaf will drop. If the rod is brought still nearer, the leaf may rise again. Explain why.

* Actually, of course, this finding has been demonstrated only for conducting bodies. Later evidence will show that the statement is true of nonconducting bodies as well. The more general statement is made here to avoid the introduction of unfruitful distinctions.

29

ELECTRIC CHARGE

True knowledge can only be acquired piecemeal, by the patient interrogation of nature.

Sir Edmund Whittaker (1951)*

The last chapter discussed, in a qualitative way, the behavior of electric charge in a few situations, and explained how to find out whether a charge is positive or negative. As one should by this time have learned to expect, further progress depends on devising a way of attaching numbers to electrical phenomena, so as to make quantitative statements about charge.

29–1. Defining a Unit of Electric Charge. We have seen that the nature of an electrical effect, for example whether given charges attract or repel one another, depends on some peculiarity of the body we happen to be dealing with. No one has suceeded in expressing this peculiarity in terms of masses, distances, and times. Therefore our kilogram, meter, and second do not constitute an adequate set of units for measuring electrical effects, and we have to augment them with a unit of a new kind. We do this by selecting a unit of charge.

Recall Newton's Law of Gravitation (Article 8–2), expressed in the equation

$$F = G\frac{Mm}{d^2}\cdot$$

The law states that the gravitational force F, with which two bodies attract one another, is proportional to the product of their masses M and m, and is inversely proportional to the square of the distance between them. The quantity G is a constant that can be determined by experiment.

* In *A History of Theories of Aether and Electricity* (London: Thomas Nelson & Sons, Ltd., 1951). Although written for scholars, this book contains much that can be understood by a beginning student. Sir Edmund is a well-known mathematician.

In 1785 a French scientist named Coulomb showed that the *electrical* attraction or repulsion of two small charged bodies at rest is inversely proportional to the square of the distance between them.* Figure 29–A is a sketch of the apparatus he used.

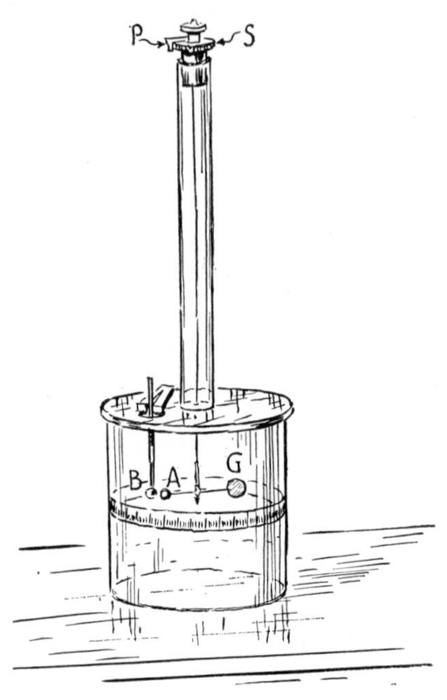

FIGURE 29–A. Coulomb's apparatus for studying the force between two charges.

An insulating bar *AG* hangs on a very fine wire. The top end of the wire is fastened to a spindle that can turn in a socket at the top of the chimneylike tube. The bar carries a pith ball at *A* and a little paper counterweight at *G*. A second pith ball hangs at *B*, on the end of a stationary insulator. With the balls *A* and *B* uncharged, Coulomb turned the spindle so that *A* just touched *B*. Then he reached in with a charged pin and placed a charge on the pith balls. *A* swung away from *B*. By turning the spindle, thereby putting more twist in the wire, Coulomb could bring *A* back toward *B* by any desired amount. By means of the pointer *P* and scale S, he could tell how much the wire had to be twisted in order to bring *A* to various positions near *B*. From previous purely mechanical experiments, he knew how the twist in the wire was related to the force acting at *A*. Hence by measuring the twist he could find the force of repulsion. His device is a kind of a balance; the electrical force

* It is stipulated that the bodies be small so that "the distance between them" may have a definite meaning.

is balanced by the force produced by a twisted wire. Since the wire can be made very fine, the balance can be made very sensitive. He found that in order to halve the distance AB, he had to quadruple the force that the twisted wire produced at A; cutting the distance to a third took nine times the force. Consequently, Coulomb concluded that the electrical force between the charged pith balls is inversely proportional to the square of the distance between them.

Coulomb showed, moreover, that the charged bodies can have numbers Q and q assigned to them, such that the force of electrical interaction will be expressed by the equation

$$F = K\frac{Qq}{d^2}$$

where d is the distance between the bodies (see Figure 29–B). The quantities Q and q are called the *charges* on the bodies.* The relationship embodied in the equation is called *Coulomb's Law*: The force of repulsion between two small charged bodies at rest is proportional to the product of their charges, and is inversely proportional to the square of the distance between them.

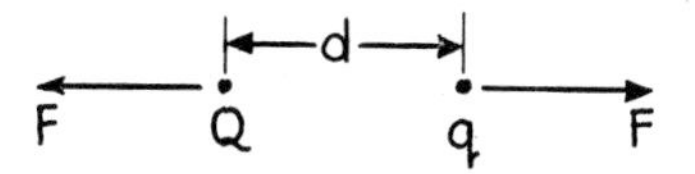

FIGURE 29–B. The interaction of two small charged bodies.

The actual measurement of charge, and even the fixing of a unit of charge, are somewhat complicated matters. Basically, charges are measured in terms of the forces they exert on other charges. It would be nice if some standard charge could be kept in a vault in Washington or Paris. Then another charge could be compared with it by comparing the forces that it and the standard exert on some third charge. Since there are no perfect insulators, however, no charge can be preserved permanently; the unit of charge has to be fixed by a more roundabout method.

There is a manifest similarity between Newton's Law of Gravitation and Coulomb's Law, but there is also an important difference. The Law of Gravitation ($F = G\,Mm/d^2$) relates forces and masses. The masses are defined on the basis of inertia, and measured by comparison with a durable standard, the kilogram, entirely independently of the Law of Gravitation. By measuring the masses, distance, and force in a given gravitational situation, the constant G can be determined by experiment (Article 8–3). Charges, on the other hand, are to be defined in terms of the interaction described by Coulomb's Law, and there is consequently an interdependence between the size of the unit of charge and the size of the constant K.

* Note that F is a repulsion. If the charges Q and q have opposite signs, then the equation gives a negative result for the repulsion. This is appropriate, because charges of opposite signs *attract* one another, and an attraction is a negative repulsion. Therefore the designations "positive" and "negative" for the two kinds of charge turn out to be mathematically convenient.

By international agreement, the numerical value of K is set at 8.99×10^9.* (This peculiar value is chosen because it reconciles the meter-kilogram-second system and the system of electrical measurements developed in the early days by practical electricians.) The customary unit of charge, called the *coulomb*, is the unit of such size that

$$F = K\frac{Qq}{d^2}$$

is a valid equation when K has the assigned value and F is measured in newtons, d being measured in meters. In other words, the coulomb is the unit of charge such that two identical charges of 1 coulomb each, placed 1 meter apart, repel each other with a force of 8.99×10^9 newtons. This force is of course very large, implying that 1 coulomb is a charge much bigger than any we find on laboratory objects. Thunder clouds sometimes carry charges of several coulombs; if two clouds carry similar charges of 10 coulombs each and are 10 miles apart, they repel each other with a force of about 750 pounds. A highly charged rubber rod carries less than a millionth of a coulomb. Nevertheless, when we deal with electric currents, the coulomb will be a unit of very convenient size.

29–2. Electric Fields. Coulomb's Law applies in an exact sense only to charges that are ideally small—so-called "point charges." In most cases of actual interest, at least one of the charges will be spread over a considerable area, and Coulomb's Law will not help us.

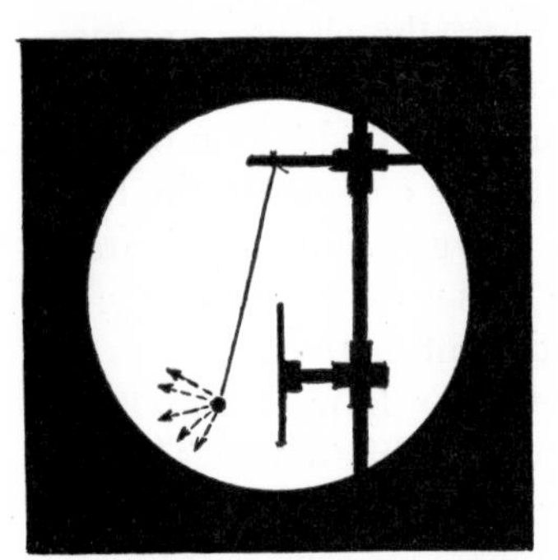

FIGURE 29–C. A charged pith ball repelled by a charged plate.

Figure 29–C shows the shadow thrown on a screen by a small positively charged ball of pith near a positively charged metal plate.† The charge on the plate is clearly not all at the same distance from the pith ball, and therefore the d in Coulomb's Law has no meaning in this case. Moreover, as suggested by the diagram, different parts of the plate urge the pith ball in different directions. Calculations based on the calculus can untangle the effects of various parts of the plate and permit the use of Coulomb's Law even in situations like this, but a far simpler approach is normally used.

If pith balls bearing various charges were brought near the plate, one at a time, it would be found that at any given place near the plate the

* Since the force depends somewhat on what is between the charged bodies, it is agreed that this value of K be applied when there is *nothing* between the bodies, that is when they are in a vacuum. The force is not much different when the bodies are in air.

† For example, the plate of an electrophorus.

force of repulsion would be proportional to the charge on the pith ball.* Therefore we can say

$$F = EQ$$

where F is the force of repulsion, Q is the charge on the pith ball, and E is a constant of proportionality. The usefulness of this equation springs mainly from the vivid physical significance that can be attached to the constant E. The force on any charge depends on how big the charge is, and it also depends on the magnitude and location of the neighboring charges. That is, the force on a charge Q depends on the magnitude of Q and also on its environment. The proportionality constant E is a factor that measures the effect of the environment.

Since the charge Q is not touched by the neighboring charges that exert forces on it, one thinks of the force on Q as being caused by a special condition of the space in which Q is situated. A region of space in which a stationary charge is acted on by an electric force is called an *electric field.* The factor E mentioned in the last paragraph describes quantitatively the electric condition of the space in which Q is located. We shall call E the *electric field strength.* Since we have selected the coulomb as our unit of charge, electric field strength must be expressed in newtons/coulomb.

At each point in an electric field, a charge will experience a force in a particular direction. A specification of the electric field strength entails, therefore, an indication of the direction in which positive charge would be urged. (The force on a negative charge would be in just the opposite direction.) The electric field strength, E, is consequently a vector quantity (Article 6–2).

The combination of plate and suspended pith ball in Figure 29–C affords a fine demonstration of an electric field. The field set up by the charge on the plate is made apparent by the behavior of the charged pith ball dangling on its string and being urged away from the plate with greater intensity as it is brought nearer to the plate.

29–3. Electric Potential. When the pith ball is near the plate, the slope of the string shows in Figure 29–C that the force exerted by the string has a horizontal component directed toward the plate. In other words, a force toward the plate must be exerted on the ball in order to hold it near the plate. (This fact would be clear even without the figure, because we know from earlier experience that two positively charged bodies repel one another.) Therefore if the ball is released, it will travel away from

* This proportionality is to be expected on the basis of Coulomb's Law, because each tiny bit of charge on the plate exerts a repulsion proportional to the charge on the pith ball, and therefore the total repulsion, whatever its magnitude or direction, will be proportional to the charge that is being repelled.

the plate, acquiring K.E. under the action of the force of repulsion. This means that when the charge is near the plate, it has energy of position, which is P.E. How much P.E. it has depends on how big a charge it is, and also on where it is. The amount of the P.E., divided by the amount of charge, gives a measure of the effect of the environment. It is called the *potential* of the point where the charge is situated, and it can be expressed in joules/coulomb because it is an energy divided by a charge. The joule/coulomb is a unit used so frequently that it is given a name of its own—it is called a *volt*:

$$1 \text{ volt} \equiv 1 \text{ joule/coulomb}.$$

EXPERIMENT. Suspend a pith ball near a positively charged plate. After it has acquired a positive charge by touching the plate, constrain the ball with a glass rod so that most of the string is vertical, as in Figure 29–Da. When the ball is released, it swings away from the plate, acquiring K.E. and gravitational

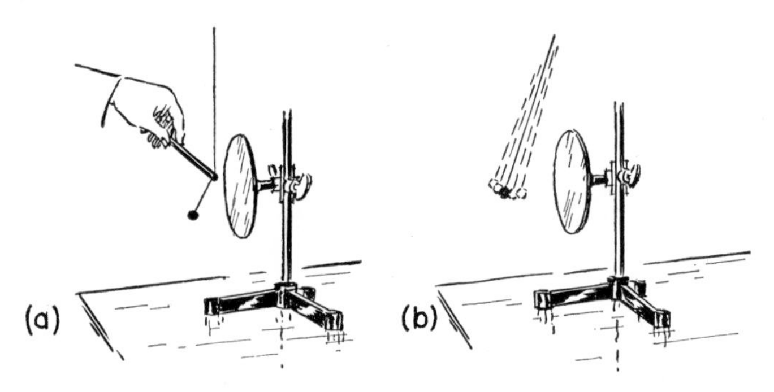

FIGURE 29–D. Potential energy and kinetic energy in an electric field.

P.E. (Figure 29–Db). Then it swings toward the plate, and the gravitational and kinetic energies are converted into electrical P.E. When the ball gets close to the plate, it "springs" away again, illustrating vividly the fact that it has energy due to its position.

In calculating the potential of a point, it is agreed to use the potential energy that *positive* charge would have at that point.

Since the concept of P.E. is useful simply in calculating the work that can be done, or the P.E. that can be acquired, when a body or a charge moves from one place to another, it is only *differences* of P.E., and differences of potential, that are important.

EXAMPLE. The potential of one terminal of a certain electric-light socket is 110 volts higher than the potential of the other terminal. How much P.E. is lost by a charge of 2 coulombs when it passes through a lamp plugged into the socket?

$$\text{P.E. lost} = \text{Decrease in potential} \times \text{Charge}$$
$$= 110 \frac{\text{joules}}{\text{coulomb}} \times 2 \text{ coulombs}$$
$$= 220 \text{ joules.}$$

An incandescent lamp converts most of this energy into heat. Some of it is converted into light, which is also a form of energy. In a fluorescent lamp, a larger fraction of the energy is converted into light.

29-4. Positive and Negative Potential. Even though the important aspect of potentials is their difference, it is often useful to measure potentials the way we measure most other things, by setting up a scale that has a zero. In most electrical work, it is customary to assign zero potential to the ground. If a positive charge has more P.E. at some point than it would have if it were in the ground, then the point in question has *positive potential.* A point has *negative potential* if a positive charge at that point would have less P.E. than it would have in the ground.

By imagining a simple experiment, it is usually easy to tell whether the potential of a point is positive, negative, or zero. This "thought experiment" consists in carrying a positive charge from the ground to the point in question. A positive charge would gain P.E. in going from the ground to a point that has positive potential. In order to produce this increase in P.E., one would have to do work on the charge. If the point were not at positive potential, there would be no increase in P.E.; no work would have to be done on the charge to move it from the ground to the point. Therefore, to find out whether a point has positive potential, imagine carrying a positive charge from the ground to the point. If an electric field opposes the motion, so that you have to do work to move the charge to the point, then the point has positive potential.

In a different situation, the positive charge might be capable of doing work in order to get from the ground to a certain point. In this case, the charge would lose P.E. in moving from the ground to the point. The point must therefore have a potential lower than that of the ground; this means that the potential of the point is negative.

If a charge in the ground could be moved to a certain point with no net change in P.E., then the point has zero potential.

A positive charge at a positive potential is like a mass raised above the surface of the earth. Work had to be done to get it there, and it will do work in order to get to a place where its P.E. is lower.

A positive charge at a negative potential is like a mass that has been dropped into a hole in the earth. It will do work in order to get there, and work has to be done in order to move it back to the ground level.

What can be said of a negative charge at a positive potential?

Summary

It has been found possible to measure charge by measuring the forces of attraction or repulsion that charges exert on one another. This is done on the basis of Coulomb's Law, by assigning to each charge a magnitude such that the force of repulsion between two charges is given by the equation

$$F = 8.99 \times 10^9 \frac{Qq}{d^2}$$

where Q and q are the magnitudes of the charges and d is the distance between them. The unit of charge that makes the equation hold when F is expressed in newtons, and d in meters, is called the coulomb. (A given charge can always be specified by its particular magnitude, say Q, no matter what other charge it may be exerting a force on. Therefore the number Q describes the charge itself, and does not depend on where the charge is.)

Any region in which a stationary charge experiences a force is called an electric field. The field is usually produced by other charges in the neighborhood. The force on any charge Q is proportional to the magnitude of Q, and therefore obeys the equation

$$F = EQ.$$

The factor E is called the strength of the electric field. It can be expressed in newtons/coulomb, and it is a vector quantity.

The electric potential of a point is related to the P.E. possessed by charge at that point. The potential is the potential energy divided by the charge. It is normally expressed in joules/coulomb, a unit given the name of "volt."

Questions

1. What is a coulomb?
2. What is an electric field?
3. Why is the concept of electric field a useful one?
4. How is electric field strength defined?
5. What governs the strength of an electric field? How would you go about producing a strong electric field?
6. What is electric potential? In what unit is it commonly measured?
7. Two circular plates of metal, each 0.2 m in diameter, are mounted on insulating supports. The plates are parallel to one another, and about 0.02 m apart. One plate carries positive charge; the other, negative. Which one is at the higher potential? How do you know?
8. What is the direction of the electric field in the region between the plates in Question 7?
9. If a point has negative potential, what can you say about the electric field in the region between the point and the ground?

Suggestion for Further Reading

W. F. Magie, *A Source Book in Physics* (New York: McGraw-Hill Book Co., Inc., 1935). Contains excerpts (pp. 408–13) from Coulomb's account of the discovery of his law.

30

ELECTRIC CURRENTS

If the labours of Men of science should ever create any material revolution, direct or indirect, in our condition, and in the impressions which we habitually receive, the Poet will sleep then no more than at present; he will be ready to follow the steps of the Man of science, not only in those general indirect effects, but he will be at his side, carrying sensation into the midst of the objects of the science itself.

WORDSWORTH (1800)

We have already noticed that electricity can pass from a charged body to the earth, or some other body, through certain materials called conductors. For example, a charged electroscope loses its charge when touched by the finger of an experimenter, because the human body is a fairly good conductor. The motion of charges through conductors is responsible for most of the effects that make electricity useful.

30–1. Electric Current. Any motion or flow of electric charge is called an *electric current.* The direction of the current is taken to be the direction of motion of positive charge. For instance, if a positively charged body is connected to the earth through a conductor (Figure 30–Aa), the current is away from the body; if the negatively charged body in Figure 30–Ab is connected to the earth, the current is toward the body. Until the nature of conduction was understood, there was no way of telling what was actually moving in a material sense. As has already been pointed out, however, "uncharged" bodies actually contain both kinds of charges. In other words, a negatively charged body is a body with a deficit of positive charges, and a

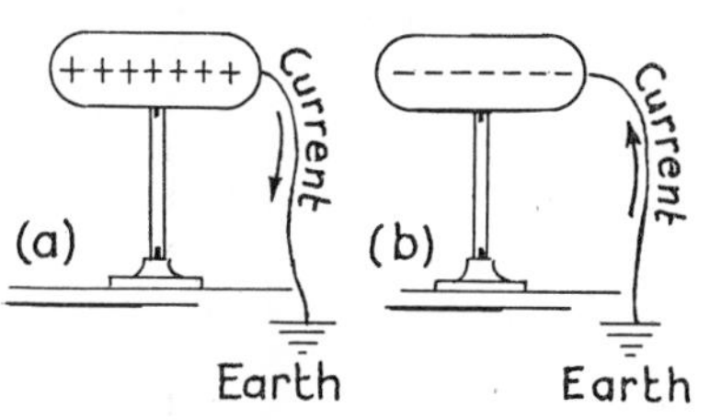

FIGURE 30–A. The convention assigning direction to an electric current. In both (a) and (b), the charge on the cylinder is decreasing, and the arrow shows the direction assigned to the current.

motion of negative charges in some direction is therefore equivalent to a motion of positive charge in the opposite direction. We shall discover later that charge is sometimes transported by positively charged particles, sometimes by negatively charged particles, and sometimes by both kinds of particles moving in opposite directions. Being able to assign a direction to the current, regardless of what the little carriers of charge happen to be, will enable us to make brief statements that will cover a variety of situations.

30–2. Producing Current with the Electric Machine. The electric machine has already been mentioned (Article 28–7); it uses the process of charging by induction to place opposite charges on two metal knobs. Imagine a little charge to be held in position, perhaps on a pith ball, somewhere between the charged knobs. It will be attracted by one knob and repelled by the other, because the knobs are oppositely charged. This shows that there is an electric field between the knobs, a field that can be made strong by placing large charges on the knobs. Now air is ordinarily a good insulator, but it becomes a conductor when it is in an electric field of sufficient strength. Therefore, when enough charge is placed on the knobs of the electric machine, the air between the knobs becomes a conductor. Charge then passes from one knob to the other, and the passage of charge constitutes the current.

By putting work into an electric machine, one can replenish the charge on the knobs as it leaks off through the air or through some other conductor connected to the knobs. A current could be maintained by coupling the electric machine to a steam engine or a water wheel, but if better means than this had not been found for producing currents, electricity would scarcely have attained its present importance.

Alessandro Volta, whose life span closely coincided with Thomas Jefferson's, was the son of a penniless Milanese nobleman. He received a classical education in the endowed schools of the Jesuits. Family pressure then urged him toward the law, but his strong interest in natural phenomena eventually prevailed, and he began to teach physics. For many years, he was professor of that subject at the University of Pavia. He was an active, thoughtful, and ingenious experimenter; his research leading to the electric battery capped a career that already included valuable work on the composition and properties of gases, and on the production and measurement of electric charge.

The continuous currents produced by the battery broadened old fields of research and opened up new ones. Volta described his battery in a letter to the Royal Society of London. Within a few weeks, it was being used in England to induce chemical decomposition. One speedy result was the discovery of several previously unknown elements.

Alessandro Volta
(1745–1827)

30–3. Electric Cells. About 1792 an Italian biologist named Galvani discovered, by patiently tracing down the cause of an effect that he had observed quite accidentally, that if two skewers, or needles, made of different metals, are touched together at one end while their other ends are imbedded in the leg muscles of a dead frog, then the leg will twitch as if alive. Linking this discovery with the fact that an electric shock in one's arm produces an involuntary contraction of the arm muscle, Galvani correctly concluded that the twitching of the frog's leg was caused by electricity. It was thus that a biologist set off the development of the vast electrical industry of today, which has given us telephones, radio, talking pictures, vacuum cleaners, and night bombing, and has made possible the use of power tools in shops too small to survive if they were dependent on steam or water power. It has of late been argued that the scientist should govern his activity in accord with its probable social consequences, but the impossibility of foreseeing those consequences is vividly illustrated by Galvani and his dead frog.

FIGURE 30–B. An electric cell.

Galvani thought that the electricity had its origin in the animal tissue, but a few years later Volta, another Italian, showed that one can get along perfectly well without the frog. Volta took a plate of copper and a plate of zinc, dipped them in salt water, and found that positive charge accumulates on the copper plate, and negative charge accumulates on the zinc plate. Such a device, two dissimilar conductors in a conducting solution, is called an *electric cell* (Figure 30–B). The two "terminals" of the cell are screws, or other means of attachment, for connecting a wire to each of the two dissimilar conductors.

EXPERIMENT. The charges that accumulate on the terminals of an electric cell are too small to affect the usual gold-leaf electroscope unless the experimenter resorts to a trick. Let a horizontal metal plate be fastened to the electroscope, and let a similar disk with an insulating handle be placed on top of the first one, with a layer of Cellophane between them for insulation. If one terminal of an electric cell is connected to each plate, the plates will acquire charge from the cell terminals, as in Figure 30–Ca. The charges on the two plates are unlike and attract one another. Each plate can therefore acquire a considerable charge before repulsion prevents more charge of the same kind from going from the cell to the plate. If the cell is then disconnected, the charges are trapped on the plates; and if the top plate is then also removed, the charges on the lower plate are no longer held there by attraction. Their mutual repulsion causes some of them to pass down into the electroscope, whereupon the leaf stands out to proclaim their presence (Figure 30–Cb). Testing with a rubber rod shows that the charge gained from the zinc plate is negative, and the one from the copper plate is positive.

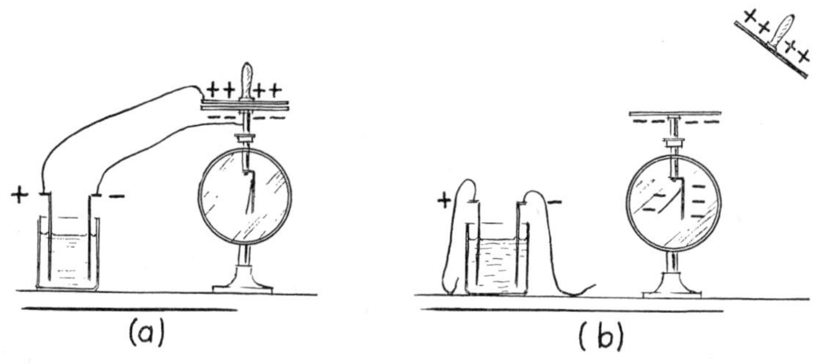

FIGURE 30–C. Demonstrating that the terminals of an electric cell are charged.

Consider now the potentials of the copper and zinc plates, by thinking of the P.E. that positive charge would have at each plate. Since the copper plate already carries positive charge, this plate would repel another positive charge brought near for test purposes. On the other hand, the zinc plate, with its negative charge, would attract the test charge. Therefore, if the test charge were transported from the copper plate to the zinc one, the electric forces would do work on it while it was in transit. The test charge, then, must have more P.E. at the copper plate than at the zinc one; in other words, the copper plate has a higher potential than the zinc one. If we provide a conducting path from one terminal of the cell to the other, then charge will pass through the wire, losing P.E. as it does so.

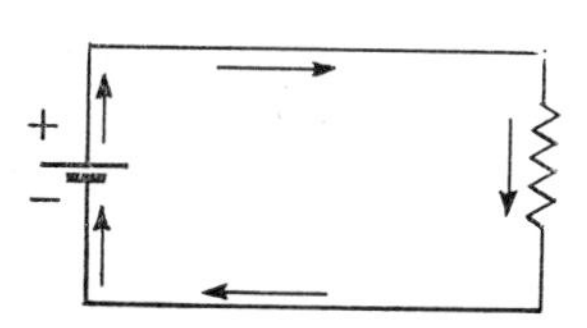

FIGURE 30–D. A conventional diagram to represent the circulation of charge through a cell and a wire.

If a thin copper wire is connected between the terminals of a cell of the kind used in automobiles, the wire will get noticeably warm. In fact, if it has previously been given a thin coating of paraffin, the wire will smoke. Clearly the P.E. of the charge on the cell terminals is being converted into heat. This heating is sustained, so there must be a *sustained circulation* of charge through the wire and the cell. In Figure 30–D, the jagged line represents the wire, and the two bars represent the terminals of the cell. The arrows show the direction of the current. The charge *loses* energy in passing through the wire, so it must *gain* energy in passing through the cell, for the charge simply circulates as shown in the diagram. (By means to be discussed later, it can be found that each coulomb gains about 2 joules in passing through the cell.) One naturally wonders where this energy comes from. Investigation shows that certain chemical reactions go on in a cell; and that these reactions are of an exothermic sort, that is, they are reactions which release chemical energy and make it available in some other form. In this case, the chemical energy is transformed into electrical P.E., which in turn is transformed into heat as charge passes through the wire. Later we shall see how electrical P.E. can be converted into mechanical work, by means of the electric motor.

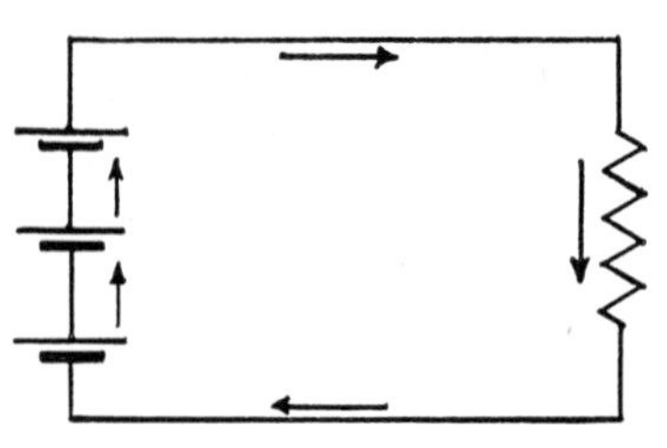

FIGURE 30–E. Diagram of an electric circuit consisting of a three-cell battery and a wire.

If the charge is allowed to pass through three cells in succession, then each of the cells will do work on it, and the charge will acquire three times as much potential energy as in the previous case. The wire consequently gets hotter, perhaps red hot. Figure 30–E is a diagram of this situation. The common incandescent lamp is simply a wire that can be made very hot by passing a current through it. Of course this wire must be made of some material with a high melting point.

A closed conducting path, such as the one just under discussion, is called an *electric circuit.* A set of cells connected together is called a *battery.*

30–4. A Quantitative Definition of Current. The phrase "electric current" has been defined to mean "flow of positive charge." The phrase is also used in a slightly different sense: *An electric current is a rate of passage of charge.** This means that the current is the amount of charge passing divided by the time during which the passage occurs:

$$\text{Current} = \frac{\text{Charge transferred}}{\text{Time of passage}}.$$

Just as the flow of traffic over a bridge is measured in cars per hour, so the flow of charge in a circuit is measured in coulombs per second. In honor of a French investigator of the early nineteenth century, the coulomb/second is called an *ampere.*

$$1 \text{ ampere} \equiv 1 \text{ coulomb/second}.$$

An instrument for actual laboratory measurement of currents will be discussed in a later chapter.

* In one sense, "current" means an event; in the other sense, it means a number associated with the event. Whether one is speaking of the number or the event is always clear from the context.

30–5. Ohm's Law. The heating of a wire by a current shows that the charge passing through the wire loses P.E. There must therefore be a potential difference between the two ends of the wire. By experiment, one finds that the current in the wire is proportional to this potential difference.* The customary symbol for potential difference is V (reminding us of *volts*), and that for current is I. Using these symbols, the proportionality of potential difference and current can be expressed thus (Article 9–2):

$$V \propto I$$

or

$$V = RI$$

where R is a constant that depends on the particular wire one is using. R can be taken as a measure of a property of the wire, called its *resistance*. If the wire is long and thin and made of a poor conductor, a large potential difference V between its ends will produce only a relatively small current I. For such a wire, therefore, the constant R will be large; the wire will have a large resistance.

The equation $V = RI$ expresses a relationship known as Ohm's Law. It is the cornerstone of electrical engineering, but we shall need it only once, when we discuss the common laboratory instruments for measuring currents and differences of potential.

30–6. Electric Power. Power is the rate of doing work, or the rate of expending energy. It is interesting, and from the engineering point of view very useful, to consider the rate at which energy is expended in a conductor. If the ends of the conductor differ in potential by an amount V, then each charge Q that passes through the conductor loses an amount of energy $V \times Q$ because V is the energy change per unit charge. Since $V \times Q$ is the energy expended, the *rate* at which energy is expended is $V \times Q/t$. But $Q/t = I$, because the rate of passage of charge is the current. Therefore the rate at which energy is expended is $V \times I$.

$$\text{Power expended} = \text{Potential difference} \times \text{Current}.$$

* The experiment is not described here, because it is complex and its result is interesting to us only as a basis for the "voltmeter" described in Chapter 33. The general plan of the experiment is simple: The potential difference between the ends of the wire is proportional to the number of cells connected to it as in Figure 30-E. The experimenter must then devise a means of measuring the rate at which charge passes through the wire.

The proportional relationship stated in the text does not hold strictly unless the temperature of the wire remains fixed, but this complication will be of no concern to us.

To check the reasoning, examine the units on the right side of this equation. They are

$$\text{Volts} \times \text{Amperes} = \frac{\text{Joules}}{\text{Coulomb}} \times \frac{\text{Coulombs}}{\text{Second}} = \frac{\text{Joules}}{\text{Second}} = \text{Watts}.$$

Therefore a potential difference times a current does equal power.

Summary

The expression "electric current" means "flow of electric charge" if used in a general sense, or "rate of flow of electric charge" if used in a quantitative sense.

A current exists whenever a charge moves through a conductor, for example when the charge on an electroscope leaks off through an experimenter's body. If the charge can be replenished as fast as it passes through the conductor, the current can be maintained continuously. Small currents can be maintained by an electric machine.

In the early nineteenth century, it was discovered that if two dissimilar metals are placed in a conducting solution, then a difference of potential will exist between them. Therefore charge will pass from one to the other if there is a conducting wire between them, and a current can thus be maintained. If there is no conducting path between them except the solution, the two pieces of metal will simply accumulate opposite charges. The combination of two dissimilar conductors in a conducting solution is called an electric cell. A simple example consists of a copper and a zinc plate immersed in dilute sulfuric acid. The fact that charges do accumulate on the terminals of such a cell can be demonstrated with an electroscope.

The difference of potential of the cell terminals implies that the cell gives energy to charge that passes through it. This energy comes from an exothermic chemical reaction that goes on in the cell.

Since current is the rate of passage of charge, it is measured in coulombs/second. This unit is called the ampere.

Ohm's Law: The current in a wire is proportional to the difference in potential of the ends of the wire. The ratio of potential difference to current is called the resistance of the wire.

Questions

1. What is an electric current? In what units is it measured?
2. When is air an insulator, and when is it a conductor?
3. What is an electric cell? Describe one that Volta made.
4. How can one show that a charge gains energy as it passes through an electric cell?

5. What is the relation between the current in a wire and the potential difference between the ends of the wire?
6. How can the current in a circuit be controlled as to magnitude?
7. The potential difference at the terminals of an automobile battery is about 6 volts. When the car is started, the battery may send about 300 coulombs through the starter. What energy does the battery supply? How does this energy compare with the P.E. lost by a 46-kg woman who falls from a second-story window and drops 4.0 meters?

Suggestion for Further Reading

W. F. Magie, *A Source Book in Physics* (New York: McGraw-Hill Book Co., Inc., 1935). Contains excerpts from the writings of Galvani and Volta.

31

MAGNETISM

Although no connection between them was apparent for a long time, electricity and magnetism turn out to be closely related. Before pursuing the subject of electric currents any further, it is desirable to learn something about magnetism.

31–1. Magnets. From at least as early as the time of Thales, it has been known that certain black, heavy stones have the property of attracting

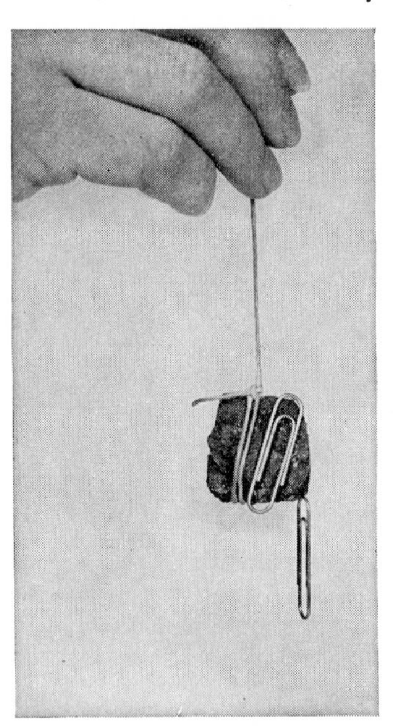

FIGURE 31–A. A lodestone.

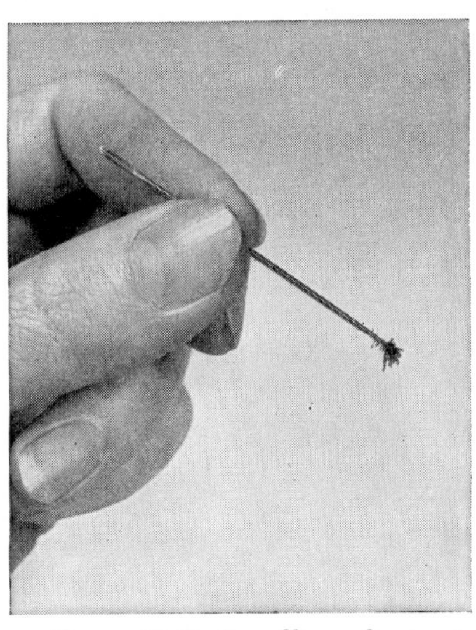

FIGURE 31–B. Iron filings clinging to one pole of a magnet, which was made by rubbing a needle on the lodestone in Figure 31–A.

iron, as pictured in Figure 31–A. This property of attracting iron is called *magnetism*, and any body that exhibits it is called a *magnet*. At first the only available magnets were the black stones mentioned above, called "lodestones." Later it was found that a piece of iron could be made into a magnet by rubbing it on a lodestone. Still later, chemical analysis showed lodestones to consist chiefly of the iron oxide Fe_3O_4. Iron is not, however, the only substance that can be magnetized—nickel, cobalt, and some of their alloys show strong magnetic behavior.

If a needle is rubbed on a lodestone and then dipped into iron filings, the filings will be attracted to the needle (Figure 31–B), and they will cling most strongly around the ends of the needle. Each magnet normally does have two regions where its magnetic effect is strongest; these regions are called the *poles* of the magnet. In long thin magnets, the poles are usually near the ends.

31–2. The Magnetic Compass. It is a familiar fact that if a magnet is suspended so that it is free to turn, then one end will turn toward the north and the other toward the south, until the line joining the magnet poles points nearly north and south. Such a device is called a "magnetic compass"; it was known to the Chinese about a thousand years ago, but seems to have been first used as an aid to navigation by Arabic peoples in the eleventh century, and by Europeans not long afterward. The pole that turns toward the north is called the "north-seeking pole," or simply the *north pole*, of the magnet; the other pole is called the "south-seeking," or *south*, pole.

31–3. Magnetic Fields. Magnets not only affect ordinary iron, but in a more complicated way they affect one another. By bringing two suspended magnets near one another, it can be easily shown that like poles

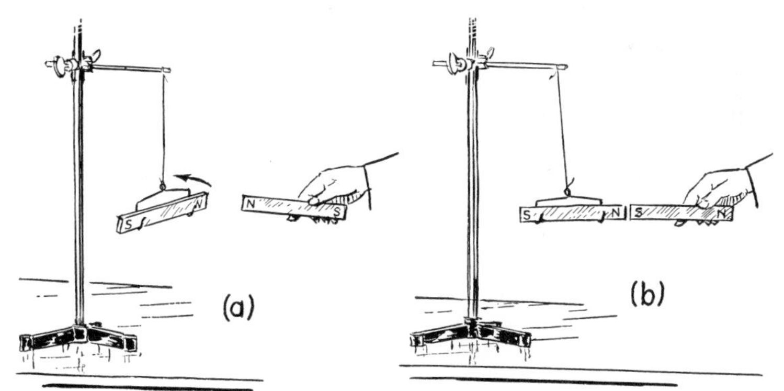

FIGURE 31–C. (a) Two like poles repel one another. (b) Two unlike poles attract one another.

repel one another, but unlike poles attract one another (Figure 31–C). For example, a south pole attracts a north pole, but repels a south pole. When a compass is near other magnets, therefore, it may not point north. The turning of one magnet, owing to the mere proximity of another, is interpreted to mean that a magnet can be affected by some property of the space it is in. Regions in which magnetic forces act are called "magnetic fields." *A magnetic field is any region in which a magnet shows a tendency to turn because of its magnetism.* A magnetic field, at any point, is assigned a *direction,* namely the direction in which a tiny compass would point if it were placed at the point.

Magnetic fields will remind the reader of electric fields, which are regions in which forces are experienced by stationary electric charges. The definitions imply that electric and magnetic fields are different. This implication is correct, although we shall find later that the two kinds of fields do have some kinship.

Since a suspended magnet becomes oriented in a north–south direction, it is clear from the definition of magnetic field that the whole region near the earth is a magnetic field. A study of this magnetic field shows that it is due to the earth itself, which acts like a huge magnet whose poles are near the geographical poles. Why the earth does act like a magnet is still a subject of research.

31–4. Induced Magnetization. A simple experiment demonstrates how it is that a magnet can attract a piece of ordinary iron.

Experiment (Figure 31–D). A piece of ordinary iron is held in the field of a magnet and at the same time dipped in iron filings. The iron filings cling to

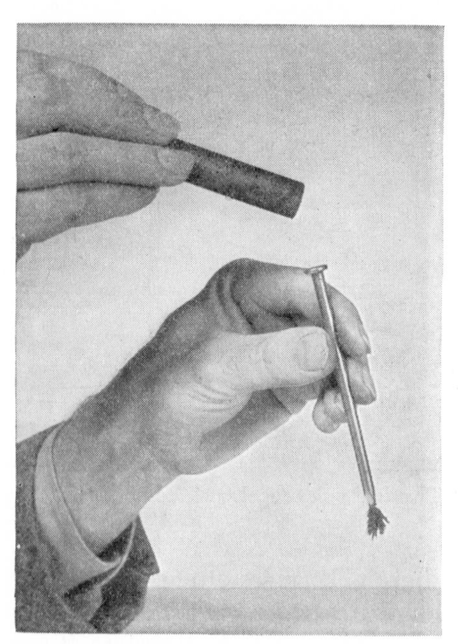

Figure 31–D. Induced magnetization. A nail becomes magnetized when in the magnetic field of the magnet above it.

the ordinary iron, showing it has become a magnet. Removing the first magnet will cause the iron filings to drop off the ordinary iron, showing that the magnetization of the ordinary iron is caused by the magnetic field of the first magnet.

The experiment shows that in a magnetic field, ordinary iron becomes magnetized. This is called *magnetization by induction,* and ordinary iron under the influence of a magnetic field is called an *induced magnet.* Induced magnetization explains how a magnet can pick up nails or iron filings. A magnet attracts a nail because it makes the nail into an induced magnet. The fact that there is attraction between them, instead of repulsion, implies that the adjacent poles are opposite, as shown in Figure 31-E.

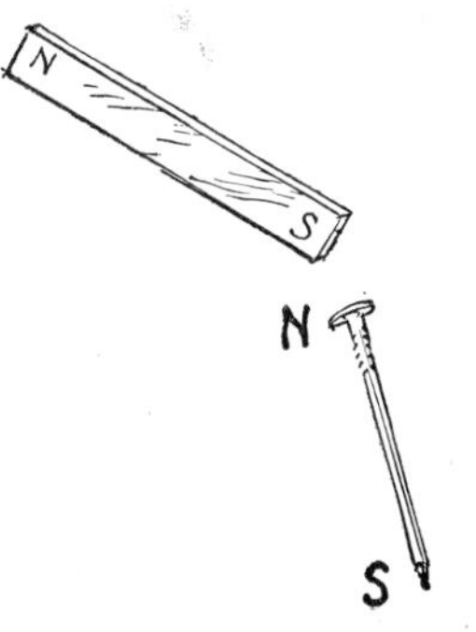

FIGURE 31-E. A magnet attracts a nail because its presence makes the nail an induced magnet, with poles as shown here.

Induced magnetization also affords a very convenient means for examining magnetic fields. If iron filings are sprinkled in the field of a magnet, each bit of iron becomes an induced magnet, and tends to act like a tiny compass. By tapping the support on which the filings rest, one can make them free to move, and they will arrange themselves in threadlike patterns that show the direction of the magnetic field. Moreover, the filings group themselves most densely in the regions where the magnetic field is strongest. Figure 31-F is a photograph of such an experiment. If one needs a strong magnetic field, having the same direction over

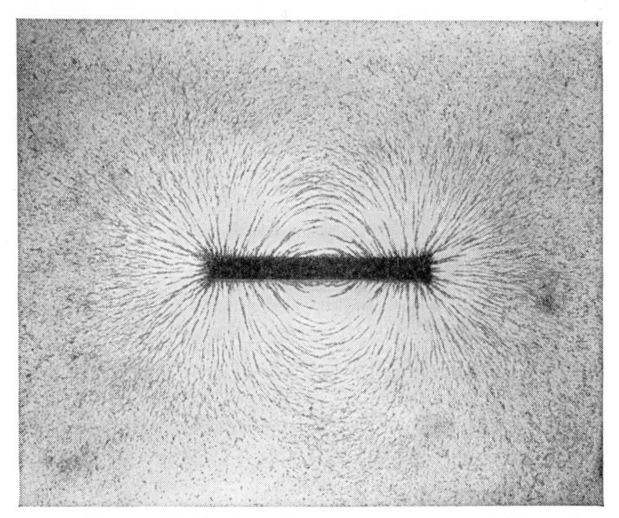

FIGURE 31-F. Iron filings in a magnetic field.

a considerable region, it is desirable to use the field between two opposite magnetic poles. These poles can belong to different magnets, as in Figure 31–G, or they can be the poles of one magnet which is bent in the form of a horseshoe.

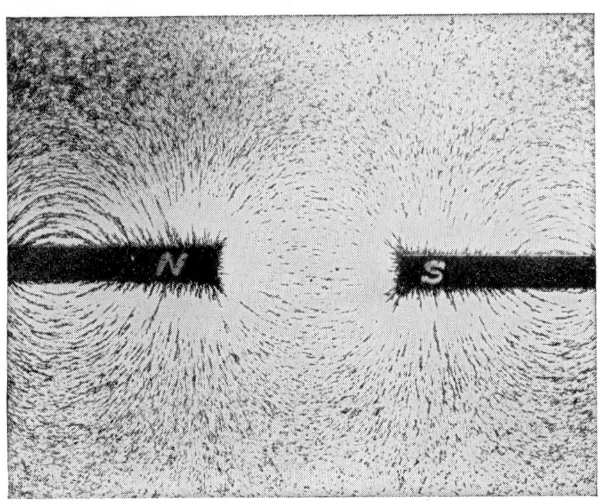

FIGURE 31–G. The magnetic field near two unlike poles. Note that the direction of the field is nearly the same throughout the region between the two poles.

Quantitative treatment of magnetic fields will be discussed in the next chapter, but these qualitative considerations should help you to feel at home with the new concept.

31–5. The Domain Theory of Magnetism. Thus far, our discussion of magnetism has been little but a recital of facts. One naturally wants to "explain" the facts, i.e., to coordinate them with reference to some central principle. The problem affords another nice illustration of scientific method. Recall from Article 3–4 that physical science proceeds by observation, classification, invention of a hypothesis, construction of a theory, and experimental test of the theory.

We have already observed that magnets exist, and we can classify them as natural magnets and induced magnets. Two further observations can be made. The first, which has already been mentioned by implication, is that induced magnetism is often temporary, as in the example of the filings clinging to the iron in a magnetic field (Figure 31–D), but sometimes it is more or less permanent, as in the case of a needle rubbed on a lodestone. Careful observation permits the following classification: induced magnetization is less strong in the harder types of iron and steel, but it is also more permanent in these materials. Furthermore, in the hard materials, induced magnetization can be enhanced by jarring or hammering the material while it is in the inducing field. The second observation that can be made is that induced magnetism can be made stronger, up to a certain point, by using a stronger magnetic field, but beyond this point increasing the strength of the field does not induce more magnetization.

We are now ready for a hypothesis, which was originally put forward early in the nineteenth century by Ampère, the Frenchman whose name is commemorated in our unit of electric current. In a form which is acceptable today, the hypothesis states that the atoms in iron are banded together in small groups called "domains," that these domains are actually little magnets, and that they have more freedom of movement in soft iron than in steel.

From the hypothesis, the theory follows immediately. When soft iron is in a magnetic field, the domains behave like little compasses and line themselves up in the direction of the field. The magnetic fields produced by the domains themselves cancel one another when the domains have a helter-skelter arrangement. When the domains all have the same orientation, however, they cooperate to produce a strong effect. In steel, the domains do not readily orient themselves under the influence of a magnetic field; but if the steel is hammered, the domains get shaken up and have a chance to turn, or perhaps to change size so that domains that are aligned with the field grow at the expense of those that are not. When the inducing field is removed, the domains in steel do not readily return to their former condition, and the retained alignment makes the iron a permanent magnet.

The hypothesis accounts for the observation that induced magnets cannot be made stronger indefinitely. After all of the domains are aligned with the field, making the field stronger cannot produce further changes within the iron.

The next step is to devise an experiment to test the theory. Perhaps the simplest one involves the behavior of permanent magnets. If their magnetization is due to the alignment of the domains, then heating the iron should remove its "permanent" magnetism, because when the iron is at a high temperature, its particles are in violent motion. If violent enough, this motion should wipe out the alignment of the domains. The theory can therefore be tested by heating a permanent magnet.

EXPERIMENT. A magnetized steel rod, heated to redness in a gas flame and then tested with iron filings, is found to have lost magnetization.

Figure 31–H provides even more direct and striking confirmation of the hypothesis and the theory. It is a pair of photographs, under high magnification, of the surfaces of two blocks of a magnetic alloy. Both blocks were made white hot (1300° C) and then slowly cooled. The only difference in the treatment of the blocks is that the one on the right cooled in a magnetic field. The pictures clearly show that the magnetic field produces an orderly orientation of the dark clumps of atoms. The sample on the right is a magnet, but the one on the left is not. The pictures therefore support the theory.

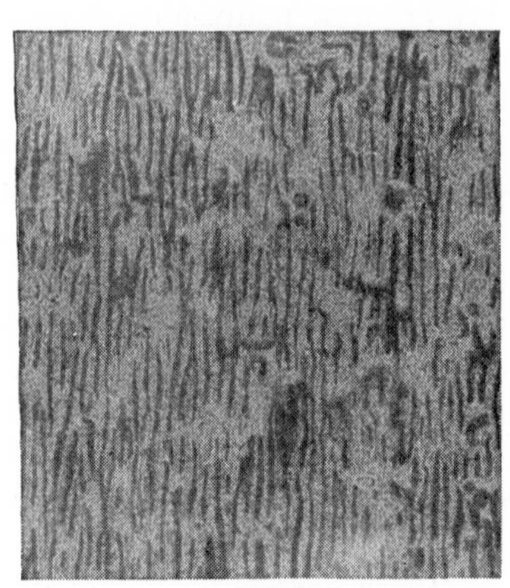

Bell Telephone Laboratories

FIGURE 31–H. The structure of a magnetic alloy. The two metal samples are alike in every respect, except that the one at the right was in a magnetic field when it was cooled, but the one at the left was not. The surfaces are seen under high magnification; the average distance between the black stripes on the right is about 10^{-5} inch.

In Article 3–4, it was mentioned that a theory should, if possible, be made quantitative. The theory of magnetism has been placed on a reasonably satisfactory quantitative basis, but the qualitative outline given here will suffice for the purposes of this book. The reason for discussing the theory is that much of our knowledge about molecules and atoms has been gained by studying the way they, and their component parts, behave in magnetic fields. We must therefore use magnetic fields fairly often, and the theory has been given in order to make them seem less mysterious.

At this point you may object that the theory is not very satisfying, for it simply says that iron can be magnetized because it is made of tiny magnets, and this does nothing toward explaining what magnetism is. It is true that the theory, as presented so far, is not very satisfying. That, however, did not prevent it from being useful. The magnetization of iron plays such a vital role in the electrical industry that an incomplete theory, if correct as far as it goes, is of very great utility. In recent years, moreover, it has been found that iron atoms are themselves magnets, that they are made of parts that are magnets, and that magnetism seems to be in fact an inherent property of matter that cannot be explained in terms of something else. We shall revert to the peculiarities of the iron atom in a later chapter.

Summary

Magnetism is the property of attracting iron as the lodestone does. It is a property exhibited chiefly by iron, and by its oxide Fe_3O_4 which constitutes lodestone, but it is also exhibited in an appreciable degree by a few other metals and alloys. A body that exhibits magnetism is called a magnet. The two parts of the magnet that show the strongest magnetism are called the poles of the magnet.

If a magnet with poles at its ends is pivoted so that it is free to turn in a horizontal plane, it will align itself in a nearly north–south direction. The device is called a magnetic compass. The pole that turns toward the north is called the north pole of the magnet; the other pole is called the south pole. It is found by experiment that unlike poles attract one another, and like poles repel one another.

Regions in which magnetic forces act are called magnetic fields. The direction assigned to a magnetic field is the direction toward which a tiny compass would point if it were placed in the field. The space around the earth is an example of a magnetic field.

When iron is placed in a magnetic field, the iron becomes magnetized. Iron in this condition is called an induced magnet. In soft kinds of iron, induced magnetization is exhibited strongly, but it disappears when the inducing field is removed. In steel, the induced magnetism is less strong, but it is retained more or less permanently. Magnetic fields can be studied by means of the patterns formed by iron filings sprinkled in the field. The individual filings become magnetized and act like little compasses, showing the direction and relative strength of the field by their orientation and bunching.

The facts of magnetism have been explained by assuming that iron consists of groups of atoms called domains, each of which is itself a magnet. This question will be pursued in a later chapter; meanwhile experiments employing magnetic fields will tell us a great deal about the structure of atoms.

Questions

1. What is a magnetic field?
2. How is a direction assigned to a magnetic field?
3. Where would you expect to find a magnetic field?
4. Distinguish between a magnetic field and an electric field.
5. Can the same region of space ever be an electric field and a magnetic field at the same time? Explain.
6. Give a reason for believing that the magnetization of iron results from the alignment of tiny magnets in the iron.
7. How does the domain theory of magnetism account for induced magnetization?

32

THE EFFECTS OF ELECTRIC CURRENTS

Having become acquainted with magnetic fields, we can profitably return to the subject of electric currents. What a current is has already been discussed; the present chapter describes what a current does.

Electric currents can produce three principal kinds of effects: the heating effect, which is used in toasters and incandescent lamps, as well as in some industrial processes; the magnetic effect, which is responsible for the action of electric motors and also is a most important tool in atomic research; and the chemical effect, which also has great industrial importance that will be mentioned from time to time, but which interests us particularly because it can tell us so much about atoms.

32–1. The Heating Effect. We have already observed that electric currents heat the conductors through which they pass, and that the heat generated in the conductor is equal to the P.E. lost by the charge passing through the conductor. Sometimes, as in a toaster or a lamp, the heating is desirable. Sometimes, as in the wires that carry current from the powerhouse to one's home, the heating is undesirable because the heat is wasted. In any case, heating by electricity is comparatively expensive, because electrical P.E. is expensive. Engineers can control the heating by making each part of the circuit have an appropriate amount of electrical resistance.

32–2. The Magnetic Effect. Electricity and magnetism both began to attract serious experimental study about 1600, but no connection between them was found until 1820. In that year Oersted, a professor at Copenhagen, won lasting fame by discovering that a link between electricity and magnetism does exist. He found that a compass needle moved when a current was established in a nearby wire.

Experiment. In Figure 32–A a wire extends in a north–south direction above a compass needle. If a current of a few amperes is switched on in the wire, the compass needle will swing away from the northerly direction.

The discovery shows that *a current-bearing wire has a magnetic field.* The field can be examined by means of the compass, but iron filings are perhaps more effective.

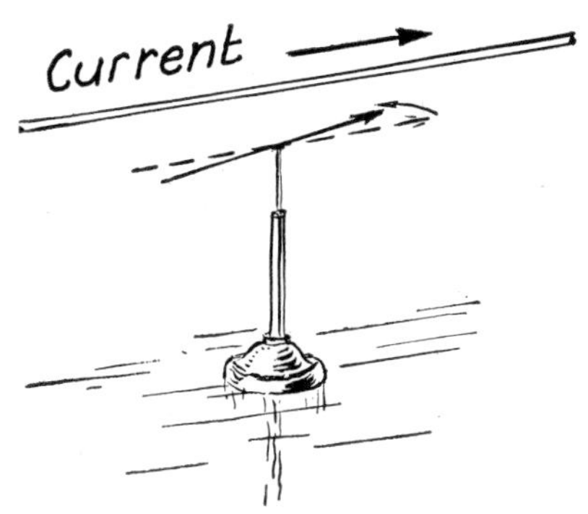

FIGURE 32–A. An electric current sets up a magnetic field.

EXPERIMENT. By sprinkling iron filings on a horizontal plate (Figure 32–B), pierced by a vertical wire that carries a current, one can verify the existence of a magnetic field around the wire. The field has circular symmetry, its center being at the wire. The field is strongest at the center.

By bending the wire, one can make the magnetic fields of the various sections of the wire overlap. Consequently, the field set up by a loop of wire is somewhat like that set up by a thin magnetized disk (Figure

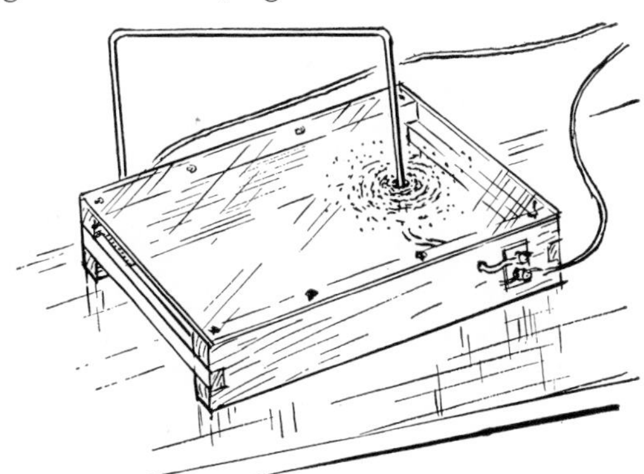

FIGURE 32–B. Iron filings mapping the magnetic field of a straight current-bearing wire.

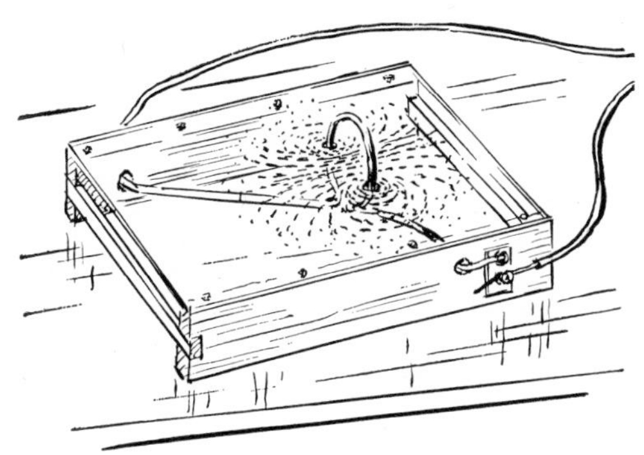

FIGURE 32–C. Iron filings mapping the magnetic field of a current-bearing loop of wire.

FIGURE 32–D. Iron filings mapping the field of a current-bearing coil. Note the resemblance to Figure 31–F.

General Electric Co.

FIGURE 32–E. An industrial electromagnet, lifting a "skull-cracker" for breaking up scrap iron.

32–C), and the field set up by a long coil is like that of a bar magnet (Figure 32–D).

The magnetic field set up by a current-bearing coil can be enhanced by placing a soft-iron core in the coil, where it becomes magnetized by induction. Such a device, called an "electromagnet," is very useful for establishing strong magnetic fields. The electromagnet in Figure 32–E is lifting a ball that weighs 4 tons.

Strong permanent magnets can be made by placing steel bars inside of current-bearing coils, and tapping the bars in order to facilitate the alignment of the domains. Iron can be magnetized more strongly in this way than by rubbing it on a lodestone.

Experiments to be described in later chapters will frequently involve magnetic fields. These fields are almost always obtained by using electromagnets, often like the one in Figure 32–F. Not only can the field of an electromagnet be made very strong, by using a large current and many turns of wire, but it also has the advantage of being readily adjusted in strength, by adjustment of the current in the coil.

FIGURE 32–F. A laboratory electromagnet.

32–3. Currents in Magnetic Fields. Return now to the simple fact that a current-bearing wire exerts a force on a magnet. According to Newton's Third Law of Motion, forces occur in pairs; therefore if the magnet experiences a force, we may suppose that the wire does too. This inference can easily be verified by experiment.

Experiment. Near the strong magnet in Figure 32–G, a wire is suspended in such a way that it is free to swing. If a current of perhaps 10 amperes is set up in the wire, the wire swings to one side. Reversing the current reverses the force on the wire.

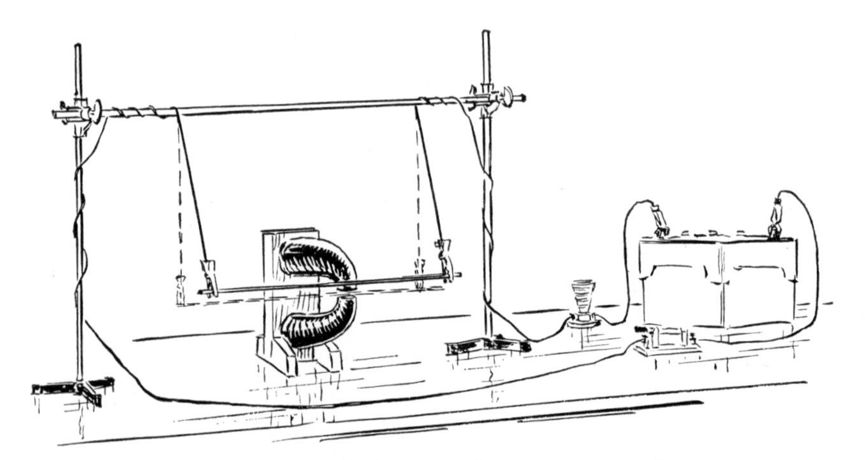

Figure 32–G. A magnetic field causes a force on a current-bearing wire.

The force on the current-bearing wire when it is near the magnet can be ascribed to the influence of the magnetic field on the charge moving in the wire, because no force acts unless the charges in the wire are moving. One noteworthy aspect of the force is that it is always perpendicular to the wire and to the magnetic field. Experimenting with various situations shows that the direction of the force is always related to the directions of the magnetic field and of the current in the way shown in Figure 32–H. The forces that act on moving charges in magnetic fields will be so important in our later work that it is advisable to memorize the set of directions involved when the velocity of the charge is perpendicular to the field. They can easily be called to mind by holding the thumb, forefinger, and middle finger of one hand at right angles to one another, and associating the thumb with the field, the *m*iddle finger with the *m*otion of the charge, and the *for*efinger with the *for*ce that the field exerts on the charge. (Do not confuse the direction of the force with the direction in which the charge is actually moving.) This scheme gives the directions properly, provided the *right* hand is used for *positive* charge, and the *left* hand for *negative* charge; it is pictured for positive charge in Figure 32–I.

The force that a magnetic field exerts on a current-bearing wire is what makes electric motors turn; it is therefore of profound economic and social importance. All sorts of machine tools, like lathes and saws, can be run from electric power instead of from steam. This makes it possible for small shops to engage in mechanized processes at some distance from primary sources of power, such as waterfalls and steam plants. Consequently, industrial activity can be much more widely dispersed than it was in the early nineteenth century, and it can be carried on profitably in shops that are too small to use a steam engine economically.

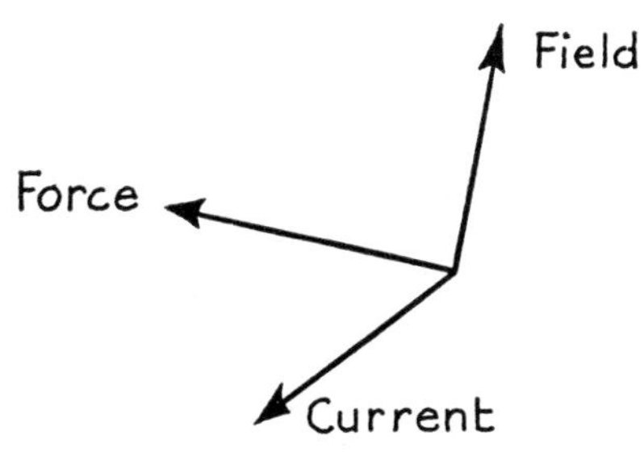

FIGURE 32–H. The directions involved when a magnetic field causes a force on an electric current.

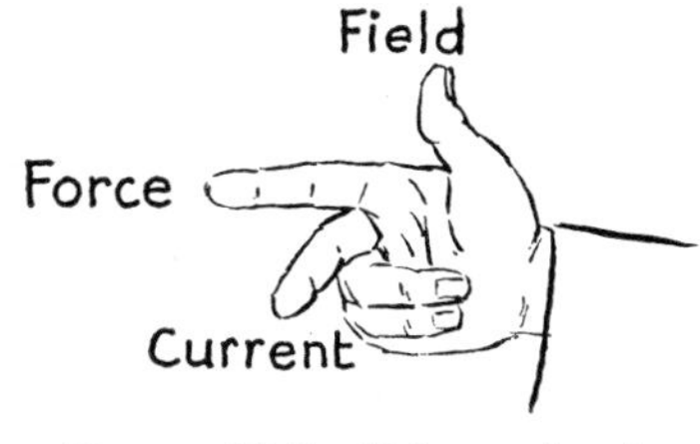

FIGURE 32–I. Using a hand to recall the directions of magnetic field, motion of charge, and force, when the charge moves at right angles to the field.

Studying the construction of the motors that convert electrical energy into mechanical energy, or of the closely related dynamos that convert mechanical energy into electrical energy at the powerhouse, would take us too far off our subject. The interaction of moving charges with magnetic fields will play an important part, however, in our study of atoms.

32–4. The Chemical Effect. As soon as the invention of the electric cell had given experimenters a means of maintaining fairly large electric currents, they began to try the effect of passing electricity through various liquids. Alcohol, kerosene, water, and many other liquids are insulators, but electricity does pass through some liquids. Certain substances are insulators when they are solid, but become conductors when molten, or make conducting solutions when they are dissolved in water. These substances are called *electrolytes*; all others are called *nonelectrolytes*.

EXPERIMENT. Figure 32–J shows a small lamp connected in a circuit made up of a battery and a pair of terminals dipping into a dish of liquid. When a solution of table salt or copper sulfate or sulfuric acid is placed in the dish, the lamp lights, showing that those solutions are fairly good conductors, although the dissolved substances are insulators when solid. As judged by the same test, however, pure water proves to be a nonconductor. So does a solution of sugar in water. When the dish is filled with water drawn from the faucet, the lamp will glow dimly if the water contains dissolved impurities that are electrolytes.

FIGURE 32–J. Testing the conductivity of liquids.

The apparatus in the experiment, applied to a large number of substances that are readily available around the laboratory, gives results such as the following:

Electrolytes	Nonelectrolytes
Sodium chloride	Sugar
Copper sulfate	Methyl alcohol
Sulfuric acid	Glycerin
Silver nitrate	Acetone
Sodium hydroxide	Formaldehyde
Hydrochloric acid	Urea

The experiment brings to light a remarkable fact that has been verified by extensive trials. *Acids, bases, and salts are electrolytes, and all other substances are nonelectrolytes.** This special electrical behavior of acids, bases, and salts implies very strongly that there must be some fundamental connection between chemistry and electricity.

The metal conductors through which electric charge passes into or out of a conducting solution are called *electrodes.* When electricity passes through a solution of sulfuric acid, one can see bubbles form on the electrodes. The bubbles eventually break loose and rise to the surface. If, by apparatus like that in Figure 32–K, the bubbles are all collected, it is found that twice as much gas is given off at the negative electrode as at the positive one. Furthermore, if a glowing splint is thrust into the smaller sample of gas, the splint bursts into flame, showing that this gas is oxygen. If a lighted match is held to the other gas, there is the explosive "pop" that is characteristic of hydrogen. The production of oxygen

* There are some apparent exceptions, but they are substances that react with water, thereby producing an acid or a base in the solution. An example is sulfur dioxide: $SO_2 + H_2O \rightarrow H_2SO_3$.

The metallic oxides, which conduct when molten, can be brought within the rule by adopting a more modern view than the one we have been taking, and considering these oxides to be salts whose parent acid is water (Article 37–6).

and hydrogen in a volume ratio of 1:2 shows that the passage of electricity through the solution causes a decomposition of the water into its constituent elements. The oxygen and hydrogen used in industry are sometimes procured in this way. Chemical decomposition under the action of an electric current is called *electrolysis.*

An interesting result is produced by the passage of electric charge through a solution of copper sulfate, using electrodes made of zinc or platinum. After a little while the negative electrode becomes coated with copper, showing that the transport of charge through the solution is associated with a transport of matter.

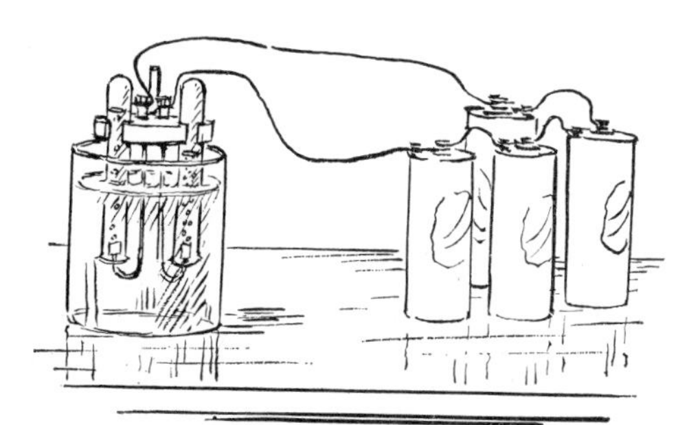

FIGURE 32–K. The electrolysis of water.

These experiments show that electric currents can influence the behavior of the particles of a dissolved substance, and suggest that a detailed study of solutions will yield further information about atoms and about electricity. We shall therefore proceed almost immediately to a study of solutions. In order to be ready, however, for the electrical aspects of the study, it will be well to gain some acquaintance with the laboratory devices that are used for measuring electrical quantities. The next chapter will be devoted to these devices.

Summary

We have discussed three effects of electric currents: the heating effect, the magnetic effect, and the chemical effect.

The heating effect is caused by the electrical resistance of the conductor through which the charge is passing, and can be controlled by controlling that resistance. The effect is due to a conversion of electrical P.E. into heat.

The magnetic effect is an interaction between moving charges and magnetic fields. It has two aspects: a current (moving charge) has a magnetic field of its own, and a magnetic field produces a force on a moving charge. The magnetic field of a current-bearing wire is utilized to make electromagnets, which produce strong and easily controlled magnetic fields. The force that a moving charge experiences when it is in the field of some magnet is used in electric motors and in experiments that reveal important facts about atoms.

Electric currents also have a chemical effect: they can induce chemical change in some liquids. For example, when charge passes through a solution of copper sulfate, copper is deposited on one of the electrodes. Studying such phenomena in detail will give us important information about electricity and about atoms.

The metal conductors through which electric charges pass into or out of a solution are called electrodes. Electrolytes are those substances that are insulators when they are solid, but that become conductors when they are liquid, or that form conducting solutions. All other substances are classed as nonelectrolytes. Experiment shows that acids, bases, and salts are electrolytes; all other substances are nonelectrolytes.

Chemical decomposition in a liquid under the action of an electric current is called electrolysis.

Questions

1. Formulate a simple theory to account for the heating of a wire when a current passes through it.
2. Give evidence that a wire carrying current has a magnetic field.
3. Describe the construction and operation of an electromagnet.
4. When the operator of the magnet in Figure 32–E is ready to drop the iron ball, what should he do?
5. Name two advantages of using an electromagnet instead of a simple magnet.
6. If a positive charge is traveling east in a magnetic field that is directed north, what is the direction of the force exerted on the charge by the field?
7. What is a nonelectrolyte?
8. What is electrolysis? Give an example.
9. Would you expect a nonelectrolyte to undergo electrolysis? Justify your answer.

33

ELECTRICAL MEASUREMENTS

Thus far in our discussion of electrical phenomena, we have been careful to state exactly how each quantity (except one to be mentioned shortly) can be measured. For example, charges can be measured by placing them near other charges and measuring the forces of attraction or repulsion. Through such statements we can be sure of exactly what we are talking about in any discussion of electricity. For actual experiments, however, the laboratory worker needs more convenient methods of measurement. This chapter discusses instruments that can be calibrated once and for all by reference to the operational definitions, and can then be used as meters for making laboratory measurements.

There is one important quantity for which a definition has not yet been given. We have spoken of magnetic fields, but have said nothing about how to measure them, i.e., how to associate numbers with them. This deficiency will now be made good.

33–1. Magnetic Field Strength. A magnetic field can be measured by means of the force it produces on a wire that is carrying current. The

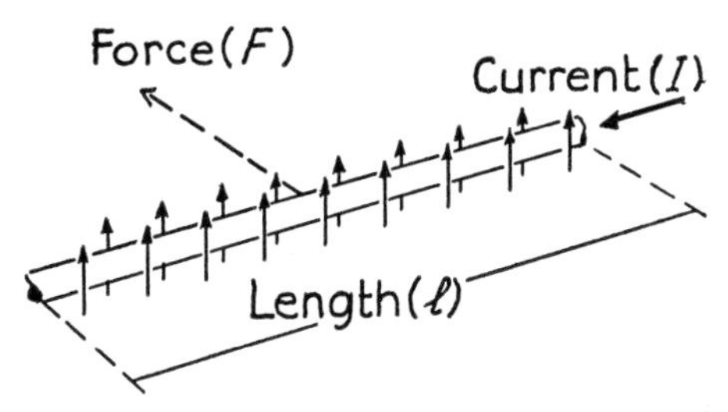

FIGURE 33–A. A wire carrying current at right angles to a magnetic field.

force is a maximum when the wire is at right angles to the direction of the field, as in Figure 33–A. (See also Figure 32–G.) When the wire is in a fixed position in any given field, the force is proportional to the current, and it is also proportional to the length of the wire if the field is the same throughout. If l is the length of the wire, I the current, and F the force on a wire that lies perpendicular to the field direction, then

$$F \propto Il, \quad \text{or} \quad F = BIl.$$

The constant of proportionality, B, is different in different magnetic fields. It is taken as a measure of the field, and it is called *magnetic field strength.* Since

$$\text{Force} = \text{Magnetic field strength} \times \text{Current} \times \text{Length of wire},$$

it follows that

$$\text{Magnetic field strength} = \frac{\text{Force}}{\text{Current} \times \text{Length of wire}}.$$

The quantities on the right can be measured. From them, the strength of the magnetic field can be calculated, and then the magnetic field can be used in a quantitative way in more complex experiments.

33–2. The Galvanometer. Let a rectangular coil of wire be suspended in a magnetic field, as shown in Figure 33–B, in such a way that the coil can be part of a current-bearing circuit. Then, because of the current in the wire of the coil, parts of the wire will experience a sideward thrust in the magnetic field. (There is no thrust on a wire carrying current parallel to a magnetic field, and therefore the top and bottom sections of the coil in the figure will not experience any thrust.) The force acting on the sides of the coil in the figure will tend to move the left side out of the paper, and the right side into the paper, as can easily be seen by applying the rule given in the last chapter. Therefore the coil, if suspended so that it can turn, will turn when there is a curent in it. The suspension of the coil can be arranged so that the motion of the coil is opposed, but not prevented, by the twisting of the supporting wire. With such an arrangement, a bigger current will twist the coil farther than a smaller one, and the device will therefore provide an indication of the size of the current if a pointer is attached to the coil. The device is called a *galvanometer.* If it is carefully made, and calibrated by means of known currents, it can be used to measure other currents. (Each of the major governments has a standardizing laboratory where currents and other quantities can be measured in terms of their operational definitions. These laboratories supply instrument makers with the services necessary for their trade.)

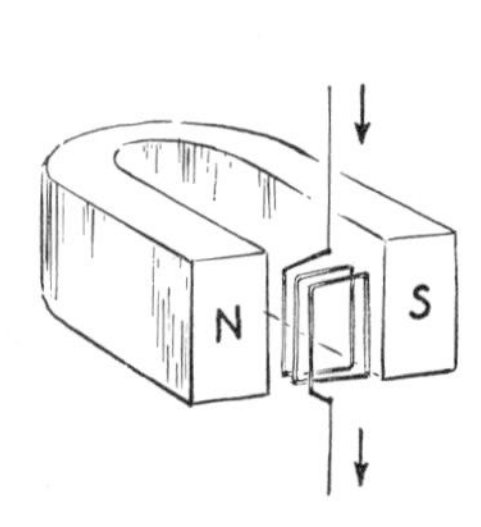

FIGURE 33–B. The structure of a galvanometer.

The galvanometer is the commonest instrument for measuring current. It can be made sensitive and portable.

Although not readily portable, galvanometers like the one in Figure 33–C find widespread use. The coil hangs from a fine wire that runs up through the vertical tube. The dark rectangles beside the coil are the

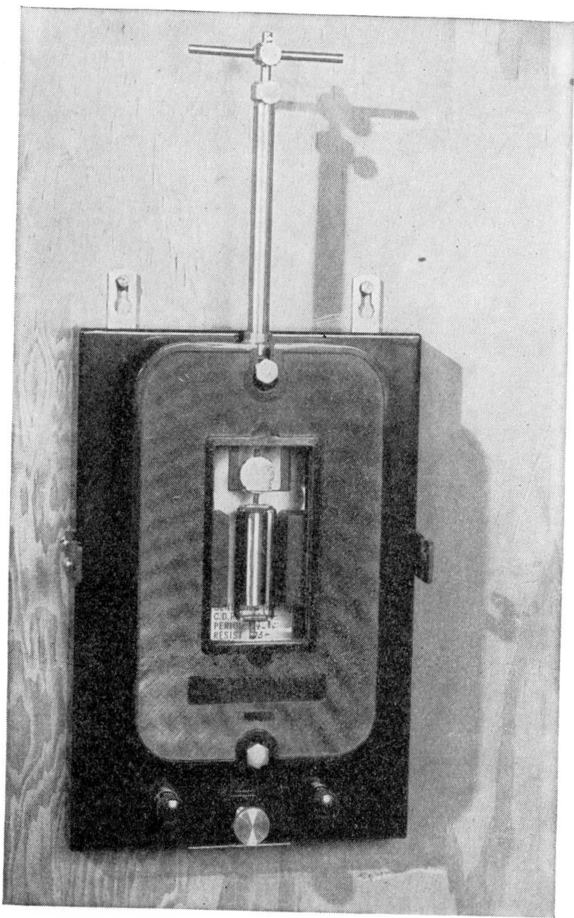

Leeds & Northrup Co.

FIGURE 33–C. A laboratory galvanometer.

magnet poles; the iron cylinder inside the coil shapes the magnetic field in such a way that the rotation of the coil is accurately proportional to the current. The "pointer" that shows the position of the coil is a beam of light reflected from the little round mirror just above the coil. By letting the light fall on a ruled scale that may be several feet away, the experimenter has the advantage of a long pointer at no cost in weight.

In instruments that must be portable and rugged, the coil is often pivoted in jeweled bearings instead of being suspended by a wire, and a spring restrains the motion of the coil. Figure 33–D shows such an instrument without its case.

Weston Electrical Instrument Corp.

FIGURE 33–D. A portable galvanometer mechanism.

When currents as large as an ampere are to be measured, it is usual to let most of the current pass through an auxiliary conductor and to let only a small known fraction pass through the galvanometer. Figure 33–E shows how the conductor is connected; its purpose is to minimize the resistance introduced into the circuit by the measuring device. A galvanometer equipped with this auxiliary conductor is called an *ammeter,* because it can be calibrated in amperes.

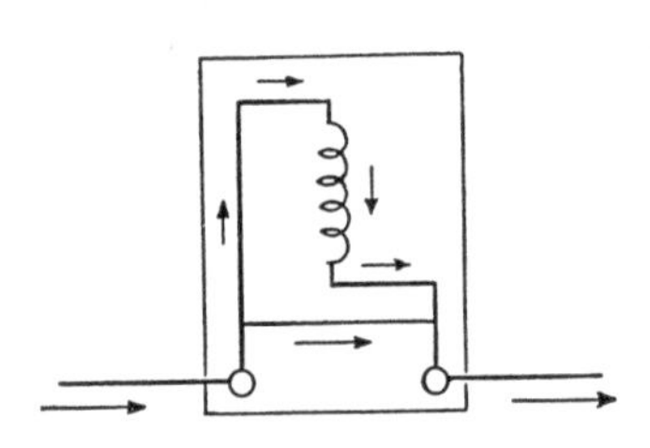

FIGURE 33–E. The connections in an ammeter.

33–3. The Voltmeter. Measurements of potential difference are very important to electrical workers of all sorts. You will recall that the potential of a point is the P.E. of a charge at that point, divided by the amount of charge present (Article 29–3). It is measured in volts, which are joules/coulomb. Potential is a useful quantity because the P.E. gained or lost by a charge when it passes between two points is equal to the charge multiplied by the difference of potential of the two points.

$$\text{P.E. gained or lost} = \text{Charge} \times \text{Difference of potential.}$$

Since one is often interested in the energy changes that a charge experiences, measurements of potential difference are very commonly needed. Any instrument for making these measurements is called a *voltmeter*.

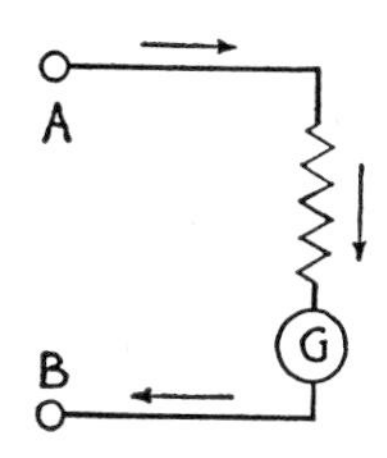

FIGURE 33-F. Scheme for measuring differences of potential.

Potential differences are usually measured by resorting to an ingenious trick. Suppose it is necessary to measure the potential difference of the points A and B in Figure 33-F. A and B may be the terminals of a battery, the terminals of a lamp, or the like. Let a current pass from A to B through a galvanometer, G, the current being limited to some small value by means of a conductor whose resistance is large. Let the amount of resistance in the conducting path be R, and let the current be I. Then by Ohm's Law (Article 30-5), we know that I and R are related in such a way that

$$RI = V,$$

where V is the potential difference between A and B. Now the resistance R can have a known value, and the current I can be measured by means

Weston Electrical Instrument Corp.

FIGURE 33-G. A voltmeter.

of the galvanometer, and therefore V can be calculated readily. In practice, the calculation is often performed by the manufacturer of the voltmeter, who puts the galvanometer and a conductor of sufficient resistance together in a box, and puts behind the galvanometer pointer a scale that is properly ruled off in volts. The voltmeter in Figure 33–G contains the galvanometer that appears in Figure 33–D, as well as a spool of wire that raises the resistance of the instrument to a suitable value.

33–4. Measuring Electric Fields.* The practical job of measuring an electric field is sometimes a complicated one, but in the situations we shall be discussing it can be done very simply. In these situations, the electric field is produced by opposite charges on flat plates that are parallel to one another. Remember that the electric field strength is the force on a positive charge in the field, divided by the amount of the charge (Article 29–2). Therefore

$$\text{Field strength} \times \text{Charge} = \text{Force on charge.}$$

If the charge is allowed to move in the direction of the field, it loses P.E., just as a stone does if it falls in the earth's gravitational field from a high place to a lower one. The P.E. lost is the work that would have to be done to restore the charge to its original position, and this is simply the force on the charge multiplied by the distance it moves.

$$\text{P.E. lost} = \text{Force on charge} \times \text{Distance moved.}$$

Putting in what we know about the force on the charge, we have

$$\text{P.E. lost} = \text{Field strength} \times \text{Charge} \times \text{Distance moved.}$$

Suppose the charge moves all the way across the field, from one plate to the other. Then the distance moved is simply the distance between the plates, and the P.E. lost is equal to the amount of charge that moves, multiplied by the potential difference between the plates. We have then,

$$\begin{aligned}&\text{Potential difference of plates} \times \text{Charge}\\ &\qquad = \text{Field strength} \times \text{Charge} \times \text{Distance between plates.}\end{aligned}$$

Canceling out the charge, we have

$$\text{Potential difference of plates} = \text{Field strength} \times \text{Distance between plates,}$$

or,

$$\text{Field strength} = \frac{\text{Potential difference of plates}}{\text{Distance between plates}}.$$

The potential difference of the plates can be measured with a voltmeter, and the distance can easily be measured. Therefore the field strength can be calculated from easily measured quantities.

* This article completes the discussion of how to measure the electrical quantities of interest in atomic science, but it need not be digested in order to understand what comes later.

Summary

Magnetic field strength is measured in terms of the force on a current-bearing wire. It is the ratio of this force to the product of current and length, when the wire is placed at right angles to the direction of the field. $B = F/Il$.

In practice, the laboratory worker needs instruments for measuring electrical quantities. Sometimes these instruments are based directly on the operational definitions of the electrical quantities; sometimes the instruments are based on some more convenient phenomenon and have to be calibrated by the manufacturer. Meters for measuring currents and differences of potential fall in the latter category.

A galvanometer consists of a coil of wire suspended in a magnetic field, its motion being restrained, but not prevented, by the twisting of the supporting wire or of a spring. When there is a current in the coil, the coil turns by an amount that depends on how big the current is. By passing known currents through the coil and measuring how far the coil turns, one can calibrate the instrument as a meter for measuring currents.

Potential differences are measured by instruments called voltmeters. The commonest type consists of a galvanometer and a conductor with a known high resistance. By measuring the current that passes in the conductor when it is connected between two points, the potential difference of the points can be calculated from Ohm's Law. The calculations can be performed in advance by an instrument manufacturer, for different values of current, and he can rule off the instrument scale directly in volts.

The strength of the electric field between two parallel plates at different potentials can be calculated in terms of quantities that are easy to measure. The electric field strength turns out to be equal to the potential difference of the plates divided by the distance between them.

Questions

1. Describe in a general way the phenomenon that is used for specifying the strength of a magnetic field. Then state the definition of magnetic field strength.
2. In what units is magnetic field strength to be measured?
3. A bar of copper 0.30 meter long carries a current of 20 amperes at right angles to a certain uniform magnetic field. As a consequence, it experiences a force of 0.50 newton. Find the strength of the magnetic field.
4. Describe the construction of one type of galvanometer.
5. Describe the construction of a voltmeter, and explain the principle on which the device operates.
6. What instruments would you need in order to determine the strength of the electric field between two flat parallel plates that are connected to a battery?

GENERAL VIEW OF SECTION V

Primitive experiments show the existence of electric charge, of which there are two kinds arbitrarily labeled "positive" and "negative." More refined experiments permit the definition of a unit of charge (the coulomb) in terms of the force of repulsion between two like charges. Moving charges constitute electric currents, measured in coulombs per second (called amperes). These currents exist when any charged body is discharged, but they are then usually brief. They can be maintained by electric cells or batteries, in which chemical activity replenishes the charge on the terminals. A charge can do work in passing from one place to another if the passage reduces the P.E. of the charge. It is customary to describe the electrical state of any point by the P.E. of a positive charge there, divided by the amount of the charge. This quantity is called electrical potential; it is measured in joules per coulomb (called volts).

Moving charges can produce three principal effects: they can produce heat, they can interact with magnets, and they can separate the constituents of some chemical compounds. The magnetic effect of a current is used as the basis for several of the instruments on which the laboratory worker depends for measuring electrical quantities.

The section has introduced a variety of electrical phenomena with no attempt at an explanation. Actually very little explanation is possible—charges and magnets, and their interactions, are the fundamental facts upon which the science of electricity is built. Nobody knows, for example, why a positive charge attracts a negative one. Nevertheless, one conclusion of prime importance can be drawn: if chemical activity can replenish the charge on the terminals of a battery, and if the passage of charge through a solution can deposit chemical elements on the electrodes, then there must be an intimate connection between electricity and chemistry. A better understanding of electricity will in fact be reached by learning more about the structure of matter, using as tools many of the electrical phenomena that have been introduced in this section.

VI

Solutions

Earlier sections have established that a gas consists of particles, which move about independently of one another if the pressure is not too great, and further that these particles are molecules made up of atoms. This view of gases is based on their mechanical, thermal, and chemical behavior. The next big step in understanding the structure of matter was made by studying solutions, and in particular by following up the discovery that the passage of electricity through a solution produces chemical change.

34

SOLUTIONS

An analogy in condition exists between the parts of a body in solution, and those of a body in a vaporous or gaseous state.

FARADAY (1833)

In our earlier and very brief consideration of solutions (Article 19–4), we noted experimental evidence for the belief that in solutions the particles of one substance are dispersed among the particles of another substance. It is now clear that this intimate mingling does not involve chemical union. In a chemical union, the constituents of the resulting compound are always present in definite proportions (Article 20–3). In a solution, the proportions of the constituents can be altered by simply adding more of one constituent or the other. Solutions, then, are not compounds; the next step is to decide what they are.

34–1. The Nature of Solutions. The simplest state of matter is the gaseous one, because in a gas the molecules move about independently, affecting one another only when they happen to collide. Consequently, the simplest kind of solution is that composed of two gases. Here the nature of the solution is obvious: Since no chemical combination occurs, the molecules of both gases simply fly about in the same space, independent of one another except during collisions.

Consider now the solution of a solid in a liquid. What happens when a small amount of sugar or copper sulfate is shaken up with water is clearly different from what happens when mud is shaken with water. The mud settles out on standing, but the sugar or copper sulfate does not. The mud in water is a mechanical mixture, called a "suspension," which separates under the mechanical influence of gravity. Sugar and water, or copper sulfate and water, do not separate on standing, except when the water leaves the scene by evaporation. How can we explain the behavior of the sugar and water? Two clues are available: Any part of the solution tastes sweet, and the sugar does not settle out. The obvious explanation is that the sugar is present throughout the solution and that it is so finely divided that the particles of sugar are comparable in size with the particles of the water in which they are dispersed. This hypothesis views the solution of a solid in water as being very much like the solution of two gases. The particles of the dissolved substance move freely among the particles of the water. The thermal motion counteracts the tendency for the heavier particles to separate from the lighter ones.* The hypothesis is supported by the behavior of an unstirred solution of a colored substance.

EXPERIMENT. If several blue crystals of copper sulfate are placed in the bottom of a tall glass jar, which is then filled with water, the copper sulfate will dissolve and make a blue solution. At first the color is concentrated at the bottom, but as days go by the color gradually diffuses throughout the fluid. The migration of the dissolved particles is much slower than migration in a gas would be, because the particles of the liquid are more closely crowded, but the experiment confirms the idea that the dissolved particles are approximately the same size as the particles of water.

It is not so easy to form a mental picture of what happens when a gas dissolves in a solid, or when a solid dissolves in a solid. To form such a picture, one must know something about the structure of solids. At this stage of our study, it is best to postpone these questions and to concentrate on solutions of solids in water.

34–2. Solution and Crystallization. A substance is said to be "soluble in water" if a detectable amount of it will dissolve in water; otherwise, it is called "insoluble." One would classify sugar as "very soluble," limestone as "slightly soluble," and sand as insoluble, or nearly so. These terms are loose ones, but they are useful. The water, or any other liquid that plays the same role, is called the *solvent*; the dissolved solid is called the *solute.*

If more and more of a solid is added to a beaker of water, then in most cases there sooner or later comes a time when no more of the solid will dissolve in the water. Any additional solid just sits there. Suppose now that the beaker stands until some of the water has evaporated. One finds that the solid builds up; some of the solute reverts to the solid condition,

* The sizes of the particles in solution vary over a considerable range. In some solutions, a beam of light is scattered by the dissolved particles, so that the path of the beam is made visible. The effect is like that of a searchlight beam passing through a fog, or a beam of sunlight passing through dusty air. Solutions of this sort are called "colloidal" solutions. In other solutions, a beam of light is not made visible by the particles of the dissolved substance, because they are too small to produce visible scattering. These solutions are called "true" solutions. This classification has no fundamental significance, but it happens that the solutions of interest in this book will nearly always be "true" solutions. A solution of soap in water is colloidal; sugar in water forms a "true" solution.

often in the form of sizable crystals which grow as the solvent evaporates. The solute is said to *crystallize* from the solution. The crystal in Figure 34–A grew in this way. Less spectacular crystals are easily made from solutions of alum, potassium sulfate, or photographer's hypo.

Evidently a soluble solid comes apart under the action of water. During the solution process, particles of the solid enter the solution. Is there any reason to suppose that a soluble crystal can ever sit in a solution without having some of its particles pass into solution? Even during crystallization, it could lose particles, but nevertheless grow, if it simply gained particles faster than it lost them. If the rate of loss exceeded the rate of gain, the crystal would dissolve. If the two rates were equal, the size of the crystal would not change. These considerations lead to the hypothesis that solution and crystallization are opposing processes that go on simultaneously whenever a soluble crystal is exposed to water. A very simple experiment gives convincing support to this hypothesis. If a broken crystal is hung in a solution which already contains as much of that substance as will dissolve, then the shape of the crystal gradually changes in such a way as to perfect the regularity of the crystal. The change shows that the situation is not a static one, even though the amount of dissolved substance remains the same. Solution and crystallization take place simultaneously, with the crystallization proceeding most rapidly in those places where the natural structure is deficient.

Bell Telephone Laboratories

FIGURE 34–A. A large crystal grown from a solution. The material is ammonium dihydrogen phosphate, $NH_4H_2PO_4$, prized for certain electrical uses.

34–3. Saturation and Solubility. Imagine a soluble crystal placed in pure water. At first, since there is no solute in the solution as yet, the solid cannot gain particles; all it can do is lose. As soon as there are some solute particles in the solution, it is possible for the solid to repossess some of them, but collisions of the solute with the solid will at first be infrequent. The solid therefore gains particles slowly while losing them rapidly. Figure 34–Ba is a cartoon of this situation. As the solution becomes more densely populated with solute particles, however, there will be an increase in the rate at which such particles bump into the solid and rejoin it. The rate of net loss therefore goes down. In short, the solid dwindles more slowly after some of it has dissolved than it did at first.

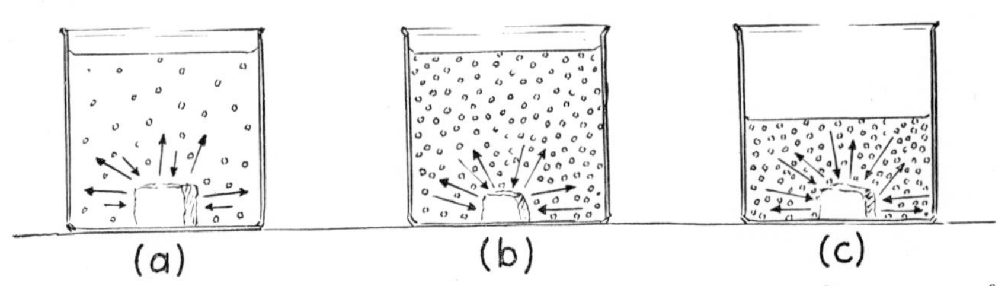

FIGURE 34–B. (a) A crystal dissolving. (b) Equilibrium between the processes of solution and crystallization. (c) A solution crystallizing .

(This deduction is in accord with experience.) If enough solid is present, there will eventually be enough particles in solution so that the rate at which they are rejoining the solid will just counterbalance the rate at which other particles are leaving the solid (Figure 34–Bb). This pair of opposite processes going on at the same rate, producing no net change, is an example of what is called *equilibrium.* Equilibrium, in the present sense, is the state of balance between two opposing processes that occur at equal rates.

When a solution is in equilibrium with the undissolved solid, the solution is called a *saturated* one. A familiar example is the solution of sugar in iced tea, when the user has been a little too generous with the sugar. After a certain amount of sugar has dissolved, no amount of stirring will persuade the rest to go into solution. If the excess solid is removed from a saturated solution, nothing else being changed, the solution is still called a saturated one. This statement involves an extension of the definition to include solutions that would be in equilibrium with undissolved solid if any were present.

Now suppose that heat is applied to a saturated solution that contains some excess solid. The solution and the solid will both rise in temperature. The increased temperature implies more rapid motion of all of the particles, whether of the solvent, the solute, or the solid. Collisions between the solute particles and the solid will become more frequent, and there may be a change in the probability that a colliding particle will stick to the solid. It is reasonable to expect, therefore, that the rate of crystallization will change. It is also reasonable to expect that the rate of solution will change, because the more violent agitation of the particles in the solid may change the rate at which they escape into the fluid. If these two rates change by different amounts, equilibrium will no longer

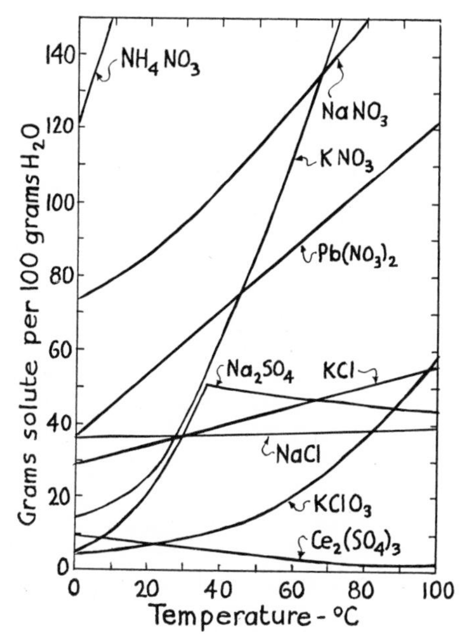

FIGURE 34–C. Graphs of solubility.

exist. If the solution process now predominates, more solid will go into solution until either a new equilibrium is reached or the solid is all used up. Experiment, or even common experience, shows that the temperature does affect the amount of solute that will dissolve in a given amount of solvent. Most substances are more soluble in hot water than in cold.

The *solubility* of a substance is the ratio of weights of solute and solvent in a saturated solution. Since this quantity is different at different temperatures, the temperature must be specified. For example, we say that the solubility of sodium nitrate ($NaNO_3$) is 96 grams per 100 grams of water at 30° C. Figure 34–C is a graph of the solubilities of several substances over a range of temperatures. The variety of curves reflects the complexity of the factors that determine the rates of solution and crystallization. An *unsaturated* solution is one that contains less solute than the amount that would produce saturation.

34–4. Supersaturation. We have been supposing, in accord with our hypothesis, that equilibrium between solution and crystallization is what sets a limit to the amount of solute that a solution can hold. It is easy to gain additional support for this assumption. We have been limiting our attention to solutions in which some of the solid remains undissolved. In these cases, the undissolved solid provides a framework on which crystallization can take place. We should expect that removal of this framework would discourage crystallization and thereby increase the amount of solute that the solution can hold. This inference is correct. If a saturated solution is cooled,* and some excess solid is present, then some of the solute crystallizes. If no excess solid is present, then a small drop in temperature may not produce any crystallization. The solution then contains more solute than it would if it were merely saturated; it is called a *supersaturated* solution. If a crystal of the solid were introduced, there would not be an equilibrium. Instead, the rate of crystallization would exceed the rate of solution (Figure 34–Bc), and some of the solute would come out of solution.

Experiment. A tiny crystal of sodium acetate is dropped into a supersaturated solution of that substance, made by allowing a warm saturated solution to cool. The solution crystallizes very rapidly. A thermometer in the solution will show an abrupt rise in temperature, because the solute particles lose potential energy as they "fall" into place in the crystal structure. The lost P.E. appears as K.E. of the particles, and the temperature rises (Article 17–4).

If a supersaturated solution is cooled to a sufficiently low temperature, crystallization occurs even before it is brought about by introduction of a "seed" crystal. Sometimes the crystallization is started by the presence of some dust particle that has a crystal structure similar to that of the solute. Sometimes it seems likely that the crystallization is entirely spontaneous; no doubt a few solute particles eventually take on by accident the same relative positions that they would have in a crystal, and they then act as a framework on which further crystallization proceeds.

Supersaturation confirms the view that saturation is an equilibrium between solution and crystallization. If no crystal is present for the dissolved particles to build on, the amount of dissolved substance can exceed the amount that will produce saturation.

34–5. Hydrates. If the deep-blue crystals of copper sulfate stand for a while in warm dry air, they crumble into a pale-blue powder. Experiment shows that the change comes about because the crystals give off water.

* We assume here that the solute is one whose solubility decreases as the temperature falls.

EXPERIMENT. If a deep-blue crystal of copper sulfate is crushed and placed in a test tube, heating makes it turn white. Droplets of water accumulate near the mouth of the test tube.

If copper sulfate is kept at about 240° C in a current of dry air until no more water is carried away by the air, it turns into a white powder. Analysis shows that this powder consists entirely of copper, sulfur, and oxygen; the relative weights of the constituents fit the formula $CuSO_4$. Since this substance contains no water, it is called *anhydrous* cupric sulfate. The water given off by the deep-blue crystals, when they are being heated to make the anhydrous salt, can be caught and weighed. It always amounts to 36.1 percent of the weight of the original crystals. These deep-blue crystals therefore have a definite composition, and qualify as a chemical compound. Since the water can so easily be removed as vapor, however, we suppose that the molecules H_2O retain their identity in the structure of the substance. If 36.1 percent of the substance is water and 63.9 percent is cupric sulfate, the substance must have the composition indicated by the formula $CuSO_4 \cdot 5H_2O$, where the dot indicates a chemical union which nevertheless does not break up the water molecules. Such a compound of any substance and water is called a *hydrate*. The water in it is called *water of hydration*.

There are three hydrates of copper sulfate. Each has a definite composition and a characteristic color. Which one is formed depends on how much water is available. The deep-blue crystals, $CuSO_4 \cdot 5H_2O$ (cupric sulfate pentahydrate), form when copper sulfate crystallizes from a water solution. On exposure to moderately dry air, they lose water and form the pale-blue $CuSO_4 \cdot 3H_2O$ (cupric sulfate trihydrate). Heating this powder to about 100° C converts it into the bluish-white $CuSO_4 \cdot H_2O$ (cupric sulfate monohydrate). The remaining water of hydration comes off at a still higher temperature, leaving $CuSO_4$.

When anhydrous cupric sulfate dissolves in water, the solution is blue although the solid was white. When the excess water evaporates, the solute crystallizes as cupric sulfate pentahydrate. Along with the process of solution and crystallization, there has been the reaction

$$CuSO_4 + 5H_2O \rightarrow CuSO_4 \cdot 5H_2O.$$

Note that the hydrated salt is not wet. It is a dry solid that has water molecules as one of its constituents.

Other common hydrates are washing soda, $Na_2CO_3 \cdot 10H_2O$, and the mineral gypsum, $CaSO_4 \cdot 2H_2O$. Controlled heating of gypsum drives off some water and produces the hemihydrate $(2CaSO_4) \cdot H_2O$ called "plaster of Paris." When this substance is mixed with water and poured into a mold, the added water soon becomes water of hydration, forming $CaSO_4 \cdot 2H_2O$, and the plaster solidifies in the mold. Ordinary cement is more complicated, because it is a mixture of substances, but it works in much the same way as plaster of Paris.

The facts of hydration are mentioned here in order to avoid giving the impression that solutes never react with the water in which they dissolve. Such reactions sometimes occur, but they will cause us no further concern for some time. Later, when we are formulating a general theory of chemical behavior, hydration will have to fit into the picture.

Summary

A fluid solution is matter in which one substance (or several) is dispersed throughout another in the form of particles so small that thermal motion prevents gravity from separating the substances. If one of the substances is normally a liquid and the other is not, then the liquid is called the solvent and the substance dissolved in it is called the solute.

Crystallization, in the sense that is of interest here, is the formation of crystals by solute material that comes out of solution and reverts to the solid state. If part of a solid enters into solution and the rest is in contact with the solution, then the processes of solution and crystallization go on simultaneously. When these two opposing processes occur at the same rate, there is no net change in the amount of dissolved substance. We call a situation like this an equilibrium, and a solution in equilibrium with undissolved solid is called saturated. The solubility of a substance is the ratio of weights of solute and solvent in a saturated solution. Solubility changes with temperature, because temperature affects differently the rates of solution and of crystallization.

If no undissolved solid is present, then there is no framework on which the solute particles can build, and this lack retards the process of crystallization. Consequently, the solution can hold a denser population of solute particles than it could if it were in equilibrium with undissolved solid. If more solute is present than is necessary for saturation, the solution is called supersaturated. The phenomenon of supersaturation confirms the hypothesis that crystallization and solution occur simultaneously when undissolved solid is present. The dependence of solubility on temperature also favors the hypothesis.

Although solutions are not chemical compounds, some substances do react with water in which they are dissolved. The reactions lead to compounds called hydrates, in which water molecules are attached to the rest of the compound in some simple ratio. Cement and some crystals are hydrates.

Questions

1. To what extent does the solution of a solid in a liquid resemble a gas?
2. When are two processes in equilibrium?
3. What is a saturated solution?
4. How can a saturated solution be changed to an unsaturated one without changing the amount of solvent or the amount of solute?
5. Define solubility.
6. How would you test the extent to which a given substance is soluble in water? Take into account the possibility that the substance may be only slightly soluble.
7. Why does stirring hasten the process of solution?
8. Some pure water is added to a beaker that contains a saturated solution and a lump of the undissolved solid. Describe what one would see, and explain it in terms of the particles.
9. Suppose that a certain solution of sugar is a saturated one, and that some common salt is added to it. Do you think that the salt will dissolve? Give your reasoning.
10. Given a solution of sodium acetate, how could you tell whether it was unsaturated, saturated, or supersaturated?
11. Why would it be wrong to say that a saturated solution is a solution that contains all of the solute that it can hold?
12. What is a hydrate?
13. Analysis shows that a certain compound contains 36.1 percent of water, and that the rest of the compound is cupric sulfate. Show that the formula $CuSO_4 \cdot 5H_2O$ fits the compounds.
14. Distinguish between the process of solution and the process of melting.

35

SOME SUGGESTIVE PROPERTIES OF SOLUTIONS

> And although the arguing from Experiments and Observations by Induction be no Demonstration of general Conclusions; yet it is the best way of arguing that the Nature of Things admits of.
>
> NEWTON

In discussing the behavior of particles in solution, the last chapter threw no light on what the particles are. It is natural to consider the possibility that the particles are molecules, but other possibilities certainly exist. For example, the particles might be little clumps of two or three molecules. Remember, moreover, that the belief in molecules rests on experiments wtih gases. Those experiments give no real assurance that molecules exist at all in liquids or in solids. We can reasonably hope to find some clue to the structure of solids by finding out what kind of particles they contribute when they go into solution in water. We shall find that in some cases these particles actually are not molecules.

35–1. Concentration. The proportion of solute to solvent is called the *concentration* of a solution. A "dilute" solution is one that contains relatively little solute, and a "concentrated" solution is one that contains a large proportion of solute. These are merely qualitative terms. Concentration can be specified quantitatively by telling the weight of the solute and the weight of the solvent. For some purposes, such as manufacturing, this method is satisfactory. For making a scientific study of solutions, however, it is desirable to specify the number of particles dissolved in some standard amount of water. In order to do so, we must take into account the fact that the particles of different substances have different weights. We therefore resort to the use of molecular weights (Article 22–3).

Molecular weights are the relative weights of molecules. Let samples of two substances be weighed out so that the weight of each sample is proportional to the molecular weight of the substance. Specifically, consider 1 gram of methyl alcohol (CH_3OH, mol. wt. 32) and 2 grams of sulfur dioxide (SO_2, mol. wt. 64). If these samples consist of molecules at all, then they must contain the same number of molecules, because the weights of the samples are in proportion to the relative weights of the molecules, 1:2. To see this point clearly, consider two sacks of carefully graded potatoes. Suppose sack A contains potatoes that all have the same weight. Sack B shall also contain potatoes that are all alike, but each shall weigh twice as much as one of the potatoes in sack A. Then it should be clear that if sack A weighs 100 pounds and sack B weighs 200 pounds, they must each contain the same number of potatoes. In the general case, if the weights of the sacks are in proportion to the relative weights of their respective potatoes, each sack will contain the same number of potatoes. Similarly, if two substances have weights in proportion to the relative weights of their respective molecules, then *the samples must contain the same number of molecules.* It is easy to choose weights that are proportional to the relative weights of the respective molecules. All we have to do is make the weight of each sample numerically equal to the molecular weight of the substance. When this is done with the gram as the unit of weight, then the sample is called a *mole* of the substance. For example, since oxygen (O_2) has molecular weight 32, a mole of oxygen is 32 g of oxygen. One mole of hydrogen (H_2) is 2 g of hydrogen; 1 mole of water (H_2O) is 18 g of water; 1 mole of sugar ($C_{12}H_{22}O_{11}$) is 342 g of sugar. These weights are different, but each of them comprises the same number of molecules.

Returning for a moment to the sacks of potatoes, we recognize that, on the basis of the information given, we cannot know how many potatoes are in the sacks. All we can infer is that the number in each sack is the same; to find what that number is, we should have to know the weight of one of the potatoes. It is the same with a mole. We know that a mole of hydrogen and a mole of steam contain the same number of molecules. This knowledge in itself is useful. Later, we shall find a way of knowing how many molecules there are in a mole, but in the practice of chemistry this number is surprisingly unimportant.

It is easy to see that the mole is well suited to specifying the concentration of a solution. Of the several ways that this can be done, the most convenient for our purposes is to specify how many moles of solute are dissolved per 1000 grams of water. The concentration, so expressed, is called the *molality* of the solution. A 2-molal solution is one that contains 2 moles of solute in 1000 g of water, or 1 mole in 500 g, or the equivalent.

35–2. The Freezing of Solutions. If a solution is cooled sufficiently, some of the water in the solution will eventually form crystals of ice. The ice is pure water, not a solution. The temperature at which ice and the solution are in equilibrium is called the *freezing point* of the solution. It is always lower than 0° C, which is the freezing point of pure water.

To understand why a dissolved substance lowers the freezing point of water, consider the equilibrium between freezing and melting. In the case of water, freezing is the building up of an ice crystal, and melting is the disintegration of the crystal into the less orderly arrangement that is water. The rate of melting simply depends on the temperature. The rate of freezing, however, depends on the temperature and also on the rate at which water particles strike the ice. If solute particles are present, they strike the ice but cannot fit into its crystalline structure. Hence the effect of the solute particles is simply to reduce the rate at which the water particles strike the ice. At 0° C, therefore, the rate of freezing is less in a solution than it is in pure water. To produce equilibrium between melting and freezing, in spite of the presence of solute, the temperature must be brought below 0° C.

If the foregoing reasoning is correct, then the freezing point of a solution should depend on how the number of solute particles compares with the number of water particles. If the solute particles are molecules, then 1 mole of any solute should have the same effect as 1 mole of any other solute. This idea can be tested by measuring the freezing point of 1-molal solutions of various substances. It turns out that 1-molal solutions of many substances do have the same freezing point (−1.86° C). Not all substances behave alike, however. Table 35–I shows the freezing points observed for solutions of various substances in water.

TABLE 35–I

THE FREEZING POINTS OF SOME SOLUTIONS

Solute		1-Molal Solution	0.1-Molal Solution	0.01-Molal Solution
Acetone	C_3H_6O	−1.79° C	−0.185° C	−0.0186° C
Glucose	$C_6H_{12}O_6$	−1.92	−0.186	−0.0186
Glycerine	$C_3H_5(OH)_3$	−1.92	−0.187	−0.0186
Ethyl alcohol	C_2H_5OH	−1.83	−0.183	−0.0183
Urea	$CO(NH_2)_2$		−0.185	−0.0185
Hydrochloric acid	HCl	−3.94	−0.352	−0.0360
Nitric acid	HNO_3	−3.58	−0.351	−0.0364
Sodium hydroxide	$NaOH$	−3.44	−0.342	−0.0355
Potassium hydroxide	KOH	−3.60	−0.342	−0.0365
Sodium chloride	$NaCl$	−3.37	−0.346	−0.0360
Silver nitrate	$AgNO_3$	−2.63	−0.332	−0.0360
Potassium chloride	KCl	−3.25	−0.345	−0.0361
Lithium chloride	$LiCl$	−3.80	−0.352	−0.0360
Barium chloride	$BaCl_2$	−5.20	−0.470	−0.0503
Cobalt chloride	$CoCl_2$	−6.31	−0.488	−0.0511
Magnesium nitrate	$Mg(NO_3)_2$	−5.78	−0.474	
Magnesium chloride	$MgCl_2$	−6.35	−0.494	−0.0514
Potassium carbonate	K_2CO_3	−4.51	−0.456	−0.0520

Note that although the data are not all the same, they do fall into groups. The grouping is particularly apparent for the dilute solutions.

In the first group, the 1-molal solutions all have nearly the same freezing point; this sameness implies that they contain the same concentration of solute particles. Now these solutions, if their solute particles are molecules, will all contain the same concentration of molecules, because they are all 1-molal solutions. Therefore, we may consistently assume that the solute particles are molecules. The assumption is of course merely an assumption, but it does not do violence to the experimental data. The difference between 0° C and the freezing point, which is called the *freezing-point depression,* is just about one-hundredth as great for the 0.01-molal solutions as it is for the 1-molal solutions. This fact supports the hypothesis that the freezing-point depression is proportional to the relative abundance of the dissolved particles. Since the substances in this group have a behavior that can be so easily explained, they are said to show a "normal" lowering of the freezing point.

The second group in Table 35–I behaves quite differently. The freezing-point depression is greater, and it is not so nearly proportional to the concentration as it is in the "normal" case. The greater depression implies a greater number of dissolved particles. Consequently, one is led to assume that in these solutions the dissolved particles are not molecules, but something smaller. In the dilute solutions, the freezing-point depression has nearly twice the normal value. It therefore seems as though the dissolved particles are nearly twice as numerous in these dilute solutions as they would be if they were molecules.

The same considerations apply to the third group, except that here the freezing-point depression for the dilute solutions is nearly three times the normal value, suggesting the possibility that the solute furnishes three particles instead of one molecule.

On looking for some obvious distinction between the substances in the different groups in Table 35–I, one notices that *the solutes that affect the freezing point abnormally are all either acids, bases, or salts.* Note that these are just the classes of compounds whose water solutions will conduct electric current (Article 32–4).

These experiments on the freezing of solutions have suggested some assumptions, or hypotheses, but they have furnished no proofs. The first hypothesis, made because it is simple and plausible, is that substances with a normal effect on the freezing point exist in solution as molecules. The second hypothesis is that substances with an abnormal effect on the freezing point exist in solution as particles that are smaller than molecules. When faced with dubious hypotheses like these, conjured up from meager evidence, the scientist has a standard procedure. He tries to wring from the hypotheses some conclusion, perhaps only a qualitative one, that can be tested by a simple experiment. If the facts are in accord with the conclusion, then the hypotheses are entitled to more respect, and some version of them may be used as the basis for a theory (Article 3–4). Now in this case an easily tested conclusion does suggest itself: If some substances exist in solution as molecules, and other substances exist as some smaller subdivision of matter, then solutions of these two classes may be characterized by different chemical behavior. The next step is to test this conclusion.

35–3. Reactions in Solutions. Some simple experiments show that solutions of acids, bases, and salts actually do behave differently than solutions of other substances.

EXPERIMENTS. (a) Ethyl alcohol (C_2H_5OH) is a hydroxide, but it is not a base. It does not feel soapy or affect litmus. Compare its behavior in solution with that of sodium hydroxide ($NaOH$), which is a base. Sodium hydroxide in solution added to copper sulfate in solution immediately produces a precipitate of copper hydroxide. Adding a solution of ethyl alcohol to one of copper sulfate results in no immediate reaction.

(b) Since ethyl alcohol is not a base, ethyl chloride (C_2H_5Cl) is not a salt, although sodium chloride ($NaCl$) is. Mixing a solution of sodium chloride with one of silver nitrate results in the immediate formation of a nearly insoluble white substance, silver chloride ($AgCl$). There is no discernible reaction, however, when a solution of ethyl chloride * is added to a silver nitrate solution.

The following equations sum up the results of these experiments: †

$$\text{(a)} \begin{cases} 2NaOH + CuSO_4 \rightarrow Cu(OH)_2 \downarrow + Na_2SO_4 \\ C_2H_5OH + CuSO_4 \quad \text{no immediate reaction} \end{cases}$$

$$\text{(b)} \begin{cases} NaCl + AgNO_3 \rightarrow AgCl \downarrow + NaNO_3 \\ C_2H_5Cl + AgNO_3 \quad \text{no immediate reaction} \end{cases}$$

The base in (a) and the sodium salt in (b) are able to enter into reaction with no detectable delay. More experiments of the same kind give the same result: acids, bases, and salts, when in solution, react immediately with other solutions in the same category, if they react at all. A solution of any other substance reacts slowly, if at all. These results bear out the idea that solutions of acids, bases, and salts are fundamentally different from solutions of other substances.

The quick reaction of acids, bases, and salts, when in solution, supports the inference that in these solutions, the solute particles are smaller

* Ethyl chloride is only slightly soluble in water, but the outcome of the experiment is the same if the solution contains alcohol to increase the amount of ethyl chloride that will dissolve.

† The symbol ↓ indicates that the substance preceding is insoluble and precipitates (Article 26–5) as it is formed by the reaction.

than molecules. It seems, for example, that the hydroxide in a solution of sodium hydroxide has much more freedom than it does in a solution of ethyl alcohol. This observation is consistent with the hypothesis that ethyl alcohol goes into solution as whole molecules, whereas sodium hydroxide goes into solution as particles that are smaller than molecules. The indications are that sodium hydroxide breaks up into sodium particles and hydroxide particles. Similar indications come from the colors of solutions.

35–4. Color in Solutions. A very simple kind of experiment gives a valuable clue to the way that salts break up when they go into solution.

EXPERIMENT. The cupric salts $CuCl_2$, $CuCl_2 \cdot 2H_2O$, $CuSO_4$, $CuSO_4 \cdot 5H_2O$, and $Cu(NO_3)_2 \cdot 4H_2O$ are respectively yellow, green, white, blue, and blue. Fiftieth-mole samples of them will all contain the same amount of copper. When dissolved in 100 g of water, these samples make solutions that all have the same blue color.

Potassium dichromate ($K_2Cr_2O_7$) and sodium dichromate ($Na_2Cr_2O_7 \cdot 2H_2O$) are somewhat different in color, but fiftieth-mole samples dissolved in 100 g of water make solutions that are the same yellow-orange in color.

The solutions of copper salts in the experiment resemble one another in two respects—their copper content and their color. It is therefore reasonable to attribute the color to the copper content, and to suppose that in solution the salts break up into copper particles and chloride, nitrate, or sulfate, particles.

Similarly, the yellow-orange color of the second set of solutions can be attributed to dichromate particles.

35–5. The Distinctive Behavior of Electrolytes. Electrolytes are the substances that are insulators when solid, but that conduct electricity when they are dissolved or molten (Article 32–4). Experiment shows that all acids, bases, and salts are electrolytes, whereas other substances are all nonelectrolytes. The substances that show normal and abnormal depression of the freezing point are therefore nonelectrolytes and electrolytes, respectively. Furthermore, it is the electrolytes whose solutions have shown the ability to enter into immediate reaction. Whatever it is about acids, bases, and salts that sets them apart from other substances, it seems to have a threefold aspect. Solutions of these substances conduct electricity, produce abnormal depression of the freezing point, and enter into reaction quickly when there is any reaction at all. The last two properties suggest that these substances, when in solution, break up into particles that are smaller than molecules.

As the introduction to this chapter points out, there is no objection to thinking that solute particles are not molecules. We might indeed suppose that whatever the solute particles are, their nature is the same in all kinds of solution. The experimental facts, however, are in clear conflict with such an assumption. Electrolytes and nonelectrolytes have entirely different behaviors in solution, so we are forced to assume that the dissolved particles are of different sorts in the two cases.

In their nonreactivity in solution and in their effect on the freezing point, nonelectrolytes behave as if the dissolved particles are molecules. Solutions of electrolytes, on the other hand, definitely behave as if these compounds somehow come apart in solution. To account for the conduction of electricity in solutions of electrolytes, all we have to do is assume that the particles in these solutions carry electric charges. At any rate, it seems clear that a better understanding of the questions raised in this chapter can be reached by further study of the conduction of electricity by solutions.

In putting before you the body of evidence and conclusions that comes from a study of solutions, it has seemed best to keep the story as simple as possible. One word of warning is in order. The reasoning given here is relatively easy, and it might seem that any good scientist could acquire the experimental data and draw the conclusion in an afternoon or two. Actually, the job spread over a large part of the nineteenth century. Along with the correct ideas outlined here, many incorrect ones reared their heads. Moreover, the evidence in the case had to be sifted out of an enormous stockpile of experimental data spread throughout the domain of chemistry. The arguments in this chapter are therefore somewhat idealized. Nevertheless, they are true to the nature of scientific thought.

Summary

The concentration of a solution is a measure of the amount of solute in relation to the amount of solvent or the amount of solution. There are several ways of specifying concentration; some of the most convenient ones are based on the mole. A mole of any substance is an amount whose weight in grams is numerically equal to the molecular weight of the substance. The mole is a useful unit because a mole of one substance contains the same number of molecules as a mole of another substance. One useful way of expressing concentration is by stating the number of moles of solute per thousand grams of water. Concentration so measured is called molality.

The freezing point of a solution is the temperature at which ice and the solution are in equilibrium. It is always lower than 0° C, which is the freezing point of pure water. The lowering of the freezing point occurs because the presence of solute particles interferes with the formation of ice crystals.

Experiment shows that 1-molal solutions of many substances all freeze at nearly the same temperature: −1.86° C. This uniform behavior, which is called normal, supports the belief that freezing in these solutions is hampered by solute particles that are molecules. There are many substances, however, whose 1-molal solutions have freezing points lower than −1.86° C. This behavior is called abnormal; it suggests that these 1-molal solutions contain more solute particles than the solutions that behave normally, and that these particles are therefore smaller than molecules.

The substances that affect the freezing point abnormally are the acids, bases, and salts. All such substances, and no others, exhibit the abnormal behavior. The class of substances with abnormal freezing-point depressions is identical with the electrolytes, the substances whose solutions are electric conductors.

Further experiments show that electrolytes in solution can enter into immediate reaction, whereas other substances in solution do not. This fact supports the idea that electrolytes come apart in solution so that the solute particles are not molecules. The colors of solutions also support this idea, since solutions of different salts with a common constituent often have the same color, even when the salts themselves have different colors.

Questions

1. What is a mole? Why is the mole a useful quantity?
2. Define "concentration" of a solution, and state one way to express concentrations.
3. Define "freezing point."
4. Consider a solution at 0° C, and suppose it contains some ice. How does the rate of freezing compare with the rate in pure water at 0° C? What will happen to the ice? How would cooling affect the rate of melting? How would cooling affect the rate of freezing? Is it to be expected that equilibrium between melting and freezing can exist at some temperature below 0° C? What would this temperature be called?
5. How does the existence of a "normal" freezing-point depression indicate that the solute particles in some solutions are molecules? Does it prove that they are molecules?
6. How many moles of water are there in 1000 grams of water? How many moles of solute are there in a 1-molal solution? How many moles of water are there in a 1-molal solution? If the solute particles are molecules, and the water particles are molecules, how does the number of solute molecules in a 1-molal solution compare with the number of water molecules?
7. State three differences between electrolytes and nonelectrolytes.
8. How many grams of sodium hydroxide ($NaOH$) must be dissolved in 100 g of water to make a 0.20-molal solution?

9. Methyl alcohol (CH_3OH) was added to the radiator of a car in the ratio 320 g of alcohol to 1000 g of water. What is the molal concentration of the solution? What is its freezing point?
10. Two aqueous solutions have the same freezing point. One solute is an electrolyte, but the other is not. Which solution is more concentrated? Explain your answer.
11. Suppose that you have tested a given substance and found that it is not an electrolyte. Show how you could determine its molecular weight from the freezing point of a solution.

36

FARADAY'S LAW OF ELECTROLYSIS

Although we know nothing of what an atom is, yet we cannot resist forming some idea of a small particle, which represents it to the mind; and though we are in equal, if not greater, ignorance of electricity . . . yet there is an immensity of facts which justify us in believing that the atoms of matter are in some way endowed or associated with electrical powers, to which they owe their most striking properties, and amongst them their mutual chemical affinity.

FARADAY (1839)

Of the several exceptional properties possessed by solutions of electrolytes, perhaps the most striking is electrical conductivity with an accompanying transport of matter. It is this phenomenon, more than any other, that has made possible an understanding of solutions.

36–1. Ions. When electric charge passes through a solution of copper sulfate, the negative electrode acquires a coat of copper (Article 32–4). How the copper gets there can be seen by using apparatus in which the electrode is separated from the solution of copper salt. The experiment is somewhat more colorful, and also more instructive, if the salt is copper dichromate instead of copper sulfate.

EXPERIMENT. The apparatus in Figure 36–A is a U-tube with platinum electrodes at the top. At the bottom is a green solution of copper dichromate ($CuCr_2O_7$) containing about 5 percent of gelatin. Higher in each arm there is a solution of potassium chloride (KCl) similarly stiffened with gelatin. Still higher, the electrodes dip in little pools of potassium chloride solution. The gelatin keeps the solutions from becoming mixed, and the clear columns of potassium chloride solution provide conducting windows through which to observe the regions near the electrodes. When the electrodes are connected to a battery, electric charge passes through the solutions. A blue coloration slowly moves into the window around the negative electrode, and a yellow one moves into the other window. These colors, blue and yellow, are known from a previous experiment (Article 35–4) to be characteristic of copper particles and dichromate particles in solution.

The experiment shows that the passage of charge through the solutions causes the solute particles to migrate. Since the solute particles are what make the solution a conductor, it is easy to infer that the particles move because they are charged. The motion of these charged particles con-

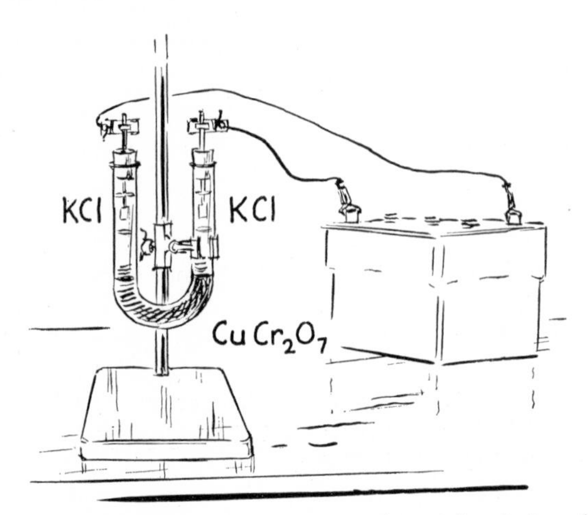

FIGURE 36–A. Experiment on the migration of particles during electrolysis.

stitutes an electric current in the solution. The copper particles, which are attracted to the negative electrode, must be positively charged. The dichromate particles, which go toward the positive electrode, must have negative charge.

MICHAEL FARADAY, whose father was a London blacksmith, put in seven years' apprenticeship to a bookbinder. Having become interested in science by reading books that passed through the bindery, he attended popular lectures on science and performed in his lodgings simple experiments in chemistry and electricity. His scientific career is closely connected with the Royal Institution, which was founded in 1799, under the leadership of Count Rumford, to "teach the application of science to the useful purposes of life." When he was 21, Faraday left bookbinding to become a laboratory assistant at the institution. He rose to be its professor of chemistry.

Aside from matters mentioned in the text, Faraday did noteworthy work on light, sound, alloy steels, lighthouse lamps, and electric eels. He also exerted great influence through his skill as a public lecturer. His success as an industrial consultant brought him fees that amounted to many times his salary, but after a few years of this work, he gave it up completely in order to devote all of his time to science. The decision proved fortunate for industry; not long afterward, he discovered the principles that have made possible the electric dynamo and the electric transformer, which have revolutionized the use of power in factories.

From a painting by Henry William Pickersgill
By courtesy of the Fisher Collection of Alchemical and Historical Pictures

MICHAEL FARADAY
(1791–1867)

Because of their migration in electrolysis, the particles of electrolytes in solution are called *ions*, from a Greek word meaning "to go" or "to travel."

36–2. The Process of Electrolysis. Having recognized the existence and migration of ions, we can form a fairly satisfactory picture of what goes on during electrolysis. When the electrodes are connected to a battery, the resulting charge on the electrodes produces an electric field in the electrolyte. Because of their charge, the ions experience a force in this field, and they begin to migrate toward the electrodes. The positive ions go toward the negative electrode, and the negative ions go the other way. Any ion that reaches an electrode has its charge neutralized there by an opposite charge that comes from the battery. If it is a copper ion, it helps to build up a coating of copper atoms on the electrode. If it is a hydrogen ion, it contributes to the formation of a bubble of hydrogen which eventually grows large enough to break loose and float to the surface of the solution. If it is a radical ion, it decomposes when its charge is neutralized. For example, hydroxide radicals break up to form water and oxygen; the oxygen bubbles to the surface. Metallic ions and hydrogen ions always accumulate on the negative electrode, showing that they have positive charge. On the other hand, nonmetallic ions always exhibit negative charge.

The material deposited by the discharge of an ion in electrolysis is always either an element or the products of decomposition of a radical. The ions are therefore more closely related to atoms and radicals than they are to molecules. From the amount by which various electrolytes depress the freezing point, it seems clear that the maximum number of particles (ions) they can furnish to the solution is equal to the number of atoms or radicals they contain (Table 35–I, p. 288). For example, sodium chloride (NaCl) produces in dilute solution about twice the normal freezing-point depression, implying that it dissolves as two ions instead of one molecule. An ion must therefore be of the same general character as an atom, except that an ion has an electric charge. Consequently, the discharging of one ion at an electrode will deposit one atom or radical there.

36–3. Faraday's Law of Electrolysis (1833). Experiments on electrolysis began shortly after Volta's invention of the electric battery in 1800 (Article 30–3). The early experimenters tried electrolyzing many solutions, and in this way discovered several new elements. Chlorine was one of them; it had been obtained before by other means, but had been considered a compound. This early research in electrolysis culminated in the work of Michael Faraday, one of the great experimenters of all time. Among other things, he studied the amount of material deposited during electrolysis. He found a simple relation, called Faraday's Law of Electrolysis, that has a deep significance. It deals with the electrodeposition of different elements by the passage of a given charge. The law can be stated thus: the same amount of charge will deposit different weights of different elements; the weight deposited is proportional to the atomic weight of the element and is inversely proportional to its valence.*

To see the meaning of this law, consider an experiment that is like some that Faraday did. Imagine five jars containing the solutions designated in Figure 36–B. Let each jar contain a pair of electrodes, and let these be wired together as shown, the end ones going to a battery and switch.

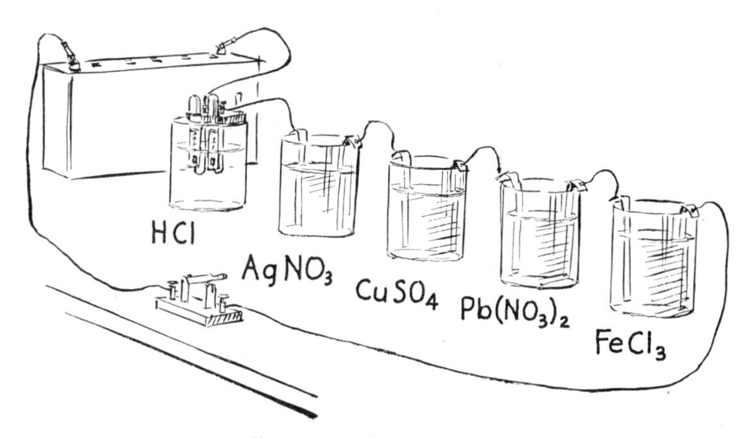

FIGURE 36–B. An illustration of Faraday's Law of Electrolysis.

When all is ready, close the switch. Charge will pass from the positive terminal of the battery into the nearest solution, go through that to the next, and so on around to the negative terminal. The same amount of charge passes through all of the solutions, ferried across on the ions. Let the flow of charge continue until 1.008 g of hydrogen has been liberated from the hydrogen chloride solution. Then find the weight of the chlorine, and of the metals deposited from the solutions in the other jars. The result will be: chlorine, 35.5 g; silver, 107.9 g; copper, 31.8 g; lead, 103.6 g; and iron, 18.6 g.

Arbitrarily, the charge allowed to pass through the solution was just enough for the liberation of 1.008 g of hydrogen, an amount chosen because 1.008 is the atomic weight of hydrogen. As a finding of the experiment, the amount of chlorine liberated was 35.5 g. Now 35.5 is the atomic weight of chlorine. The relative weights of the liberated samples are the same as the relative weights of the liberated atoms, namely,

* If the element can exhibit more than one valence, then the one to be used here is the one the element exhibits in the compound that is used in the electrolysis.

35.5:1.008. Therefore the two liberated samples must contain the same number of atoms. But this implies that the two samples were liberated by the discharge of the same number of ions. The experiment therefore shows that equal numbers of hydrogen and chlorine ions will transport the same charge. The simplest explanation of this astonishing fact is that one hydrogen ion carries the same charge (except for sign) as one chlorine ion.*

The relative weights of silver and hydrogen deposited in the experiment were 107.9:1.008, the same as the ratio of the atomic weights. The preceding line of reasoning leads to the conclusion that a silver ion carries the same charge as a hydrogen ion.

Now consider the bivalent elements, copper and lead. The relative weights of the copper and hydrogen were 31.8:1.008. This ratio is just half the ratio of the atomic weights. It follows that the electrolysis deposited only half as many copper atoms as hydrogen atoms. The inference is that each copper ion carries twice as much charge as a hydrogen ion does. The same argument applies to lead. By the same reasoning, the ferric ions carry three times as much charge as hydrogen ions do.

The account of this experiment has had two purposes. In the first place, it illustrates in some detail the meaning of Faraday's Law of Electrolysis, a law that is firmly based on observable quantities. Secondly, the account shows that the law, taken in conjunction with some plausible assumptions, implies that the charges on different kinds of ions are very simply related. Specifically, it implies that all univalent ions carry the same charge, bivalent ions carry twice as much, and trivalent ions carry three times as much. The simple relation between charge and valence indicates some very fundamental connection between chemical union and electricity.

36–4. A Deduction and a Speculation. The matters discussed in the last article lead to another important conclusion. If all univalent ions have the same charge, and if all other ions have charges that are larger by a multiple of 2, 3, or some other integer, then the charge on ions in electrolytes comes in small indivisible bits. A univalent ion carries one bit, a bivalent ion carries two bits, and so on. No ion carries 3/4 bit or 3/2 bits.

The commonly used scientific term for an indivisible bit is *quantum* (plural *quanta*), a Latin word meaning "how much." Anything that comes in quanta is said to be *quantized.*

* This is not the only possible explanation. It is conceivable that what we observe in electrolysis is only a statistical truth, like those in life-insurance tables, true *on the average* for a large number of events, but not implying that the events are all identical. As usual, we make the simpler assumption and see whether its consequences are consistent with later experiments.

The quantization of charge on ions opens the way to an interesting speculation. Suppose we designate the quantum of electric charge as e, and consider the electrodeposition of some number, n, of univalent atoms by the transport of a given charge Q, then

Charge transported = Charge on each ion × Number of atoms deposited,

or

$$Q = en.$$

Furthermore, if M is the mass deposited and m is the mass of a single atom of the element, then

$$M = mn,$$

because

Mass deposited = Mass of one atom × Number of atoms deposited.

Dividing one equation by the other gives

$$\frac{Q}{M} = \frac{en}{mn}; \quad \text{hence,} \quad \frac{Q}{M} = \frac{e}{m}.$$

In words,

$$\frac{\text{Charge transported}}{\text{Mass deposited}} = \frac{\text{Charge on each ion}}{\text{Mass of one atom}}.$$

Now we can measure Q by measuring the current and the time during which it passes, and we can measure M by weighing (Article 8–1). Hence, we can find e/m, although we cannot as yet find e or m separately. If, however, we could somehow measure e, the quantum of charge, we could then calculate m, the actual mass of an individual atom.

Summary

In solutions of electrolytes, electric current is a motion of charges that reside on the solute particles. Faraday named these charged particles "ions." Freezing-point data indicate that except for their charge, ions are of the same general character as atoms or, in some cases, radicals. Metallic ions migrate to the negative electrode; they must therefore have positive charge. Nonmetallic ions migrate in the opposite direction, showing that they have negative charge. When an ion reaches an electrode, its charge is neutralized by the charge on the electrode. When they lose their charge, radical ions decompose and other ions turn into atoms.

Faraday's Law of Electrolysis states that the same amount of charge will deposit different weights of different elements, the weight deposited being proportional to the atomic weight of the element and inversely proportional to its valence. The law rests directly on experiment. In conjunction with some plausible assumptions about ions, the law implies that univalent ions all carry the same charge, that bivalent ions carry twice this charge, and so on for larger valences. The law therefore suggests that the charge on ions is quantized.

Because it links charge, atomic weight, and valence, Faraday's Law shows that there is a connection between chemistry and electricity.

Questions

1. Describe the passage of electric charge through a solution of an electrolyte.
2. What evidence shows that metallic ions have positive charge?
3. How could you coat a copper ornament with silver?
4. State Faraday's Law of Electrolysis.
5. Illustrate the meaning of Faraday's Law of Electrolysis.
6. Suppose the same amount of charge passed through several solutions of electrolytes and liberated 16 g of oxygen from one of them. Assuming that the proper solutions were used, find what weight of each of the following elements would be deposited: iodine, zinc, trivalent chromium.
7. In an experiment on the electrolysis of molten $ZnCl_2$, the amount of chlorine liberated was 3.55 g. How much zinc was deposited on the negative electrode?
8. Compare the weights of metal that would be deposited by passing the same charge through solutions of ferrous sulfate and ferric sulfate.
9. What experiment would you do to determine the sign of the charge carried by a specified kind of ion?
10. How can one tell that the solute particles of nonelectrolytes are not charged?
11. In electrolysis, what is the relation between valence and charge? Why is this relation of interest?
12. Justify the conclusion that electric charge on ions in electrolytes is quantized.
13. Give the argument for believing that all univalent ions carry the same charge.
14. If it is true that each ion of copper in a solution has the same charge, what relation would you expect to find between the current in an electrolysis experiment and the rate at which copper is deposited on the positive electrode? Devise an experiment that would test your conclusion. What apparatus would you need?

> Of all electrical phenomena electrolysis appears the most likely to furnish us with a real insight into the true nature of the electric current, because we find currents of ordinary matter and currents of electricity forming essential parts of the same phenomenon.
>
> MAXWELL (1873)

37

THE ARRHENIUS THEORY

The two preceding chapters discuss some of the facts about solutions that became known during the nineteenth century. They present the topics in an order that makes for easy understanding, but this order is not a chronological one. Although electrolysis and the freezing of solutions began to be studied about the same time (1800), the quantitative regularities were formulated for freezing-point depressions (Raoult, 1883) almost fifty years later than for electrolysis (Faraday, 1834). Faraday, with his great insight, interpreted his Law of Electrolysis to mean that the charge on ions is quantized. At that time, however, the whole atomic theory of chemistry was in the doghouse, because the distinction between atoms and molecules had not yet been made clear by the acceptance of Avogadro's hypothesis (Articles 21–2, 21–4). Arguments about the nature of solute particles were therefore highly speculative.

Later in the century the whole outlook was different. In the hands of Joule and others, the dynamical theory of gases (Article 17–3) had made it reasonably certain that matter does consist of small particles. Furthermore, the acceptance of Avogadro's hypothesis, about 1860, had cleared away the difficulties that had been caused by confusing molecules with atoms. By 1880 the dynamical theory of gases had been worked out in great detail. The thought occurred to a few scientists that the theory of gases might be applicable to solutions. In a gas, the molecules fly about in space, colliding with the containing vessel and with one another. In a solution, the solute particles may also fly about independently, making collisions with the containing vessel, with the surface of the solution, with the solvent particles, and with one another. The dynamical theory of gases, by then a precise and familiar tool, should clearly be tried on solutions. Hence the experiments with molal mixtures (1883) and the discovery of the freezing-point regularities that appear in Table 35–I.

37–1. The Arrhenius Theory. The dovetailing of facts and inferences in the two past chapters shows how the science of solutions stood in about

1885. The subject was in the forefront of chemical and physical research, because it gave clear promise of unveiling the nature of electricity and the nature of matter, as well as the nature of chemical union. A theory that seemed to correlate all of the known facts was put forward by a young Swedish chemist, Svante Arrhenius. His hypotheses are as follows:

1. Electrolytes (acids, bases, and salts), when dissolved in water, in part break up into charged particles smaller than molecules. The particles are called "ions," and the breaking up is called "electrolytic dissociation."
2. There exists an equilibrium between the electrolyte molecules and the ions; dilution favors the formation of more ions.
3. The ions move independently of one another and independently of the other particles present.

The first of these hypotheses simply formulates an idea that has already been expressed in our previous discussion. Each of the others deserves a word of comment.

The equilibrium proposed in the second hypothesis is easy to imagine. It demands that there be two opposing processes taking place continually: a separation of molecules into ions, and a coming together of ions to form molecules. For some degree of dissociation, these two processes will occur at equal rates; in other words, they will be in equilibrium. It is

---

SVANTE ARRHENIUS grew up in Uppsala and attended the university there. Embarking on a doctoral research in physics at the time when science was just beginning to make headway in the study of solutions, he sought a means of finding the molecular weight of a solute from the electrical conductivity of a solution. The work led him to the hypothesis of dissociation in electrolytes, which he used in 1884 as the basis of his doctor's thesis. Perhaps because he was working on the border which at that time separated chemistry and physics, the thesis did not receive a high enough grade to admit him to teaching status at the university. Some of the leading German scientists, however, recognized its worth, and he spent most of the next five years in Germany, working with chemists and physicists there, supported by his private income. Later, he held in turn a professorship of physics at Stockholm and the directorship of the Nobel Institute of Physical Chemistry, which was set up for the purpose of keeping him in Sweden.

Arrhenius' work embraced all of the physical sciences. Aside from studies that refined or exploited his theory of dissociation in solutions, he worked on electric conduction in flames and hot gases, on the velocity of reactions in nonelectrolytes, on volcanoes, on hydroelectric installations, on serum therapy, on various aspects of meteorology, and on astrophysics. He was active not only as a research scientist but as teacher, university administrator, government commissioner, corporation director, and author of popular books about the current state of science.

By courtesy of the Akademische Verlagsgesellschaft

SVANTE ARRHENIUS
(1859–1927)

entirely reasonable that dilution should favor the formation of more ions, because the presence of more solvent particles will hinder ions from finding mates, but will not affect the rate of dissociation. In order for the rate of recombination to equal the rate of dissociation, the number of ions must therefore become larger when the solution is diluted.

The third hypothesis, that the ions move as independent particles, made it possible to use the dynamical theory of gases to calculate the effect that the ions have on the freezing point and on other properties of the solution.

Arrhenius was not the first to suggest any of these hypotheses, but he made an important contribution by showing that, when taken together, these hypotheses provide a base on which to construct a fairly successful theory of electrolytes. We can examine the most important consequences of the theory.

37–2. The Degree of Dissociation. The solutes in Table 35–I (page 288) fall into three groups. The first, the nonelectrolytes, all depress the freezing point of a 1-molal solution by about the same amount. The electrolytes in the second group do not all produce the same freezing-point depression in 1-molal solutions, but they do in more dilute solutions. The same is true of the electrolytes in the third group. Arrhenius' postulate about equilibrium between molecules and ions accounts for these facts with some success. In very dilute solution, silver nitrate produces about twice the normal freezing-point depression. On Arrhenius' theory, this behavior means that each molecule of the silver nitrate has furnished two ions to the solution, Ag^+ and NO_3^-. The 1-molal solution contains a hundred times as much silver nitrate as the 0.01-molal solution, but the freezing-point depression is not a hundred times as great. According to the theory, this shows that not all of the silver nitrate is dissociated. It is easy to calculate what fraction of the silver nitrate must be dissociated in a 1-molal solution in order to produce the observed depression of 2.63 Centigrade degrees. (The answer is a little over 40 percent.) Arrhenius compared the degree of dissociation deduced from freezing-point data with the degree of dissociation deduced in the same way from the electrical conductivities of dilute and less dilute solutions. He found that the two kinds of measurements give nearly the same result for the degree of dissociation.

It is now time to confess that the substances listed in Table 35–I were chosen with some bias. Not all electrolytes fall so obviously into the second or third groups in the table. Acetic acid ($HC_2H_3O_2$) is an example. It causes a freezing-point depression of 1.79 Centigrade degrees in 1-molal solution and 0.190 degree in 0.1-molal solution; yet it is an electrolyte.

Experiment. If the conductivity of pure acetic acid is tested with the apparatus in Figure 32–J, the lamp does not light. Adding a little water makes the lamp glow dimly. Acetic acid is therefore an electrolyte. Successive dilutions make the lamp glow brighter and brighter.

The experiment gives a clue to why acetic acid, in 1-molal or 0.1-molal solution, produces practically a normal freezing-point depression. These solutions are poor conductors. Interpreted in terms of Arrhenius' theory, the near-normal depression and poor conductivity indicate a low degree of dissociation. Arrhenius calculated that in 1-molal solution, only about one acetic acid molecule out of a hundred is dissociated. At greater dilutions, there is more dissociation, as manifested by the increased brightness of the lamp.

Substances that show a low degree of dissociation, except in very dilute solutions, are called *weak electrolytes.* Acetic acid is a typical example. Substances that show a high degree of dissociation in 1-molal or 0.1-molal solutions are called *strong electrolytes.* With very few exceptions, salts are strong electrolytes. Most acids and bases are weak electrolytes; notable exceptions are HCl, HNO_3, H_2SO_4, NaOH, KOH, and $Ca(OH)_2$. These exceptional acids and bases are called "strong"; they were recognized as exceptional long before Arrhenius' time, because they are chemically so active.

Experiment. If the last experiment is repeated with hydrochloric acid in place of the acetic acid, the lamp glows brightly even when the acid is very concentrated. This fact shows that HCl is a strong electrolyte.

Arrhenius' theory successfully correlates the conductivity and the freezing-point depression of weak electrolytes. If these substances had been included in Table 35–I, they would have made the message of the table much harder to decipher. Of course, Arrhenius and his predecessors had nobody to censor the facts of nature for them by culling out a collection like Table 35–I. Arrhenius' accomplishment lay largely in seeing that the varied behavior of electrolytes can be explained fairly well by postulating different degrees of dissociation.

37–3. A Critique of the Arrhenius Theory. There are some things about the Arrhenius theory that are not very satisfactory. One of them appears plainly in Table 35–I. In 1-molal solution, most of the substances in the second group produce freezing-point depressions that are a little less than twice the normal one. The theory attributes this behavior to incomplete dissociation. This is fine, but a few substances show *more* than twice the normal depression. Surely, the dissociation cannot be more than complete.

Another trouble is that, although the degree of dissociation comes out *nearly* the same when calculated from the conductivity or the freezing point (page 306), nevertheless it does not come out exactly the same. The discrepancy is worse for high concentrations.

These shortcomings of an otherwise serviceable theory suggest that the hypotheses may be oversimplifications. One of them is particularly open to question. Arrhenius assumed that the ions move independently of one another. Since the ions are charged, however, they certainly will affect one another when they are close together. The situation is reminiscent of the dynamical theory of gases (Article 17–3). There, the simple theory assumed that the particles did not influence one another, and the result agreed with experiment when the pressure was not too high. For higher pressures, the influence of the particles on one another had to be taken into account. The ions in a solution resemble the molecules in a gas, with the difference that the ions are charged so that they affect one another even when they are not in contact. The failure of the original Arrhenius theory at high concentrations is very much like the failure of Boyle's Law at high pressures.

Although later work has led to some revisions of Arrhenius' hypotheses, the structure of the theory is essentially sound. The rest of this chapter will describe some of the successes of the original theory.

37–4. Dissociation. The ions in a solution can often be identified by noting what collects at the electrodes when the solution undergoes electrolysis. Radical ions decompose when they are discharged at the electrode, but their presence can be inferred from the products of the decomposition. In solutions of salts, the ions are those of the elements or radicals that form the salt (Article 26–5). The symbol for an ion is that of the element to which it is related, with a set of signs to represent its charge. The signs are + or − according to the kind of charge, and their number is equal to the valence of the ion. Each sign therefore represents one quantum of charge. The following dissociations are representative:

$$KBr \rightleftharpoons K^{+} + Br^{-}$$

$$K_2SO_4 \rightleftharpoons 2K^{+} + SO_4^{--}$$

$$K_3PO_4 \rightleftharpoons 3K^{+} + PO_4^{---}$$

$$CuCl_2 \rightleftharpoons Cu^{++} + 2Cl^{-}$$

$$AlCl_3 \rightleftharpoons Al^{+++} + 3Cl^{-}$$

$$MgSO_4 \rightleftharpoons Mg^{++} + SO_4^{--}$$

$$Al_2(SO_4)_3 \rightleftharpoons 2Al^{+++} + 3SO_4^{--}$$

The sign $\rightleftharpoons$ indicates that dissociation into ions and recombination into molecules are going on at the same time, in accord with Arrhenius' hypothesis of equilibrium.

Notice that when a compound breaks up into ions, the total charge on the ions is zero, because the nonmetallic valences always balance the metallic ones. Therefore, a solution of an electrolyte does not exhibit any net charge.

37–5. Acids and Bases. The common constituent of all acids is hydrogen (Articles 26–2, 26–3), and acids differ from other hydrogen compounds in that the hydrogen in acids very readily enters into reactions. Examples of these reactions are the replacement of hydrogen by metals (Articles 27–2, 27–6) and the neutralization of an acid by a base to form water and a salt (Articles 26–4, 26–5). Moreover, acids are electrolytes, and in their electrolysis hydrogen is deposited at the negative electrode. Taken together and interpreted in terms of the Arrhenius theory, these facts point clearly to the distinction between acids and other hydrogen compounds: An acid is a hydrogen compound that furnishes hydrogen ions when dissolved in water.

By the same sort of reasoning, the Arrhenius theory distinguishes a base as a hydroxide that, when in solution, furnishes hydroxide ions. A few examples will show how these conceptions clarify the similarities of acids to one another, and of bases to one another.

$$HCl \rightleftharpoons H^+ + Cl^- \qquad NaOH \rightleftharpoons Na^+ + OH^-$$
$$H_2SO_4 \rightleftharpoons 2H^+ + SO_4^{--} \qquad Ca(OH)_2 \rightleftharpoons Ca^{++} + 2OH^-$$
$$HC_2H_3O_2 \rightleftharpoons H^+ + C_2H_3O_2^- \qquad NH_4OH \rightleftharpoons NH_4^+ + OH^-$$

Notice that acetic acid, $HC_2H_3O_2$, contains some hydrogen that forms an ion and readily enters into reaction, and also some hydrogen that does not itself form an ion but is part of the acetate radical. In this acid, as in many that are not so widely known, some of the hydrogen contributes to the acid character of the compound and some does not. One step further away are the hydrogen compounds that are not acids at all.

37–6. Water. The Arrhenius theory leads to some important conclusions about water. Although pure water is an extremely poor conductor of electricity, it does conduct to some extent. It must therefore be classed as an electrolyte, but its poor showing as a conductor proves that the water particles are nearly all molecules.*

A few simple chemical observations enable us to identify the ions that are formed when water dissociates. For instance, a water solution of

* At room temperature and with the same electrical arrangements, the electric current through pure water is less than a millionth as large as the current through a saturated solution of sodium chloride. By comparing the electric conduction in pure water with that in solutions in which the concentration of ions is known, it has been determined that, at room temperature, only one water molecule in over 500 million is dissociated into ions.

sodium acetate ($NaC_2H_3O_2$) turns litmus from pink to blue and behaves in other respects like a solution of a base. We can explain this behavior by assuming that hydroxide ions are present, as a result of the dissociation of water. That is, we assume that the dissociation of water takes the form

$$H_2O \leftharpoondown\!\!\!\rightharpoonup H^+ + OH^-,$$

where the short arrow points to the less numerous particles.

Sodium acetate, being a salt, has a high degree of dissociation when dissolved in water:

$$NaC_2H_3O_2 \rightleftharpoons Na^+ + C_2H_3O_2^-.$$

The solution therefore contains the ions H^+ and $C_2H_3O_2^-$; because acetic acid is a weak acid, these ions have a strong tendency to combine and form molecules:

$$H^+ + C_2H_3O_2^- \rightleftharpoons HC_2H_3O_2.$$

This formation of acetic acid molecules removes H^+ ions from the solution. To restore the equilibrium described by the first equation, more water ionizes. In equilibrium, therefore, the solution contains more OH^- ions than were present in the water before the sodium acetate dissolved in it.

Solutions of some salts turn litmus from blue to pink, taste sour, and otherwise behave like solutions of acids. This behavior is caused by the hydrogen ions formed by dissociation of the water. The dissociation is enhanced by the presence of the salt. Ammonium chloride is one salt that will produce this effect. The water and the salt dissociate:

$$H_2O \leftharpoondown\!\!\!\rightharpoonup H^+ + OH^- \qquad NH_4Cl \rightleftharpoons NH_4^+ + Cl^-.$$

Ammonium ions combine with hydroxide ions to form ammonia and water:

$$NH_4^+ + OH^- \rightleftharpoons NH_3 + H_2O.$$

This removal of OH^- ions from the solution affects the equilibrium of the water with its ions, and more water dissociates. In the final equilibrium, there is a considerable population of H^+ ions, and the solution therefore has acid properties.

The reaction of the ions of a salt with the ions of water is called "hydrolysis"; such a reaction occurs if its products remove hydrogen ions or hydroxide ions by incorporating them into molecules.

Pure water dissociates so little that it does not noticeably exhibit the behavior of an acid or of a base. Since water contains both hydrogen ions and hydroxide ions, however, the Arrhenius theory demands that water be regarded as being both an acid and a base. This view of water, which can be brought to the fore by writing water's formula as HOH, is a distinct improvement in classification. For example, it brings under a single heading the reactions (Chapter 27) in which a metal replaces hydrogen in water or in some stronger acid:

$$Ca + 2HOH \rightarrow H_2 + Ca(OH)_2$$
$$Ca + 2HCl \rightarrow H_2 + CaCl_2.$$

37–7. Reactions in Solution. The Arrhenius theory explains why it is that electrolytes in solution react so quickly. As an example, consider solutions of sodium chloride and silver nitrate. When these solutions are mixed, silver chloride precipitates immediately. In conventional symbols, the equation for the reaction is:

$$AgNO_3 + NaCl \rightarrow AgCl \downarrow + NaNO_3.$$

In the light of Arrhenius' theory, this equation can be replaced by one that attributes the reaction to ions:

$$Ag^+ + NO_3^- + Na^+ + Cl^- \rightarrow AgCl \downarrow + Na^+ + NO_3^-.$$

The silver chloride contributes a negligible number of ions to the solution, because it is nearly insoluble in water.

Notice that Na^+ and NO_3^- appear on both sides of the last equation. They take no part in the reaction, which is simply the union of the Ag^+ and Cl^- to form AgCl:

$$Ag^+ + Cl^- \rightarrow AgCl \downarrow.$$

Since any soluble silver salt will furnish silver ions, and any soluble chloride will furnish chloride ions, silver chloride can be made from a variety of starting materials. Whatever the starting materials, the ionic reaction that forms the silver chloride is always the same. The reaction occurs swiftly because the particles that enter into it do not have to become disengaged from any partners; their earlier partnership ended when the materials went into solution, and the ions are free to react as soon as they come into contact with suitable new partners.

It is now possible to state conditions under which electrolytes in solution will react. Notice that the formation of silver chloride removes ions from the solution, because the silver chloride is insoluble. By contrast, consider the problem of making potassium nitrate (saltpeter). Although this substance occurs in nature, its widespread use * has created a need to make it from other raw materials that are more plentiful. Suitable materials are sodium nitrate and potassium chloride, both of which exist in large natural deposits. When mixed together in dry form, they do not

* Saltpeter is an ingredient of black gunpowder. It is also used for preserving meat.

react. When in solution, both of them are almost completely ionized. Suppose these solutions are mixed. In ionic form, the result will be:

$$(K^+ + Cl^-) + (Na^+ + NO_3^-) \rightarrow K^+ + Cl^- + Na^+ + NO_3^-.$$

All that happens is that the resulting solution contains four kinds of ions. It would be improper to say that any reaction has occurred. Nevertheless, a reaction can be made to occur, by an instructive trick.

It happens that of the four salts, KCl, $NaNO_3$, NaCl, and KNO_3, the desired KNO_3 is the least soluble in cold water (Figure 34–C). Therefore, if the solution is cooled below about 20° C and part of the water allowed to evaporate, some potassium nitrate will crystallize out of the solution. The crystals will eventually be in equilibrium with the K^+ and NO_3^- ions in the solution:

$$K^+ + Cl^- + Na^+ + NO_3^- \rightleftharpoons KNO_3 + Na^+ + Cl^-.$$

Further cooling will produce further crystallization, during which the population of K^+ and NO_3^- ions will be correspondingly reduced.

The foregoing situation is clearly a highly special one, but it teaches a very general lesson: reactions between electrolytes in solution occur when the reaction removes ions from the solution. The two most common situations that remove ions are:

1. The formation of a compound that is insoluble, or only slightly soluble.
2. The formation of a compound that is not much dissociated.

The formation of silver chloride (page 311) is an example of the first situation, and the formation of any weak electrolyte is an example of the second. For instance, the addition of hydrochloric acid to a solution of sodium acetate will produce acetic acid, which is a weak electrolyte:

$$(Na^+ + C_2H_3O_2^-) + (H^+ + Cl^-) \rightarrow HC_2H_3O_2 + Na^+ + Cl^-.$$

Any neutralization reaction depends on the formation of a substance that is not much dissociated, namely water:

$$(H^+ + NO_3^-) + (Na^+ + OH^-) \rightarrow H_2O + Na^+ + NO_3^-.$$

Summary

The Arrhenius theory correlated many of the facts about electrolytes. The theory rests on the assumptions that when an electrolyte is in solution, some of it dissociates into ions that move about independently, and that there is an equilibrium between the ions and the undissociated molecules, such that dilution favors dissociation. The principal tenet of the theory is that when electrolytes dissolve in water, the solute is partly or entirely dissociated into ions. Substances that dissociate to a great extent are called strong electrolytes; those that dissociate but slightly, except in very dilute solution, are called weak electrolytes.

This theory not only accounts in an approximate way for the observed electrical conductivities and the observed freezing-point depressions, but also it explains much of the chemical behavior of acids, bases, and salts. It characterizes acids as those hydrogen compounds that furnish H^+ ions to a solution, and bases as those hydroxides that furnish OH^- ions. Dissociation explains why electrolytes in solution react very quickly, if they react at all. The theory also makes clear the condition under which reaction in solution will occur. A reaction occurs if it removes ions from a solution; the removal commonly occurs through the formation of a compound that is nearly insoluble or one that, though soluble, is not much dissociated.

These successes make the Arrhenius theory a useful one, even though it fails quantitatively when the concentration of ions is high enough so that the ions do not move independently.

Questions

1. What is electrolytic dissociation?
2. Distinguish between weak and strong electrolytes. To which class do most salts belong? To which class do most acids belong?
3. State Arrhenius' hypotheses about electrolytes.
4. What limits the success of the Arrhenius theory when it is applied to strong electrolytes?
5. Why does the Arrhenius theory apply better to dilute solutions than to concentrated ones?
6. Describe briefly how Arrhenius' hypotheses account for the distinctive properties of electrolytes in solution.
7. Show how Arrhenius' theory accounts for the facts described by Faraday's Law of Electrolysis.
8. Why is it possible to use a concentrated solution of boric acid (H_3BO_3) as an eyewash, although even very dilute sulfuric acid would cause serious damage if it were so used?
9. In the early days of electrolysis, it was commonly believed that solutions of electrolytes contained only a few ions, but that the supply of ions was replenished by dissociation as fast as they were removed by the electric field. State an experimental fact that conflicts with this assumption, and revise the assumption to fit the fact.
10. In terms of the Arrhenius theory, what differentiates acids from other substances?
11. What do the terms "strong" and "weak" mean when they are applied to acids and bases? Give examples.

12. Write an equation to describe the dissociation of each of the following compounds when in solution: $NaCl$, $ZnSO_4$, Na_2CO_3, $Pb(NO_3)_2$, and $Cr_2(SO_4)_3$.
13. State a condition under which the mixing of solutions of two electrolytes will give rise to a reaction.
14. Write the ionic equation for the reaction of a soluble copper salt with a base, to form cupric hydroxide.
15. Show that the ionic reaction for neutralization is always the same, no matter what acid and base react.
16. How does dilution favor dissociation?
17. When mixed with a solution of any sulfate, a solution of barium chloride always reacts to form barium sulfate. What can you conclude about the solubility of barium sulfate? Do you see a way in which this reaction can be useful in the chemical laboratory?

GENERAL VIEW OF SECTION VI

The evidence shows that a solution is in some ways much like a gas. In this analogy, the solvent particles take the place of empty space, and the solute particles play the role of gas molecules.

Experimental study of solutions brings to light a number of differences between solutions of electrolytes and nonelectrolytes. Solutions of electrolytes conduct electricity; they also enter into chemical reactions very quickly, and they depress the freezing point abnormally. Moreover, the color of a solution of an electrolyte is characteristic of the constituents of the solute. Nonelectrolytes have none of these properties. The behavior of electrolytes in solution implies that these solutions contain particles smaller than molecules. The particles, called ions, in some cases resemble atoms, except that ions have electric charge. In other cases, the ions are charge-bearing radicals. The Arrhenius theory accounts for the observed behavior of electrolytes in solution, provided the ion population is not too dense.

Faraday's Law of Electrolysis strongly suggests that the electric charge on ions is quantized, univalent ions carrying one quantum; bivalent ions, two quanta; and so on. This situation, which relates valence and charge, puts electricity at the very heart of chemistry. The study of solutions was therefore one of the most significant steps in the merging of chemistry and physics.

VII

The Classification of the Elements

Classification is one of the first steps in the application of science to any domain of nature. After recognizing a distinction between metals and nonmetals, therefore, chemists tried as a matter of course to achieve a more detailed classification of the elements. The first step was the grouping together of elements into small families whose members showed a noteworthy amount of chemical similarity. Eventually, Mendeléeff, a Russian chemist, saw how to lay out all of the known elements in a two-dimensional table that groups similar elements together and helps to give order to their similarities and their differences.

38

THE HALOGENS

After classifying the elements into the two categories metal and nonmetal, it is natural to look for subdivisions of these categories. Are some metals more closely similar to one another than to the other metals? Do some nonmetals have characteristics that set them off from other nonmetals? These questions form the basis for that systematizing which is so necessary for the advance of any science. Both of them have affirmative answers. There are small families of elements that have chemical properties not shared by other families. This chapter will give a somewhat detailed account of one such family called the *halogens*. The discussion will clarify, by example, the meaning of "family."

38–1. The Halogens. The halogens are fluorine, chlorine, bromine, and iodine. Within a few years of their being recognized as elements, it became clear that they strongly resemble one another in their general chemical properties. They are all nonmetals with a valence of 1. Their sodium compounds, NaF, NaCl, NaBr, and NaI, called the "sodium halides," all have the same crystal form and appearance. The halogens combine with hydrogen to form the "hydrogen halides," which are all acids. HCl, HBr, and HI are strong acids, but HF is not. This difference in the acids is typical of the fact that fluorine, although definitely a member of the halogen family, departs a little from the behavior of the other members of the family. Because the chemical kinship of the halogens manifests itself in their compounds more clearly than in the elements themselves, we shall consider some of the compounds first and then discuss the elemental substances. When fluorine cannot be included in a remark about the other halogens, the fact will simply be noted; later the exceptional aspects of fluorine compounds will get separate description.

The halogens are chemically so active that they do not exist in nature as uncombined elements. Science and industry get their halogens mainly from natural salts. Because chlorine, bromine, and iodine compounds are for the most part soluble in water, they occur chiefly in the sea and in or

International Salt Co.

FIGURE 38–A. The interior of a salt mine, showing an electric shovel and many tons of broken salt.

near salt lakes. They also occur, however, in important underground deposits. The mine in Figure 38–A exploits a mass of nearly pure sodium chloride.

38–2. The Hydrogen Halides. The chemical similarity of the halogens is illustrated by the similarity of the compounds they form with hydrogen. At room temperature, the hydrogen halides are all gases, soluble in water. They may be prepared by letting a properly chosen acid act on a halide.

EXPERIMENT. When concentrated phosphoric acid is poured over about 5 g of sodium chloride in a test tube, slight heating will produce a reaction that has a gaseous product. The reaction is *

$$2NaCl + H_3PO_4 \rightarrow 2HCl \uparrow + Na_2HPO_4.$$

A similar reaction ensues when sodium or potassium bromide or iodide is used instead of sodium chloride:

$$2NaBr + H_3PO_4 \rightarrow 2HBr \uparrow + Na_2HPO_4$$

$$2KI + H_3PO_4 \rightarrow 2HI \uparrow + K_2HPO_4.$$

* The symbol $\uparrow$ in the equation indicates that the substance preceding it is gaseous, and that the gas leaves the scene of the reaction.

These three hydrogen halides all show the following behavior:

1. Blowing across the mouth of the test tube causes the gas to fume, because the gas dissolves in the moisture of the breath and makes fine droplets.
2. Moist blue litmus paper turns red when held in the gas, showing that a water solution of the gas is acidic.
3. If the stopper from a concentrated solution of ammonia is held in the gas, white clouds appear. The clouds are small particles of the ammonium halide. For example,

$$NH_3 + HCl \rightarrow NH_4Cl.$$

By their similar responses to these three tests, the hydrogen halides demonstrate the chemical similarity of the halogens.

The acids formed when the hydrogen halides dissolve in water are called hydrofluoric, hydrochloric, hydrobromic, and hydroiodic acids. The first will be mentioned again in the article on fluorine compounds (page 323), and the last two have few important uses. Hydrochloric acid, however, is important in many ways. A great quantity of it is used in the steel industry to remove the oxide layer that forms on the steel that is rolled into sheets while hot. Hydrochloric acid plays an important part in the manufacture of glue from horns and hooves, and in the manufacture of "corn syrup" from starch. It is a constituent of the gastric juices in the human stomach.

The halogens form oxyacids as well as hydracids, but the oxyacids have no particular interest for us.

38-3. The Silver Halides. The family resemblance of the halogens appears very strikingly in the silver halides. Since (except for the fluoride) they are nearly insoluble in water, they can be prepared by mixing solutions of a soluble halide and a soluble salt of silver.

Experiment. When a solution of silver nitrate is added to solutions of sodium chloride, sodium bromide, or sodium iodide, the silver halide precipitates. The precipitates resemble one another, except that the chloride is white, the bromide is pale yellow, and the iodide is a stronger yellow.

If a portion of each precipitate formed in the experiment is placed in sunlight, it will turn dark. This unusual property of the silver halides forms the basis of photography (Article 66-1).

38-4. The Uncombined Halogens. The similarity of the halogens is a similarity in their chemical behavior and in the properties of their compounds. The uncombined elements have no physical resemblance except that they are all nonmetals. At room temperature, two are gases, one a liquid, and one a solid.

Fluorine, one of the gases, has the distinction of being the most active of all the nonmetals. Even such an inactive metal as silver, if warmed a little, will ignite and burn when put in fluorine. The element can be obtained by electrolysis of any molten fluoride.

Chlorine is a greenish-yellow gas that is obtained on an industrial scale by electrolyzing a solution of sodium chloride. It is used for bleaching textiles and paper, and for other industrial processes.

Bromine at room temperature is a dark-red liquid that gives off a disagreeable and poisonous red vapor.

Iodine is a black crystalline solid; dissolved in alcohol, it has been widely used as an antiseptic.

Fluorine is too active to be easily prepared, but the other halogens are readily evolved when a gram or two of their hydracid is heated in a large test tube with about the same quantity of manganese dioxide. (They are all somewhat poisonous; the reaction should be stopped with cold water as soon as the yield is sufficient.) The reactions are of the form

$$MnO_2 + 4HBr \rightarrow MnBr_2 + 2H_2O + Br_2.$$

The variety and violence of the reactions that the elemental halogens can take part in are illustrated by the following examples:

(a) *Reaction With Metals.* If a strip of copper is heated and thrust into a tall glass cylinder containing a liter or two of chlorine, the metal glows as it reacts exothermically with the chlorine. Drops of molten copper chloride fall to the bottom of the cylinder; when dissolved in water, they produce the blue color that is characteristic of copper ions.

A hot piece of iron picture wire, thrust into a similar jar of chlorine, will glow and give off clouds of reddish-brown smoke, $FeCl_3$.

Powdered antimony, even when cold, will ignite with a shower of sparks when it is thrown into a jar of chlorine, forming antimony trichloride.

(b) *Reaction With Nonmetals.* All of the halogens combine directly with many of the nonmetals. Fluorine, chlorine, and bromine enter into these reactions too exothermically for safe trial with simple equipment. Iodine reacts less violently. If a piece of white phosphorus the size of a pea is covered with pulverized iodine, the whole being on a thick asbestos mat, the two elements react with very satisfying vigor. The resulting cloud contains phosphorus triiodide, phosphorus pentoxide, and iodine vapor. (White phosphorus is inflammable and very poisonous. Handle it only as directed by laboratory manuals.)

(c) *Reaction With Hydrogen.* A burning jet of hydrogen continues to burn when immersed in chlorine, the flame then being whitish instead of nearly colorless. See also the experiment in Article 27–5.

(d) *Reaction With Compounds.* The halogens react not only with many elements, but also with many compounds. The variety of such reactions is in fact enormous; a single example will suffice to call attention to the possibilities.

If a scrap of cloth soaked in turpentine ($C_{10}H_{16}$) is put in a tall glass jar of chlorine, the chlorine will react with the turpentine. Soon there will be a burst of flame and copious clouds of black smoke, which is carbon. The chlorine combines with the hydrogen of the turpentine and sets the carbon free.

38-5. Fluorine Compounds. Uncombined fluorine behaves chemically very much as the other halogens do, except that fluorine reacts more violently. Fluorine compounds, however, do not act quite like the corresponding compounds of other halogens. For example, the fluorine compounds that occur in nature are not very soluble in water; therefore no great amount of fluorine is found in the sea. The chief source of fluorine for industry is the mineral called fluorspar or fluorite, which is natural calcium fluoride (CaF_2).

In the discussion of the hydrohalic acids (page 321), hydrofluoric acid was left out because it differs from the others in several respects. The most striking difference is that hydrofluoric acid reacts with glass.

EXPERIMENT. Hydrogen fluoride can be made by putting perhaps 10 g of concentrated sulfuric acid on a similar quantity of calcium fluoride in a lead dish. The reaction is *

$$CaF_2 + H_2SO_4 \rightarrow 2HF \uparrow + CaSO_4.$$

The dish can be covered immediately with a sheet of paraffin-coated glass on which a design has been scratched, so that parts of the glass are exposed to the hydrogen fluoride. After exposure for an hour or so, washing off the paraffin with hot water will reveal that the gas has etched the design on the glass. Glass consists mainly of calcium and sodium silicates and silicon dioxide. Hydrogen fluoride reacts with each of these substances. (One of the products is water; another is silicon tetrafluoride, SiF_4, which at room temperature is a gas.)

Hydrofluoric acid differs from the other hydrohalic acids in that it is a weak acid. Furthermore, hydrofluoric acid readily forms acid salts, such as KHF_2, although the other hydrohalic acids do not. The solubilities of the fluorides bear little resemblance to those of the other halides. Silver fluoride, for example, is highly soluble in water, although the other silver halides are scarcely soluble at all. These differences set fluorine apart from the other halogens. Nevertheless it is clear that fluorine should be counted as a member of the halogen family, since it can enter into most of the same reactions as the other halogens do, and it bears little chemical resemblance to any elements except the other halogens.

* Measurements of the molecular weight of gaseous hydrogen fluoride show that its molecule is not always diatomic. At room temperature and 0.76 meter-of-mercury, it seems that HF, H_2F_2, H_3F_3, H_4F_4, and H_5F_5 exist together in an equilibrium. At somewhat higher temperature or lower pressure, nearly all the molecules are HF.

38–6. Gradations Within the Halogen Family. Although the halogens are chemically very much alike, there are differences even among chlorine, bromine, and iodine. One difference is typified by the manner in which the various halogen elements combine with hydrogen. When the elements are mixed, fluorine combines explosively with hydrogen even in the dark. Chlorine and hydrogen also combine explosively, but at room temperature the reaction does not start in the dark. The combination of bromine with hydrogen is not an explosive one, and iodine reacts with hydrogen hardly at all, even at high temperatures. This set of reactions is typical in that it shows fluorine as the most active of the halogens and iodine as the least active, with chlorine and bromine in between. Nearly all of the other chemical, and even physical, properties of the halogens vary in this same order. Table 38–I gives a few examples.

TABLE 38–I

THE GRADATION IN SOME PROPERTIES OF THE HALOGENS

	Fluorine	Chlorine	Bromine	Iodine
State at room temperature	Gas	Gas	Liquid	Solid
Atomic weight	19.0	35.5	79.9	126.9
Boiling point	−187° C	−34.6° C	58.7° C	184° C
Energy released in reaction with hydrogen, calories per mole	64.0	22.0	8.65	—5.93
Boiling point of hydrogen halide	+20° C	−85° C	−67° C	−35° C
Energy released in reaction with sodium, calories per mole	136	98	86	70
Melting point of sodium halide	980° C	804° C	755° C	651° C
Amount of sodium halide that will dissolve in 100 g H_2O at 100° C.	5 g	40 g	120 g	302 g
Energy released when 1 mole of sodium halide dissolves in H_2O	−0.48 cal	−1.3 cal	−0.19 cal	+1.4 cal

In all of these examples, bromine fits between chlorine and iodine. Fluorine fits at the beginning of the series in some of the examples, but in others it does not. One of the great triumphs of atomic science has been the attainment of an explanation for the family resemblance of the halogens, for the gradations in their properties and in those of their compounds, and even for the peculiarities of fluorine and its compounds. These matters will unfold in a later section. At present we shall pursue the problem of simply classifying the elements, and the halogens will serve as examples of elements that must be classed together. After the classification has been developed, we shall seek its underlying foundation.

Summary

The halogens are the elements fluorine, chlorine, bromine, and iodine. They are called a family of elements because their chemical properties are much the same. The similarity appears principally in their compounds.

The halogens unite with hydrogen to form the hydrogen halides, of which HCl is the best known. These compounds, which at room temperature are gases, are acids that are highly soluble in water.

The silver halides have the property of changing under the influence of light, and this property forms the foundation of photography.

At room temperature, fluorine and chlorine are gases, bromine is liquid, and iodine is solid. The elements all combine directly with many metals and nonmetals, as well as with hydrogen. These reactions are mostly exothermic, in some cases very much so. The fluorine compounds often have properties that differ appreciably from the corresponding compounds of the other halogens.

The halogens and their compounds have properties that vary progressively from one halogen to another when they are arranged in the order fluorine, chlorine, bromine, and iodine, except that fluorine compounds often do not follow the rule.

Questions

1. State a few facts in support of the statement, "The chemical properties of chlorine, bromine, and iodine show differences in degree, but not in kind."
2. Give two reasons for classifying fluorine as a halogen.
3. When chlorine reacts with turpentine ($C_{10}H_{16}$) as on page 323, a light cover being set on the jar to keep air from entering, then the products are hydrogen chloride and carbon. Write the equation for the reaction.
4. Compare the reactions of chlorine with those of oxygen.
5. Comment on the possibility of making the silver halides by the direct action of the hydrohalic acids on silver.
6. How would you prove that a given substance was a fluoride?
7. What enables the reaction of H_3PO_4 with NaCl to proceed until one of these substances is used up, instead of merely reaching an equilibrium? How would the presence of water affect the reaction?
8. Why is there nothing inconsistent in the statements, "Hydrofluoric acid is a weak acid" and "Hydrofluoric acid attacks glass"?

39

CLASSIFYING THE ELEMENTS

When I was undertaking to write a book called *Principles of Chemistry,* I had to decide on some systematic grouping of the elementary substances, in order to be guided by some definite principle rather than by chance or instinct. . . . Any system based on exact observed numbers will, of course, deserve preference over other systems that lack numerical support. . . . The numerical data concerning elementary substances are at present limited. . . . Everyone knows, however, that throughout all the changes in attributes of an elementary body a *something* remains unaltered. . . . In this connection, we know only one thing that has a numerical measure, and that is the element's atomic weight.

MENDELÉEFF (1869)

The halogens are by no means the only easily recognized family of elements. A brief description of a few other families will afford a further basis for appreciating the problem of classification.

39–1. Families Other Than the Halogens. In chemical opposition to the halogens stands a family of elements called the *alkali metals,* listed in Table 39–I in the order of their atomic weights.

TABLE 39–I

THE ALKALI METALS

Element	Symbol	Atomic Weight
Lithium	Li	6.94
Sodium	Na	23.0
Potassium	K	39.1
Rubidium	Rb	85.5
Cesium	Cs	132.9

As the halogens are the most active nonmetals, so the alkali metals are the most active metals. They stand at the top of the replacement series (Article 27–6). They all have valence 1. They are all soft metals with low melting points. They all react with water to form soluble hydroxides that are strong bases. The properties of the alkali metals and their compounds show gradations within the family, although they differ from the halogens in that the alkali metal with the *largest* atomic weight is the most active, has the lowest melting point, and in general exhibits the family characteristics most strongly. As with the halogens, however, the lightest member of the family behaves a little unlike the other members.

Another well-defined family is that of the *alkaline-earth metals.* These are calcium, barium, strontium, and radium. Calcium is a constituent of bones, teeth, shells, chalk, lime, and many rocks. Compounds of the other alkaline-earth metals are too scarce to be familiar. All members of the family have metallic valence 2 and form compounds that have pretty much the same character no matter which member of the family they contain, although there is the usual gradation of properties within the family. The uncombined elements all react with water and liberate hydrogen, but they do not do so as rapidly as the alkali metals do.

In contrast with these two families of highly reactive metals, the *platinum family* consists of six metals that have so little tendency toward chemical reaction that they occur in nature as uncombined, or free, elements. They are ruthenium, rhodium, palladium, osmium, iridium, and platinum; usually all are found together in small nuggets or granules. All are heavy metals with high melting points, and they all resist attack even by most strong acids. Although they are rare, platinum being the most plentiful, their hardness and resistance to corrosion make them very useful for special jobs. The point of your fountain pen is probably tipped with some of them.

Lastly, we may mention two rather exceptional families of elements. The elements with atomic weights in the range 139 to 175 have chemical properties that are very nearly identical. In fact, these elements can be separated only with difficulty. They are called the *rare-earth metals.* Since there are fifteen of them, none being plentiful or familiar, we shall not list their names here. Their existence is worth keeping in mind, however, because their close similarity is a challenge to any explanation of chemical behavior.

Another peculiar family is that of the *inert gases,* helium, neon, argon, krypton, xenon, and radon. These elements have no chemical properties at all, or perhaps we should say that their one chemical property is refusal to enter into chemical combination. At ordinary temperatures, they are all gases, and the gases are monatomic. Except for radon, the inert gases occur in the air, from which they can be separated by exploiting the fact that they boil at temperatures different from the boiling points of nitrogen and oxygen (Article 25–2). Although the inert gases have some industrial uses, their chief interest for us is that their atoms will not enter into chemical union.

Dmitri Ivanovich Mendeléeff
(1834–1907)

39–2. Döbereiner's Triads (1829). The German chemist Döbereiner made the first fruitful attempt to connect the chemical properties of the elements with some quantitative principle. He pointed out that elements with similar properties seemed to come in threes, or, as he called them, "triads." In his time, many elements were as yet undiscovered, and many of his triads were mere parts of what we now know as families. Among his triads were three halogens, three alkali metals, and three alkaline-earth metals. Using modern values, the relation of their atomic weights is as follows:

Chlorine	35.46	Lithium	6.940	Calcium	40.08
Iodine	129.92	Potassium	39.096	Barium	137.36
Average	81.19		23.018		88.72
Bromine	79.92	Sodium	22.997	Strontium	87.63

Döbereiner emphasized the fact that the atomic weight of one member of a triad lies very nearly halfway between the atomic weights of the other two members. He also called attention to the fact that, in each triad, the member that has intermediate atomic weight also has intermediate chemical activity.

Döbereiner's paper had no immediate effect on the course of atomic science. It was published just at the time when chemists were beginning to become absorbed in the prodigiously rich and varied chemistry of carbon, and also at a time when knowledge of the elements was too fragmentary to permit much progress in classifying them. Atomic weights were at the focus of Döbereiner's attention, and it was not until the acceptance of Avogadro's hypothesis (Article 21–4) that a reasonably correct table of atomic weights could be worked out (about 1860). Soon thereafter, several chemists tried classifying the elements in terms of their atomic weights. Each of these attempts went farther than Döbereiner's, but all others were quickly overshadowed by the great classification of the Russian chemist Mendeléeff, which is substantially the one we use today.

39–3. Mendeléeff's Periodic Table (1869). The central idea of Mendeléeff's classification is this: When the elements are arranged in

---

Dmitri Ivanovich Mendeléeff, after a childhood in his native Siberia and university study in Russia, France, and Germany, became a professor of chemistry in St. Petersburg (now Leningrad). He was a highly successful teacher. Political tension and his advanced pedagogical ideas led to his resignation in 1890, but he later received the directorship of the Bureau of Weights and Measures. He was an extremely prolific researcher and writer in nearly all phases of chemistry, but his claim to immortality rests on his founding of the Periodic Table.

order of increasing atomic weight, the properties encountered as one goes along the array are repetitive, or "periodic." He started a new row whenever the properties began to repeat. When they seemed to be needed, he left blank spaces to accommodate elements that had not as yet been discovered. Table 39–II reproduces, with minor simplifications, the upper portion of one of Mendeléeff's first tabulations.

The table shows several signs of resting on some fundamental principle. Note first that the halogens all appear in one column or group, the alkali metals in another, and the alkaline-earth metals in still another. It is true that they would not all fall so neatly into place, except for the gaps left for supposed undiscovered elements. The first gap, however, does not appear until after calcium. Putting Cl under F fixes the positions of all the other elements that come before this gap. With no other arbitrary adjustment, Li, Na, and K fall in the same column, and in these first rows the metals fall on the left and the nonmetals on the right. Moreover, in going from left to right there is a progressive increase in the highest valence that the element exhibits in oxides, as exemplified by

$$Na_2O \quad MgO \quad Al_2O_3 \quad SiO_2 \quad P_2O_5 \quad SO_3 \quad Cl_2O_7.$$

There is a similar progressive change in the compounds that these oxides form with water. Those on the left form bases, but those on the right form acids, and there is a gradual transition from NaOH, a strong base, to $HClO_4$, a strong acid. The compounds with hydrogen are, for this same set of elements,

$$NaH \quad MgH_2 \quad AlH_3 \quad SiH_4 \quad PH_3 \quad H_2S \quad HCl.$$

Here, too, there is an orderly change, but the valence toward hydrogen grows from 1 to 4 and then drops again to 1.

In the rows below the one that begins with Na, the propriety of Mendeléeff's classification is not so obvious. For example, it is somewhat surprising to find copper and silver grouped with the alkali metals, or manganese with the halogens. Nevertheless, in order to have the rest of the table look sensible, these groupings are necessary, and they are not really absurd. Copper and silver do have some things in common with the other elements in Group I; they are metals, and they often have valence 1. Manganese, a hard gray metal, certainly does not look like a halogen, and for the most part it does not behave like one. However, it does form salts called "permanganates" (e.g., $KMnO_4$) that resemble the perchlorates (e.g., $KClO_4$).

In spite of a very few groupings that were hard to understand, Mendeléeff's table expressed so many correlations among the elements as to leave no doubt that some fundamental principle lay behind it. Mendeléeff himself emphasized that the table was open to improvement

TABLE 39–II

Part of an Early Version of Mendeléeff's Periodic Table

The lower part of the table is not reproduced here; more than half its entries are blanks, and most of the others are elements not yet mentioned in this book.

Group I	Group II	Group III	Group IV	Group V	Group VI	Group VII	Group VIII
H							
Li	Be	B	C	N	O	F	
Na	Mg	Al	Si	P	S	Cl	
K	Ca	–	Ti	V	Cr	Mn	Fe Co Ni
Cu	Zn	–	–	As	Se	Br	
Rb	Sr	Y(?)	Zr	Nb	Mo	–	Ru Rh Pd
Ag	Cd	In	Sn	Sb	Te	I	
Cs	Ba	Di(?)	Ce(?)	–	–		
.	.	.					
.	.	.					
.	.						
.	.						
.							
.							

based on further acquaintance with the elements, but he was so convinced of the table's essential validity that he used it to prophesy the properties of some elements that had not yet been discovered. When these elements came to light a few years later, their properties agreed admirably with Mendeléeff's predictions. Table 39–III compares a few of the predictions with the facts for the element that later filled the gap under silicon in Table 39–II.

TABLE 39–III

SOME PROPERTIES OF GERMANIUM

Property	Value Predicted by Mendeléeff in 1871 *	Modern Value for the Element Discovered in 1886
Atomic Weight	72	72.3
Weight of 1 milliliter of element	5.5 g	5.36 g
Formula for the oxide	GeO_2	GeO_2
Weight of 1 milliliter of the oxide	4.7 g	4.703 g
Formula for the chloride	$GeCl_4$	$GeCl_4$
Boiling point of the chloride	somewhat under 100° C	83° C
Weight of 1 milliliter of the chloride	1.9 g	1.879 g

* He of course did not predict that the symbol would be Ge!

39–4. Atomic Volumes. Mendeléeff's table is based on the repetition, or "periodicity," of certain properties, when the elements are arranged in the order of increasing atomic weights. The discussion above has been concerned with chemical behavior. Periodicity is also exhibited by some simpler properties of the elements. One such property is the "atomic volume" of the element. By the same argument used in connection with the mole (Article 35–1), it is easy to see that, if samples of various elements have weights that are numerically equal to their atomic weights, then they contain the same number of atoms.* If the elements are all in the solid state, then the volumes of the samples will be proportional to the volume occupied by one atom of the respective elements. It is therefore possible to measure the atomic volumes of the elements, on a relative scale, without knowing how many atoms each sample contains.

Although Mendeléeff laid some stress on atomic volumes, their periodic property was more strikingly pointed out by one of the other chemists who were working on the classification of the elements at about the same time. He plotted the atomic volume of the elements against their atomic weights, as in Figure 39–A. The resulting graph shows clearly the periodic variation in atomic volume. Note that the different members of the chemical families occupy similar positions on the graph,

* If the weight in grams is numerically equal to the atomic weight, then the sample is called a "gram atom" or "gram atomic weight."

although the graph deals with a physical quantity. The boiling points and some of the other physical properties of the elements also vary periodically with increasing atomic weight.

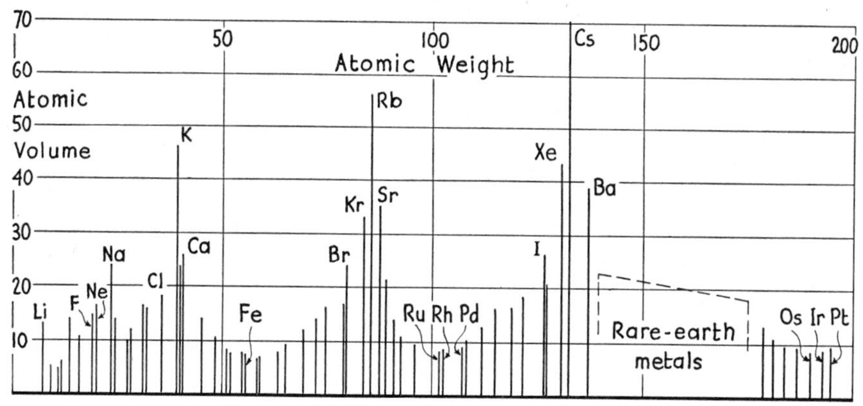

FIGURE 39-A. The periodicity of atomic volumes.

SUMMARY

Some of the noteworthy chemical families are the alkali metals (very active), the alkaline-earth metals (less active), the platinum metals (not very active), and the inert gases (completely inactive). The rare-earth metals are a large family of elements with chemical properties so much alike that these elements can be separated only with difficulty. The existence of still other families has long been recognized.

Early in the nineteenth century, Döbereiner called attention to the fact that certain triads of chemically similar elements have atomic weights that differ in a systematic way. The element with intermediate chemical properties has an atomic weight that lies nearly midway between the atomic weights of the other two.

By about 1870, the knowledge of atomic weights had progressed enough to permit the discovery that many properties of the elements show a strong correlation with the atomic weights. Of several nearly simultaneous attempts to classify the elements on the basis of the atomic weights, the most successful was that of Mendeléeff. He showed that there is a periodic, i.e. repetitive, change in the properties of the elements when they stand in order of increasing atomic weight. By setting the elements down in this manner and starting a new row when the properties begin to repeat, he made a table that classifies the elements in a way that has proved very useful. Elements of the same family fall in the same vertical group, and elements in the same horizontal row show orderly changes from left to right.

Questions

1. Name the alkali metals, give their symbols, and state three ways in which these metals are alike.
2. Name one way in which members of the platinum family differ from the alkaline-earth metals.
3. Name three of the inert gases, give their symbols, and state the distinctive property of this family.
4. What is meant by the statement, "Many properties of the elements vary periodically with the atomic weights"?
5. Refute a superficial critic who claims that Mendeléeff's table (page 331), is so arbitrary that it does not indicate any real regularity in the relations of the elements to one another.
6. Contrast the positions of the metals in Figure 39–A with the positions of the nonmetals.
7. In a few sentences, describe two methods of finding atomic weights. (See Chapter 22.)
8. The discovery of the periodic properties of the elements came just a few years after an important development in chemical theory. Name that development, and show how it bears on Mendeléeff's work.

40

THE PERIODIC TABLE

The classification of the elements has not only a pedagogical importance, as a means for more readily learning assorted facts that are systematically arranged and correlated, but it has also a scientific importance, since it discloses new analogies and hence opens up new routes for the exploration of the elements.

MENDELÉEFF (1871)

The elements are classified today in tables very much the same as Mendeléeff's. The difference is that the modern Periodic Table contains more elements than Mendeléeff knew, and there are a few places where the order of the atomic weights has had to be violated in order to make the elements fall in places that fit their chemical behavior. This chapter will examine the table to see how it points up the relationships of elements that are already familiar from previous chapters. This is also a good place to introduce a few facts that would have seemed like a mere miscellany if they had been brought in earlier. The Periodic Table fits them into a coherent pattern.

40–1. Modern Forms of the Periodic Table. Although the Periodic Table is sometimes put in other forms for special purposes, it normally appears either as the "short table" (Figure 40–A) or the "long table" (Figure 40–B). The short table resembles Mendeléeff's arrangement, but there are a few significant changes. All of the spaces are now occupied by known elements. Furthermore, the zigzag arrangement in each column has been modified; the new arrangement is less regular than Mendeléeff's, but more in accord with chemical similarities.

The horizontal divisions are called *periods.* The first period comprises only hydrogen and helium. The next two, called the *short periods,* have eight elements in each; the rest are called *long periods.* The vertical divisions are called *groups*; each of them is divided into a *main group* and a *subgroup.* In Group I, the alkali metals form the main group, while copper, silver, and gold form the subgroup. In the long table, there is no need for subgroups. The elements that comprise the subgroups in the short table fall in the middle of the long table, where they form a bridge, or transition, between the two ends.

The integers in the boxes in Figures 40–A and 40–B are serial numbers showing the position of the element in the table. They are called the *atomic numbers* of the elements. An element can be designated by its atomic number instead of by its name, but the numbers are usually used merely in conjunction with the name or symbol, as a reminder of the element's position in the table: $_2$He, $_7$N, $_{16}$S.

I	II	III	IV	V	VI	VII	VIII		
1 H							2 He		
3 Li	4 Be	5 B	6 C	7 N	8 O	9 F	10 Ne		
11 Na	12 Mg	13 Al	14 Si	15 P	16 S	17 Cl	18 A		
19 K	20 Ca	21 Sc	22 Ti	23 V	24 Cr	25 Mn	26 Fe	27 Co	28 Ni
29 Cu	30 Zn	31 Ga	32 Ge	33 As	34 Se	35 Br	36 Kr		
37 Rb	38 Sr	39 Y	40 Zr	41 Nb	42 Mo	43 Tc	44 Ru	45 Rh	46 Pd
47 Ag	48 Cd	49 In	50 Sn	51 Sb	52 Te	53 I	54 Xe		
55 Cs	56 Ba	Rare-earth metals	72 Hf	73 Ta	74 W	75 Re	76 Os	77 Ir	78 Pt
79 Au	80 Hg	81 Tl	82 Pb	83 Bi	84 Po	85 At	86 Rn		
87 Fr	88 Ra	Actinon metals							

FIGURE 40–A. The Periodic Table, in short form.

The filling out of the table by discovery of new elements needs little comment. The positions of the blank spaces were a guide to the searchers, telling them what to expect of the element they were looking for. The table was, of course, of no help in finding the inert gases. When they did become known, their atomic weights, with one exception, showed that their proper place lay between the halogens and the alkali metals. It is usual to place them in Group VIII, although they bear no resemblance at all to the triads that Mendeléeff put in Group VIII. In the long form of the table, the inert gases are alone in Group VIII. In the short form, which should be looked on as a folded-up version of the long form, the triads in Group VIII must be regarded as intruders that are "just passing through."

In the short table, Mendeléeff's zigzag arrangement has given way to a less balanced one consisting of a main group and a subgroup, the division being made on the basis of family resemblance. Sodium clearly resembles the alkali metals more than it resembles copper or silver; no considerations of symmetry should keep it out of the left side of the column. Similar remarks hold for other columns. There still exists a unifying regularity: the subgroups appear only in the long periods, and they occur there in a regular way.

I	II	TRANSITION ELEMENTS										III	IV	V	VI	VII	VIII
H 1																	He 2
Li 3	Be 4											B 5	C 6	N 7	O 8	F 9	Ne 10
Na 11	Mg 12											Al 13	Si 14	P 15	S 16	Cl 17	A 18
K 19	Ca 20	Sc 21	Ti 22	V 23	Cr 24	Mn 25	Fe 26	Co 27	Ni 28	Cu 29	Zn 30	Ga 31	Ge 32	As 33	Se 34	Br 35	Kr 36
Rb 37	Sr 38	Y 39	Zr 40	Nb 41	Mo 42	Tc 43	Ru 44	Rh 45	Pd 46	Ag 47	Cd 48	In 49	Sn 50	Sb 51	Te 52	I 53	Xe 54
Cs 55	Ba 56	† 57-71	Hf 72	Ta 73	W 74	Re 75	Os 76	Ir 77	Pt 78	Au 79	Hg 80	Tl 81	Pb 82	Bi 83	Po 84	At 85	Rn 86
Fr 87	Ra 88	†† 89-															

† Rare-earth metals

La	Ce	Pr	Nd	Pm	Sm	Eu	Gd	Tb	Dy	Ho	Er	Tm	Yb	Lu
57	58	59	60	61	62	63	64	65	66	67	68	69	70	71

†† Actinon metals

Ac	Th	Pa	U	Np	Pu	Am	Cm	Bk	Cf		Ct
89	90	91	92	93	94	95	96	97	98	99	100

FIGURE 40–B. The Periodic Table, in long form.

Putting the inert gases into the table brought up in acute form a problem that arose when the technique of measuring atomic weights had improved to the point of giving three-figure accuracy. Placing argon between chlorine and potassium upsets the order of atomic weights, which is Cl 35.47, K 39.096, A 39.944. Nevertheless, argon is certainly an inert gas, and the atomic weights of all the other inert gases fit between the halogens and the alkali metals. Argon must therefore be placed just after chlorine in the table. There are three other cases where a heavier element has to be placed before a lighter one, if the grouping of the elements is to be consistent with their chemical and physical properties. (See the Periodic Table under the back cover.) This means that in order to retain the plausibility of the table, the principle on which it was formed has to be violated. The only possible conclusion is that the atomic weights are not the determining factor in the properties of the elements. The table shows that there is a very high degree of correlation between this determining factor and the atomic weight, but it gives no hint as to what the determining factor may be. The table is not a theory, however; it is a tool. The atomic weights were a guide to its construction, but it has a purely empirical origin. It can be used, and for two generations was used, without any theoretical foundation. The rest of this chapter will therefore be devoted to the use of the table as a tool.

40–2. The Long Periods. We have already remarked (Article 39–3) on the progressive change from metallic to nonmetallic in the course of one of the short periods. The long periods are not quite so simple. The short ones consist of eight elements, one in each group. The first two long periods consist of eighteen elements; the third long period has thirty-two elements. There are two additional complications. Each of the long periods contains a triad of elements so much alike that they are placed in the same group. (See Figure 40–A.) Furthermore, in the third long period there is one box containing fifteen rare-earth metals. The last period is still different: it stops in Group III, in a box containing a whole family of elements somewhat like the rare-earth metals. This last family in the table is of interest because it includes uranium and plutonium, elements that find use in "atomic" bombs and other devices for using "atomic energy."

There is not complete agreement on just how the main groups and subgroups should be set down in the short table. In Figure 40–A, a very simple convention is followed. A main-group element has its symbol on the left side of the box, and a subgroup element has its symbol on the right. Other tables you see may be arranged differently.

In each long period, the first two members are main-group elements. Occupancy of the subgroups begins in Group III and continues (except in the last period) through Group II. The rest of the elements in the period are in main groups.

The subgroup elements differ from the main-group elements in the same group, but the subgroup elements in any period bear a strong resemblance to one another. They are all metals when in the uncombined state, and in compounds they can all act as metals, although some can act as nonmetals also.* All of them can have valence 2, but nearly all can have other valences as well. Because they provide a succession of small steps in the passage from the main-group elements in column II to those in column III, the subgroup elements are called *transition elements.* With few exceptions, each transition element has at least some salts that make colored solutions (remember copper sulfate). As we have seen

* Examples of nonmetallic behavior: the salts potassium permanganate, $KMnO_4$, and lead chromate (chrome yellow), $PbCrO_4$, in which manganese and chromium occur in acid radicals.

earlier, the color is characteristic of the ion. Ions of main-group elements do not produce color in solutions. These facts imply that there really is some physical distinction between main-group elements and transition elements; the subgroups are not simply a fiction that is maintained for the sake of making the Periodic Table look more plausible.

40–3. Metals and Nonmetals in the Periodic Table. The position of an element in the replacement series (Article 27–6) can be taken as a measure of the degree to which that element behaves like a metal. Thus, zinc is more metallic (in the chemical sense) than copper, since zinc will replace the copper in solutions of copper salts, whereas the reverse reaction will not occur. In symbols,

$$Zn + Cu^{++} \rightarrow Zn^{++} + Cu.$$

Instead of saying "more metallic," we sometimes say "more active as a metal."

In the Periodic Table, there is a strong correlation between the position of an element and the extent to which it acts as a metal or a nonmetal. There is a simple rule that applies to all but a few elements. In any main group, any element is more metallic than those above it; in a subgroup, any element is less metallic than those above it. For example, rubidium (atomic number 37) is more metallic than potassium, which in turn is more metallic than sodium. Copper (atomic number 29) is more metallic than silver, which lies below it in the subgroup.

The same rule, properly interpreted, carries over to the nonmetals. If an increase in nonmetallic character is taken to be equivalent to a decrease in metallic character, then even among the halogens the most metallic (least nonmetallic) is at the bottom.* Fluorine, which plays the nonmetallic role far more vigorously, is at the top of the group.

The rule is a reliable guide in the outer groups of the Periodic Table. In the central groups, the rule holds in a general way, but there are a few main-group elements that are more active than the ones immediately below them. For instance, aluminum, which lies above gallium in the Periodic Table, also lies above it in the replacement series. The rule, however, covers a host of facts that would be a nuisance to memorize. The Periodic Table displays them clearly to anyone who can memorize a simple rule and a small number of exceptions.

Another simple rule is that in any period, metallic character in the main groups is most pronounced for the elements toward the left and declines as one goes rightward to Group VII. If metallic behavior is strongest at the left and at the bottom of the table, and nonmetallic

* Calling iodine the most metallic of the halogens is not very farfetched. Iodine has a luster much like that of a metal.

behavior is strongest toward the right and the top, then we should expect that any dividing line between metals and nonmetals would divide the table in some diagonal way, leaving the metals on the lower left and the nonmetals on the upper right. Such a dividing line can indeed be drawn, but one must remember that in the short table, all of the subgroup elements are metals. The dividing line can apply only to main-group elements.

Figure 40–C shows the best dividing line that can be drawn between metals and nonmetals. The elements near the dividing line are only weakly metallic or nonmetallic. In fact, they usually have some metallic characteristics and some nonmetallic ones. Silicon is a good example. It conducts electricity, though not very well, and it has a luster almost like that of a metal. On the other hand, its hydroxide, $Si(OH)_4$ or H_4SiO_4, is an acid, not a base. It does

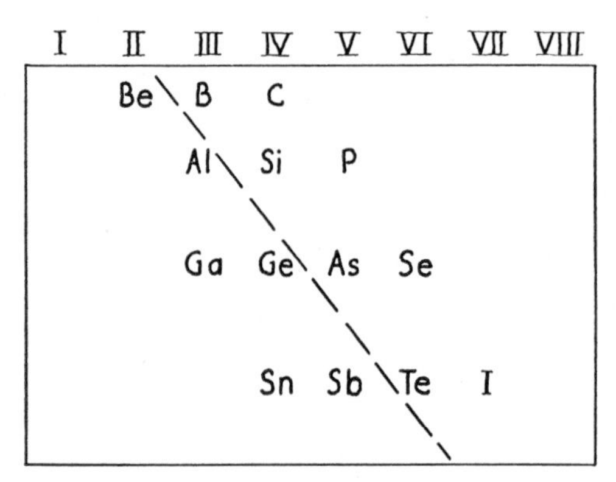

FIGURE 40–C. The dividing line between metals and nonmetals in the Periodic Table.

not play the role of a metal in salts. Since silicon acts chemically as a nonmetal, and does not have physical properties that are truly metallic, it is classed as a nonmetal. Aluminum, on the other side of the dividing line, has all the physical characteristics of a metal, and it plays the metallic part in many salts, such as aluminum nitrate, $Al(NO_3)_3 \cdot 9H_2O$. Aluminum hydroxide acts as a base, in that it reacts with acids to form a salt and water. Nevertheless, aluminum does show some nonmetallic behavior, because aluminum hydroxide will also react with a strong base to form a salt and water. Whether aluminum hydroxide acts as a base or an acid depends on its chemical environment:

$$Al(OH)_3 + 3HCl \rightarrow 3H_2O + AlCl_3$$

$$Al(OH)_3 + 3NaOH \rightarrow 3H_2O + Na_3AlO_3.$$

A hydroxide that can act as either an acid or a base is called "amphoteric."

40–4. The Value of the Periodic Table. In the past, the Periodic Table rendered several services that were important at the time but are now only of historical interest. Of these, perhaps the most important was the guidance the table gave to those who looked for undiscovered elements. The value of the table in such a quest has already been mentioned in connection with the discovery of germanium (Article 39–3). The table not only gave some idea of how to hunt for unknown elements, but also it told when to stop. A few years ago, the last blank space was filled; we are pretty certain now that no unknown element is lying about undetected.*

The great use of the table, however, is now and always has been the giving of order to what would otherwise be a mass of unrelated data. An acquaintance with the Periodic Table makes it unnecessary for each chemist to learn all of the properties of all of the elements. When he knows the behavior of a few representative elements, one or two in each group, the table will give him a very good idea of what to expect of the other elements. He may never have seen selenium or any of its compounds, but the table shows him that selenium (atomic number 34) is related to sulfur in much the same way that bromine is related to chlorine. He can therefore estimate pretty well the properties of hydrogen selenide (H_2Se) and selenic acid (H_2SeO_4) by calling on his experience with hydrogen sulfide (H_2S) and sulfuric acid (H_2SO_4). For exact data, of course, he must depend on experiments made with the actual substance he is interested in. It may be that these experiments have already been performed and are recorded in the chemical literature; perhaps they are yet to be done. Usually an estimate based on the Periodic Table will tell the chemist whether the unfamiliar substance is likely to be of such interest to him as to warrant a search of the literature or the performing of a new experiment.

40–5. Some Curious Aspects of the Periodic Table. Although the Periodic Table is so useful that it soon became the accepted way to classify the elements, there are some things about it that were very puzzling. For one thing, the short table arranges the transition elements in a way that seems to place an undue emphasis on valences that are not at all common. Copper, for example, is more commonly bivalent than univalent, yet it falls in Group I. Worse yet is the case of manganese, which exhibits valences of 1, 2, 3, 4, and 6, as well as the valence of 7 that accords with the placing of manganese in Group VII.

* The last section of the book will describe the manufacture of elements, with atomic numbers higher than 92, that have only a transient existence. If they ever existed in nature, they have not lasted until now, but they can be made in the laboratory. Manufacture of new elements of this sort may extend the table.

Another puzzling feature of the table is the number of elements in each period. The first period has two elements, the next two have eight, the next two have eighteen, and the next thirty-two. Do these numbers have any significance? One can scarcely ignore this question after noticing that the numbers are related as follows:

$$2 = 2 \times 1^2$$

$$8 = 2 \times 2^2$$

$$18 = 2 \times 3^2$$

$$32 = 2 \times 4^2$$

There was a time when the discovery of a relation like this would have been considered a sufficient reason for the lengths of the periods to be what they are, and the discoverer of the relation would have enjoyed great renown. Since about the time of Galileo, science has put little emphasis on numerical graces; nevertheless, such a relationship as this certainly begs for an explanation.

Perhaps the most intriguing of all aspects of the Periodic Table is the principle that determines the order of the elements. Why does the atomic weight have any connection with the order in the table? Why is the order *nearly* the same as the order of atomic weights, but not *quite* the same?

We have already noted that the order in the table depends on something that is closely correlated with, but different from, the atomic weights of the elements. Mendeléeff had no way of knowing what it is that governs the behavior of atoms and their position in the table, but some of his contemporaries were pursuing lines of research that ultimately led to a complete understanding of the table. This great work is the subject of the next section.

Summary

Modern forms of the Periodic Table are not very different from Mendeléeff's table, except that there are now no gaps for undiscovered elements. The horizontal divisions are called periods, and the vertical ones, groups. The position of the element in the table is designated by a serial number called the atomic number of the element. In a few cases, the order of the atomic numbers is not the same as the order of atomic weights. The only possible conclusion is that the atomic weight is not the determining factor in the properties of the elements, although there is a strong correlation between this factor and the atomic weight.

The Periodic Table is a useful tool to the working chemist, as well as to the beginning student of chemistry. It is like a filing system which gives access to a large amount of information at the cost of learning a few rules.

Questions

1. In the Periodic Table, what are (a) groups, (b) main groups, (c) subgroups, (d) periods, (e) short periods, (f) long periods, (g) transition elements, (h) atomic number?
2. Devise a rule (not an explanation) for the presence of subgroups in the Periodic Table.
3. Why would it be undesirable to stretch out the third long period into more boxes, by putting each rare-earth metal into a separate box?
4. What does "empirical" mean? Justify the statement that the Periodic Table had a purely empirical origin.
5. Construct a simple long Periodic Table in which each box contains only the symbol for its element. (Use a single box for the rare-earth metals and another single box for the similar family that lies below them in the table.) Put in a heavy dividing line between the metals and the nonmetals. How does the number of metallic elements compare with the number of nonmetallic ones?
6. State one property shared by all the transition elements, and another property that is shared by most of them.
7. Do you consider the use of the Periodic Table, as discussed thus far, to be scientific or unscientific? Defend your contention.

GENERAL VIEW OF SECTION VII

The chemical resemblances of certain elements led chemists to the concept of the family of elements. We have discussed one family, the halogens, in some detail, in order to show what a family is like. As soon as the acceptance of Avogadro's hypothesis had resulted in a valid set of atomic weights, Mendeléeff showed that a tabular arrangement of the elements was capable of displaying all of the family relationships and many other regularities as well. His Periodic Table, as revised by later workers, has given order to a vast body of data about the elements.

The earlier sections concerned with chemical topics have dealt mainly with the *observation* of chemical behavior. This section has dealt with *classification* of chemical behavior. In our discussion of Galileo's work on motion, the step called classification was almost trivial; it consisted simply in classifying some motions as falling motions, and it was certainly not original with Galileo. The job of classifying the elements was much more complex; it made nearly as strong demands on Mendeléeff's imagination as on his knowledge.

For the *invention of a hypothesis* and the *construction of a theory* to account for the Periodic Table, it was necessary to wait until more knowledge about atoms became available. The resultant understanding of the Periodic Table is one of the most beautiful fruits of physical science. It forms the subject of the next section.

VIII

The Structure of Atoms

Although the Periodic Table was invented by a chemist, and is useful primarily to chemists, an understanding of the table was achieved through studies of electricity and light. The experiments that led to this understanding of the Periodic Table were not the result of over-all planning. Various workers in various countries simply worked on investigations that seemed to them to be interesting, and eventually the principles behind the Periodic Table were uncovered. No doubt very few of the workers saw any connection between what they were doing and the Periodic Table.

If just for the fun of it, however, we take advantage of hindsight, a plausible starting point for an investigation of the Periodic Table can be selected. The last two sections introduced three ideas that are by no means disconnected—the ionization of some solutions, the quantization of charge, and the Periodic Table. When we recall that the valence of an ion is equal to the number of quanta, or "bits," of charge that it carries, and that the valence of an atom is to some extent related to its position in the Periodic Table, we can well believe that the arrangement of elements in the Periodic Table is somehow connected with the bits of charge. Perhaps, therefore, a better understanding of the Periodic Table (and a better understanding of atoms) can be reached by finding out more about charge.

Studying the conduction of electricity through solutions disclosed so much about charge that one might expect to learn something further by studying the conduction of electricity through gases, which in several important respects are simpler than solutions. With this "expectation," based on hindsight, as an excuse, we shall turn to a study of conduction in gases. There is little doubt that the early investigators in this field were attracted to it by the beauty of the phenomena themselves, rather than by any prevision of what they would accomplish. Nevertheless, the work did lead to our present detailed understanding of the chemical properties of the elements, and to rational explanation of the Periodic Table.

41

THE PASSAGE OF ELECTRICITY THROUGH GASES

The first experiments with the conduction of electricity through gases were done with air, even though air is a mixture of different gases. One normally thinks of gases as being insulators, but of course it is well known that if air is in a sufficiently strong electric field, then the air does become a conductor and there is a spark. For example, sparks will occur between the terminals of the electric machine discussed in Article 28–7.

41–1. The Gaseous Discharge. Sparking at atmospheric pressure occurs only when the electric field is very strong. Early in the nineteenth century it was found that if most of the air is removed from an enclosure, then the remaining air will conduct electricity even when the electric field is not very intense. The result is not a spark, but a fascinating glow.

We shall digress here to make a general observation about the progress of science. Faraday, having made such important discoveries through the study of conduction in solutions, spent some time on a study of conduction in gases. No great result ensued from this work. In this case, as in many others on which we have not commented, advance in scientific experiment had to wait for advance in technology. A generation later, one of Faraday's own discoveries had been exploited to make a device called an "induction coil," which is better than an electric machine for producing large differences of potential (thousands of volts). Furthermore, great improvements in vacuum pumps had made possible much reduced pressures, in which the phenomena of gaseous conduction are simplified.

The principle on which the induction coil operates will be in the direct line of our thought in a later chapter, so it will be best now to accept the device as a tool, with the understanding that its operation will be explained later. On the other hand, vacuum pumps are mechanical devices whose principles of operation have no direct bearing on our other business. Let us accept them as tools without pausing to study them, as a politician accepts a television transmitter.

By courtesy of the Cavendish Laboratory, Cambridge University

SIR J. J. THOMSON
(1856–1940)

Return now to the fact that air and other gases glow and conduct electricity if the pressure is of the order of 10^{-3} meter-of-mercury, and if the gas is in a moderately strong electric field.

EXPERIMENT. By means of an induction coil, a potential difference of several thousand volts is applied to metal electrodes sealed into the ends of a long glass tube. As air is pumped out of the tube, the remaining air becomes conducting, and incidentally gives off a pink light. (Commercial neon signs operate on this principle. Neon is used instead of air because it gives a more vivid red. Other gases are used to give other colors.) As more air is removed from the glass tube, the glow gets fainter and eventually disappears; when it is gone we observe another glow, this time green, coming from the glass wall of the tube. When the tube is evacuated still further, conduction through the tube ceases.

The same effects can be observed by using a set of glass tubes that have been evacuated to various low pressures and then sealed.

A tube containing a pair of electrodes and a gas at low pressure is called a "discharge tube." The electrode that is at the higher potential is called the *anode*; the other electrode is the *cathode*.

We shall not attempt to trace the whole history of the understanding of electrical conduction in gases. Various workers developed techniques of experimentation, and collected information, for about forty years before they made any significant progress. Progress was slow largely because vacuum pumps were still relatively crude. Eventually pumps became good enough so that they could decrease the population of gas particles in a tube until, with luck, a particle could travel all the way across the tube without bumping into other particles.* Then the particles interfered very little with one another, and the electrical phenomena became relatively simple.

* It is interesting that improvement in pumps sprang from economic considerations: Edison's invention of the incandescent electric lamp produced a commercial demand for evacuated bulbs.

JOSEPH JOHN THOMSON entered the University of Cambridge as an undergraduate, and spent the rest of his life as one of its members. After a brilliant start as a theoretician, he was elected to the professorship of experimental physics while still in his twenties. His laboratory speedily assumed leadership in research on electrical phenomena in gases. The portrait opposite shows some of the apparatus with which he discovered the electron.

Thomson's researches brought him many honors, including a Nobel prize (1906) and a knighthood (1908). In later years, he took much satisfaction in the many successes achieved by men who had trained under him as graduate students. His preoccupation with higher things did not result in a complete indifference to money. After his death, his friends learned with surprise that by shrewd investment of his savings he had accumulated a substantial fortune.

41–2. Cathode Rays (1876). The first progress toward real understanding was made by studying the "discharge," or conduction, that occurs when the pressure is so low that the light comes mostly from the walls of the tube. As is shown in the following experiment, the glow from the glass is produced by something emanating from the cathode and traveling in straight lines. This "something" is called *cathode rays,* because it issues from the cathode along straight lines.

EXPERIMENT. In the discharge tube in Figure 41–A, a metal plate in the form of a cross stands in front of the cathode. The anode is sealed into one side of the tube. The pressure in the tube is about a millionth of atmospheric pressure, or about a million times as much as the best vacuum now obtainable.

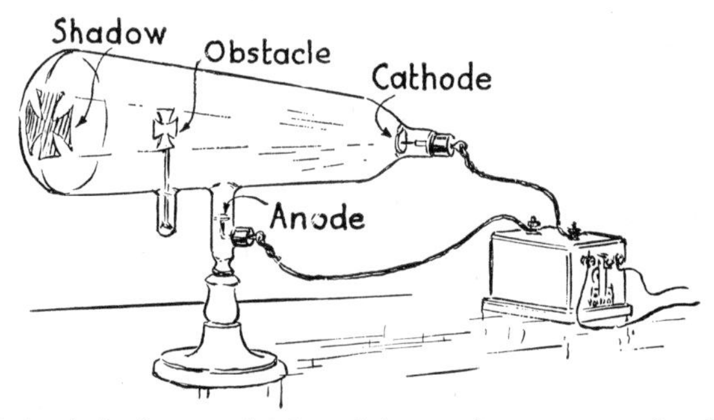

FIGURE 41–A. A discharge tube for exhibiting the existence of cathode rays.

Some of the rays coming from the cathode are obstructed by the cross. The cross casts a sharp "shadow" on the glowing end of the tube, showing that the glow is produced by something that does come, along straight lines, from the cathode.

About 1890 the nature of the cathode rays was in the forefront of physical research, and opinion about the rays was divided. Most German investigators thought them to be a kind of invisible light somewhat like the ultraviolet, which does make some things glow. On the other hand, most of the British investigators believed the rays to consist of charged particles.

41–3. The Nature of Cathode Rays. If the cathode rays are charged particles in motion, then they constitute an electric current, and this current will experience a sideward thrust when in a magnetic field (Article 32–3). By experiment it was shown that if a magnet is brought near a beam of cathode rays, so that the beam is in a magnetic field, then the beam is in fact deflected. The experiment can easily be repeated by holding a magnet near the discharge tube in Figure 41–A. The shadow of the cross then takes a new position, showing that the cathode rays have been urged sideward by the magnetic field.

An alternative demonstration that cathode rays are bent by a magnetic field can be achieved by confining the rays to a narrow beam, as in Figure 41-B. An anode, pierced by a slit, can be placed in front of the cathode. Most of the cathode rays then strike the anode, but a narrow beam of the rays will pass through the slit in the anode and strike a plane surface inserted diagonally in the tube. The trajectory of the cathode rays is made visible by coating the plane with zinc sulfide or some other salt that glows when struck by the rays. When a magnet is brought near the beam of rays, the glowing streak becomes curved, as in the figure, showing that the rays are being affected by the magnetic field. The trajectory is curved because the magnetic field exerts a force that is perpendicular to the velocity. Such a force produces an acceleration that is perpendicular to the velocity, and the result is a curved path (Article 6-4).

FIGURE 41-B. Cathode rays are deflected by a magnetic field.

The sideward thrust exerted on the beam of cathode rays by a magnetic field was a strong indication that the rays are streams of charged particles. Taking the directions of the field and of the motion into account (Article 32-3), the experimenters always found that the direction of the thrust was the direction in which *negatively* charged particles would be urged. The fact that the cathode rays actually do consist of negatively charged particles was clinched by J. J. Thomson, Professor of Physics in Cambridge University. Thomson constructed a discharge tube like the one in Figure 41-C. It contained an auxiliary electrode which was connected only to an electroscope. With the tube in operation, Thomson could deflect the rays with a magnet in such a way that they struck the auxiliary electrode. When they did so, the electroscope registered the presence of a charge. Since the charge was of the same kind as that acquired by a rubber rod by contact with fur, the most skeptical investigators were convinced that the cathode rays actually are streams of negatively charged particles.

FIGURE 41-C. Proving that the cathode rays are streams of charged particles.

If we have charged particles traveling in a discharge tube, we naturally wonder whether these particles are the same as the ions encountered in electrolysis. In fact, as the next chapter will explain, the cathode-ray particles are different and more fundamental.

Summary

Gases at low pressure (about 10^{-3} meter-of-mercury, or less) become conducting in electric fields of only moderate strength.

A discharge tube is a glass vessel, usually of cylindrical shape, containing a pair of metal electrodes and a gas at low pressure. When a potential difference of several thousand volts is established at the electrodes, the gas becomes conducting. It glows with a light that depends on what the gas is and what its pressure is.

If the pressure is low enough, the glow in the gas is faint, perhaps invisible, and the observer sees a glow coming from the glass walls of the tube. This glow is caused by rays issuing from the cathode. The cathode rays cause the generation of light when they strike glass or certain other substances. They are deflected in a magnetic field, and Thomson showed that they consist of negatively charged particles.

Questions

1. What is a discharge tube? What are the cathode and anode of a discharge tube?
2. Describe what is seen in a discharge tube when the pressure in it is gradually lowered while there is a large potential difference between the electrodes.
3. Describe how cathode rays may be observed. Why are they so named?
4. Cite evidence that cathode rays are streams of negatively charged particles.

42

THE DISCOVERY OF THE ELECTRON

The cathode rays having been identified as negatively charged particles, it became very desirable to obtain further information about them. Are they perhaps the same as the negative ions found in solutions? One can tell best by subjecting them to measurements. Simply making measurements on the bending of the rays in a magnetic field is not very helpful, because the amount of deflection in a magnetic field depends, as will be explained below, on the charge carried by each particle, on the velocity of the particle, and on its inertia, or mass.

Being charged, the cathode-ray particles also experience a force when they are in an *electric* field. After several other people had failed because of faulty apparatus, Thomson succeeded, in 1897, in deflecting the cathode rays by an electric field. As shown below, he was able to measure the velocity of the cathode-ray particles, and knowing the velocity he was able to get other information.

We did not have to worry about the velocity of the ions in electrolysis, because we could get information about them by weighing the material that was liberated from the solution. In dealing with cathode rays, we get no weighable deposit and must therefore make a more roundabout attack.

42–1. The Velocity of the Cathode Rays. Thomson's method of determining the velocity of the cathode rays employs both electric and magnetic fields.

Recall (Article 32–3) that a charge moving in a magnetic field experiences a force. If the current and the field are perpendicular to one another, and we use our usual system of units, then the force on a current-bearing wire (Article 33–1) is

$$\text{Force} = \text{Magnetic field strength} \times \text{Current} \times \text{Length of wire}.$$

In the case of cathode rays we have a rather unusual situation because the moving charges are not in a wire. It can be shown that the last equation can be applied to individual charged particles by modifying it as follows:

$$\text{Force} = \text{Magnetic field strength} \times \text{Charge} \times \text{Velocity.*}$$

In symbols,

$$F = Bqv,$$

where v is the velocity of the particle.

The force exerted on the charged particles by an electric field, of strength E, is (Article 29–2):

$$\text{Force} = \text{Electric field strength} \times \text{Charge}.$$

In symbols,

$$F = Eq.$$

Suppose that the particles are subjected to electric and magnetic fields simultaneously, as shown in Figure 42–A. The particles are to be

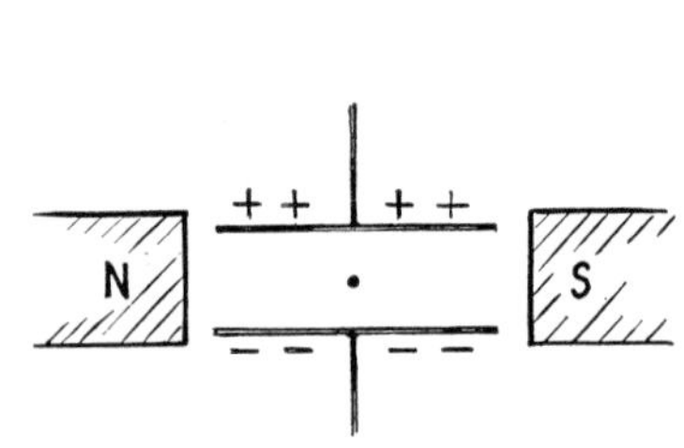

FIGURE 42–A. A region of "crossed" magnetic and electric fields. The magnetic field is horizontal; the electric field, vertical. The dot represents a stream of charged particles coming out of the page.

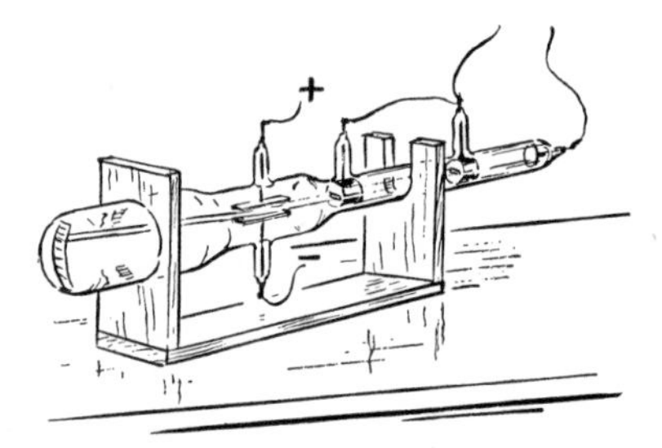

FIGURE 42–B. One of Thomson's discharge tubes for investigating the cathode-ray particles. The plates in the center are used to establish an electric field, and an auxiliary magnet establishes a magnetic field at right angles to the electric one, as in Figure 42–A.

imagined as coming toward you, out of the page. The electric field will urge the particles *up*, and the magnetic field will thrust them *down*. (Use the rule in Article 32–3, remembering that the particles here are nega-

* In this equation, the product (charge) × (velocity) occupies the place held by (current) × (length of wire) in the previous equation. That this substitution is *plausible* follows from the fact that the first product is measured in units (coulombs) × (meters/second), or coulomb-meters/second, while the second is measured in (amperes) × (meters), or (coulombs/second) × (meters), or coulomb-meters/second. Therefore the two products have the same physical significance. That it is *correct* to substitute one for the other has been shown by experiments on charged objects moving in magnetic fields.

tive.) By proper adjustment of the electric field, we can make its upward force on the negative particles just big enough to balance the downward thrust due to the magnetic field. To do this, we use a discharge tube like the one in Figure 42-B, in which cathode rays pass between two charged plates that produce an electric field. The electric field can be varied by changing the potential of the plates. The magnetic field may be produced by an iron magnet or by a current-bearing coil. We make the electric field just strong enough so that the particles strike the end of the tube in the same place when the two fields are present as it does when they are both turned off. In this situation, the forces exerted by the two fields being equal, we have

$$Eq = Bqv,$$

whence

$$v = \frac{E}{B}.$$

Notice that the charge cancels out and therefore need not be known.

On performing this experiment in 1897, Thomson found that for the cathode-ray particles in the discharge tube he was using, $v = 2 \times 10^7$ m/sec, or about 10,000 miles/second. (It is found that the velocity depends on the difference of potential between cathode and anode.)

EXPERIMENT. An old cathode-ray tube, of the sort Thomson used, or a modern one which is put to many uses in the electrical laboratory, can be used to observe the deflection of the cathode rays by electric and magnetic fields. In a television receiver, the intensity and deflection of the cathode rays are controlled so that the beam traces out a picture.

42-2. The Charge-to-Mass Ratio of the Cathode-Ray Particles. Now suppose that the electric field is removed, so that only the magnetic field acts on the particles. Then the particles experience a force, and therefore an acceleration, at right angles to their direction of motion. In Article 6-4, we found that an acceleration perpendicular to the motion is characteristic of uniform circular motion, and that the magnitudes of the acceleration, velocity, and radius are related by the equation

$$\text{Acceleration} = \frac{(\text{Velocity})^2}{\text{Radius}}.$$

But by Newton's Second Law of Motion,

$$\text{Force on particle} = \text{Mass of particle} \times \text{Acceleration}.$$

Therefore

$$\text{Force} = \text{Mass} \times \frac{(\text{Velocity})^2}{\text{Radius}}.$$

In symbols,

$$F = m\frac{v^2}{r}\cdot$$

Now the force is exerted by the magnetic field, so that

$$F = Bqv.$$

Combining these last two equations, we have

$$Bqv = m\frac{v^2}{r},$$

where the term on the left is the force, and the term on the right is Mass $\times$ Acceleration. Now v can be measured by the method described in the last article, B can be measured by the force it exerts on a known current in a wire, and r can be measured by observing the bending of the beam of particles. Therefore if we put the last equation into the form

$$\frac{q}{m} = \frac{v}{Br},$$

all the quantities on the right side are observable ones, and we can therefore determine q/m. That is, we can measure the *ratio* of charge to mass, although the experiment gives no information about charge or mass individually. The result is

$$\frac{q}{m} = 176{,}000{,}000{,}000 \text{ coulombs/kilogram},$$

or 1.76×10^{11} coulombs/kg, *regardless of the kind of gas or the electrode material used in the tube.* This indicates that the cathode-ray particles are all alike, and that they are found in all materials that can be used as a cathode, i.e. in all conductors. From this it is reasonable (and, as it turns out, correct) to guess that the cathode-ray particles are found in all matter.

42–3. The Electron (1897). When studying electrolysis, we saw how to find a relation between the mass of an atom and the charge of its ion in a solution. In fact, if e represents one quantum of charge and m represents the mass of the atom, then in the simple case of univalent ions, each of which carries just a single quantum of charge, we found (Article 36–4) that

$$\frac{e}{m} = \frac{\text{Total charge transported}}{\text{Total mass liberated}}\cdot$$

Measurements of this sort show that for hydrogen $e/m = 9.57 \times 10^7$ coulombs/kilogram, and that for all other elements e/m is smaller. But we have just seen that the charge-to-mass ratio for the cathode-ray particles is much larger. Therefore, under the reasonable assumption that the mass of an ion is not much different from that of the corresponding atom, *the cathode-ray particles are not the same as the charged particles encountered in solutions.*

The cathode-ray particles, with their larger charge-to-mass ratio, clearly have a larger charge or a smaller mass than do hydrogen ions. It had been discovered about 1890 that if a very thin metal foil is used as a window at the end of a cathode-ray tube, the rays falling on the window will pass right through it. Since no gas will leak through such a foil, it seemed probable that the cathode-ray particles are smaller than any atoms. Moreover, they are present, in identical form, in all kinds of matter. Professor Thomson jumped to the conclusion that these particles are *parts* of atoms,* and in fact are "building blocks" that enter into the construction of atoms. They were named *electrons.*

Atoms under ordinary circumstances are electrically neutral, and electrons are electrically negative; there must therefore be another kind of building block which is positive.

If the electron is actually one of the primordial components of which atoms are made, then an atom that has lost an electron (which can apparently happen very easily, since cathode rays are easy to produce) will be left with a positive charge. An atom that has more than its normal quota of electrons will have a negative charge. We see at once that this explains what an ion is, and it explains why the charge on ions comes in bits. An ion is an atom (or in some cases a group of atoms) that has a surplus or a deficit of electrons. If it has a surplus of one electron, then it has a negative charge of one quantum; if it has a deficit of, say, two electrons, then it has a positive charge of two quanta, and so on. It is clear that the quantum of negative charge is simply the charge of an electron.

From the fact that charge on ions is quantized, it can be surmised that an atom loses or gains whole electrons when it turns into an ion—that it never loses or gains only a fraction of an electron. This in turn leads one to suppose that the electron is indivisible. The facts that have been presented so far are not sufficient to guarantee the correctness of this assumption, of course, but it is a fact that in fifty years of experimentation nobody has ever observed a fraction of an electron. Because the electron is believed to be indivisible (as of 1955!), it is called a *fundamental particle.* We shall meet other fundamental particles in later chapters.

* The word "atom" comes from a Greek word meaning "indivisible," but Thomson's work indicated that the atom actually is divisible, because it is composed of parts.

Summary

Thomson determined the charge-to-mass ratio for the cathode-ray particles, by studying their behavior in electric and magnetic fields.

The first step in Thomson's study was to determine the velocity of the particles he was using. He did this by exerting forces on the particles by means of an electric field and a magnetic field. The fields were directed so that they exerted opposing forces on the moving negative particles, and the strengths of the fields were adjusted so that the forces just balanced one another and the particles were not deflected. The force exerted by the magnetic field depends on the velocity of the particles, but the force exerted by the electric field does not. Consequently, the velocity of the particles can be calculated from a knowledge of the field strengths that produce balanced forces on the particles. Thomson's particles had a velocity of about 10,000 miles/second.

Knowing the velocity of the particles, one can calculate their charge-to-mass ratio by finding the radius of the curved path they follow when they are acted on by a magnetic field only. The charge-to-mass ratio turns out to be independent of the kind of gas or the electrode material used in the tube; the cathode-ray particles must therefore be all alike, and they are found in all kinds of matter.

The charge-to-mass ratio of the cathode-ray particles is several thousand times as large as the charge-to-mass ratios of ions found in solutions. Moreover, the cathode-ray particles can pass through thin sheets of solid metal. These two facts indicate that the cathode-ray particles are smaller and less massive than any atoms. They were named "electrons," and Thomson correctly concluded that they are one of the fundamental components of which atoms are made.

An ion is an atom that has either more or fewer electrons than its normal quota. The fact that the charge on ions comes in bits is therefore understandable. The ion has one bit of charge for each electron missing from, or in addition to, its normal quota. The quantum of negative charge is the charge of an electron.

Questions

1. Without using equations, describe how the velocity of cathode rays can be measured.
2. State the order of magnitude of the velocity of Thomson's cathode rays.
3. Without using equations, describe how the charge-to-mass ratio of the cathode-ray particles can be determined.
4. Cite a connection between the study of planetary motion and the study of cathode-ray particles.

5. Cite a connection between the study of cathode-ray particles and the entertainment of the American people.
6. Compare the charge-to-mass ratio of cathode-ray particles with that of the ions found in solutions. On what assumption about the mass of an ion is your answer based?
7. What is some of the evidence for the belief that the cathode-ray particles are parts of atoms?
8. Outline the connection between the cathode-ray particles and the ions found in solutions.

Suggestions for Further Reading

J. J. Thomson, "Cathode Rays," *Philosophical Magazine,* Series 5, vol. 44, pp. 293–316 (1897). Most of this paper is reprinted in W. F. Magie, *A Source Book in Physics* (New York: McGraw-Hill Book Co., Inc., 1935), pp. 583–97.

Sir J. J. Thomson, *Recollections and Reflections* (New York: Macmillan Co., 1937). A delightful autobiographical volume by one of the outstanding figures in modern physics. Pages 325–43 deal with the electron. There are also some astonishing descriptions of baseball and American football.

43

THE QUANTUM OF CHARGE AND THE MASSES OF ATOMS

The last chapter described Professor Thomson's discovery of the electron. He was able to measure neither the charge nor the mass of an electron, but only the ratio of charge to mass. As soon as either the charge or the mass could be measured separately, the other quantity could be calculated from their ratio. When Thomson's hypothesis that the electron is one of the primordial building blocks of matter was accepted, it seemed fairly certain that the charge of the electron was just one quantum of charge; the problem of determining the size of the quantum of charge therefore took on a new importance.

Attempts to measure the quantum of charge had of course been made even before the discovery of the electron, but the first measurement that had any claim to accuracy was made by the American physicist Millikan, by an experiment that is beautiful in its simplicity and directness.

43–1. Millikan's Oil-Drop Experiment (1909). Millikan sprayed oil from a nozzle that broke it up into tiny droplets, some of which fell through a hole into the space between two horizontal metal plates, as shown in Figure 43–A. The drops were so tiny that they fell slowly, because on such a light object the retarding effect of air resistance will counterbalance the weight, even though the drop is not moving very fast.* By watching an individual droplet through a microscope, Millikan could measure its rate of fall. From the rate of fall and some experimental laws concerning air resistance, he could calculate the radius of the drop (about one ten-thousandth of an inch); knowing the radius of the drop and the weight of a given volume of the oil, he readily computed the weight of the drop.

* This does not conflict with the work of Galileo, which applies only when the falling object is heavy enough, and slow enough, so that air resistance is negligibly small compared to the weight of the object.

Having measured the rate of fall, Millikan connected the upper plate to the positive terminal of a battery, and the lower plate to the negative terminal, so that the region between the plates became an electric field. The drop would then fall at a different rate, showing that the electric

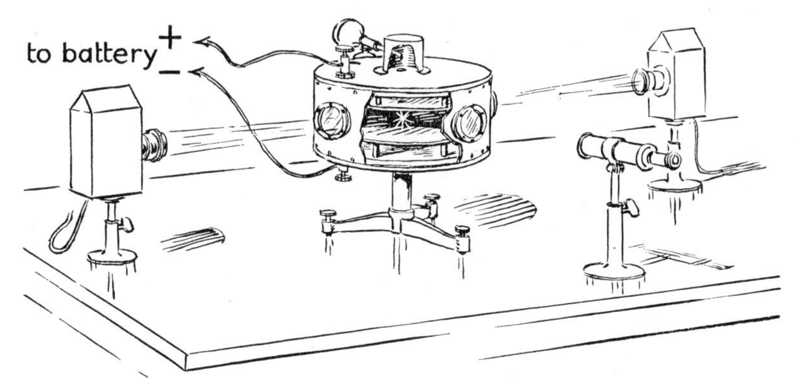

FIGURE 43–A. Apparatus for Millikan's oil-drop experiment.

field was exerting a force on it. This effect indicated that the drop had become charged when it was blown out of the nozzle, in the same way that a rubber rod becomes charged from contact with fur. By adjusting the battery voltage, Millikan could make the electric field just strong enough to support the droplet. When this balance prevailed, then

$$\text{Electric field strength} \times \text{Charge on drop} = \text{Weight of drop.}$$

The weight of the drop was known, and the strength of the electric field could be calculated from the battery voltage and the separation of the plates (see Article 33–4). Therefore the charge on the drop could be calculated from experimental data.

The following table contains, in the first column, the charges that Millikan actually found on some of his droplets. The second column contains a small integer, found by trial and error, which when divided into the charge gives the quantity shown in the third column.

Observed Charge	Integer	Quotient
8.20×10^{-19} coulomb	5	1.64×10^{-19} coulomb
6.55	4	1.64
16.37	10	1.64
13.11	8	1.64

It is clear that each of the observed charges is an integer multiple of 1.64×10^{-19} coulomb. In other words, the charges come in bits whose size is 1.64×10^{-19} coulomb; the first charge in the list amounted to 5 bits, or 5 quanta, the second to 4 bits, the third to 10 bits, and so on. Now the drops acquired these charges through contact with the nozzle, and the experiment therefore showed that charges produced by contact come in bits.

Immediately there arose the important question: Are the bits of charge that are transferred by contact the same as the bits of charge that are found on ions? Millikan was easily able to answer this question. Occasionally one of the drops collided with a stray ion in the air, and this of course changed the charge on the drop. Such collisions announced themselves by a sudden change in the electric field that was needed to counterbalance the weight of the drop. By measuring the charge on a drop before and after a collision with an ion, and taking the difference, *Millikan could measure directly the charge on an ion.* He found that it was always either 1.64×10^{-19} coulomb, or some small multiple of this quantity.

Millikan's experiment had a threefold result: He proved that the charge acquired by contact comes in quanta, he proved that these quanta are the same as the ones observed on ions, and *his measurements established the size of the quantum of charge.* The measurements quoted above were among the first that he made, before he discovered a small error in his technique for measuring the size of the droplet. With improved technique, he and others have measured the charges on thousands of droplets.* Within the limits of error of the experiments, the charges have all been some integer multiple of

$$1.6021 \times 10^{-19} \text{ coulomb}.$$

This is the quantum of electric charge, usually denoted by the symbol e. Since the charge of an electron is one quantum, the charge of an electron will hereafter be denoted by e instead of the more general symbol q.

* Instead of adjusting the electric field to balance out the weight of the drop as nearly as possible, it is easier to get approximate balance and then to see how fast the drop rises or falls in the known field. The equations for this case are not much more complicated than that in the text.

Robert Andrews Millikan grew up in Iowa and then worked his way through Oberlin as acting director of the college gymnasium. He trained professionally in physics at Columbia University and, as was customary at that time, in Germany. Then, at the infant University of Chicago, he applied himself to teaching and research. One result was a set of high-school and college textbooks that did much to set the pattern of American physics teaching for the next half-century. Having served in the Army as scientific adviser during World War I, he went to the California Institute of Technology, where he helped to bring that school to the eminent position in science that it now enjoys.

Millikan was one of the first Americans to receive a Nobel prize. Unlike most physicists, he did his best research after he was 40. He did vital work not only in measuring the quantum of charge, but also in other fields mentioned later in this book: spectroscopy, the photoelectric effect, and cosmic rays.

ROBERT ANDREWS MILLIKAN
(1868–1953)

43–2. The Masses of Atoms. Having measured the quantum of charge, Millikan was able to compute the mass of an electron, because the value of e/m for an electron had already been determined by Thomson (Article 42–2) to be 1.76×10^{11} coul/kg. It is easy to calculate that the mass of an electron is 9.1×10^{-31} kg.

For a problem that is in some ways more fruitful, we can calculate the mass of a hydrogen atom. From electrolysis experiments involving the liberation of hydrogen, we find, as has already been mentioned (Article 42–3), that

$$\frac{e}{m_H} = 9.57 \times 10^7 \text{ coul/kg},$$

where m_H is the mass of a hydrogen atom.

But

$$e = 1.602 \times 10^{-19} \text{ coulomb},$$

so

$$\frac{1.602 \times 10^{-19} \text{ coul}}{m_H} = 9.57 \times 10^7 \text{ coul/kg}.$$

Hence

$$m_H = \frac{1.602 \times 10^{-19} \text{ coul}}{9.57 \times 10^7 \text{ coul/kg}},$$

or

$$m_H = 1.67 \times 10^{-27} \text{ kg}.$$

The mass of any other atom can be found from the mass of the hydrogen atom by multiplying by the ratio of their masses, which is simply the ratio of their atomic weights. For example, the mass of a gold atom is

$$\frac{197.2}{1.008} \times 1.67 \times 10^{-27} \text{ kg},$$

which is

$$3.27 \times 10^{-25} \text{ kg}.$$

43–3. The Number of Molecules in a Mole. It has already been noticed, in Article 35–1, that a mole of any substance contains the same number of molecules as a mole of any other substance. It is this fact that makes a mole worth talking about. Knowing how many molecules there actually are in a mole is sometimes not important. Nevertheless a better appreciation of molecular phenomena results from knowing how many molecules there are, for example, in a spoonful of water.

Knowing the actual masses, and hence the actual weights, of atoms, as we do from the calculations in the last article, we can find the number of molecules in a mole. First a quick review may be useful. A mole of a substance is an amount whose weight in grams is numerically equal to the molecular weight of the substance. Suppose we have a substance A whose molecular weight is 50, and another substance B whose molecular weight is 100. Then each molecule of B weighs twice as much as a molecule of A, and hence a 100-gram sample of B will contain the same number of molecules as a 50-gram sample of A. Therefore a mole of B contains the same number of molecules as a mole of A. Convince yourself that a 25-gram sample of D, whose molecular weight is 25, will contain this same number of molecules. Similarly, 2 grams of H_2 contains the same number of molecules as 18 grams of H_2O.

We can now find out how many molecules there are in a mole of H_2, and therefore how many molecules constitute a mole. (We use H_2 for the computation simply because the mass of an atom of H has already been figured out above.) Since it contains two H atoms, a molecule of H_2 has a mass of

$$2 \times 1.67 \times 10^{-27} \text{ kg} = 3.34 \times 10^{-27} \text{ kg},$$

and hence a weight of 3.34×10^{-24} g (because a kilogram weighs 1000 g).

A mole of H_2 weighs

$$2 \times 1.008 \text{ g} = 2.016 \text{ g}.$$

But

$$\text{Weight of a mole} = \text{Weight of 1 molecule} \times \text{Number of molecules in a mole},$$

so

$$2.016 \text{ g} = 3.34 \times 10^{-24} \text{ g} \times N,$$

where N is the number of molecules in a mole. Solving this gives

$$N = \frac{2.016 \text{ g}}{3.34 \times 10^{-24} \text{ g}} = 6.02 \times 10^{23}.$$

That is,

$$N = 602{,}000{,}000{,}000{,}000{,}000{,}000{,}000.$$

The number of molecules in a mole is so much beyond our experience that we can scarcely form any idea of it. If a small raindrop evaporated by losing only a million molecules per second, it would take about a million years to evaporate. An indirect but entertaining way of seeing what a large number of molecules there are in a mole is to consider the poison drunk by Socrates. If the potion consisted mostly of water, and he drank a cupful (about 10 moles) of it, and if that water has now become thoroughly mixed with the other water on the earth, then a modern cup of coffee contains over 1000 of those fateful molecules.

Summary

Millikan measured the charges on tiny drops of oil, by measuring the forces exerted on them by electric fields of known strength. He found that the charge on any droplet was some multiple of 1.60×10^{-19} coulomb; this amount is therefore the quantum of charge, denoted by the symbol e.

When the quantum of charge had been measured, the masses of the various ions could be calculated from the previously measured charge-to-mass ratios. This leads to a knowledge of the actual masses and actual weights of atoms, and hence also of molecules.

By taking the weight of a mole of any substance, and dividing it by the weight of one molecule of that substance, we can find how many molecules there are in one mole; there are about 6×10^{23} molecules in a mole.

Questions

1. Describe the essential parts of Millikan's apparatus for measuring the charge on the electron.
2. For what purpose did Millikan measure the rate of fall of his oil drops when the electric field was turned off?
3. In his oil-drop experiment, what forces did Millikan employ?
4. How did Millikan find the quantum of charge from the charges on his oil drops?
5. How could Millikan determine the charges carried by ions?
6. Using the measured value of the quantum of charge, and Thomson's value for the charge-to-mass ratio of a cathode-ray particle (Article 42–2), calculate the mass of an electron.
7. The text calculates the number of molecules in a mole. Suppose that somebody gave you this number of small dice, a quarter of an inch on each edge. If you stacked them neatly and evenly over the whole land area of the United States, how thick a layer would you get? (The land area of the United States is 2.97×10^6 square miles. Disregard the fact that it is bumpy.)
8. Compare the mass of an electron with the mass of a hydrogen atom. Use this comparison to show that the mass of an ion in electrolysis is about the same as the mass of the corresponding atom.
9. Show that Millikan's oil-drop experiment can be regarded as measuring the charge-to-mass ratio of a body that is large enough so that its mass can be found from an auxiliary measurement.

44

CANAL RAYS AND ISOTOPES

We have seen that the cathode rays in a discharge tube are streams of negatively charged particles, called electrons. We now turn to another aspect of electrical discharges in gases—one which has been almost as fruitful as cathode rays in enhancing our understanding of atoms.

44–1. Canal Rays (1886). Even before the nature of the cathode rays was understood, a German investigator discovered another sort of rays in a discharge tube. He found that if the cathode of a discharge tube has a hole cut in it, as in Figure 44–A, the gas behind the cathode glows in such a way as to suggest that rays of some kind are passing through the hole. These rays are called, not very aptly, *canal rays.* (They pass

FIGURE 44–A. A discharge tube for exhibiting canal rays.

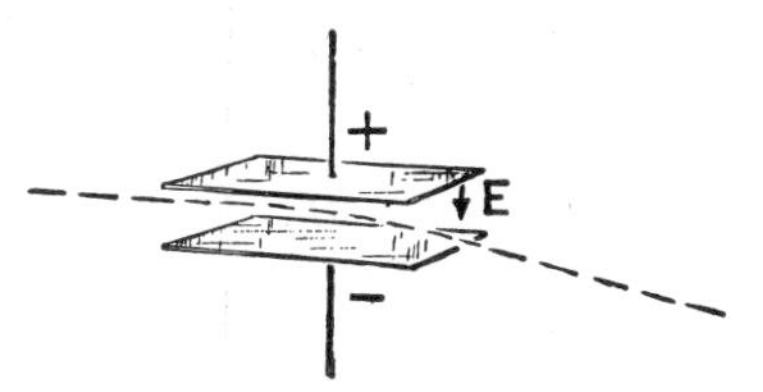

FIGURE 44–B. Canal rays being deflected in an electric field.

through a "canal" connecting the space behind the cathode with the region in which the discharge takes place. A ray is anything that travels in a straight line if not interfered with.) When in the region of discharge, the canal rays clearly travel toward the cathode, so one immediately suspects that they are positively charged particles. To verify this guess, one of course tests to find out whether the rays are bent by passage through an electric or magnetic field. The first attempts at deflecting the rays were unsuccessful, but when strong enough electric and magnetic fields became available, the canal rays were bent. If, for example, the rays are passed through the electric field set up between a pair of oppositely charged plates (Figure 44–B), they are bent in the direction of the field, i.e. toward the negatively charged plate. This deflection shows that the rays actually do carry positive charge.

44–2. The Nature of the Rays. As we have already seen in the case of the electrons in cathode rays, one of the observable properties of a charged particle is its charge-to-mass ratio. It will be useful to recapitulate the method that Thomson used to measure the charge-to-mass ratio for electrons, in order to judge whether the same scheme can be applied to the canal-ray particles. The force that a charge experiences in an electric field depends on how big the charge is, but the force a charge experiences in a magnetic field depends not only on how big the charge is

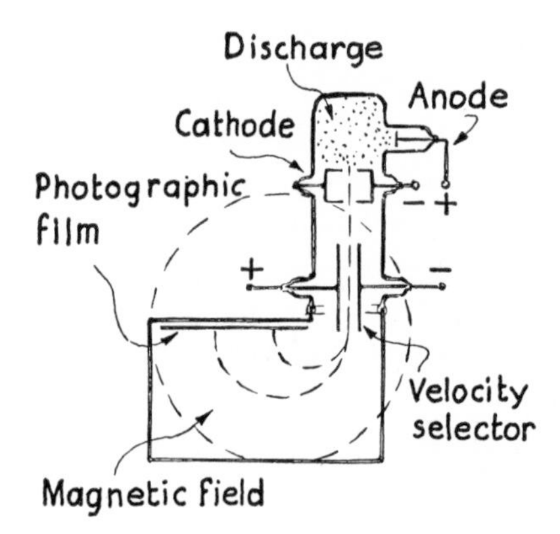

FIGURE 44–C. A "mass spectrograph," for measuring the charge-to-mass ratios of canal-ray particles.

but also on how fast it is moving. Thomson passed his cathode rays through electric and magnetic fields whose strengths were adjusted so that the forces they exerted on the beam were equal and opposite, and the beam was not deflected at all. The requisite strength of the magnetic field being proportional to the velocity of the charged particles, he was able to determine the velocity of his particles (Article 42–1). Then by observing how much the particles were deflected by a known magnetic field acting alone, he was able to calculate the charge-to-mass ratio for the particles (Article 42–2).

Except for one difficulty, Thomson's method can be used to measure the charge-to-mass ratio for the particles in canal rays. The difficulty is that the canal-ray particles do not all have the same velocity. The way in which Thomson's method has been modified to cope with this complication is typical of the schemes that a modern experimenter must resort to. As shown in Figure 44–C, the canal rays emerge in a narrow beam from a long canal connected to a discharge tube. Then they pass into the electric field between two plates that are parallel and close together. In the diagram, this electric field urges the particles to the right. The plates, however, lie between the poles of a large magnet, which produces a magnetic field directed out of the paper toward the reader. This magnetic field urges the charged particles to the left. The electric field exerts the same force on all of the particles that carry the same charge, in accord with the equation.

$$\text{Electric force} = \text{Electric field strength} \times \text{Charge},$$

or

$$F_{\text{electric}} = Eq.$$

On the other hand, the magnetic field exerts a large force on the fast particles and a smaller force on the slower ones, in accord with the equation

$$\text{Magnetic force} = \text{Magnetic field strength} \times \text{Charge} \times \text{Velocity of charge},$$

or

$$F_{\text{magnetic}} = Bqv.$$

For particles of some velocity, the force exerted by the magnetic field will exactly counterbalance the force exerted by the electric field, and these particles will pass through the narrow channel between the plates without being deviated. All slower particles will be deflected to the right, and all faster ones will be deflected to the left; they will bump into the charged plates and will be removed from the beam. Reference to the equations above shows that for those particles that get through the plates,

$$Eq = Bqv,$$

or

$$v = \frac{E}{B}.$$

After these selected particles emerge from the electric field between the plates, they are acted on by the magnetic field only. The situation then corresponds to the second part of Thomson's experiment on cathode rays. The force exerted by the magnetic field is perpendicular to the direction of motion of the particle. The particle therefore experiences an acceleration at right angles to its motion, and consequently it moves in a curved path. The argument of Article 42–2 applies without change, and the charge-to-mass ratio of the canal-ray particles is given by the equation

$$\frac{q}{m} = \frac{v}{Br},$$

where B is the strength of the magnetic field and r is the radius of the circular path in which the particles move when acted on by the magnetic field alone. By letting the particles strike a photographic film, which they affect as light does, one can find where they strike and can therefore determine the radius of the path they followed. Then all of the quantities on the right side of the equation are known, and q/m can be determined.

When the canal rays come from a discharge tube filled with hydrogen, several points of impact appear on the photographic film. The particles causing one of the spots turn out to have the same charge-to-mass ratio as we found for the H^+ ion in electrolysis, and the charge-to-mass ratio for the particles hitting the other spot is just half as great. This means that some of the canal rays in a hydrogen-filled discharge tube are H^+ ions, whereas others, having twice as much mass, are H_2^+ ions. The latter are molecules of hydrogen that have had an electron removed by the jostling and colliding that goes on in the discharge. There is also a spot caused by H_3^+ ions, which have a very brief existence in the discharge.

If oxygen instead of hydrogen is used in the discharge tube, the measurements show the canal rays to consist of O^+ ond O_2^+ ions. If the discharge is sufficiently violent, there will be other oxygen ions that have two or more quanta of positive charge, resulting from the loss of two or more electrons. Such experiments show that the canal rays are *ionized atoms* or *ionized molecules*, and the conduction of electricity in gases therefore resembles in some ways the conduction in solutions. One important difference is that in solutions, as we can see from freezing-point tests, the ions exist whether electricity is actually being transported or not. In gases, on the other hand, almost all of the ions are produced by the electric discharge.

The details of the process of discharge in gases are extremely complex. They seem to be pretty well understood in the main, but are not of much concern in our particular line of study. Curiosity will perhaps demand at least a short statement about the process. In brief, the ions are created when gas molecules are struck by previously created ions, or by the cathode rays. The cathode rays, in turn, are electrons that get knocked out of the cathode when it is struck by the positive ions. The discharge is started in the first place by the presence in the tube of a few ions that are created by other processes, notably by the radioactivity that forms the subject of the next chapter.

44–3. Isotopes (1912). Canal rays are of interest to us because, in the hands of Thomson and his successors, they have revealed something about atoms that was not previously suspected. The canal rays from hydrogen and oxygen discharges are complicated by the presence of ionized molecules. Tin vapor, being monatomic, could be expected to produce just a single spot on the photographic film, made by the Sn^+ ion. When the canal rays from a discharge in tin vapor are tested, however, one is shocked to find ten spots on the film, showing that there are ten kinds * of tin atoms! Assigning to the oxygen a mass of 16 units,† and ascribing to each tin ion a charge of one quantum, we find that the various kinds of tin atoms have masses of 112, 114, 115, 116, 117, 118, 119, 120, 122, and 124 units. Figure 44–D is made from a photographic film struck by ions from a discharge in the vapor of tin. The numbers are the masses corresponding to the various positions on the film.

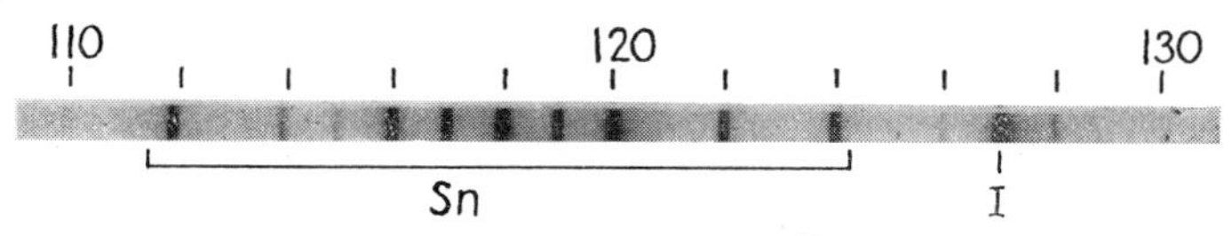

K. T. Bainbridge, Harvard University

FIGURE 44–D. The isotopes of tin. The spot corresponding to a mass of 127 units was made by ions of iodine, which was present in the discharge; only one kind of iodine atom occurs in nature, so the iodine produces only one spot.

In deciding whether an atom is a tin atom or not, a chemist is guided by its chemical behavior, not by its mechanical behavior. Therefore differences in the masses of atoms do not prevent the chemist from classifying them as being alike. It is true that the chemist is interested in atomic weights, but he always deals with very large numbers of atoms at a time. In determining atomic weights, therefore, he measures the *average* atomic weight of a group of atoms whose chemical properties are the same. In the case of tin, he concludes that the atomic weight is 118.70. All samples of tin found in nature have this same atomic weight, showing that the ten kinds of tin atoms are uniformly intermixed.

In physical experiments, the different kinds of atoms of a single element can be distinguished from one another. The physicist therefore needs separate names for them, and assigns to the various tin atoms the names Sn^{112}, Sn^{114}, . . ., Sn^{124}. Since atoms that differ only in mass are atoms of the same element and fit in the same place in the Periodic Table, they

* The spots cannot be explained as coming from tin atoms that have lost various numbers of electrons, because in that case the other charge-to-mass ratios would be 2, 3, 4, 5, up to 10 times the smallest one. Actually the charge-to-mass ratios differ by only a few percent. This shows that the kinds of tin ions differ in mass rather than in charge. The multiple-charged ions that can be produced in a more violent discharge make still other spots, well separated from the ones we mention.

† Fortunately oxygen atoms are overwhelmingly, although not entirely, of one kind. This kind is assigned a relative mass of 16. The fact that some few oxygen atoms are different from this one results in a slight difference between the scale of atomic masses and the scale of atomic weights, because the latter is based on nature's mixture of oxygen atoms. Since the two scales differ only by a factor of 1.000272, the difference will not be important to us.

are called *isotopes* of the element. "Isotope" comes from Greek roots meaning "same place."

Because the apparatus under discussion spreads out atoms of different masses in the same way, superficially speaking, as a prism spreads light of different colors into a spectrum, the apparatus is called a *mass spectrograph.*

There are some elements, among them argon, iodine, and gold, of which nature provides only a single kind of atom. Most elements, however, occur in several isotopes. Hydrogen occurs as H^1 and H^2, although the existence of the latter was for some time obscured by the fact that its atomic weight, 2.015, is nearly the same as the molecular weight of H^1_2, which is 2.016. The heavier isotope of hydrogen is called *deuterium,* from the Greek word for "second." Isotopes of the other elements do not have special names.

In the early nineteenth century it was thought that atomic weights were all integers. When methods of measurement improved, chlorine was found to have an atomic weight of about 35.5, which is certainly not an integer. Later work gives 35.46 for chlorine, and puts decimal places on all of the other atomic weights that have been accurately measured. When we put chlorine in the mass spectrograph, however, we find it to be a mixture of two isotopes, Cl^{35} and Cl^{37}, each of whose atomic weights is *very nearly* an integer. The actual figures are 34.9707 and 36.9676. The lighter isotope is about three times as plentiful as the heavy one, so the average atomic weight is about 35.5, in agreement with the figure obtained by chemical means.

The existence of isotopes means that there are more kinds of atoms than we had supposed, but since the atomic weights of individual atoms are much closer to being integers than we had thought, the discovery of isotopes reveals that the relationship of atoms to one another must be unexpectedly simple.

Summary

If there is a hole, or canal, in the cathode of a discharge tube, there pass through it rays which consist of positively charged particles. Deflection in electric and magnetic fields shows that these particles are ions of the gas in the discharge tube, and that not all of the ions of a given element have the same mass. An element therefore may, and in fact usually does, consist of several kinds of atoms.

The different kinds of atoms of a single element are called isotopes. They are distinguished from one another by adding to the chemical symbol for the element a number showing the relative mass of the atom, the abundant isotope of oxygen being assigned a mass of 16 to make the physical scale of atomic masses coincide very nearly with the chemical scale of atomic weights.

Accurate measurement of the atomic masses shows that they are nearly, but not quite, integers. The chemically determined atomic weights are the relative weights, on the average, of large numbers of atoms that are chemically alike but physically not all alike.

QUESTIONS

1. Under what circumstances are canal rays observed? What do these rays consist of?
2. The problem of measuring the charge-to-mass ratio for canal-ray particles is somewhat like that of measuring the charge-to-mass ratio of electrons. State one similarity and one difference between these two problems.
3. The velocity of the particles that get through the velocity selector in Article 44–2 is $v = E/B$. The same equation was obtained for the velocity of the cathode rays in Article 42–1. Explain.
4. What are isotopes?
5. How does the study of canal rays bring to light the existence of isotopes?
6. What sort of revision of Dalton's hypotheses (Article 20–4) does the discovery of isotopes make necessary?
7. If a small proportion of Pb^{204} is disregarded, then in round figures the isotopic constitution of lead is: one-half Pb^{208}, one-quarter Pb^{207}, and one-quarter Pb^{206}. Assume that the atomic weights of these isotopes are integers, and calculate the atomic weight of lead. Compare your result with the experimental value listed in the table of atomic weights in the Appendix.

45

RADIOACTIVITY

Fluorescence, which is emission of light incited by light of another color, or by some other agent, is in these days a familiar phenomenon. It is seen in fluorescent lamps, where the stimulating agent is light, and in television tubes where the stimulating agent is a pencil of cathode rays. Many salts exhibit fluorescence. Some of the most striking of these are salts of uranium. It was while experimenting with fluorescence that a Frenchman named Becquerel, about the turn of the century, ushered in the atomic age by the chance discovery that uranium salts emit something that is not light, but that will affect a photographic film.

45–1. The Discovery of Radioactivity (1896). Becquerel found that if a photographic film, protected from light by a wrapping of black paper, is left for a day or so in the neighborhood of a uranium compound and then developed in the usual way, the film is blackened as if it had been exposed to light. He soon discovered that *all* uranium compounds show this effect, whether they exhibit fluorescence or not, and he found that uranium metal itself shows the effect even more strongly. This fact shows that the effect arises from atoms rather than from some molecular combination, and shows also that it has nothing to do with fluorescence. The effect is called *radioactivity*.

Experiment. A smooth slab of rock containing specks of the uranium-bearing mineral uraninite was placed on a photographic film for two days, and then the film was developed without ever having been exposed to light. Figure 45–A shows the result. The film turned dark at the spots where it was exposed to uraninite, and the rock took its own picture.

Whatever it is that emanates from radioactive material will not only affect a photographic film, but it also produces ionization in the air near the material.

Experiment. An electroscope, whether positively or negatively charged, loses its charge when a uranium-bearing rock is held near it. This loss occurs because some of the air molecules are broken up into ions, and ions of the appropriate sign are attracted to the electroscope and neutralize its charge.

Since it is quick and lends itself readily to quantitative measurements, detection of radioactivity by electrical means is more convenient for most purposes than the photographic detection that led to the initial discovery.

(a) (b)

FIGURE 45-A. (a) A uranium-bearing rock, photographed in the usual way. (b) The same rock, photographed by means of its radioactivity.

45-2. Radium. By 1898 Pierre and Marie Curie had found that there are elements that are more radioactive than uranium, in the sense that a given quantity of the substance will discharge an electroscope faster. They named one of the new elements "polonium," after Marie Curie's native country, and the other they called "radium." These elements occur in nature along with uranium, but they have different chemical properties.

Radium was found by treating uranium ore with acids, and separating the resulting salts by exploiting the differences in their solubilities in water, ammonia, and other solvents. After each separation, the radioactive substance was located by testing the chemicals for radioactivity with an electroscope. Among other elements, the uranium ore contained appreciable amounts of barium. The chemical treatment yielded barium chloride, and when this was separated from the uranium, most of the radioactivity went along with it. Now barium itself is not radioactive, so the Curies concluded that with their electroscope they had found a new element, chemically similar to barium, and present in the form of a chloride in their solution of barium chloride. This new element, radium, has now had its atomic weight and other properties well determined, and you will notice that it fits just below barium in the Periodic Table. The Curies found that although radium chloride is chemically very much like barium chloride, it is a little less soluble in a mixture of alcohol and water, and this difference makes it possible to separate the two substances by repeated crystallizations.

45–3. The Radioactive Rays. Simple experiments with "shadows" cast by substantial objects, such as the gun mechanism in Figure 45–B, show that the agency that blackens photographic films and ionizes air has the property of traveling in straight lines, and it may therefore be said to consist of rays.

As with the cathode rays, one faces the question whether these rays are streams of particles. If they are particles, then very likely they are fragments of uranium atoms, or of other radioactive atoms, and if so, they might be expected to carry a charge. By letting the rays pass through a couple of slits bounded by thick lead plates, as in Figure 45–C, one can confine the rays to a narrow beam. When this beam traverses a sufficiently strong electric field and falls on a photographic film, one finds that part of the beam is slightly deviated in the direction of the electric field, show-

---

PIERRE CURIE, like a notable number of other nineteenth-century scientists, never went to school; he studied at home until ready for the University of Paris. As professor of physics in a small technical school, he did research of enduring value, first on the mathematical and physical properties of crystals, later on magnetism. MARIE CURIE, *née* Marya Sklodowska in Warsaw, worked for years as a governess in Poland before saving enough money to enter the University of Paris, where she took master's degrees in physics and mathematics. After marrying Pierre in 1895, she began as a doctoral research the work that culminated in their discovery of polonium and of radium. The photograph on the opposite page was taken on one of their brief outings at this time. As a widow, Marie took Pierre's place as professor of physics at the Sorbonne.

The Curies are supreme examples of devotion to science. Handicapped as they were by inadequate equipment and by pitiful salaries that destroyed their health, they made discoveries that not only changed our conception of matter, but also provided what was for many years the only effective therapy for cancer. They decided that the spirit of science did not allow them to patent their process for extracting radium, although they knew that the patent would relieve them from want. Pierre was a physicist of the first rank, but Marie was unique. She was the first woman to hold a professorship at the Sorbonne. The only other woman who has received a Nobel Prize in physical science is one of her daughters, and Marie is the only person to have received the prize twice (in Physics, 1903; in Chemistry, 1911).

By courtesy of the Bettmann Archive

Pierre Curie and Marie Curie
(1859–1906) (1867–1934)

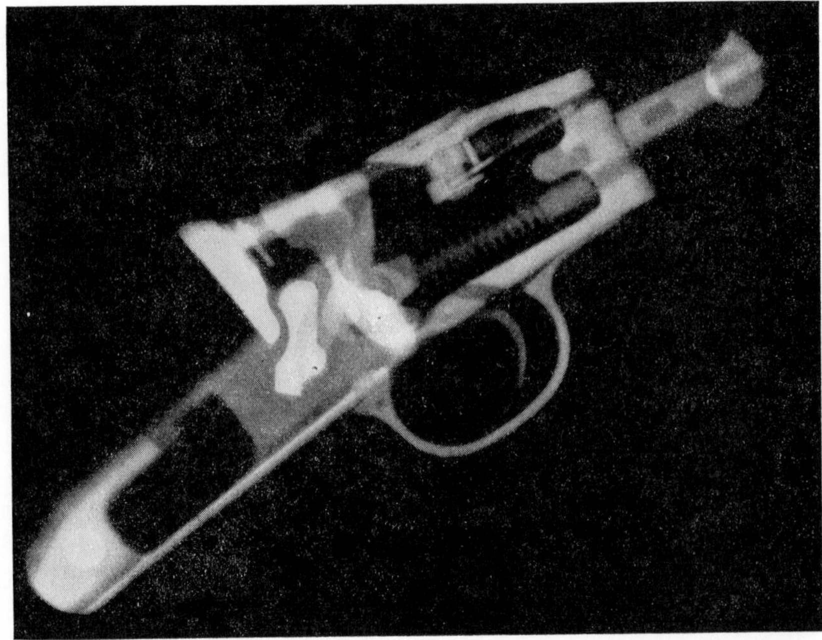

Tracerlab, Inc.

FIGURE 45–B. The "shadow" cast by a gun mechanism resting on a photographic film exposed to a radioactive substance. Note that the wooden stock and some other parts are nearly transparent to the rays and do not noticeably hinder the blackening of the film.

ing that it consists of positively charged particles; another part of the beam is strongly deviated in the opposite direction, showing that it consists of negatively charged particles. A third set of rays is not influenced by the electric field; therefore it either consists of uncharged particles or else resembles light. (Although we have not studied light yet, you know that it affects a photographic film, and you are not surprised to hear that it is not electrically charged and that therefore a beam of light is not bent when it passes through an electric field. Actually the third set of rays does resemble light, and for this reason as well as others we cannot postpone some study of light very much longer.) The three types of rays are

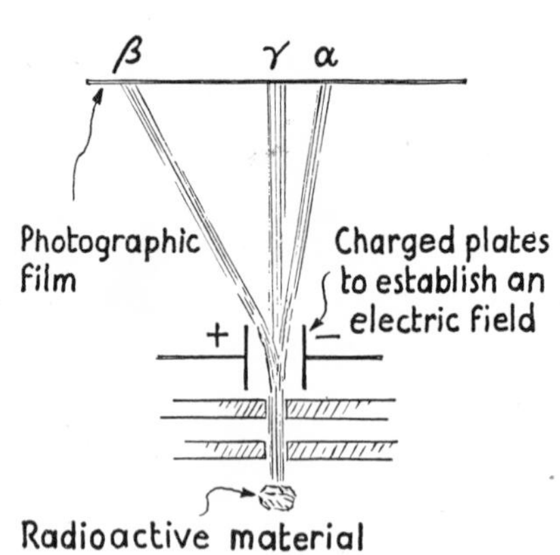

FIGURE 45–C. The rays from radioactive substances are of three different types.

called α- (alpha), β- (beta) and γ- (gamma) rays, because names were needed for them before anyone knew what they were.

One very simple distinction concerning the rays can be drawn at once. The alpha-rays have very little ability to penetrate matter, being stopped by a piece of paper or by a couple of inches of air at atmospheric pressure. The beta-rays will penetrate about a fiftieth of an inch of aluminum, and the gamma-rays are not seriously impeded by an inch of aluminum.

Progress in the study of gamma-rays was slow, and we can profitably put them off until later. Since the alpha- and beta-rays are charged particles, they can be investigated as the cathode and canal rays were, by deflection in electric and magnetic fields. The β-rays, which are easier to experiment with because they are more penetrating and more easily deflected, were identified first.

45–4. The Beta-Rays. By subjecting them to the kind of experiment that Thomson did with cathode rays, Becquerel found that the β-ray particles have the same charge-to-mass ratio as the cathode-ray particles. He therefore, correctly, identified them as electrons. They differ from cathode rays only in the way they are produced, and in their speed and kinetic energy. Not all β-particles, even from a single substance, travel with the same velocity. Roughly speaking, however, they have 100 to 1000 times as much kinetic energy as Thomson's cathode rays. In order to give electrons in a cathode-ray tube as much energy as the β-particles have, one must let the cathode rays move through a difference of potential of hundreds of thousands, or for some β-rays over a million, volts. (The difference of potential through which the electrons "fall" in a cathode-ray tube is usually only a few thousand volts.)

45–5. The Electron-Volt. Even though the β particles travel at tremendous velocities, near 300 million meters, or 186,000 miles, per second, their mass is so small that their kinetic energy is only about one ten-millionth of a millionth of a joule, or 10^{-13} joule. We therefore need a smaller unit of energy for use in dealing with atoms. Recall that the difference of potential between two points is the energy acquired by a charge in moving from one point to the other, divided by the size of the charge. A volt is a joule per coulomb; that is, a coulomb of charge passing between two points will gain or lose a joule of potential energy if the difference of potential is one volt. One could say, then, that a joule is a coulomb-volt. The unit of energy used in the atomic domain is the energy acquired, not by a coulomb, but by a single quantum of charge, when it falls through a potential difference of one volt. That is, it is the energy acquired by an electron when it passes between two points whose potentials differ by one volt. The unit is called the *electron-volt.* Since the charge of an electron is only 1.60×10^{-19} coulomb, 1 electron-volt = 1.60×10^{-19} joule. This unit is of a very convenient size in much atomic work. Very frequently, however, one deals with energies in millions of electron-volts, and the abbreviation Mev is used to designate a million electron-volts. The energy of β-rays is frequently about 1 Mev.

If any ion with a charge of 1 quantum falls through a potential difference of 10 volts, it gains an energy of 10 electron-volts. The mass of the ion does not matter—if it is a massive ion, it will not acquire as much velocity as a light ion or an electron would, but it acquires the same K.E.

45–6. The Alpha-Rays. The job of identification was more difficult for the α-rays than for the β-rays. Tests with electric and magnetic fields disclosed the velocity of the particles. Then deflection in a magnetic field, to determine their charge-to-mass ratio, showed this quantity to be half as large as it is for H^+ ions (see Article 44–2). The simplest assumption to make would be that the α-particles have a charge of 1 quantum and a mass of 2 units on the atomic-mass scale, which would make them H_2^+ ions. Following the clue that helium is always found in radioactive rocks, and seldom found anywhere else on the earth, a young worker named Rutherford, who afterward became the most distinguished of all atomic physicists, showed in 1909 that the α-particles are not hydrogen ions, but are doubly charged ions of helium. (Check for yourself that the latter ions will have a charge-to-mass ratio that is the same as that for the H_2^+ ion.) Rutherford's proof consisted in putting a sample of radioactive material near a discharge tube in which there was no helium, the material being separated from the discharge tube only by a glass window so thin that the alpha-particles could go through it. After a couple of days, the light given out by the tube when a discharge passed through it contained a yellow component that is typical of the discharge in helium (see Chapter 49).

45–7. The Detection of Single Alpha-Particles. The photographic and ionizing effects of the α-particles permitted workers to observe the behavior of streams of these particles. In 1903 a way of following the fortunes of a single α-particle was devised, thereby making possible the first observations on the behavior of single particles of atomic or subatomic size. It was well known that some salts, for example zinc sulfide, fluoresce when struck by a stream of cathode rays. It was found that zinc sulfide also fluoresces when struck by α-particles, and that viewing the salt through a low-power microscope makes visible a scintillation, or brief speck of light, every time an α-particle strikes the area you are looking at.

Experiment. The end of a short metal tube is coated on the inside with zinc sulfide, which can be viewed through a magnifying lens at the other end of the tube. Supported near the zinc sulfide is a speck of radioactive material which emits α-particles. Provided one's eye has been in darkness for a few minutes, the scintillations caused by the impact of the individual α-particles can be seen with the aid of the lens.

Luminous watch dials of the better grade are made with some fluorescent salt and a trace of radioactive material that emits α-particles. The scintillations that make the dial visible in the dark can be seen individually in a dark room, with the aid of a magnifying lens.

The ability to observe the impact of individual subatomic particles opened up a new realm of possibilities. Hitherto, all atomic experiments had to be based on the average behavior of large numbers of atoms; now research on single atomic events could begin.

Summary

Uranium and some other elements of high atomic weight are radioactive. That is, they emit radiations that can be detected by the effect which they produce on a photographic film, or by the ionization which they produce when they pass through air.

By letting the rays from radioactive substances pass through an electric field, one finds that there are three kinds of rays, called alpha, beta, and gamma. The α-rays are positively charged particles, the β-rays are negatively charged particles, and the γ-rays are not charged at all. The nature of the γ-rays will have to be explained later. Experiments on the charge-to-mass ratio of the α- and β-particles show that the α's are doubly charged helium ions, and the β's are swiftly moving electrons.

In the atomic domain, the joule is too large for convenience. A new unit called the electron-volt is therefore introduced. It is the amount of energy gained by an electron, or any other particle bearing a single quantum of charge, when it falls through a potential difference of 1 volt. A million electron-volts is abbreviated Mev.

An α-particle striking a suitable crystal, such as zinc sulfide, produces a flash of light that is visible to the dark-adapted eye. This phenomenon made possible the first observations on individual atomic events.

Questions

1. Describe the discovery of radioactivity.
2. State two effects by which radioactivity may be detected.
3. Show how the Periodic Table bears on the procedure that the Curies used when they isolated radium.
4. Cite evidence that there are three kinds of rays that emanate from radioactive substances. Name the three kinds, and distinguish between them.
5. State the nature of α-particles, and tell how it was ascertained.
6. What is meant by "an energy of 1 Mev"?

46

THE ATOMIC NUCLEUS

In the opening years of this century, the passage of α- and β-particles through gases and solids was the subject of many investigations, because it was hoped that the behavior of these particles in their interaction with atoms would give clues to the constitution of the atoms. One obvious problem was to find out how the particles could make their way through solid films of celluloid or metal. Rutherford, who had earlier determined the nature of α-particles (Article 45–6), saw the value of observing the α-particles individually in researches of this kind.

46–1. The Discovery of the Nucleus (1911). With some of his students, Rutherford used the scintillation technique to study the passage of α-particles through very thin sheets of gold, and later of other metals that can be made into foils. Using the scheme sketched in Figure 46–A, they found that most of the particles that passed through the foils were deviated from their courses by less than 1°, but that some particles were deflected through much larger angles. Rutherford reasoned that the deflections were due to the electric forces exerted on the (positively charged) α-particles by the charged constituents of the atoms in the metal foil. Now we have seen that an α-particle has almost 8000 times as much mass as an electron, because it has 4 times as much mass as a hydrogen ion, which in turn has almost 2000 times as much mass as an electron. Therefore if an α-particle and an electron have an encounter in which they exert forces on one another, then the α-particle, by virtue of its larger inertia, will not be much affected; it will go right on like a sailboat that

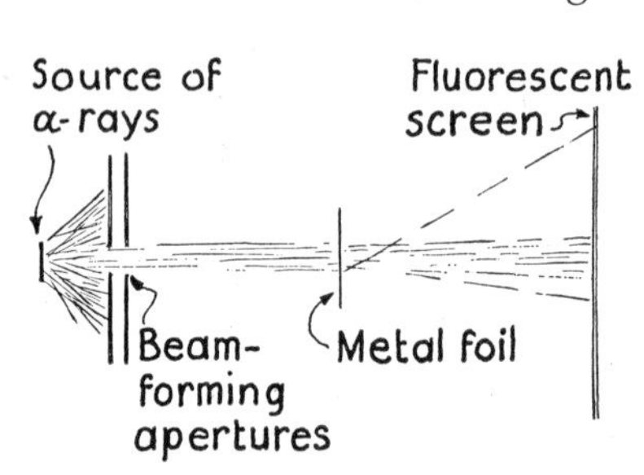

FIGURE 46–A. Rutherford's experiment on the scattering of alpha-particles by a metal foil.

hits a floating bottle. Rutherford concluded that the deflection of the α-particle was caused by electric forces exerted by the more massive parts of the atoms in the foil. These massive parts presumably carried a positive charge, since the electrons are negative and the atom as a whole is neutral.

At this time, ideas about the structure of the atom were not very definite. Perhaps the most specific suggestion was one that had been put forward by Thomson, whose position as leader of atomic research had not yet been passed on to Rutherford. After his discovery that atoms contain electrons, Thomson had advanced the hypothesis that the atom is a sphere of positive electricity, in which enough electrons to neutralize the charge are imbedded like raisins in a bun.

One thing that was definitely known about atoms was their approximate size. By studying the differences between real gases and the idealized model of a gas which we discussed in Chapters 17 and 18, one can estimate the sizes of atoms. Those chapters are far enough back so that a review of the point may be helpful. We mentioned that the law $pV = cT$ does not hold when the pressure is high enough so that the molecules are crowded close together. Under these conditions, the space taken up by the molecules themselves has to be subtracted from the volume of the box in order to get the effective volume in which the molecules are free to move. The space actually occupied by the molecules can therefore be found by experimenting with the pressure–volume relationship in gases at high pressure. It is easy then to estimate the size of an individual molecule. If the gas is monatomic, this is the size of the atom. Measurements of this kind show that the radius of an atom is in the neighborhood of 10^{-10} m.

In order to get information about the gold atom from the behavior of his α-particles, Rutherford calculated the force that the positive part of an atom exerts on an α-particle. This can be done by using Coulomb's Law, which says that the force exerted by a concentrated charge Q on another concentrated charge q is

$$F = K\frac{Qq}{d^2},$$

where d is the distance between the charges. Now this law is similar in form to Newton's Law of Gravitation, which says that a planet, for example, is attracted toward the sun with a force that is inversely proportional to the square of their distance apart. In symbols,

$$F = G\frac{Mm}{d^2}\cdot$$

One important difference between these two situations is that the planet is *attracted* to the sun, but the α-particle is *repelled* by the positive part of the gold atom. You will recall that the planet moves about the sun in an ellipse, a fact which was observed by Kepler and which was shown mathematically by Newton to be a consequence of the Law of Gravitation. In the same way it can be shown that if a small positively charged particle passes near a massive one, the path of the particle will be another of the conic sections of Apollonius, a hyperbola (Article 2–5).* Figure 46–B shows several such paths. The closer the α-particle comes to the other charge, the more it will be deflected from its original direction. Rutherford found that some of the α-particles were deflected so much that they must have passed within about 10^{-13} meter of the positive charge. Remembering that the atom has a radius of about 10^{-10} meter, we see that if the positive charge were spread throughout the atom as Thomson had supposed, then the α-particle would be penetrating to the interior of the positive charge, which would therefore not act as if it were concentrated at a point, and Coulomb's Law would not govern the situation. But Rutherford observed what percentage of the α-particles was deflected at various angles, and he showed that the distribution of deflections was correctly predicted by Coulomb's Law. Therefore Thomson's idea of the atom had to be abandoned, and Rutherford had to assume that all of the positive charge, along with most of the mass, is *concentrated in a little region less than 10^{-13} meter in radius,* although the radius of the atom is a thousand times larger. This means that practically all of the mass of the atom is concentrated in about one billionth † of the volume of the atom, in a little positively charged core which Rutherford christened the *nucleus.* The rest of the atom is occupied only by a few electrons, so most of the atom must be empty space! We can now see why an α-particle, or an electron, can pass through a "solid" foil of metal.

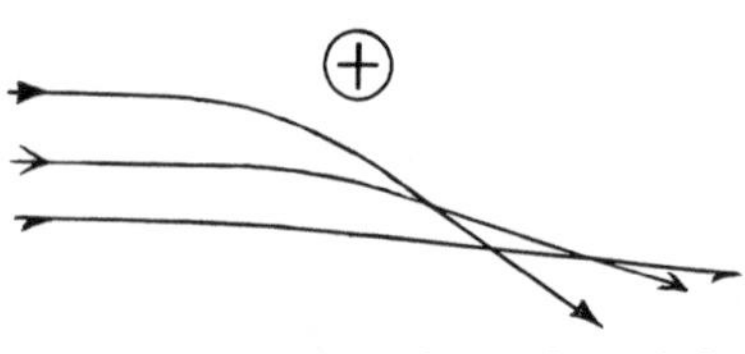

FIGURE 46–B. Three hyperbolic paths of deflected alpha-particles.

46–2. The Nucleus and the Periodic Table. In skillful hands, the passage of α-particles through metal foils reveals a still more majestic truth. Knowing now that the positive charge is concentrated in a nucleus, Rutherford was able to derive a formula for the number of α-particles deflected through a given angle, say 40°. This formula contains a factor involving the charge on the nucleus. By measuring the number of particles deflected through 40°, or some other convenient angle, by foils of

* In the gravitational case, when there is an "inverse square" law of *attraction,* the orbit *can* be hyperbolic, and it is so for some comets.

† The volume of a sphere is proportional to the cube of its radius. Therefore when the radii of two spheres differ by a factor of a thousand, the volumes differ by a factor of a thousand cubed, which is a billion.

different elements, Rutherford's students determined that *the number of quanta of charge on the nucleus is just equal to the atomic number of the element,* where by "atomic number" we mean (Article 40-1) the number that gives the position of the element in the Periodic Table. Thus, the aluminum nucleus has a positive charge of 13 quanta, which is neutralized by a surrounding swarm of 13 electrons. It is this fact that gives aluminum the thirteenth place in the Periodic Table. Here, then, is the hidden foundation of the Periodic Table.

Summary

Rutherford used the scintillation phenomenon to study the deflection of α-particles when they pass through thin foils of gold and other metals. In order to get a quantitative explanation of the deflections he observed, he had to give up the prevailing idea of atomic structure, and assume that all of the positive charge of an atom, along with most of its mass, is concentrated in a tiny nucleus. The nucleus is not more than 10^{-13} m in radius, although the radius of the atom is 1000 times as large (10^{-10} m). The nucleus is surrounded by electrons, but most of the atom is empty space.

By observing the deflections of α-particles by atoms of various elements, Rutherford's students were able to prove that the number of quanta of charge on the nucleus, and therefore the number of electrons in the nonionized atom, are just equal to the atomic number of the atom. (The atomic number of an atom is the number that gives the position of the atom in the Periodic Table. Hydrogen has atomic number 1; uranium has atomic number 92.) The chemical behavior of an element, and its position in the Periodic Table, are determined by the number of electrons in its nonionized atoms.

Questions

1. State two important aspects of atomic structure that were discovered by Rutherford and his students through their experiments with alpha-particles.
2. Describe the experimental equipment by means of which Rutherford learned that atoms have small nuclei.
3. Explain the part that Coulomb's Law played in the discovery of the atomic nucleus.
4. In what respect does the motion of an alpha-particle near the nucleus resemble the motion of a planet? Name one respect in which these two motions differ.
5. What aspect of an atom's constitution determines the place of that atom in the Periodic Table?

6. How did Rutherford's students measure the charge of certain nuclei?
7. Why can one not measure the charge on the nucleus of, say, aluminum, or gold, by experimenting with canal rays?

Suggestion for Further Reading

J. Chadwick, "The Charge on the Atomic Nucleus and the Law of Force," *Philosophical Magazine,* Series 6, vol. 40, pp. 734–46 (1920). A fine example of actual research reporting.

47

LIGHT WAVES

Light seeking light doth light of light beguile.

Love's Labour's Lost, I, i

Thus far in our survey of atomic science, the subject of light has been mentioned only casually. The time has now come, however, when a discussion of light can be postponed no longer.

The study of light began very early in the history of science. Euclid wrote a book on it. It was one of the few branches of science that advanced during the Dark Ages, when it was studied by the Moslems (who were by no means in the dark). The early work was mostly concerned with the way light is influenced by mirrors, lenses, prisms, and the like. This is a very interesting subject, and anybody who does laboratory work in atomic science needs to know something about it, but it need not be studied in order to understand the material in this book. The first discovery about light that has to concern us was made by an Italian Jesuit named Grimaldi, who was of an age to be Galileo's son or Newton's father.

47–1. Diffraction (1665). Grimaldi discovered that light does not always travel exactly in straight lines. He admitted sunlight into a darkened room through the very small hole *CD*, Figure 47–A, and let it pass through another small hole *GH* in an opaque screen. If light travels strictly in straight lines, then the region from *O* to *N* will be illuminated by rays that pass through the holes, but no light will reach any point below *O* or above *N*. Grimaldi, having calculated the distance *NO* by trigonometry, found that the illuminated portion of the wall covered a larger space,

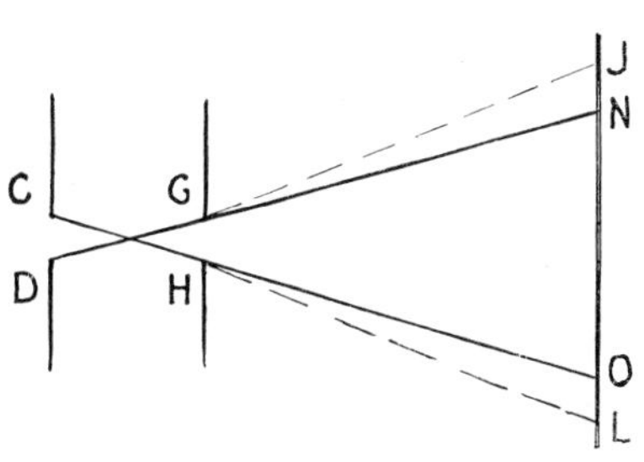

FIGURE 47–A. Grimaldi's discovery of diffraction.

JL. He therefore concluded that light does not travel in straight lines when it passes the edge of an obstacle.

The bending of light around the edge of an obstacle is called the *diffraction* of light.

47–2. Interference (1800). The next discovery that commands our attention was made in the Napoleonic period by Thomas Young, who read the English Bible at four, the Hebrew Bible at thirteen, did several pieces of scientific work of the first importance, practiced and taught medicine, and was one of the first to decipher the Egyptian hieroglyphics. This genius comes into our story because of his least spectacular and most enduring accomplishment, the correct interpretation of a very simple

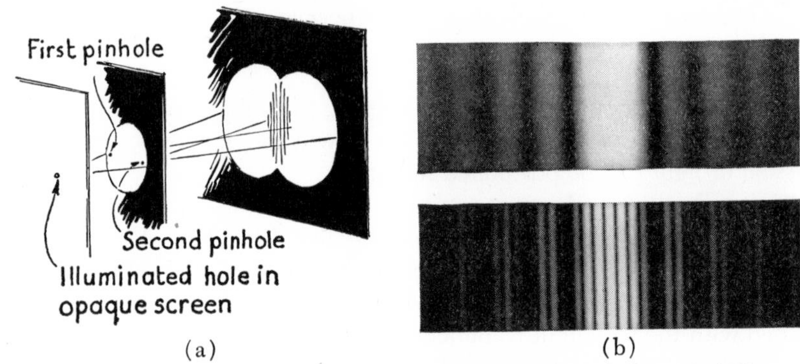

From F. W. Sears, Optics, *1949, Addison-Wesley Publishing Co.*

FIGURE 47–B. (a) Young's pinhole experiment. (b) The result of an experiment like Young's except that the light passed through slits instead of pinholes. For the upper half of the photograph, one of the slits was covered, so that we see how the light spreads by diffraction from one slit; in the lower half, light passes through both slits, and the areas receiving light from both of them are striped by bands of darkness.

observation. Figure 47–B shows how he let light enter a dark room through a pinhole in a window shade, and then let it pass through two other small openings very close together. When this is done, the region illuminated by *both* openings is crossed by alternating bands of light and darkness. Since the two overlapping beams of light produce darkness in some places, they are said to "interfere destructively" with one another at these places.

EXPERIMENT. If a tiny source of light is viewed through two closely adjacent parallel scratches in an opaque screen, one sees bright bands of light separated by dark lines.

The screen may be a blackened photographic film on which two parallel scratches are ruled with a phonograph needle. The source may be simply a needle hole in tinfoil, illuminated from behind. The light from a sodium-vapor lamp gives a particularly clear-cut effect.

Since the two beams of light produce darkness in part of the region where they overlap, the two beams must be interacting in some way. The interaction of beams of light that emanate from a common source, and reach a common point by more than one path, is called *interference* of light.

47–3. Rival Theories of Light. Before the discovery of interference, most scientists thought that light consisted of little particles, or *corpuscles*, emanating from a hot body like bullets from a machine gun. The theory that light is a wavelike disturbance traveling through space had been suggested by the great Dutch physicist Huygens, a contemporary of Newton. Newton rejected the idea that light consists of waves, arguing that if it did, then it would bend around an obstacle as a water wave bends around a stone that protrudes from a pond. Newton knew about Grimaldi's experiment, which shows that light actually *does* bend very slightly when it passes an obstacle, but the bending is so small that he ascribed it to some sort of influence that the edge of the obstacle might exert on the corpuscles that passed near it. Even the greatest genius, put face to face with a scientific fact, can misinterpret it.

When Young discovered the interference of light about 1800, he and others showed that the facts are entirely consistent with the wave theory. On the other hand, it is hard to see how two streams of corpuscles or bullets, traveling in the same direction, could cancel one another. The corpuscular theory was forthwith abandoned in favor of the wave theory. We must therefore learn a little about waves.

47–4. Waves. A wave can be defined as any disturbance that travels through space. For our purposes, however, a simpler conception will suffice—we can for the moment think of a wave as an endless succession of humps and hollows moving along with some constant velocity. For concreteness, these can be thought of as waves on the surface of the ocean. The tops of the humps are called "crests," and the bottoms of the hollows are called "troughs." The rate at which any crest moves is called the *velocity* of the wave. Another obvious quantity relating to the wave is the distance from one crest to the next. This distance is called the *wavelength* of the wave, and is usually designated by the symbol λ (*lambda*, the Greek "l"). Figure 47–C illustrates the meaning of wavelength.

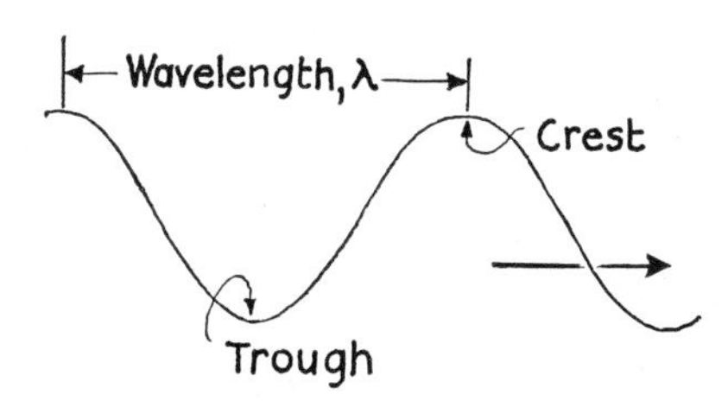

FIGURE 47–C. The meaning of "wavelength."

One of the keys to the study of wave phenomena is a relationship that exists among the wavelength and the velocity and another attribute of the wave. This attribute is the number of crests per second that pass a given point, and it is called the *frequency* of the wave. The frequency of a light wave is usually designated by the symbol ν (*nu*, the Greek "n," to remind us of "*n*umber of crests passing per second").

The relationship connecting the wavelength, the velocity, and the frequency takes the form of a simple equation. Clearly, the distance a wave travels per second is equal to the number of crests that pass a given point per second, multiplied by the distance between crests.* That is,

$$\text{Velocity} = \text{Frequency} \times \text{Wavelength}.$$

This relationship will be of use in a later chapter.

47–5. Explanation of Diffraction. The diffraction of a wave, its spreading around the edges of an obstacle in its path, is very easy to explain in a qualitative way. In order for a disturbance to be propagated from place to place, a disturbance at one point must have an effect on all nearby points. For example, if some point on a stretched clothes line is tapped with a stick, the point that is displaced by the stick will drag with it neighboring points that were not in contact with the stick. By pressing one's finger against some small area of a drumhead or a stretched table-

* Perhaps an analogy will be helpful. Suppose that you want to measure the speed of a train as it passes your parked car at a crossing. If each car is 90 feet long, and 12 cars pass in 24 seconds, then cars pass at the rate of 0.5 per second, and the train passes at the rate of 0.5 cars/sec × 90 ft/car = 45 ft/sec.

THOMAS YOUNG, like his contemporary John Dalton, was of Quaker parentage and was largely self-taught, but Young was as brilliant and versatile as Dalton was plodding and humdrum. After a very precocious childhood, Young spent his teens in the study of mathematics, a dozen languages, and the sciences. One of his favorite exercises was the translation of Shakespeare into Greek verse. Under the patronage of a rich uncle, who later willed him a comfortable income, he studied medicine at several universities and went into practice in London in 1800. While waiting for patients, he accepted the professorship of natural philosophy at the Royal Institution, which had just been founded under the sponsorship of Count Rumford. In Young's later life, physics was merely a hobby.

Although best noted for his pinhole experiment, Young is also remembered for lasting research on the optics of the human eye, on the perception of color, on elasticity and the strength of materials, and on the theory of life insurance. Perhaps his most striking accomplishment was the working out of the general principles of the Egyptian hieroglyphic form of writing, using the famous Rosetta stone, which contains part of a hieroglyphic inscription and its Greek equivalent.

From a painting by Sir Thomas Lawrence

THOMAS YOUNG, M.D.
(1773–1829)

cloth, one depresses not only the region in contact with the finger, but also neighboring regions as well. If the general level of a pond is disturbed by the piling up of water into a hump at some place, the water will run off of the hump in all directions, and will therefore raise the water level in the whole neighborhood of the hump. Suppose then that a wave encounters an obstacle with a hole in it. In order to deal with a familiar example, suppose that the obstacle is a breakwater at the entrance to a harbor. Let waves approach from the left, as shown. From time to time a crest will lie in the opening of the breakwater. As this crest passes into the harbor, it will disturb the water not only in front of it, but also on all sides of it. Therefore waves will spread out around the edges of the opening, as shown in the diagram. In other words, the wave passing through the opening will be diffracted.

FIGURE 47–D. Diffraction of a wave passing through an opening in an obstacle.

The foregoing explanation, which is essentially that given by Newton in his discussion of water waves, has a serious limitation: it is only qualitative. It shows that there will be *some* disturbance of the water in regions that from a purely geometrical point of view would be protected by the breakwater, but it says nothing about *how much* disturbance will occur at various places. The quantitative calculations demand some moderately advanced mathematics, and only their results can be stated here. It is found that the amount of spreading that occurs behind the breakwater depends on the ratio of the wavelength of the wave to the width of the opening. If the wavelength is much shorter than the width of the opening, then the spreading behind the breakwater will not amount to much; the wave in the harbor will not be much wider than the hole. If, on the other hand, the wavelength is about the same as the width of the hole, the wave in the harbor will spread out into a wide arc.

The diffraction of light not only suggests very strongly that light travels in waves, but it also gives a clue about the wavelength of light. The spreading of light when it passes through even a pinhole is so slight that only a careful observer will notice it. Therefore the wavelength of light must be appreciably smaller than the diameter of a pinhole. Measurements on the spreading permit a numerical estimate of the wavelength to be made, but a better way of actually measuring the wavelength of light will be explained shortly.

47–6. Explanation of Interference. Earlier in this chapter it was stated that the discovery of interference led quickly to the acceptance of the wave theory of light. To see that interference is easily explainable in terms of waves, consider the situation shown in Figure 47–E. There S is a small source of light, perhaps a pinhole in an opaque window shade on a sunny day. *A* and *B* are small holes or slits in an opaque screen. Light from S can pass through *A* and *B* and fall on the wall at the right. If *A* and *B* are very small gaps, the light passing through them will spread out because of diffraction. Assume, then, that light consists of waves of some sort. Waves will spread out from *A* and *B*, which will therefore act like sources. They are not independent sources, however; they owe their activity to a wave coming from S, and since *A* and *B* are equidistant from S, they will act together. That is, *A* and *B* will be sending out crests at the same time, and at some later time they will both be sending out troughs. In short, we can say that *A* and *B* act "in step" with one another.

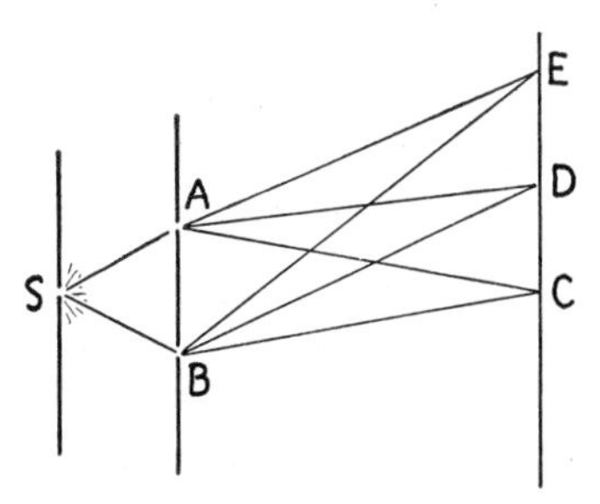

FIGURE 47–E. The relationship between two interfering waves of light.

At the point *C*, equidistant from *A* and *B*, the waves from *A* and *B* will have traveled equal distances and will therefore still be in step. When a crest is arriving from *A*, a crest will also be arriving from *B*, so the waves from *A* and *B* will augment one another, and *C* will be illuminated.

On the other hand, to reach points above *C* the wave from *B* will have to travel farther than the wave from *A*, and there will be some point *D* such that the difference in path of the two waves from *B* and *A* is just half a wavelength. At this point *D*, then, the crests from *B* will arrive in between the crests from *A*; in fact the crests from *B* will arrive at the same time as the troughs from *A*, and therefore the *waves from A and B will cancel one another*. Consequently the point *D* will not be illuminated. It is called a "point of destructive interference."

Higher up, at some point *E*, the wave from *B* will arrive a *whole* wavelength behind the wave from *A*; crests from *B* will coincide with other crests from *A*, and *E* will be brightly illuminated. In between *D* and *E* there will be some illumination, but not as much as at *E*. There will be other points above *E*, and also a whole set of points below *C*, where crest falls on crest and the light from *A* augments that from *B*. These brightly illuminated points, called "points of constructive interference," are the points such that the differences in their distances from *A* and *B* are exactly some whole number of wavelengths. We could use this fact to derive a formula for the positions of the bright spots; we shall refrain from doing so because the same time spent on the formula for a slightly more complicated case will be rewarded by more useful results.

47–7. The Velocity of Light. Since the time of Newton, astronomers have known that light takes nearly 20 minutes to travel across the earth's orbit. (This fact was discovered by noting that eclipses of Jupiter's moons appear to occur irregularly, unless allowance is made for the position of the earth in its orbit.) In the nineteenth and twentieth centuries, the velocity of light has been measured in a more refined way by terrestrial experiments. Most experiments of this kind simply measure the time required for light to travel to a distant mirror and return, the distance to the mirror being known. It is found that light travels 3.00×10^8 meters, or 186,000 miles, per second.

One successful scheme of measurement depends on an octagonal mirror near the lamp that serves as a source of light. When the octagonal mirror is in a certain position, it reflects light from the source to the distant mirror. This light returns to the octagonal mirror and is reflected into the observer's eye. The octagonal mirror can rotate about its axis at high speed, driven by a controllable motor. After the experimenter starts the motor, the rotating mirror is no longer in the same position when the light returns as it was when the light set out for the distant mirror. Therefore, if the observer sees the returned image of the lamp at all, its apparent position is in general not the same as it was when the mirror was standing still. When the octagonal mirror is made to rotate at just the right speed, however, it will make one-eighth of a turn while the light makes its round trip to the distant mirror. Then the returning light will be reflected just as if the mirror had not moved at all, and the observer will see the image in its original position. If he then measures the rate of rotation of the mirror, he can find the time that elapses while the light makes its trip over the measured course. From this time and the distance, the velocity follows immediately.

The velocity of light is one of the most accurately known of all physical constants. The average of several recent determinations is 2.99793×10^8 m/sec.

47–8. The Nature of Light. Because the diffraction and interference of light are to be expected if light is a wave motion, but are not at all to be expected if light consists of streams of particles, the corpuscular theory of light was abandoned shortly after Young's discovery of interference of light. It was agreed that light consists of waves. Waves of what? Surely not waves in air, because light will travel through glass and water, and even through an evacuated jar. In fact, the sun's light reaches us after traveling through about 93 million miles of better vacuum than any that is obtainable in a laboratory. Clearly, then, the light waves are not waves in any ordinary matter. It was decided that they must be waves in a special material called "the luminiferous ether." This ether was taken to be a kind of jelly that pervaded all of space. In order for vibrations to travel at any such rate as 3×10^8 m/sec in a jelly, the jelly had to be assumed to be very stiff—more rigid than steel, in fact—and it was hard to see how the planets could move through it unimpeded. A way out of the difficulty was found through the study of electricity, as discussed in the next chapter.

Summary

The diffraction of light is the bending of light around the edges of an obstacle.

The interference of light is the interaction of two or more beams of light that meet after traveling over different paths from the same source.

Prior to 1800 there were two rival theories of light. The generally accepted theory, which had the advantage of Newton's sanction, held that light rays are streams of particles called corpuscles. On the other hand, the great Dutch physicist Huygens had put forward the hypothesis that light consists of waves, and on this hypothesis he had built a theory that explained many optical phenomena. Both theories accounted about equally well for the known facts before interference was discovered at the opening of the nineteenth century. Interference can easily be explained by a wave theory, but it defies explanation by a corpuscular theory.

Three important and related attributes of a wave are its velocity, its wavelength, and its frequency. The velocity is the rate of motion of a crest. The wavelength is the distance between two successive crests. The frequency is the number of crests per second passing a given point. The three quantities are related by the equation

$$\text{Velocity} = \text{Frequency} \times \text{Wavelength}.$$

Diffraction occurs because if a wave disturbance exists at some point, then all of the points in the neighborhood are disturbed, and their disturbance is propagated to their neighbors on all sides. Each point disturbed by a wave is therefore itself the source of a new wave. The various parts of this new wave can interfere with one another either destructively or constructively. In general they interfere constructively in the direction in which the original wave was traveling. If they proceed from a narrow opening, they will also interfere constructively in other directions than that in which the original wave was traveling. The wave disturbance therefore spreads after passing through the opening. The spreading is not very pronounced if the width of the slit is much larger than the wavelength of the wave.

Interference occurs because two waves from different points excited from the same source can overlap either crest-on-crest, or crest-on-trough, or in an intermediate way. Where the crest-on-trough overlapping occurs, the two waves cancel one another. Two waves that start out together "in step" will be in step again when they overlap, if and only if their paths differ in length by a whole number of wavelengths.

Questions

1. What is the diffraction of light? Describe a way in which it can be observed.
2. What is the interference of light? Describe a way in which it can be observed.
3. Describe the two rival theories of light, and explain why the corpuscular theory was discarded.
4. Under what circumstances does destructive interference occur?
5. What are the wavelength and the frequency of a wave?
6. Use the quotation at the head of this chapter to support the contention that Shakespeare was familiar with the interference of light. Do you think he actually was?

48

ELECTROMAGNETIC WAVES

I have a new electromagnetic theory of light, which until I am convinced to the contrary I hold to be great guns.

MAXWELL (*ca.* 1860)

Having become convinced that light consists of waves, we proceed now to learn what kind of waves they are. In order to understand the modern theory of light, it is necessary to consider an electrical discovery made by Faraday, not long before the work that led to his Law of Electrolysis.

48–1. Electromagnetic Induction (1831). It will be recalled that a magnetic field exerts force on a current-bearing wire (Article 32–3). Faraday sought some other connection between electricity and magnetism, and he found one: he found that a changing magnetic field produces an electric field. In the course of his experiments, he connected the ends of a coil of wire to a galvanometer which would indicate any current that might be set up in the coil. Figure 48–A shows a modern form of the apparatus. He found that when a magnet was thrust into the coil, the galvanometer showed a momentary current. When the magnet was kept at rest inside the coil, nothing happened, but when the magnet was withdrawn again there was another brief passage of charge through the galvanometer. From this experiment Faraday concluded that when the magnetic field inside the coil is *changing* because of the motion of the magnet, then a current is set up in the circuit consisting of coil and galvanometer. When the magnetic field is no longer changing, the current ceases. This experiment shows that a changing magnetic field

FIGURE 48–A. A changing magnetic field produces an electric field.

exerts a force on stationary charges, or in other words *a changing magnetic field produces an electric field.* The phenomenon is called "electromagnetic induction."

Few scientific discoveries have had more momentous consequences than this one of Faraday's. Almost all of the electric power used in homes and in industry is generated by means of electromagnetic induction. An electric dynamo consists fundamentally of a coil placed near a revolving magnet, in such a way that the magnetic field in the coil is continually increasing and decreasing. The changing magnetic field sets up in the coil an electric field that accelerates electrons in the wire and sends them through whatever circuits may be connected to the dynamo. The energy required to turn the magnet can be got from a steam engine or a waterfall, and it is transmitted to the electric charges, which can carry it along wires to a distant point. Therefore the dynamo is a device for converting mechanical energy into electrical energy. At certain places, particularly at a waterfall, mechanical energy is cheap. The dynamo, based on Faraday's discovery, permits this energy to be converted into electrical energy and used anywhere within a radius of a hundred miles or more. No longer is industrial development limited to cities that possess waterfalls or cheap coal, and no longer is efficient machinery limited to enterprises large enough to employ a steam engine.

The induction coil, which was mentioned in Chapter 41 with the promise that it would be explained later, operates by virtue of electromagnetic induction. It consists of an electromagnet placed inside of a coil containing many thousands of turns of fine wire. The electromagnet is connected to a battery, but in this circuit there is an automatic switch operated by the electromagnet itself. This switch turns the current in the electromagnet off and on about a hundred times per second. The magnetic field set up by the electromagnet is therefore changing most of the time, and it produces an electric field that results in a large difference of potential (perhaps 10,000 volts or more) between the terminals of the coil.

48–2. The Work of Maxwell (1860). Faraday was an experimenter. His work on electromagnetic induction was formulated mathematically

---

James Clerk Maxwell, following up a boyhood interest in science, made a brilliant record as a student at the University of Cambridge. Elected to a professorship at Aberdeen at the age of 25, he taught for ten years and then retired to his country estate. Both as a professor and as a Scottish laird, he pursued research in several branches of "natural philosophy." Although his electromagnetic researches take first place, he also did important work in the dynamical theory of gases and in the study of color. In 1871 he went back to the University of Cambridge as its first Professor of Experimental Physics. There he founded one of the most celebrated schools of physical research.

By courtesy of the Cavendish Laboratory, Cambridge University and Dr J. C. Maxwell Garnett

JAMES CLERK MAXWELL
(1831–1879)

by a Scottish physicist named Maxwell, about the time of our Civil War. Using a mathematical argument that involves the calculus of vectors and is therefore beyond our reach, Maxwell convinced himself that if a changing magnetic field produces an electric field, then a changing electric field should produce a magnetic field. With all his mathematics, Maxwell could not *prove* this assertion. It was really just a bold and educated guess, which had to be tested by its implications.

Suppose it is true that a changing electric field produces a magnetic field. Then if the electric field is not changing uniformly, the magnetic field will not be constant, but will be changing. The changing magnetic field will produce an electric field at neighboring points, and that field can produce a magnetic field at neighboring points, and so on. Maxwell showed that the changing electric and magnetic fields will move through space like a wave, and from electrical measurements he was able to calculate the velocity that this predicted wave would have. The answer was 186,000 miles/second, which is just the velocity of light! This result led him to suspect that light is an *electromagnetic wave*, simply a propagation of changing electric and magnetic fields through space, whether the space is empty or full of transparent matter.

48–3. Electromagnetic Waves. The crux of Maxwell's theory is the prediction that an electric field that changes nonuniformly will result in an electromagnetic wave. To test the theory, one needs to produce an electric field that changes nonuniformly. This is not hard to do. An electric charge produces an electric field, and if the charge moves with constant velocity, then the field changes uniformly; but if the charge moves with a velocity that is not constant, then the electric field will change nonuniformly. Therefore, Maxwell's theory predicts that an electromagnetic wave will be generated by an electric charge that accelerates. In 1888 Hertz in Germany made electric charges oscillate rapidly back and forth in an electric circuit, and showed that waves were actually generated. Moreover, he showed that these waves have the velocity of light and that they can be reflected, made to interfere, and so on, just like light waves. One may regret that Maxwell did not live to see his theory verified by these experiments, which were the beginning of radio communication. Ten years later, Marconi, after private experimentation which achieved transmission and detection of the waves over several miles, formed a company to exploit the commercial possibilities of the discovery. In spite of pooh-poohing from all quarters, he succeeded in bridging the Atlantic in 1901. Commercial wireless telegraphy, radio, and television have followed in one lifetime. In considering technological unemployment, it is interesting to speculate on the number of jobs created by the discoveries of Faraday the experimenter, Maxwell the theorist, and Marconi the engineer and entrepreneur.

General Electric Co.

FIGURE 48-B. A generator or transmitter (right) and a detector or receiver (left) of electromagnetic waves.

EXPERIMENT. The detector and generator in Figure 48-B are suitable for demonstrating electromagnetic waves much like those used by Hertz. The generator, or transmitter, on the right consists essentially of two bent rods connected to an alternating source of charge, which is inside the rectangular case. The rods can be seen in the center of the reflector, whose purpose is to form the waves into a beam. The device in the case puts a positive charge on the upper rod, then a negative one, then a positive one, and so on in very rapid succession. The lower rod is always charged oppositely to the upper one. The charges rushing back and forth in the rods are accelerating or decelerating during nearly all of their motion, and they set up an electromagnetic wave.

The detector or receiver, on the left, contains two rods much like those in the transmitter. The electric field in the wave, when it acts on these rods, sets in motion some of the charges in the rods. This motion is a current, and it is detected by means of the sensitive ammeter that constitutes the rest of the receiver.

The wave from the transmitter can be detected many feet away by the receiver. In Figure 48-C the demonstrator is showing that the wave can be reflected from a "mirror" consisting of a sheet of metal or a metal screen.

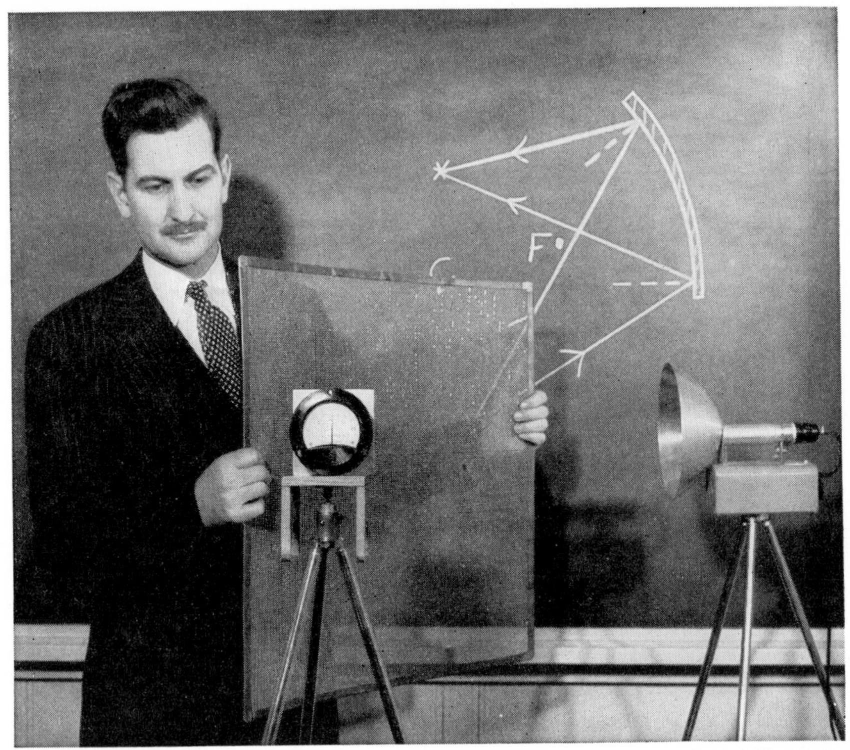

General Electric Co.

FIGURE 48–C. A demonstration of electromagnetic waves, which are being reflected toward the receiver by the sheet of conducting material.

The experimental proof that electromagnetic waves do exist is a very strong confirmation of Maxwell's guess that a changing electric field will produce a magnetic field. His idea that light consists of electromagnetic waves was accepted without further delay, and the ether eventually joined caloric in the limbo of discarded hypotheses. In order to understand a wave that can travel in empty space, it is helpful to draw a vector diagram of the electric field strength in the light wave or radio wave. At a particular instant, the electric field strength has the wavelike distribution shown in Figure 48–D. As time progresses, the wave travels to the right, or left,* at about 186,000 miles/second or 3×10^8 m/sec.

* One might ask: How does the wave know which way it is going, right or left? The answer depends on a detail of Maxwell's theory that we omitted. The theory says that if the electric field vector points toward the top of the page, then the magnetic field vector points either into the page or else out of it, being perpendicular to the electric field vector; and furthermore that if the electric field is up, then the wave travels to the left if the magnetic field points into the page, and it travels to the right if the magnetic field points outward.

Frequency has been defined as the number of crests per second passing a given point in space. Another interpretation of frequency can be drawn from Figure 48–D. Suppose we confine our attention to the fixed point in space marked by the little circle. As the wave progresses to the right, the electric field at the circled point declines to zero and then reverses its direction; eventually it declines again and then grows in the upward direction, and so on. Every time a crest passes the circled point, the electric field strength at that point is at its maximum value. But the number of times per second that a crest passes is the frequency of the wave. Hence, the frequency is also the number of times per second that the electric field strength at a given point takes on its maximum value.

FIGURE 48–D. The electric field strength in an electromagnetic wave.

The frequency of a radio wave is determined by, and is equal to, the frequency with which charge is made to surge back and forth in the transmitting antenna. The unit for measuring radio frequencies is the megacycle per second, colloquially shortened to "megacycle." One megacycle is a frequency of one million per second. Ordinary broadcasting stations use frequencies of about 1 megacycle; television and FM stations use higher frequencies, up to a few hundred megacycles.

48–4. The Transmission of Energy by Waves. One very important aspect of waves will have to be dismissed with only brief mention: waves are able to carry energy from one place to another. For example, a celluloid duck can be set in motion by agitating the surface of the water at some point in the bathtub. When the duck is in motion, it has K.E.; when it is poised at the top of a wave, it has P.E. Another more useful instance is the transmission by radio of small amounts of energy which, by means of a radio receiving set, can be made to control the power from the lighting system in one's house in such a way as to cause the piston in a loud-speaker to move back and forth. This motion generates waves in the air, which set one's eardrum into motion and convey information or pleasure. The electromagnetic wave conveys a minute amount of energy to the home, where it is used to control a large amount of energy that one buys from the electric-power company. Then this energy is converted into a sound wave that imparts K.E. to the eardrum. In a television receiver, the incoming energy controls not only the motion of a loud-speaker, but also the position and intensity of a beam of cathode rays that traces a picture on a fluorescent screen.

A third and vital example of energy transmission by waves is the transmission of energy from the sun to the earth through empty space. The violently agitated particles in the hot sun emit electromagnetic waves, some of which, on arrival at the earth, agitate the particles of the earth and make it warmer. Furthermore, some of the electromagnetic energy is converted by the plants into chemical energy, which supports our life processes when we eat the plants.

Summary

Faraday discovered experimentally that a changing magnetic field produces an electric field. About thirty years later, Maxwell, in the course of a mathematical formulation of the then-known facts of electricity, became persuaded that a changing electric field will produce a magnetic field. He concluded that an accelerated electric charge would produce a set of changing electric and magnetic fields which would be propagated through space as a wave. He showed theoretically that such a wave would have the same velocity as light waves, and suggested that light waves are in fact electromagnetic waves.

Almost another thirty years later, Hertz showed that an accelerated charge does produce electromagnetic waves, and that these waves behave in many ways like light waves. On the theoretical side, the experiments of Hertz verified Maxwell's guess about changing electric fields; on the practical side, Hertz's experiments initiated radio communication.

In an electromagnetic wave, the electric field strength, and also the magnetic field strength, have wavelike distributions in space at any instant. As time progresses, this distribution of electric and magnetic field strengths moves through space with a velocity of 3×10^8 m/sec. The wavelength of the wave is the distance between successive maxima of electric (or magnetic) field strength, and the frequency is the number per second of such maxima that occur at a given point.

An important aspect of waves is that they can carry energy from one point to another. The energy we receive from the sun is carried to us by electromagnetic waves.

Questions

1. What connection did Faraday find between a magnetic field and an electric field? By what experiment did he discover this connection?
2. State a social or economic consequence of Faraday's discovery of electromagnetic induction.

3. State the belief that led Maxwell to assert the existence of electromagnetic waves. How is this belief related to Faraday's electromagnetic induction?
4. Give a qualitative argument for the existence of electromagnetic waves.
5. Describe a way to produce electromagnetic waves.
6. What is the relation of electromagnetic waves to radio communication?
7. How is the frequency of an electromagnetic wave related to the electric field strength in the wave?
8. How is the wavelength of an electromagnetic wave related to the electric field strength in the wave?
9. The electromagnetic waves used for ordinary broadcasting have a frequency of about 1 megacycle. Find their wavelength. What is the wavelength of the waves used in television, which have a frequency of about 100 megacycles?
10. The apparatus in Figure 48–B generates electromagnetic waves that have a wavelength of 0.12 m (about 5 inches). What is the frequency of these waves? In order to set up these waves, how many times per second must the charge in the generating apparatus reverse its direction of motion?

Suggestion for Further Reading

J. R. Pierce, "Microwaves," *Scientific American*, August, 1952, pp. 43–51.

49

SPECTROSCOPY

> Do not several sorts of Rays make Vibrations of several bignesses, which according to their bignesses excite Sensations of several Colours, much after the manner that the Vibrations of the Air, according to their several bignesses excite Sensations of several Sounds?
>
> NEWTON, *Opticks* (1704)

We have already noticed that the gas in a discharge tube emits light. We know that the molecules of a gas are relatively independent of one another, especially when the pressure is low, as it is in a discharge tube. Also we know that some gases, for example neon, argon, and the vapor of mercury, are monatomic gases. That is, their molecules are single atoms. The light that these gases emit can reasonably (and as it turns out, correctly) be considered as emitted by the individual atoms of the gas. If atoms can emit light, then a study of the light they emit can be expected to give information about the atoms. This supposition has been richly confirmed. By using the phenomenon of interference to study the wavelengths of the light emitted by gases, we can make amazing advances in our understanding of atomic affairs.

49–1. The Diffraction Grating. Suppose light from some very distant source, or else from a nearby small source with lenses interposed to give the illusion of a distant source, falls on a glass plate on which many parallel scratches have been ruled very close together. The glass will be practically opaque where it is scratched, and the clear spaces between the scratches will therefore act like narrow slits in an opaque screen. Because of diffraction, light waves will spread out from each of these slits. The light waves from the various slits will interfere; they will interfere constructively, to produce bright illumination, only if they are "in step" so that crest falls upon crest. (Although we are dealing with electromagnetic waves, the situation can be visualized by thinking of water waves.) Whatever illumination proceeds in some chosen direction can be collected by a lens, as in Figure 49–A, and brought to a focus at some point E on a white wall or on a photographic film.

The condition for constructive interference is essentially the same as it is for the simple pair of slits discussed in Article 47–6. Consider two slits A and B in Figure 49–A. The waves that they send to some point E will arrive in step only if the difference in their paths is exactly a whole number of wavelengths. But their path difference is the distance MB. Therefore the condition that waves from A and B interfere constructively at E

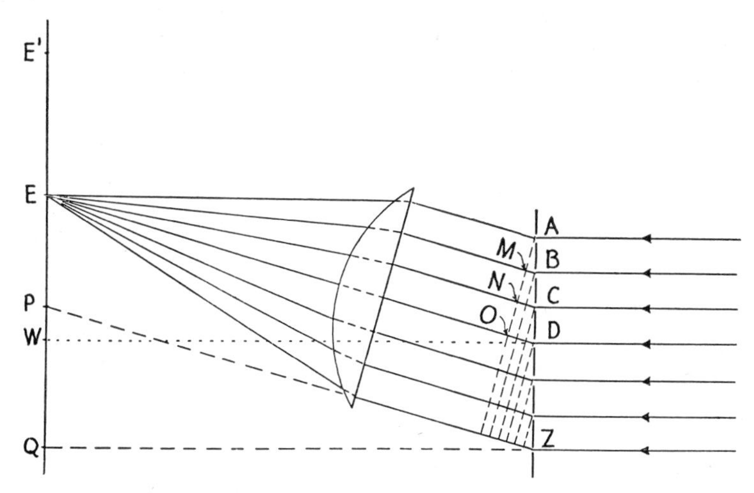

FIGURE 49–A. Measuring the wavelength of light with a diffraction grating.

is simply that E be a place for which $BM = n\lambda$, where λ is the wavelength of the light and n is some integer (0, 1, 2, 3, etc.). Suppose for the moment that $n = 1$, so that BM is simply one wavelength. Then it is clear from the diagram that CN will be exactly two wavelengths, DO will be exactly three wavelengths, and so on, so that *light waves from all of the slits will be in step when they reach* E, and E will be brightly illuminated.

In the diagram, the triangles AMB and ZQP are similar because they are right triangles with $AB \perp QZ$ and $AM \perp PZ$. Therefore

$$\frac{MB}{AB} = \frac{QP}{PZ}$$

or

$$MB = AB\,\frac{QP}{PZ}\cdot$$

If E is the spot of light formed by waves that start out in a direction such that MB is just one wavelength, we can replace MB in this equation by λ and get

$$\lambda = AB\,\frac{QP}{PZ}.$$

Since all of the quantities on the right side of the equation are distances that can be measured, we have a way of measuring the wavelength of light. By making the scratches close together, so that AB is small, we can ensure that QP will be large enough to measure accurately.

Elaborate machines have been made for ruling the scratched surfaces, which are called *diffraction gratings.* The usual grating has about 15,000 scratches per inch, and perhaps as many as 100,000 scratches altogether, all very accurately spaced at equal distances from one another. The ruling is so accurate, and such care is taken in the measurements, that wavelength measurements accurate to one part in a million are a matter of routine.

We have been tacitly supposing that the light that falls on the grating has some specific wavelength, λ. The point E will be brightly illuminated if E is the point such that $MB = \lambda$. There will, however, be other points that are brightly illuminated. For example, there will be bright illumination at the point E', which is situated so that the path lengths to it from successive slits differ by *two* wavelengths. Another point, beyond E', will involve path differences of exactly three wavelengths for waves from successive slits, and will therefore be brightly illuminated. When the slits are as numerous as they are in the usual diffraction grating, the points in between E and E' will receive almost no illumination at all; the host of waves arriving on the screen will cancel one another almost entirely unless they are actually in step.

The point W, located opposite the center of the grating, has a specially favored position. If the lens is placed so that it focuses the light from the slits onto W, then the surface of the lens will be parallel to the surface of the grating. The paths from the slits to the lens are then all of the same length. Therefore all of the waves from the slits will travel the same distance to reach the lens, and they will all be in step when they get there. The lens will then focus them onto the point W, which will be a point of bright illumination. Below W in the diagram, there will be another whole set of illuminated points like E, E', and so on, corresponding to path differences of one, two, and so on, wavelengths, with the path from A being *longer* than that from B and the path from Z being the shortest. Of all the illuminated points, the only ones we actually must work with are W and E, although the others are often useful in the laboratory.

Concentrating our attention on the points W and E, we see that they differ in a very important way. Point W receives illumination because it is located symmetrically with respect to the slits in the grating. On the other hand, E is illuminated because it is the point such that MB is just equal to one wavelength. For light of different wavelengths, MB must have different lengths in order to produce constructive interference, and different lengths for MB demand different positions for E. Therefore the position of E depends on the wavelength of the light. If light of two different wavelengths falls on the grating, *each wavelength will cause illumination at a separate position of E.* Both wavelengths will produce illumination at the point W, because W is determined by symmetry. The upshot is that the distance WE will be different for different wavelengths, and can be used to measure the wavelength. In fact it is easy to see that $WE = QP$, a quantity that appears in the equation developed on page 408. In practice, QP can best be measured by measuring WE.

In the foregoing discussion we have ignored the fact that the slits have some length. When this fact is taken into account, the illumination at C and E is of course extended along lines parallel to the slits.

49–2. The Spectroscope and Its Uses. Using an arrangement like that in Figure 49–B, let light from a narrow white source fall on a white screen

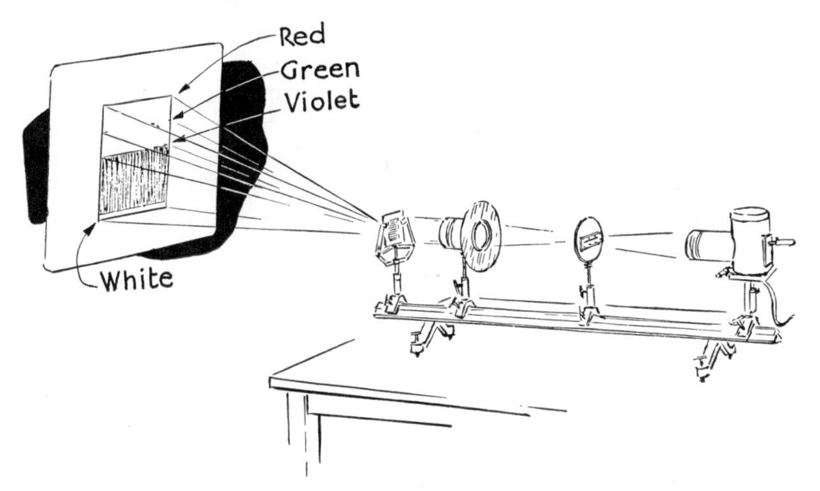

FIGURE 49–B. A rudimentary spectroscope.

after passage through a diffraction grating.* The light on the screen is spread out into an array of graduated colors, from violet to red, called

* The fixed and movable lenses in the previous scheme are here replaced by a single fixed lens; the equation derived from Figure 49–A will not hold here with mathematical exactness, but it holds to an approximation that is more than adequate for a first measurement.

a *spectrum.* This effect shows, in the first place, that white light is actually a mixture of colors. Second, the fact that different colors produce illumination at different points on the screen shows that the *different colors of the spectrum correspond to different wavelengths.* The central image is white, because it is illuminated by light of all wavelengths. The distance corresponding to WE in Figure 49–A is greater for the red light than for the blue, showing that red light has a bigger wavelength than does blue. Even this relatively crude arrangement will show, by use of the equation on page 408, that violet light has a wavelength of about 4×10^{-7} m, or about 1/60,000 inch. The wavelength of red light is about twice as great.

If light from mercury vapor glowing in a discharge tube is sent through the apparatus, then the spectrum thrown on the screen consists of a faint red line, a yellow line, a green one, and several violet ones.

Each line is an image of the slit through which light passes before it strikes the grating. The lines are in different places because the light from the mercury vapor is a mixture of light of several wavelengths.

A lamp containing sodium vapor produces only a single line bright enough to be seen throughout the room. With the apparatus described here, the lines are rather wide, but using a narrow slit and better lenses will give very narrow lines. When this is done the sodium line turns out to be *two lines* differing in wavelength by 0.1 percent.

An instrument for observing the spectrum visually is called a *spectroscope*; one for recording the spectrum photographically is called a *spectrograph.* Figure 49–C shows a spectroscope of simple design. The horizontal tube at the left ends in a slit that receives the light to be studied. Inside the tube is a lens to make the light from the slit fall on the grating in parallel rays. The other tube, which is on a movable arm, is a telescope that plays the role of the lens in Figure 49–A. By viewing the spectrum through a telescope, instead of projecting it on a screen, one can observe very faint parts of the spectra.

The spectrum emitted by hot solids is called a *continuous spectrum,* because it shades off gradually from one color to the next. The light emitted by gases is very different in character: only certain definite wavelengths are present at all, so the spectrum of a gas is a collection of more or less widely spaced bright lines. It is therefore called a *line spectrum.*

These facts were discovered in the middle of the last century, and it was soon found that each element, when in the gaseous state and excited by high temperature or electric discharge, emits light whose spectrum consists of distinctive lines. The lines in its spectrum identify an element just as surely as a set of fingerprints identifies a man. The spectra of some elements, particularly hydrogen and the alkali metals, are relatively simple, but other elements, notably those in the central columns of the Peri-

American Optical Co., Instrument Division, Buffalo, N. Y.

FIGURE 49-C. A simple laboratory spectroscope. The magnifying glasses are used for reading a scale of angles that can be seen through the horizontal windows. Measurement of *QP* and *QZ* in Figure 49-A is replaced by measurement of the angle QZP.

odic Table, have very complicated spectra. Figure 49-D shows parts of the spectra of several kinds of matter.

EXPERIMENT. Line spectra from several gases can be compared by looking through a small grating at a vertical string of slender discharge tubes containing different gases. (The diatomic gases show the band spectra mentioned below.)

When a spectroscope is finely built, so that even very weak lines become visible, observation shows that the spectrum of atomic hydrogen is the simplest of all. Even in the case of hydrogen, however, if instead of simply looking at the spectrum you let it fall on a photographic film, then when the film is developed you find there are lines that the eye does not see. Some of them have wavelengths shorter than those of violet light, and some have wavelengths longer than those of red light. These two invisible parts of the spectrum are called the *ultraviolet* and the *infrared.* Solids that are not very hot, for example stoves, radiate mostly in the infrared. The ultraviolet light is known to all sun-bathers as being responsible for their tan. It may be mentioned here that γ-rays are electromagnetic radiation of much shorter wavelength than the ultraviolet, and that radio waves have longer wavelengths than the infrared.

Our special interest in spectral lines lies in their use as a tool for investigating the construction of the atom. Nevertheless, some of their other uses should be mentioned. As already stated, the spectral lines of an element in gaseous form provide the equivalent of a fingerprint of the atoms of that element. Line spectra of elements that are ordinarily solid can be obtained by getting the element or one of its compounds sufficiently hot. When the temperature is high enough, not only will a substance turn into a gas, but the jostling of the molecules will be so violent that they will come apart into their constituent atoms, and these atoms

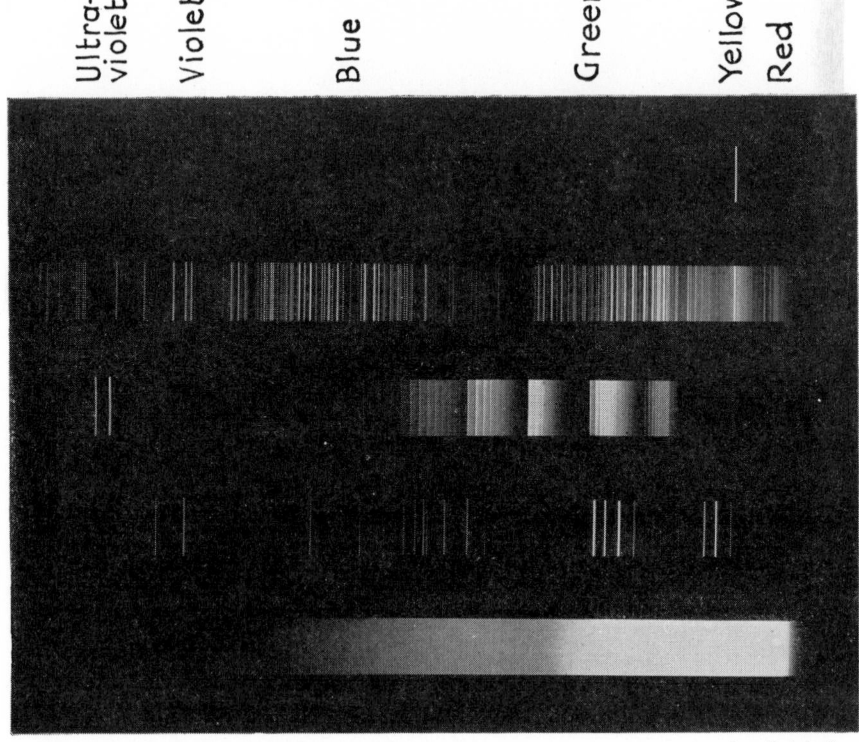

Jarrell-Ash Co.

FIGURE 49–D. Some spectra. From top to bottom, their sources are: sodium; iron; aluminum on the left, aluminum monoxide on the right; copper; a hot solid, the filament of an incandescent lamp. Each spectrum has many weak components that do not show in this photograph.

will emit line spectra. At a somewhat lower temperature, the substance can be a gas composed of unbroken molecules, and the molecules emit spectra called *band spectra* because they consist of groups of very closely spaced lines. The band spectrum in Figure 49–D is that of aluminum monoxide, AlO. Each different molecule has a different spectrum, by which it can be identified. The spectroscope therefore gives a simple and definite way of detecting the presence of an element or a compound, even though only a trace of it is present.

Spectroscopy is finding increasing use in industrial processes. In making steel, for example, the success of the operation depends on removing the melt from the furnace when most, but not all, of the impurities have been cooked out of the iron. The quality of the steel depends on the presence of just the right quantities of just the right impurities, notably carbon. Until recently, the right time to remove the melt from the furnace was determined largely by the guess of an experienced foreman, and partly by chemical analysis of a sample. The chemical analysis took so long that the melt was likely to spoil while the analysis was being made. Now a sample of the melt is examined with a spectrograph, which in a matter of minutes gives an analysis of the kind and amount of the impurities, the amount being inferred from the intensities of the spectral lines.

The most marvelous thing that the spectrograph does, however, is to perform a chemical analysis of the stars. Stars are gases so highly compressed in the interior that, like solids, they radiate continuous spectra. The outer part of a star, however, is not highly compressed, nor is it so hot as the interior. Now experiment shows that when a continuous spectrum passes through a cool gas, the gas absorbs from the spectrum those lines, or at least some of those lines, which it is capable of radiating when it is hot. Yellow light of the characteristic sodium wavelength is absorbed when it passes through sodium vapor. The light absorbed by the sodium atoms is soon reradiated, but it goes out in all directions. The amount of reradiated light that happens to proceed in the original direction is relatively small, and light of this wavelength therefore seems to be missing from the spectrum. The result is a dark line in the spectrum.

Experiment. A white wall is illuminated with yellow light from a sodium lamp. There is a gas burner between the lamp and the wall, as in Figure 49-E.

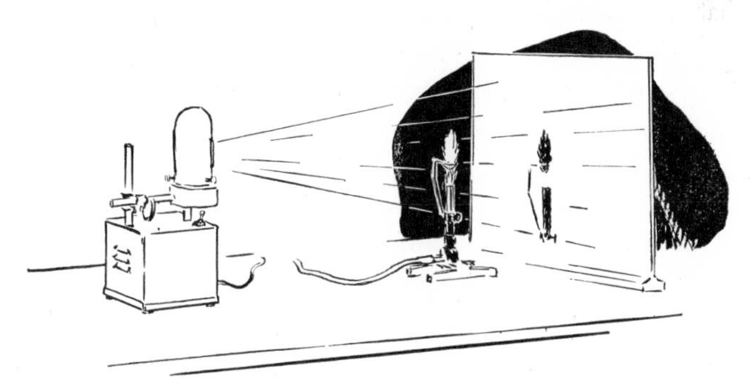

Figure 49-E. Sodium vapor absorbs the light that a sodium-vapor lamp emits.

If common salt (sodium chloride) is held in the flame of the burner, the sodium vapor thus produced absorbs the light from the lamp, and the burner flame then casts a shadow on the wall.

The foregoing experiment shows that sodium atoms absorb radiation of the same wavelength that they emit. To show that they absorb *only* radiation of the same wavelength that they emit, a more elaborate experiment is needed.

EXPERIMENT. On opposite sides of a metal chimney enclosing a Bunsen or Mekker flame, there are two vertical slits (Figure 49–F). White light from an arc lamp and lens passes through the wider slit and across the chimney, where it is focused on the narrower slit. Another lens throws an image of this slit onto

FIGURE 49–F. Sodium vapor absorbs selectively a line in the yellow part of the spectrum, at the same wavelength that characterizes the light that sodium atoms can emit.

a screen, and a grating (or a prism) interposed between lens and screen spreads the light into a continuous spectrum. If a lump of sodium is lowered into the gas flame, the chimney becomes filled with sodium vapor, which absorbs some of the light from the arc lamp. In the yellow part of the spectrum, a dark line appears, but the rest of the spectrum is unaffected. The experiment demonstrates that atoms absorb only wavelengths that they can emit.

The gases in the outer parts of the stars absorb from the starlight various spectral lines which enable astronomers to identify the absorbing atoms. The spectrum in the central bands of Figure 49–G is that of a typical star, which consists mostly of hydrogen. It is a negative print; the light lines in the figure represent dark lines in the spectrum. The outer bands contain the lines of iron atoms in a laboratory light-source. The iron lines, whose wavelengths are well known, serve as an index to the wavelengths in the stellar spectrum. Figure 49–H is the visible part of the spectrum of the sun. The dark lines in this figure represent dark lines in the spectrum.

EXPERIMENT. When the slit of a moderately good spectroscope is illuminated by sunlight, the dark lines in the sun's spectrum can be seen. It is easy to identify a dark line in the yellow, at the exact wavelength characteristic of sodium.

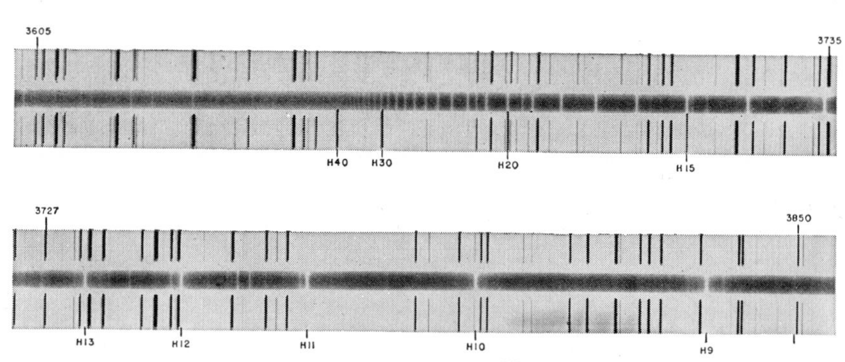

Mount Wilson and Palomar Observatories

FIGURE 49–G. Part of the ultraviolet spectrum of the star known as HD193182. The stellar spectrum is in the two central strips; the bordering spectrum is that of iron, used as a set of index marks. This is a negative print, in which the dark parts represent parts of the spectrum that are light.

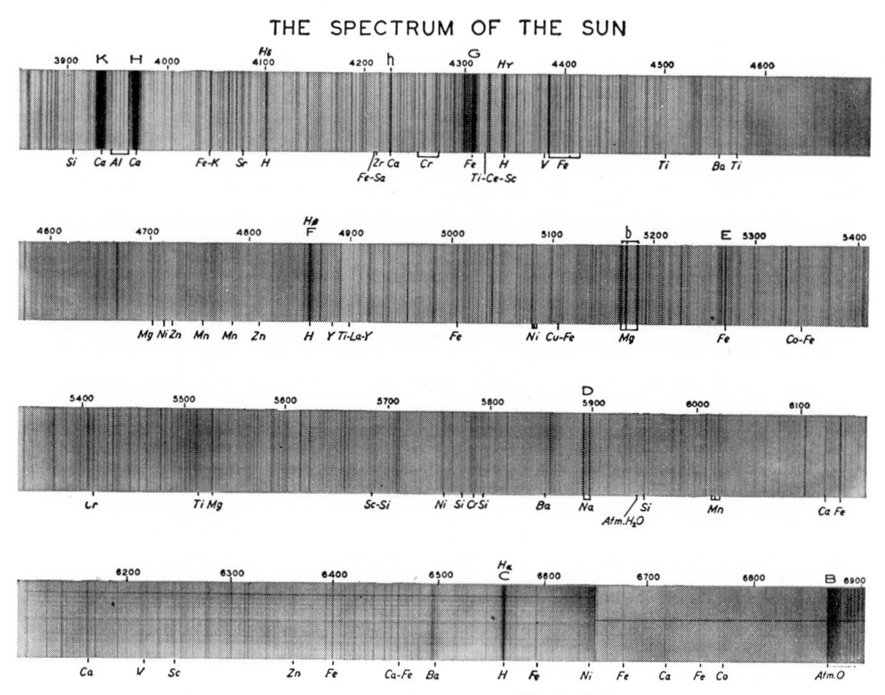

Mount Wilson and Palomar Observatories

FIGURE 49–H. The visible part of the solar spectrum. The pair of prominent lines near 5900 on the scale corresponds to the line in the first spectrum of Figure 49–D. Dark lines on this print represent dark lines in the spectrum. The numbered scale is one of wavelength, the unit of measure being 10^{-10} meter.

It is found that the same kinds of atoms exist throughout the known universe; no atom unknown on the earth has been found in a star. (Helium was so found, in the sun, but it was discovered on the earth about twenty-five years later.) Some of the cooler stars, and also the atmospheres of the planets, show by their spectra that they contain various identifiable molecules.

Summary

The phenomenon of interference provides a means of measuring the wavelength of light waves. If a grating is used, the wavelengths can be separated sufficiently to permit very accurate measurements of the wavelengths. Crude measurements are possible in the classroom.

White light is a mixture of all colors. The wavelength of red light is about twice that of violet light; yellow light, which lies in between, has a wavelength of about 6×10^{-7} m.

Hot solids emit continuous spectra.

Hot gases emit line spectra if they consist of atoms, and band spectra if they are cool enough to contain molecules.

The lines or bands are characteristic of the atoms or molecules from which they come, and can be used to identify them.

Cool gases absorb, very selectively, certain of the wavelengths that they can emit when heated or excited by the electric discharge. This absorption will produce dark lines in a continuous spectrum from a glowing solid viewed through the gas. The dark lines in the spectrum of the sun and other stars tell what atoms these stars contain; they are of the same kinds as those on earth.

There are many spectral lines in portions of the spectrum to which the human eye is not sensitive. Wavelengths somewhat shorter than the violet constitute the ultraviolet region of the spectrum; wavelengths somewhat longer than the red constitute the infrared.

Questions

1. Explain how the operation of a grating spectroscope depends on diffraction.
2. Explain how the operation of a grating spectroscope depends on interference.
3. What do the terms "ultraviolet" and "infrared" mean?
4. Describe how the spectroscope can tell us about elements and compounds in the stars.
5. Article 49–2 states that the simplest spectrum is that of atomic hydrogen. In the light of Article 46–2, do you see a possible correlation between the simplicity of the hydrogen spectrum and the constitution of the hydrogen atom?

Suggestions for Further Reading

A. G. Ingalls, "Ruling Engines," *Scientific American*, June, 1952, pp. 45–50. A description of one of the most exacting and fascinating of all mechanical problems—the ruling of a diffraction grating.

Front cover of the *Scientific American,* December, 1950. The spectra, in color, of about twenty stars visible at the same time in a telescope. Some are very much alike; others are quite different.

O. Struve, "The Fraunhofer Lines," *Sky and Telescope,* March, 1951, pp. 117–20.

> After the discovery of spectrum analysis, no one acquainted with the subject could doubt that the riddle of the atom would be solved, once we had learned to understand the language of the spectrum . . . an actual atomic music of the spheres.
>
> Sommerfeld, *Atombau und Spektrallinien* (1919)

50

THE QUANTUM ASPECT OF LIGHT

Today, I have made a discovery as important as that of Newton.

PLANCK, to his small son (1900)

Two previous chapters have dealt with the wavelike behavior of light and its explanation in terms of Maxwell's electromagnetic theory. We have mentioned how Hertz verified Maxwell's theory by producing, by purely electric means, waves that are like light waves except that they have lower frequency and longer wavelength. For a short time after Hertz's investigation, the subject of light seemed to be almost completely understood. Only one well-known phenomenon resisted quantitative explanation. Persistent scrutiny of this phenomenon disclosed it to be a tiny doorway connecting the world of human experience with the world of atoms. Just when most physicists thought that they understood the universe, Max Planck in Germany found the key to the little door and physicists began to explore the world of atoms, a world in which nothing seemed to happen in the expected way.

50–1. The Radiation From Hot Solids (1900). The phenomenon that resisted explanation was the emission of light. The radiation of light from hot gases comes from the individual molecules and atoms, and Maxwell's theory could be expected to account for it when one's knowledge of atomic structure extended to the accelerations of the radiating charges, and not before. The radiation from solids, on the other hand, could be expected to follow laws that could be deduced on the basis of available knowledge. The details are complicated, but the general nature of the problem is simple.

In a solid, the atoms are bonded together, so that they radiate light as a group rather than individually. We know from experience that the radiation depends on how energetically the atoms are moving (i.e., on how hot the body is) but does not depend very much on what kinds of atoms the solid is made of. When a solid, say a stove, gets too hot to touch, we can feel infrared radiation coming from it. If it gets still hotter, it begins to give out some red light. At a still higher temperature, it gives out yellow light as well as orange, red, and infrared. Very hot solids, like the filaments of incandescent lamps, give out green and blue light as well as light of the longer wavelengths (Figure 49–D). The hotter the body, the wider the range of wavelengths in its spectrum. The spectrum of a hot solid is *continuous*: every wavelength over a whole range is present. The process of radiation involves simply a transfer of energy from the quivering atoms of the solid to the electromagnetic field in the surrounding space. Calculating how the electromagnetic energy will be distributed among the various wavelengths looked like a straightforward problem, but everybody who tried it got an answer that did not fit the observed facts determined by spectroscopy.

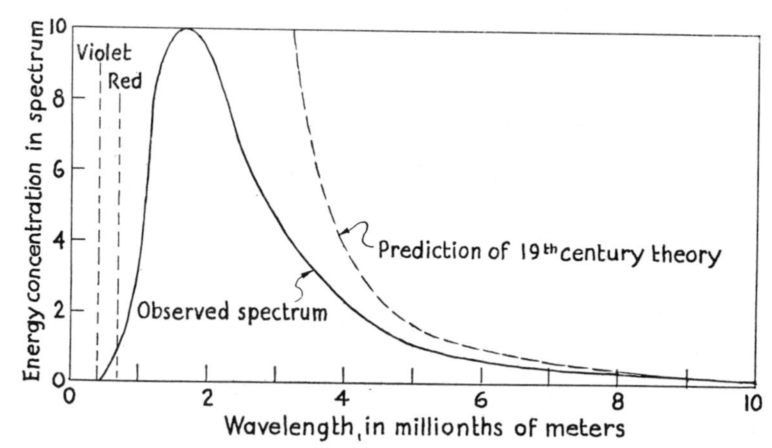

FIGURE 50–A. The spectrum of energy radiated by a solid body at 1800° A, the temperature at which iron melts. Most of the radiation lies in the infrared part of the spectrum.

In Figure 50–A, the solid curve shows how the energy radiated by a hot body is distributed among the different wavelengths. The curve can be obtained by using a diffraction grating to separate the radiations according to wavelength, and for each wavelength measuring the energy by the heating of a tiny thermocouple, or other heat-detecting instrument. The curve shows that most of the energy from the body under observation was radiated in the infrared. There was some radiation in the red part of the spectrum (0.7×10^{-6} meter) and practically none in the blue or in the ultraviolet. The dotted curve is the prediction of nineteenth-century theory, for a body at the temperature used. It asserts that more and more energy will be found as one goes to shorter wavelengths, and that an infinite amount of energy will be found in the ultraviolet! The agreement of theory with fact at one end of the spectrum, and the complete failure * of the theory for the other end of the spectrum, show that the basis of the theory is only partially correct.

After a period of years, a physicist named Planck discovered how to work the problem. He found that he got an answer in agreement with experiment if he assumed that the transfer of energy from the atoms to the electromagnetic wave has to occur in bits, or packages, or quanta. Specifically, he found it necessary to assume that the energy handed over from the group of atoms to the wave comes in packages whose size is proportional to the frequency of the wave. He expressed this relation in the equation

$$E = h\nu$$

where E is the energy that is radiated, ν is the frequency of the wave and bears a simple relation to the wavelength, and h is a constant which has been named "Planck's constant." To get agreement with experiments on radiation, h has to be assigned the value 6.63×10^{-34} joule-second. The role of h in modern physics is as important as that of π in geometry. While physicists were digesting the unexpected discovery that radiant energy is transferred in bits of a definite size, a worse shock was on the way.

* Called "the ultraviolet catastrophe."

MAX PLANCK had trouble deciding whether to make a career in physics or in music. He chose physics, although it seemed to his advisers that little or nothing of interest in that field remained to be discovered. His doctoral thesis, written when he was 21, was a commentary on the Second Law of Thermodynamics. As he put it later, the impact of this work was equal to zero. In subsequent articles, he applied the Second Law to chemical reactions and to solutions. By this route, using freezing-point data, he discovered almost simultaneously with Arrhenius that salts in solution are dissociated. His crowning work, his theory of the continuous spectrum, was the first indication that the previously established laws of physics are not always applicable to the world of atoms.

Although he owed his first faculty appointment more to family influence than to any general recognition of his merit, Planck soon was called to one of the coveted professorships at the University of Berlin, and eventually he became the highly regarded elder statesman of German science. He kept his intellect constantly refreshed by a career of Alpine mountaineering that continued well into his seventies. As a boy, he had watched the Prussian troops occupy his native Holstein in the first of Bismarck's strokes that led to a united and Prussianized Germany; he lived to see the Third Reich hammered to pieces by bombs and tanks.

By courtesy of Johann Ambrosius Barth and Annalen der Physik

MAX PLANCK
(1858–1947)

50–2. The Photoelectric Effect (1890–1915). It was discovered about 1890, as a result of an entirely accidental observation, that under certain circumstances a charged and insulated piece of metal may lose its charge.

EXPERIMENT. A freshly sandpapered zinc plate is well insulated and connected to an electroscope. If the plate is charged negatively and then illuminated by light from an electric arc, the plate loses its charge. On the other hand, if the plate is given a positive charge and then illuminated, the electroscope leaf continues to stand out, showing that the plate retains the charge.

The experiment shows that an illuminated zinc plate will lose a negative charge, but not a positive one. The loss of charge cannot be ascribed to impairment of the insulation of the plate—perhaps by ionization of the surrounding air—because if the insulation were impaired, the plate would lose charge whether it was positive or negative. The obvious conclusion is that the plate suffers a loss of negative charges that jump out of it

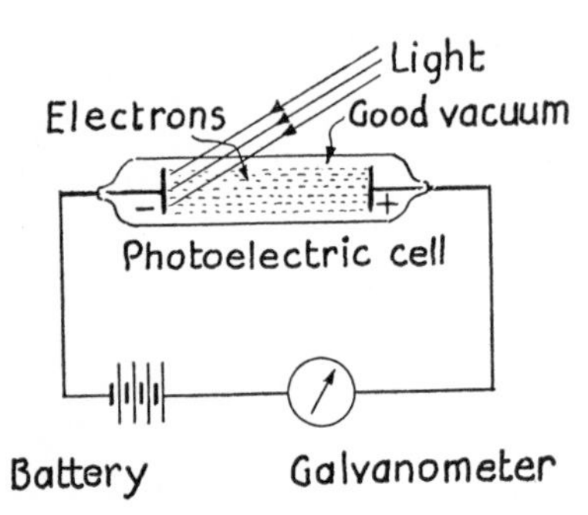

FIGURE 50–B. A circuit containing a photoelectric cell. The beam of light, striking a metal plate, ejects electrons. Under the influence of the battery, which establishes an electric field, the electrons circulate and constitute an electric current, which may be used for a variety of purposes.

when it absorbs energy from a light beam. It is natural to suppose that these charges are electrons, because we know from the phenomenon of cathode rays that the plate contains electrons that can be rather easily removed. To check this conclusion, we can place the plate in an evacuated chamber, where there is not enough air to stop the charged particles or to confuse the issue by becoming ionized. We find that when the metal plate is illuminated, it does give off negative charge which can be collected by a positively charged electrode placed in the neighborhood. The transfer of charge implies the presence of charged particles, and a measurement of their charge-to-mass ratio shows that these particles actually are electrons.* Because they are liberated from a metal plate by the

* The fact that the illuminated plate does not lose its charge when it is positive is now readily explained; the electrons that are knocked out of it are attracted right back to it if it has positive charge.

light that falls on it, they are called *photoelectrons*, and the phenomenon is called the *photoelectric effect*. The device shown in Figure 50–B is called a "photoelectric cell." Since it permits a beam of light to control an electric current, which will actuate a galvanometer or other device placed in the circuit, the photoelectric cell has many useful applications—it plays a vital role in talking pictures and in television. Our interest in the photoelectric effect lies in some astonishing information it gives us about light. When studied in more detail it shows that Maxwell's theory, successful though it is in many ways, does not tell the whole story.

The electrons in a metal are held in it by the attractive forces exerted on them by the positively charged nuclei of the atoms. Removing an electron from the metal is therefore like lifting a golf ball out of the cup and onto the green, in that both operations demand that P.E. be given to the electron or golf ball. Clearly, in the photoelectric effect the work is done on the electron by the light that strikes the metal, because without the light the electron does not come out. If the electron is supplied with more energy than it needs for escape from the metal, then the excess energy is carried off as K.E. of the electron. The situation can be described by the equation

$$\text{Energy supplied to electron} = \text{P.E. needed for liberation} + \text{K.E.}$$

In Maxwell's electromagnetic theory of light, the strength of the fluctuating electric field is related to the intensity (power per unit area) of the light. The electric field exerts a force on the electron, and can do work on it. The theory therefore predicts that by making the light more intense, so that the force on the electron is stronger, one can enhance the K.E. that the electrons have when they escape from the metal. The K.E. of the photoelectrons can be measured in many ways; one way is to measure their velocity as J. J. Thomson measured the velocity of his cathode rays, by balancing the deflections produced by electric and magnetic fields, and then using the definition K.E. $= \frac{1}{2}mv^2$. *The K.E. of the photoelectrons turns out not to depend at all on the intensity of the light that liberates them.* Making the light more intense liberates more photoelectrons per second, but they do not have any more K.E. than those liberated by a weak illumination. This is in flat contradiction to Maxwellian ideas.

Measurements like the ones just mentioned do show that the K.E. depends on the *wavelength* of the light. The shorter the wavelength of the light, the more energetic are the electrons that are liberated. Actually, red light, no matter how intense, will not liberate electrons at all from most of the pure metals. The common metals will emit photoelectrons only under the stimulus of violet or ultraviolet light, but light of longer wavelengths will eject photoelectrons from the alkali metals. For any given metal, the shorter the wavelength of the light, the more energetic the electrons. In terms of Maxwell's theory, this relation just does not make sense.

EXPERIMENT. As in the last experiment, an insulated zinc plate connected to an electroscope is illuminated by light from a carbon arc, but this time a lens or a sheet of window glass is placed between the light source and the zinc. The zinc does not now lose a negative charge that is placed on it. When the glass is taken out of the beam, then the zinc does lose its charge just as before.

The explanation is that ordinary glass is opaque to ultraviolet light, and zinc is one of the metals from which electrons cannot be liberated by light in the visible range of wavelengths.

50–3. Einstein's Photons (1905). In order to account for the photoelectric effect, Einstein suggested a very bold revision in the theory of light. Expanding on Planck's discovery that the transfer of energy from a hot body to an electromagnetic field occurs in bits, or quanta, of amount $h\nu$, Einstein proposed the hypothesis that the radiated energy actually stays in little packages when it travels through space. These packets of radiant energy are now called *photons*.

The new proposal did not involve a complete rejection of Maxwell's theory of electromagnetic waves; Einstein regarded the waves as suitable and necessary for the discussion of large-scale phenomena, but as un-

---

ALBERT EINSTEIN, the son of a small businessman in Bavaria, did so poorly in high school that he was asked to leave, but he managed to graduate from a Swiss school. By his brilliant record in mathematics, he gained admission to the Federal Institute of Technology in Zurich, where he prepared for teaching physics. Failing to get an assistantship for graduate study, or even to get an appointment in a secondary school, he took a job examining applications in the Patent Office at Bern. He pursued theoretical physics as a hobby; in 1905 he published three great papers, any one of which would have ensured his fame among physicists. One was a quantitative theory of the Brownian motion; another, his theory of the photoelectric effect; and the third, a critique of the foundations of dynamics, which contained what is now known as "the restricted theory of relativity." The portrait was made in this year.

His great successes in research brought Einstein professorial appointments, first in Zurich, then in Prague, and eventually in Berlin. In 1916 he published his "general theory of relativity," a system of mechanics which offers an explanation for gravitation. Paradoxically, the mathematical sophistication of this theory fired the popular imagination, and Einstein suddenly became a public figure, whose opinion on any subject was front-page news. When Hitler took over the government, Einstein resigned and came to the Institute for Advanced Study, in Princeton, where he spent the rest of his life. He tried to enlarge the scope of his relativity theory so that it would apply to subatomic phenomena as well as to those on a cosmic scale. This problem is still unsolved.

By courtesy of Lotte Jacobi

ALBERT EINSTEIN
(1879–1955)

suitable for dealing with the interaction between light and matter. Indeed the idea of waves was indispensable, because the amount of energy carried by each photon is $h\nu$, where h is Planck's constant and ν is the frequency of the wave. The only reason for taking such a wild theory seriously was that the orthodox and reasonable theory was clearly wrong, as far as the photoelectric effect was concerned.

Einstein's photon hypothesis did deal successfully with the photoelectric effect, and it has gone on to so many further successes that it is now considered correct. In Einstein's view, the photoelectron is liberated because the photon is absorbed and ceases to exist, and the energy balance can be expressed as follows:

$$\text{Work required to liberate electron} + \text{K.E. gained by electron} = \text{Energy of photon.}$$

Clearly the electron will never be liberated at all unless the energy of the photon is at least equal to the work required to free the electron from the metal. Now the energy of the photon is proportional to the frequency of the light ($E = h\nu$), and therefore the frequency must be greater than a certain lower limit in order for the electron to be liberated. Remembering (Article 47–4) that the frequency is inversely proportional to the wavelength, we see that in order for the electron to be liberated, the wavelength will have to be less than a certain upper limit. But this fits the facts! For zinc the wavelength has to be less than that of violet light, and for sodium it has to be less than the wavelength of green light.

Such a revolutionary proposal as Einstein's cannot be accepted without a quantitative test. Letting W stand for the energy needed to liberate an electron from the metal, and using the fact that the energy of the photon is $h\nu$, where h is Planck's constant and ν is the frequency of the light, we can write the last equation in symbolic form:

$$\text{K.E.} = h\nu - W.$$

Here W, the energy required to extract the electron from the metal, is a fixed amount of energy that depends simply on what metal is being used. Therefore as the frequency increases over the minimum value needed for the liberation of an electron, the K.E. of the liberated electron will increase in exactly the same manner, if Einstein's proposal is correct.

Quantitative experiments on photoelectrons are very difficult to perform, because of the large errors introduced by any impurities (for example a layer of the oxide) on the metal surface. A quantitative test of the predicted relation $\text{K.E.} = h\nu - W$ was carried out by Millikan a decade after Einstein put forward his photon hypothesis. Millikan used a photoelectric cell illuminated in turn by the various lines of the mercury spectrum, the frequency of each line being accurately known.* To make sure that the illuminated metal surface was clean, he used a block of pure sodium and cut it, to expose a fresh surface, *after* the cell was evacuated. Using sodium has the advantage that it is soft enough to cut with a razor blade, and also that its photoelectric sensitivity extends over a large portion of the visible spectrum. On measuring the kinetic energies of the photoelectrons, Millikan found them to be in complete accord with Einstein's hypothesis.† Einstein's incredible directness and boldness of thought are nowhere better illustrated than in this simple example; he was deterred neither by the previous triumphs of the Maxwellian theory nor by the scarcity and crudeness of the experimental data about photoelectricity that were then available.

In a sense the Einstein theory of light is a reversion to the corpuscular theory. It is open to the objection that it treats light as consisting of bits, called photons, when considering the interaction of light with matter, but that it also treats light as a wave when considering its propagation through space. A further objection is that the new theory mixes corpuscles and waves by expressing the energy of the corpuscle in terms of the frequency of the wave. To these objections one can only answer that although Einstein's mixture of waves and corpuscles seems confusing and vague, the corpuscular theory and the wave theory, taken separately, are each in flat contradiction to experimental facts. Further developments in other aspects of physics have made Einstein's theory of light seem less bizarre, although it is still not entirely clear in all details. One of its most important applications will be discussed in the next chapter.

Summary

The distribution of energy in the spectrum of a hot solid is different for different temperatures. To make theory fit the experimental facts, Planck assumed that the transfer of energy from the hot solid to an electromagnetic wave must occur in bits, or quanta, whose energy E is given by $E = h\nu$, where ν is the frequency of the wave and h is a constant.

The photoelectric effect is the emission of electrons from metals, or other substances, under the action of light or other electromagnetic radiation. The energy given to the electrons by the light depends on the fre-

* The frequency of a spectral line is found by measuring the wavelength of the light and using the relationship

$$\text{Velocity} = \text{Wavelength} \times \text{Frequency}.$$

The velocity of light has been accurately measured, and therefore the frequency can be calculated when the wavelength is known.

† Einstein's equation purports to hold, and Millikan's data showed that it does hold, only for the electrons from the surface of the metal, since electrons escaping from the interior will fritter away some of their energy in collisions before they break though the surface.

quency of the light, but not on its intensity. Unless the light has a certain minimum frequency, which is different for different materials, no electrons are emitted at all. These facts are not what Maxwell's theory would lead us to expect.

To explain the photoelectric effect, Einstein suggested that light travels in quanta whose energy is $h\nu$, where h is Planck's constant and ν is the frequency of the wave. Planck had shown that a hot body gives out radiant energy in little packages; Einstein assumed that the energy stays in the packages when it travels through space. The packages are called light quanta or photons.

On Einstein's photon hypothesis, one expects the K.E. of a photoelectron to be equal to the energy of the photon that liberates it, minus the work required to extract the electron from the metal. Millikan showed by an experiment that this idea is quantitatively correct.

Einstein's theory of light is a corpuscular theory, although it retains the idea of waves. The quantum nature of light comes to the fore when light and matter interact. The wave nature of light is important when the path of the light has to be considered.

Questions

1. How does light emitted by a solid differ from light emitted by a gas?
2. What attribute of a hot solid determines, to a major degree, the spectrum of the light emitted by the solid?
3. What assumption did Planck have to make, in order to make a successful calculation of the relation between the temperature and the spectrum of a solid?
4. What is the photoelectric effect?
5. How can the photoelectric effect be observed?
6. How does the photoelectric effect depend on the frequency of the light? How does it depend on the intensity of the light?
7. In what respect does Maxwell's electromagnetic theory of light fail, when applied to the photoelectric effect?
8. Summarize Einstein's theory of the photoelectric effect.
9. How did Millikan find experimental support for Einstein's theory of the photoelectric effect?
10. Do you think it possible to explain interference in terms of photons instead of waves?
11. What kinds of phenomena are correctly accounted for by the wave theory? What kinds by the quantum, or photon, theory?
12. What operational significance can you attach to the question, "Does light really consist of waves, or of photons?"

Suggestion for Further Reading

P. Frank, *Einstein* (New York: Alfred A. Knopf, Inc., 1947). A fine biography, by an eminent physicist.

51

BOHR'S HYDROGEN ATOM

The new discoveries made in physics in the last few years, and the ideas and potentialities suggested by them, have had an effect upon the workers in that subject akin to that produced in literature by the Renaissance.

SIR J. J. THOMSON (1909)

Spectroscopy became a lively subject in the last half of the nineteenth century. Naturally, men working in this field soon tried to find regularities in the wavelengths of the spectrum lines. The spectrum of hydrogen is particularly simple and was the first to be subjected to an algebraic formulation.*

51–1. The Hydrogen Spectrum. The visible spectrum of the hydrogen atom consists of only four lines, but these are accompanied by many more in the neighboring ultraviolet. Figure 51–A is a photograph of this spectrum. The lines constitute an orderly series in which the spacing decreases as the wavelength decreases. The set of lines is called the *Balmer series,* in honor of the man who found a formula that gives their wavelengths. His formula is

$$\lambda = 3647.05 \times \frac{p^2}{p^2 - 4} \times 10^{-10} \text{ meter},$$

where p takes on the values 3, 4, 5, 6, and so on.

* The extensive mathematical argument in this chapter is presented as a sample of the application of mathematics to an atomic problem. This particular sample is chosen because it involves only simple mathematical steps, although there is a long series of them. Most calculations in atomic physics involve higher branches of mathematics, and the nature of the problem is often so complicated that one has to be satisfied with a mathematical treatment that is only approximate. Except for these considerations, the calculation discussed here is typical. Having presented this sample, the author will feel free in later chapters to state the results of mathematical analyses without going into the details of the calculations.

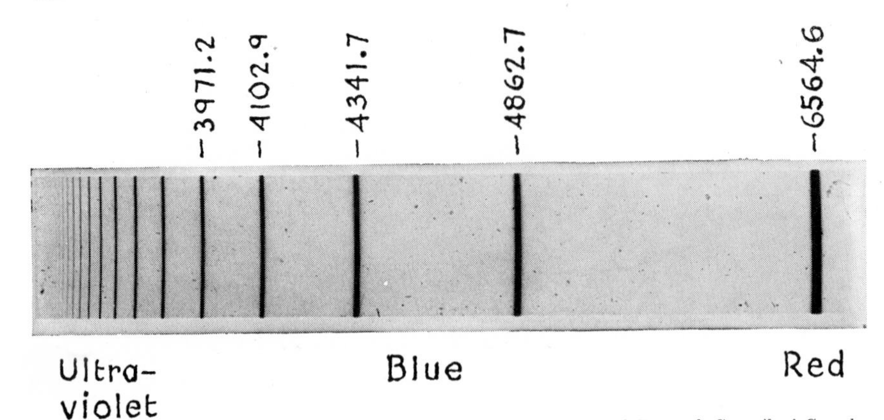

G. Herzberg, National Research Council of Canada

FIGURE 51–A. The Balmer series. The figures are wavelengths, in units 10^{-10} meter.

The Balmer formula looks a little better if written in terms of frequency instead of wavelength. It becomes

$$\nu = R\left(\frac{1}{2^2} - \frac{1}{p^2}\right)$$

where $R = 3.28806 \times 10^9$ megacycles per second, and p has the values 3, 4, 5, 6, and so on, for the successive spectrum lines.

To see how the formula works, we can calculate the frequencies of a few lines. For the first line, $p = 3$, so

$$\nu = R\left(\frac{1}{2^2} - \frac{1}{3^2}\right) = R\left(\frac{1}{4} - \frac{1}{9}\right) = \frac{5}{36}R = 4.567 \times 10^8 \text{ megacycles.}$$

For the second line, $p = 4$, and

$$\nu = R\left(\frac{1}{2^2} - \frac{1}{4^2}\right) = R\left(\frac{1}{4} - \frac{1}{16}\right) = \frac{3}{16}R = 6.165 \times 10^8 \text{ megacycles.}$$

NIELS BOHR has spent most of his life at the University of Copenhagen, where his father was a professor of physiology. He took his doctor's degree in physics there in 1911, the year that Rutherford discovered the atomic nucleus. Bohr immediately went to England to work with Thomson and with Rutherford, and his theory of the hydrogen atom ensued. He was soon made professor of theoretical physics at Copenhagen, which became the world's leading nursery of brilliant theoreticians.

When the Germans occupied Denmark in World War II, Bohr escaped to England in a small boat and was flown to the United States to take part in the development of the first atomic bombs. Directly and through his students, Bohr has had an immense influence on the whole course of modern physical theory.

By courtesy of the Bettmann Archive

NIELS BOHR
(1885–)

Notice that as p gets larger, the second term in the parenthesis gets smaller (1/9, 1/16, 1/25, and so on), so that the successive frequencies differ by less and less. This means that the lines in the calculated spectrum get closer and closer together, in accord with the experimental spectrum in Figure 51–A. The frequencies given by the formula are in good numerical agreement with the measured values.

Later another series in the spectrum of hydrogen was found in the ultraviolet, and still a third was found in the infrared. These series have frequencies given by the formulas

$$\nu = R\left(\frac{1}{1^2} - \frac{1}{p^2}\right), \quad p = 2, 3, 4, \cdots$$

and

$$\nu = R\left(\frac{1}{3^2} - \frac{1}{p^2}\right), \quad p = 4, 5, 6, \cdots$$

Here we have a most intriguing set of relationships, which nobody was able to explain until 1913, when a young Dane named Bohr came forward with a theory.

51–2. A Dilemma. At this time, atomic physicists were in a quandary. Rutherford had shown that the positive charge in an atom is concentrated in a massive but minute core called the nucleus, which is surrounded at a respectful distance by the electrons of the atom (Article 46–1). The electrons, being negatively charged, are surely attracted to the positively charged nucleus. Why does the atom not collapse? One immediately thinks of the solar system, in which the planets are attracted to the sun but do not fall into it because they are in motion. The attraction of the sun simply makes the planets travel in curved orbits instead of in the straight paths they would trace out if they were not acted on by any force. Applying the same scheme to the construction of an atom led to grave difficulty, however.

Anything moving in a curved orbit has a velocity that is changing; hence it has an acceleration. An electron moving in a curved orbit is therefore a charge that is experiencing acceleration, and consequently Maxwell's theory says that the electron must radiate electromagnetic waves. But this radiation will carry energy away from the electron, which will give up part of its own potential energy to supply the loss. The P.E. of the electron is due to its separation from the nucleus, and a decrease in the P.E. of the electron will involve a decrease in the radius of the electron's orbit. It can be calculated that the electron will under such conditions spiral into the nucleus in a small fraction of a second. Therefore there seemed to be no reason why atoms should not collapse, which they certainly do not.

51–3. Bohr's Hydrogen Atom (1913). This was a period of revolution in physics. The discoveries of the electron, of the radioactive disruption of atoms, of the nuclei of atoms, of the photoelectric effect, and of the x-rays that we shall discuss later, had so thoroughly unsettled physics that in 1913 the period before 1895 was being called "classical." In the spirit of the times, Bohr adopted the following hypotheses and built a theory on them:

I. For phenomena on the atomic scale, Maxwellian electrodynamics is not valid.

II. There are certain orbits in which an electron can revolve about the nucleus without radiating electromagnetic energy. These orbits are circles, and they are the circles whose radii satisfy the condition that

$$\text{Circumference of orbit} \times \text{Momentum of electron} = nh,$$

where n is an integer and h is Planck's constant.

III. Light is radiated from an atom when the electron jumps from one allowed orbit to another that is closer to the nucleus. The frequency of this light is given by the equation

$$h\nu = E_1 - E_2$$

where $h\nu$ is the energy of the photon, E_1 is the energy of the electron when it is in the larger orbit, and E_2 is the energy of the electron when it is in the smaller orbit.

Some comment on these postulates may be helpful. The first is simply an admission that atomic phenomena cannot be correctly described in terms of the "classical" ideas. This point of view had already been advanced by Einstein (Article 50–3). The second looks quite arbitrary; it was arrived at by a combination of three things: a mathematical sophistication that is quite beyond us in this book, the brazen imagination of a genius of twenty-seven, and some trial-and-error fiddling. This postulate specifies definite orbits in which the electron can move, and, combined with the third postulate, it provides for the emission of definite frequencies. The third postulate is Einstein's photon idea modified to fit the problem of emission.

For a test of the postulates, it is natural to apply them to the hydrogen atom. Since the atomic number of hydrogen is 1, the hydrogen atom has only one electron (Article 46–2). It is therefore the simplest atom, and for the first test of new hypotheses, a simple case is the most attractive. Therefore Bohr used his postulates as the starting point in a calculation of the frequencies that a hydrogen atom can radiate. The first step is to find what energy the electron in hydrogen has when it is in each of the permitted orbits. The electron, traveling at a uniform velocity v

in a circle of radius r, has an acceleration. From Article 6–4, this acceleration is

$$a = \frac{v^2}{r}.$$

But the force F on the electron can be calculated from Coulomb's Law, and then we can apply Newton's Second Law. The negative charge on the electron is 1 quantum, represented by the symbol e, and the positive charge on the hydrogen nucleus is also 1 quantum e, as we know from the fact that hydrogen occupies the first place in the Periodic Table. Therefore Coulomb's Law (Article 29–1) tells us that the nucleus attracts the electron with a force

$$F = K\frac{ee}{r^2} = K\frac{e^2}{r^2}.$$

Using Newton's Second Law, $F = ma$, with the value of a given above, we have

$$F = m\frac{v^2}{r}.$$

Setting these two expressions for the force equal to one another, we have

$$K\frac{e^2}{r^2} = m\frac{v^2}{r},$$

or

$$K\frac{e^2}{r} = mv^2.$$

Therefore the K.E. of an electron in the hydrogen atom is

$$\text{K.E.} = K\frac{e^2}{2r},$$

because K.E. $= \frac{1}{2}mv^2$.

To get the total energy of the electron, we must calculate its P.E. and add that to the K.E. The potential energy of one concentrated charge near another one can easily be calculated from Coulomb's Law and the definition of potential energy. It turns out to depend on the product of the charges divided by the distance between them (not squared). In the case of a raised weight, we calculated the P.E. in terms of the height h of the weight with respect to the ground. For charges, we must calculate the P.E. with respect to some specified location; we shall take that location to be at a distance d from the nucleus. This quantity d simply specifies a radius at which we take the P.E. to be zero. At any other place, the P.E. of the electron is

$$\text{P.E.} = K\left(\frac{e^2}{d} - \frac{e^2}{r}\right).$$

The total energy of the electron is

$$\text{K.E.} + \text{P.E.} = K\left[\frac{e^2}{2r} + \left(\frac{e^2}{d} - \frac{e^2}{r}\right)\right]$$

or

$$\text{Total energy} = K\left(\frac{e^2}{d} - \frac{e^2}{2r}\right).$$

The expression above gives the total energy of the atom when the radius of the orbit is r. The next job is to find out what orbits are permitted. Putting hypothesis II into symbolic form, for ease in drawing conclusions, we have

$$2\pi r \times mv = nh,$$

where r is the radius of the orbit,
m is the mass of the electron,
v is the velocity of the electron,
n is an integer,
h is Planck's constant.

In the permitted orbits, therefore, v must have the value $v = nh/2\pi rm$, as you can see by solving for v in the previous equation. But we have already seen from Newton's Second Law and Coulomb's Law that

$$K\frac{e^2}{r^2} = m\frac{v^2}{r},$$

where the left side is the force with which the nucleus attracts the electron, and the right side is the mass of the electron times its acceleration.

Putting in the square of the value that v must have in a permitted orbit gives

$$K\frac{e^2}{r^2} = m\frac{n^2h^2}{4\pi^2r^3m^2}.$$

This can be solved for r, the radius of a permitted orbit. The result is

$$r = \frac{n^2h^2}{4\pi^2mKe^2},$$

which shows that each value of the integer n corresponds to a permitted orbit with a certain radius, r being larger for the larger values of n. Here the theory makes an assertion that can be checked against a known fact. The approximate size of the hydrogen atom is known from experiments on the way hydrogen disobeys Boyle's Law at high pressures (Articles 18–1, 46–1). The radius of the hydrogen atom is about 5×10^{-11} m. We therefore pause in the development of Bohr's theory to see whether it gives a reasonable value for the atomic radius.

If hydrogen is glowing in a discharge tube and the current through it is shut off, the emission of light ceases very quickly, which shows that atoms with surplus energy quickly radiate the energy as light and subside to their state of lowest energy. This state, one would expect, would be a state in which the electron (negative) is as near as it can get to the nucleus (positive). Our formula above for the energy of the electron in hydrogen confirms this thought; the total energy is smallest when r is smallest. In Bohr's theory, the last equation above shows that r is smallest when the integer n has its smallest value, namely 1. For this smallest orbit, in which the electron will normally revolve, the formula for r reduces to

$$r = \frac{1h^2}{4\pi^2 Kme^2}.$$

All quantities on the right are known; their values, and the article in which the value has been discussed, are as follows:

$$h = 6.63 \times 10^{-34} \text{ joule sec} \qquad (50\text{–}1)$$

$$K = 8.99 \times 10^{9} \text{ nt meters}^2/\text{coul}^2 \qquad (29\text{–}1)$$

$$m = 9.11 \times 10^{-31} \text{ kg} \qquad (43\text{–}2)$$

$$e = 1.60 \times 10^{-19} \text{ coul} \qquad (43\text{–}1)$$

Putting them into the equation for r gives

$$r = 5.3 \times 10^{-11} \text{ m}.$$

This is in fine accord with the known radius! Considering how unlikely it is that the enormous powers of 10 would combine to give a correct value for r by accident, we can feel that the theory is definitely on the right track.

It is now time to combine the expression for the radius of an orbit with the expression for the total energy. In

$$\text{Total energy} = K\left(\frac{e^2}{d} - \frac{e^2}{2r}\right),$$

substitute

$$r = \frac{n^2h^2}{4\pi^2 mKe^2}.$$

The result is

$$E_n = K\left(\frac{e^2}{d} - \frac{2\pi^2 mKe^4}{n^2h^2}\right),$$

where by E_n we mean the total energy of the electron when it is in orbit number n. If the electron moves to a smaller orbit, whose value of n is n_2, from a larger orbit whose value of n is n_1, the energy lost by the electron is $E_{n_1} - E_{n_2}$, which works out to

$$E_{n_1} - E_{n_2} = -K\frac{2\pi^2 mKe^4}{n_1{}^2h^2} + K\frac{2\pi^2 mKe^4}{n_2{}^2h^2},$$

or

$$E_{n_1} - E_{n_2} = \frac{2\pi^2 K^2 me^4}{h^2}\left(\frac{1}{n_2{}^2} - \frac{1}{n_1{}^2}\right).$$

According to Bohr's hypothesis III, the energy lost by the atom goes into the creation of a photon whose energy is $h\nu$. If so, then

$$\frac{2\pi^2 K^2 me^4}{h^2}\left(\frac{1}{n_2{}^2} - \frac{1}{n_1{}^2}\right) = h\nu,$$

or

$$\nu = \frac{2\pi^2 K^2 me^4}{h^3}\left(\frac{1}{n_2{}^2} - \frac{1}{n_1{}^2}\right).$$

Suppose the electron falls from an outer orbit, numbered n_1, to the next-to-the-innermost orbit, for which $n = 2$. Then $n_2 = 2$ and n_1 has some value, greater than 2, which we can designate by p. The last equation then becomes

$$\nu = \frac{2\pi^2 K^2 me^4}{h^3}\left(\frac{1}{2^2} - \frac{1}{p^2}\right),$$

where p is an integer greater than 2. Except for the factor in front of the parenthesis, this equation looks just like the Balmer formula (page 430). The value of the factor can be calculated from the known values of K, m, e, and h; the result is

$$\frac{2\pi^2 K^2 me^4}{h^3} = 3.29 \times 10^9 \text{ megacycles/sec.}$$

This result is in spectacular agreement with the value of R that has to be used in the Balmer formula (page 430). Because it gave a rational basis for the Balmer formula, Bohr's theory of the hydrogen atom won immediate acceptance and acclaim, even though it involved a definite break with classical concepts.

51–4. A Discussion of Bohr's Hydrogen Atom. The general physical significance of Bohr's theory is easy to understand. There are orbits in which the electron can move without radiating. The number n is simply a serial number for the orbits; $n = 1$ for the innermost orbit, 2 for the next, 3 for the next, and so on, the radius of the orbit being proportional to n^2. Therefore, as in Figure 51–B, the second orbit is four times as large as the first, or innermost, one. The energy of the electron is smallest when it is in the innermost orbit. If the temperature of the hydrogen is sufficiently high, the atom may acquire, as a result of collisions with other atoms, enough energy to raise the electron to one of the larger orbits. Since the electron can lose energy by "falling" back to a smaller orbit, it will eventually do so. (The average time spent in an outer orbit has been measured to be about a hundred-millionth of a second, or 10^{-8} second, which is long enough to enable the electron to travel about 10^{-2} meter, or half an inch, and therefore to make millions of trips around the nucleus.) When the electron loses energy by falling into a smaller orbit, this energy goes into the formation of a photon, whose frequency is given by

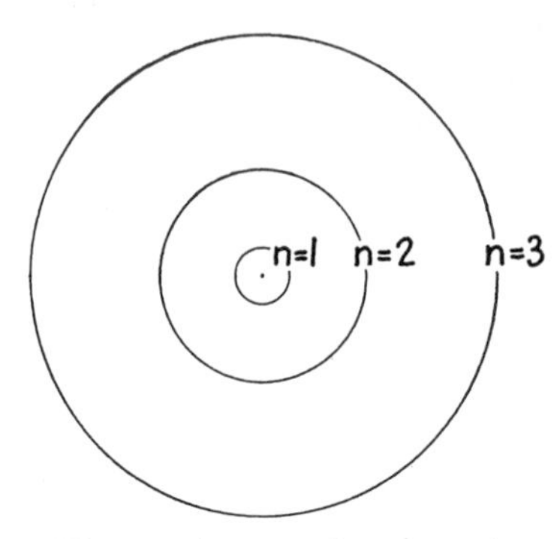

FIGURE 51–B. The first three orbits in Bohr's hydrogen atom.

$$h\nu = \text{Energy lost by electron.}$$

Therefore each line in the spectrum of hydrogen corresponds to an electron jump between two of the permitted orbits. The formulas on pages 430 and 432 now have a physical interpretation. The Balmer series of lines results from jumps from the various outer orbits to the next-to-the-innermost one, for which $n = 2$. The far-ultraviolet, or Lyman, series results from jumps into the innermost orbit, for which $n = 1$. The lines resulting from jumps into the third and higher orbits all lie in the infrared.

This theory also explains the dark lines that hydrogen produces in the solar spectrum. The hydrogen atom can *absorb* energy from a photon, thereby destroying the photon, provided the energy of the photon is just enough to move the electron from the orbit it is in to an outer one. Because only specific orbits are permitted, only specific amounts of energy can be absorbed, and these amounts of energy correspond exactly to frequencies that the atom is capable of emitting later. Therefore the dark lines that hydrogen produces in the sun's spectrum correspond exactly to bright lines that hydrogen can radiate. The same considerations apply to the production of dark-line spectra by other kinds of atoms.

Summary

At the end of the nineteenth century, it was discovered that the frequencies of various lines in the spectrum of hydrogen could be expressed by means of the algebraic formula

$$\nu = R\left(\frac{1}{2^2} - \frac{1}{p^2}\right)$$

where R is a constant and p takes on successive integer values beginning with 3. This formula had no theoretical basis—it was simply found by trial and error that this formula does correctly express the experimentally determined frequencies of a set of lines in the spectrum of hydrogen. This set of lines is called the Balmer series in honor of the man who found the formula.

The first successful theory of the hydrogen atom and its spectrum was worked out by Bohr in 1913. Bohr based his theory on the following set of radical hypotheses:

I. For phenomena on the atomic scale, Maxwellian electrodynamics is not valid.

II. There are certain orbits in which an electron can revolve about the nucleus without radiating electromagnetic energy. These orbits are circles, and they are the circles whose radii satisfy the condition that

$$\text{Circumference of orbit} \times \text{Momentum of electron} = nh$$

where n is an integer and h is Planck's constant.

III. Light is radiated from the atom when the electron jumps from one allowed orbit to another that is closer to the nucleus. The frequency, ν, of this light is given by

$$h\nu = E_1 - E_2,$$

where $h\nu$ is the energy of the photon, E_1 is the energy of the electron when it is in the larger orbit, and E_2 is the energy of the electron when it is in the smaller orbit.

Using Newton's Second Law of Motion and Coulomb's Law for the attraction between charges, Bohr was able to calculate the energy and the momentum that the electron has when it is at various distances from the nucleus. His second hypothesis restricts the momentum, and therefore restricts the radius of the orbit to certain specific values. Each of these allowed orbits entails a definite energy. Applying Bohr's third hypothesis, $h\nu = E_1 - E_2$, one can calculate the frequency of the light radiated when the electron jumps from a larger orbit to a smaller one. The resulting formula turns out to be just the Balmer formula, which had been obtained earlier by mere trial and error.

The diameter of the smallest orbit turns out to be about 10^{-10} meter; this is the diameter of a hydrogen atom in its normal condition.

The number n in Bohr's second hypothesis plays the role of a serial number for the various orbits, $n = 1$ corresponding to the smallest orbit, and larger values of n to larger orbits.

According to Bohr's theory, the hydrogen atom emits light when the electron jumps from a larger orbit to a smaller one, the energy radiated as light being just the energy released by the electron when it falls to an orbit closer to the nucleus. Conversely, the atom can absorb a photon of light if the photon has just enough energy to raise the electron from the orbit it is in to one of the larger ones. Alternatively, the energy to raise the electron to an outer orbit can be acquired in a collision with another atom, if the temperature is high enough.

Questions

1. Just after the discovery of the nucleus, what considerations suggested that an atom resembles the solar system?
2. At the time mentioned in Question 1, what difficulty stood in the way of the assumption that an atom resembles the solar system?
3. How did Bohr get around the difficulty mentioned in Question 2?
4. In Bohr's theory of the hydrogen atom, what assumption restricts the number of possible orbits?
5. How is Bohr's third hypothesis related to Einstein's theory of the photoelectric effect?
6. State two ways in which the consequences of Bohr's theory agree with experimental facts.
7. In terms of Bohr's theory, explain the fact that hot hydrogen gas emits light of certain definite frequencies.
8. In terms of Bohr's theory, describe the absorption of light by hydrogen atoms.
9. In Article 51–1, the frequencies of the first two Balmer lines are calculated from Balmer's formula. From these frequencies, calculate the wavelengths of the lines, and compare the results with the experimentally observed wavelengths that appear in Figure 51–A.

52

QUANTUM NUMBERS

> For the sake of persons of different types of mind scientific truth should be presented in different forms, and should be regarded as equally scientific, whether it appears in the robust form and colouring of a physical illustration, or in the tenuity and paleness of a symbolical expression.
>
> MAXWELL

In its original form, discussed in the last chapter, the Bohr theory of the hydrogen atom postulated a set of circular orbits in which the electron can move without losing energy in the form of radiation. The orbits were characterized by a number n, which has the value 1 for the smallest orbit, 2 for the next larger one, and so on. The theory accounted very well for the main features of the hydrogen spectrum, and it succeeded equally well for the spectrum of ionized helium, which also has a single electron. Bohr's original theory, however, was not able to account for the spectra emitted by atoms that have more than one electron. The theory was soon elaborated to make it account for minor aspects of the hydrogen spectrum, and to make it applicable to the more complicated atoms.

Practically all of this work was done in Germany between 1916 and 1932. During this period the chief business of physics was the study of spectra. Experimenters in all countries, including the United States, put a great effort into accumulating experimental information about spectral lines and the energy relationships that they imply. These facts were correlated by a relatively small number of German theorysmiths. (Many British physicists, under the leadership of Rutherford, continued to investigate the atomic nucleus.) The progress of the theory can be treated in this book only in outline, because a full understanding of the theory requires the use of advanced calculus. Even an outline, however, makes it possible to grasp the essential result of the theory, which is a rational explanation of the chemical behavior of atoms.

52–1. Elliptical Orbits. The first modification of Bohr's hydrogen atom was a fairly simple one. By analogy with the solar system, it is to be expected that the electron can move about the nucleus not only in circular orbits, but also in elliptical ones. The electron is held in its orbit by electrostatic attraction, and a planet is held in its orbit by gravitational attraction. Both kinds of attraction vary with distance in the same way: they are inversely proportional to the square of the distance from the nucleus or the sun. (See Coulomb's Law, Article 29–1, and Newton's Law of Gravitation, Article 8–2.) The similarity in the forces implies a similarity in the possible motions. Bohr's theory explained very well the Balmer and other series in the hydrogen spectrum, but it failed to account for the spectra of more complex atoms. The visible spectrum of sodium, for example, has several overlapping series, each somewhat like the Balmer series. Bohr's theory therefore had to be extended, and the obvious way to extend it was by considering elliptical orbits.

An ellipse has a property called *eccentricity*, which could just as well be called "flatness." It describes how wide the ellipse is in proportion to its length. In the extended hypothesis about permitted orbits, only ellipses of certain definite eccentricities are permitted. For $n = 1$, the only permitted orbit is a circle. For $n = 2$, there are two permitted shapes, one a circle and the other an ellipse. For $n = 3$, there are three permitted shapes, a circle and two ellipses (Figure 52–A), and so on for larger values of n. For a given value of n, the length of each ellipse is the same as the diameter of the circle. As might be expected from analogy with the solar system, each ellipse has one of its foci at the nucleus.

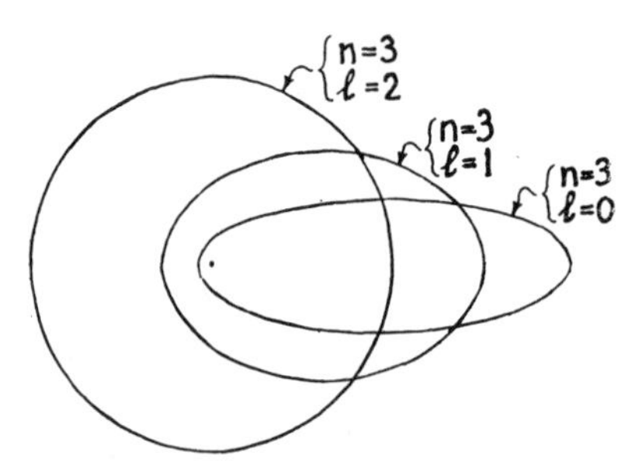

FIGURE 52–A. The shape of the permitted orbits when $n = 3$.

An orbit can no longer be described by the number n alone, because for each n greater than 1 there are several permitted shapes. We therefore assign to the orbits another number, designated by l, which indicates the flatness or eccentricity of the orbit. The flattest ellipse is designated by $l = 0$, the next flattest by $l = 1$, and so on. Since for each value of n the hypothesis permits n different shapes, the permitted values of l range from 0 to $n - 1$. For example, there are four possible shapes for which $n = 4$; the possible values of l when $n = 4$ are therefore 0, 1, 2, and 3.

For no obvious reason, the numbers n and l are called *quantum numbers*.

The hydrogen atom does not afford a good test of whether the elliptical orbits are actually occupied, because it turns out that in hydrogen the energy of the electron is practically the same in an elliptical orbit as it is in the corresponding circular orbit. In atoms that contain several electrons, the mutual repulsion of the electrons influences their energies. The electrons in elliptical orbits are influenced differently than those in circular orbits; jumps to an elliptical orbit and to a circular orbit therefore give rise to different spectrum lines, and in fact to different series. For instance, the overlapping series in the sodium spectrum are found to arise from electron jumps to orbits with different eccentricities. Instead of supporting the idea of elliptic orbits by treating these complex spectra in detail, we shall see later how the Periodic Table gives evidence for the existence of elliptic orbits.

52–2. The Orientation of the Orbits. If hydrogen atoms, or any other atoms, emit light while in a magnetic field, each spectrum line "splits" into several closely spaced lines (Figure 52–B). This splitting means that

FIGURE 52–B. The splitting of spectrum lines when the radiating atoms are in a magnetic field. Above, magnetic field turned off; below, magnetic field turned on. The spectrum is the yellow radiation from sodium atoms.

there must be different electron jumps that involve emission of the same frequency when the atom is not in a magnetic field, but that these jumps result in the emission of slightly *different* frequencies when the atom *is* in a magnetic field. The variety of jumps implies the existence of various permitted orbits in which the electrons have slightly different energies when a magnetic field is present.

EXPERIMENT. Atoms in a magnetic field emit frequencies that differ by only a little from the frequencies that they normally emit. The shift in frequency of the Balmer lines can be *seen* only by placing a hydrogen-filled discharge tube between the poles of a very strong magnet, and then viewing the discharge through an exceptionally good spectroscope. The effect of the magnetic field on the energy of the electrons can easily be shown to exist, however, by using atoms themselves as detectors of radiation.

Let light from a sodium lamp be focused on a Bunsen flame and then fall on a screen. The flame should be between the poles of an electromagnet. A bead of sodium borate on the end of a wire is put in the edge of the flame, to produce a small amount * of sodium vapor. Before the electromagnet is turned on, the sodium atoms in the vapor absorb light from the lamp and cause

* It is easy to get too much vapor, so that the Na atoms interfere with one another and spoil the effect.

a shadow on the wall (Article 49–2). The absorption occurs because the photons from the sodium lamp have exactly the energy required to raise some electrons in the sodium flame from their customary orbit to another one.

When the electromagnet is turned on, so that the sodium in the burner is in a magnetic field, the energy that characterizes each orbit in that sodium is changed a little. Absorption ceases, because the absorption line splits into several lines, none of which coincides exactly with the frequency emitted by the atoms in the sodium lamp, which is not in a strong magnetic field.

The effect of a magnetic field on spectrum lines caused a further elaboration of Bohr's postulates and theory. Again the mathematical details are beyond us, but the general idea is easy to understand. Consider the electron in a hydrogen atom, depicted in Figure 52–C. It is a moving

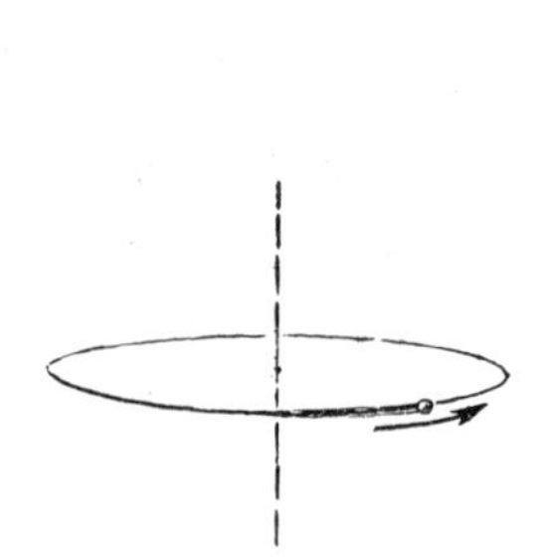

FIGURE 52–C. An electron moving in its orbit resembles a loop of current.

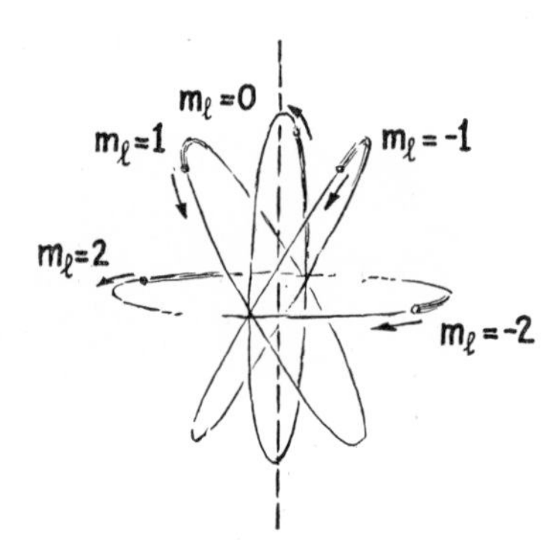

FIGURE 52–D. The five permitted orientations of an orbit that has $l = 2$, in a magnetic field that is parallel to the dashed line.

charge, and is therefore equivalent to a current. The charge moving in its orbit will behave like a current in a loop of wire—it will act like a little electromagnet, with north and south poles that will tend to line up along the direction of the magnetic field the way a compass needle or a galvanometer coil does. To change the alignment of the orbit with respect to the field, one would have to exert a force on it and move it, so work would be required. This shows that the energy stored in the atom depends to some extent on the tilt of the orbit with respect to the magnetic field. When no magnetic field is present, no energy would be needed to shift the tilt of an orbit, and therefore orbits with different orientations do not give rise to separate lines in the spectrum.

From the observed influence of a magnetic field on the energy radiated by an atom, students of spectra concluded that a small number of different orbital orientations are actually possible. The hypothesis about permitted orbits was therefore extended again, to allow the planes of the orbits to have certain definite angles of tilt with respect to the magnetic field, the amount of tilt being specified by a third quantum number called m_l, whose permitted values range from $-l$ to l. For example, if $l = 2$, then the possible values of m_l are -2, -1, 0, 1, and 2, so there are five positions in space that such an orbit can occupy. Figure 52–D shows how they lie. (There are only four positions that look different, but in an orbit that is perpendicular to the field, it makes a difference which direction the electron is going around in.) By studying the influence of the magnetic field on the spectrum, one can infer the value of l for the orbit in which the electron normally moves.

52–3. Electron Spin (1925). We now have a great variety of permitted orbits, and a variety of energy changes, but from a study of spectrum lines it was found that there are some energy changes which the theory outlined thus far does not account for. Specifically, some of the spectrum lines are actually double; the "line," when examined carefully with a good spectroscope, turns out to be two lines close together. A well-known example is the yellow doublet in the spectrum of sodium. These lines are prominent in the solar spectrum; they appear in Figure 49–H, near 5900 on the scale.

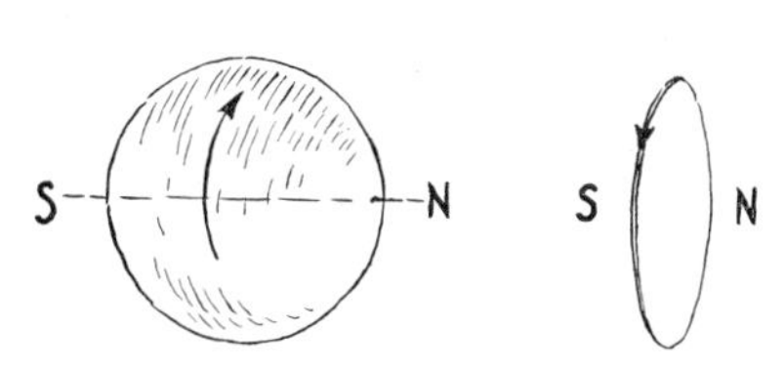

FIGURE 52–E. A spinning electron is a magnet.

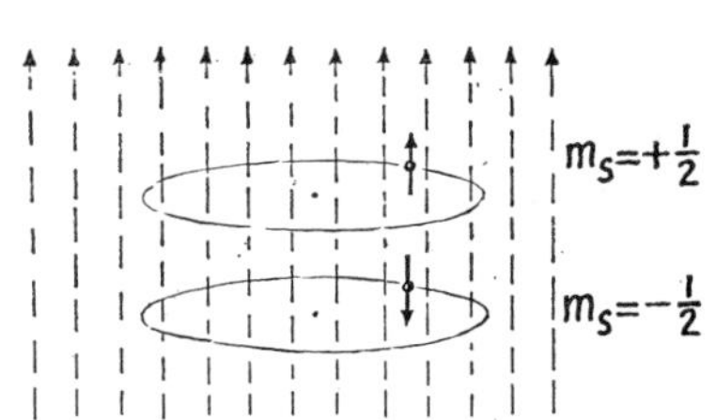

FIGURE 52–F. The possible orientations of an electron in a magnetic field.

Even the lines of the Balmer series turn out on close examination to be double. To account for this doubling, and for other effects that are observed in more complicated spectra, a couple of young Dutch physicists introduced the idea that electrons spin on their axes as the earth does. The electrons are charges, and if they spin, then the charge near their "equator" moves in a circle and constitutes a circular current which will behave like a loop of current-bearing wire. That is, the electron itself will behave like a little electromagnet having a north pole and south pole. Figure 52–E is a fanciful representation of the effect.

When a spinning electron revolves about the nucleus, the effect on the electron is the same as if the nucleus revolved about the electron. (Recall the geocentric and heliocentric explanations of the solar system.) The motion of the nucleus relative to the electron produces a magnetic field at the electron, and the electron will have less energy if it is lined up along this magnetic field than if it is lined up against the field.

The electron behaves to some extent like a compass needle in the earth's field, but there is an important difference. The compass needle will always swing so as to align itself with the field (pointing north), but the doubling of some spectral lines shows that the electron can align itself in either of two positions: *with* the field or *against* it. These two positions, shown in Figure 52–F, are distinguished from one another by means of a fourth quantum number, called m_s, which is positive when the electron is aligned with its north pole pointing in the direction of the field, and negative when the axis of the electron is aligned against the field. The quantum numbers n, l, and m_l all have integer values, but the values assigned to m_s are $+\frac{1}{2}$ and $-\frac{1}{2}$. (The fact that m_s has half-integer values, while m_l has integer values, arises in the mathematics from the fact that m_l deals with a charge revolving in an orbit while m_s deals with charge rotating on its axis.)

The discovery of electron spin greatly improves our understanding of magnetism. The electron is itself a magnet; if the electrons in an atom are predominantly oriented in one direction, they can make the atom behave as a magnet. Many such atoms, if aligned alike, will make a large-scale magnet. The magnetic properties of iron and other materials can therefore be traced to magnetism of the simplest particle we know, the electron.

52–4. The Quantum Numbers. Our aim in this chapter has been to interpret the evidence supplied by spectra, and thereby to arrive at an understanding of the arrangement of electrons in atoms. Thus far the understanding is incomplete. We have a large variety of permitted orbits, but no knowledge of how the electrons in a complicated atom are distributed in these orbits. The key to this knowledge appears in the next chapter. Before going further, however, we must be clear about the quantum numbers.

There are four quantum numbers. The first three, which describe the orbits, are n for size, l for eccentricity, and m_l for orientation. The fourth, m_s, tells how the electron is oriented in the orbit.

The patterns observed in the spectra of even very complex atoms can be accounted for in terms of changes in the quantum numbers. Therefore the quantum numbers can safely be regarded as having a fundamental significance, although the orbits themselves are not directly observable.

Summary

Guided by observations on the spectra of various atoms, theoretical physicists extended the Bohr theory to make it permit a considerable variety of different orbits. These orbits can be designated by a set of integers called quantum numbers.

The quantum number n specifies the size of the orbit—the diameter if it is a circle or the length if it is an ellipse—and has the value 1 for the smallest orbit, 2 for the next larger, and so on to infinity. The number l specifies the eccentricity, or flatness, of the orbit. The number of orbits of a given size is the same as the serial number of that size; for example when $n = 3$ there are three possible orbits, a circle and two ellipses. The flattest ellipse is designated by $l = 0$, and the less flat ellipses by successively larger values of l, the largest value of l being assigned to the circle. The largest value l can have is clearly $n - 1$; for example, when $n = 3$, l can have values, 0, 1, and 2.

The quantum number m_l designates the tilt of the orbit when the atom is in a magnetic field. It can have integer values ranging from $-l$ to $+l$. For example, an orbit that has $l = 2$ can have any of the following values of m_l: -2, -1, 0, 1, or 2. An orbit with $l = 2$ can therefore tilt in any one of five ways.

There is a fourth quantum number, m_s, which designates the direction in which the electron is spinning, and therefore designates the orientation of the north pole of the electron. The two possible orientations are designated by $m_s = +\frac{1}{2}$ and $m_s = -\frac{1}{2}$.

Questions

1. What are the symbols for the quantum numbers for an electron in an atom? What is the physical interpretation of each of these quantum numbers?
2. When $n = 2$, what values may l have? For each of these values of l, what values may m_l have? How many possible orbits are there altogether, such that $n = 2$?
3. Using the procedure outlined in Question 2, find the number of possible orbits for which $n = 3$.
4. What theoretical consideration indicated the possibility of elliptical orbits in atoms?
5. What experimental considerations suggested that electrons in atoms can occupy elliptical orbits?
6. Explain why it is to be expected that, in a magnetic field, the energy of a hydrogen atom will depend on the angle between the magnetic field and the plane of the atomic orbit.
7. What experimental fact is evidence that the energy of an atom does depend on whether the atom is in a magnetic field? What indicates that the angle of tilt of any orbit, with respect to the magnetic field, is restricted to a small number of specific values?
8. Explain why a spinning charged particle should be expected to act like a magnet.
9. What experimental fact indicates that an electron does act like a tiny magnet?

53

ELECTRON ORBITS AND THE PERIODIC TABLE

We have seen that the spectrum of hydrogen can be accounted for by devising a set of permitted orbits in which the electron in the hydrogen atom can move about its nucleus, and by assuming that the electron normally occupies the orbit closest to the nucleus. When the atom acquires energy by collision with other atoms, or by absorbing a photon, the electron moves to an outer orbit but soon reverts to the innermost one, either by jumping from the outer orbit directly to the innermost one, or else by reaching the innermost one by successive jumps with stop-overs in intermediate orbits. Each such jump involves the emission of a photon according to the relation

$$E_1 - E_2 = h\nu$$

where $E_1 - E_2$ is the energy lost in falling from one orbit to the other.

53–1. The Exclusion Principle (1924). Now consider a lithium atom. Since lithium occupies the third place in the Periodic Table, we know it has three electrons when it is not ionized. These three electrons must move in permitted orbits. How are the three electrons distributed among the infinitude of possible orbits? One would probably suppose, if there were no evidence to the contrary, that all three electrons would be in the innermost orbit, equally spaced around its circumference. Evidence to the contrary does exist, however. The spectra of helium, with two electrons, and beryllium, with four, do not resemble the spectrum of hydrogen at all. For one thing, their lines are not double, and for another they do not contain lines arranged as simply as in the Balmer series. The spectrum of lithium, however, does resemble that of hydrogen in some respects. The lines in the lithium spectrum are double, and among many other lines there is a set whose pattern resembles that of the Balmer series. This similarity suggests that in lithium, as well as in hydrogen, the spectrum comes from the orbit-to-orbit jumps of a single electron, the other two electrons being differently situated.

Consideration of the facts mentioned in the last paragraph, and of many other similar facts, led to the discovery in 1924 of Pauli's Exclusion Principle. This principle, or rule, states that *no two electrons in the same atom can have the same set of quantum numbers.* That is, no two electrons in the same atom can have exactly the same motion. No theoretical justification for the principle has ever been found, but it is apparently one of the most fundamental of all the laws of science. For one thing, it explains the positions of the atoms in the Periodic Table.

53–2. The Lithium Atom. It is easy to apply the Exclusion Principle to lithium. Start with a lithium nucleus, and bring one electron near it. The electron will fall into the innermost of the permitted orbits, for which $n = 1$, and therefore l must be 0. The only permitted orientation when $l = 0$ is the one such that $m_l = 0$. The axis of the electron will line up along the magnetic field created by the relative motion of the nucleus; this alignment is designated by $m_s = +\frac{1}{2}$. Now bring another electron near the lithium ion and let it be captured. It will fall into the orbit where its energy will be a minimum, which is the innermost orbit, where the only possible values of n, l, and m_l are 1, 0, and 0, respectively. In this orbit, the quantum number $m_s = +\frac{1}{2}$ has already been taken by the first electron, so that the second electron must have $m_s = -\frac{1}{2}$; that is, it must align its axis oppositely to that of the first electron. *The orbit for which $n = 1$ is now completely occupied.*

When the third electron is put into the lithium atom, it will have to go in one of the outer orbits, whichever one corresponds to the lowest value of energy. This is one of the orbits for which $n = 2$, and by studying the spectrum of lithium atoms when they are in a magnetic field, it has been determined that the outer orbit that is normally occupied always has the same orientation with respect to the field. Unless $l = 0$, several orientations are possible, so l must be 0, which means that the third electron in lithium occupies the flattest orbit for which $n = 2$. The lithium atom can therefore be depicted as in Figure 53–A.

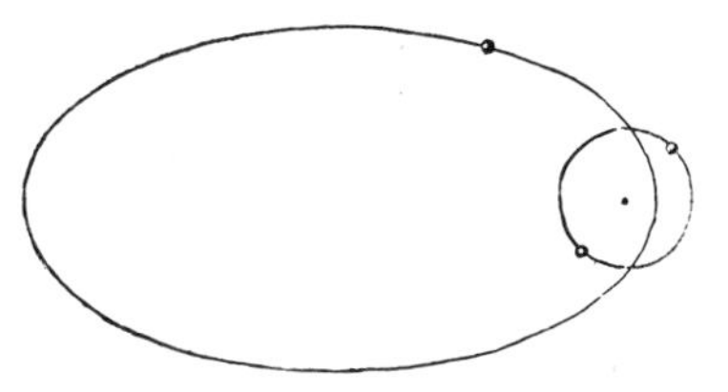

FIGURE 53–A. The Bohr model of the lithium atom.

One can jump now to a couple of conclusions. The first bears on the experimental fact that in its spectrum and in its chemical behavior, lithium to a considerable degree resembles hydrogen. It is reasonable to wonder whether this resemblance may stem from the similarity in the structures of lithium and hydrogen. In each of these atoms, there is a lone electron in the largest occupied orbit. The second speculative conclusion bears on the fact that helium is a chemically inert substance. Can this be because its two electrons just exhaust the possibilities for $n = 1$? Let us take nuclei with larger charges, and build atoms with them to see whether any generalizations can be brought to light.

53–3. Atom Building. For beryllium, the atomic number is 4, and the first three electrons will fit in the same orbits as for lithium. The fourth electron will fit in the same orbit as the third, but the axes of these two electrons must be oppositely aligned. That is, $m_s = -\frac{1}{2}$ for the fourth electron. The flattest orbit for which $n = 2$ is now filled to capacity. Therefore in building boron, with atomic number 5, the fifth electron must go into an orbit for which $l = 1$.

When $l = 1$, m_l can have the values -1, 0, and 1, and for each of these values of m_l, the value of m_s can be either positive or negative, so there are three orbits with $l = 1$, and they can accommodate six electrons.

The orbits for which $n = 2$ can therefore accommodate two electrons with $l = 0$ and six electrons with $l = 1$, making eight electrons all told for which n can equal 2. Table 53–I shows how these considerations apply to the electron arrangement in the first few elements of the Periodic Table.

TABLE 53–I

THE DISTRIBUTION OF ELECTRONS IN THE LIGHTER ATOMS

Atomic Number	Element	$n = 1$, $l = 0$	$n = 2$, $l = 0$	$n = 2$, $l = 1$	$n = 3$, $l = 0$	$n = 3$, $l = 1$	$n = 3$, $l = 2$
1	H	1					
2	He	2					
3	Li	2	1				
4	Be	2	2				
5	B	2	2	1			
6	C	2	2	2			
7	N	2	2	3			
8	O	2	2	4			
9	F	2	2	5			
10	Ne	2	2	6			
11	Na	2	2	6	1		
12	Mg	2	2	6	2		
13	Al	2	2	6	2	1	
14	Si	2	2	6	2	2	
15	P	2	2	6	2	3	
16	S	2	2	6	2	4	
17	Cl	2	2	6	2	5	
18	A	2	2	6	2	6	

The foregoing table is constructed entirely on the basis of the Exclusion Principle and the assumption that each new electron added to the atom will take on the smallest values of n and l that are still available. (This assumption, which is correct for the atoms listed in the table, can be verified by observing the spectra of atoms in a magnetic field, as mentioned earlier. For atomic numbers higher than 18, the spectra show that the assumption no longer is valid, but they also show what the values of l actually are.)

53-4. Closed Shells. The group of orbits for which n has a given value is called a *shell.* Quite arbitrarily, because the need for talking about shells arose before they were really understood, the innermost shell is called the K shell, and the outer ones, the L, M, N, and so on, shells. For example, electrons for which $n = 2$ are called members of the L shell. Electrons that have the same n and also the same l are said to constitute a *subshell.* The L shell has two subshells; the one for $l = 0$ can contain two electrons, and the one for $l = 1$ can contain six. The larger shells contain three or more subshells.

When a shell or a subshell is occupied by all of the electrons that the Exclusion Principle allows, the shell or subshell is called *closed.* For example, the K shell is closed when it contains two electrons; the L shell is closed when it contains two plus six, or eight electrons.

Using this terminology, the conclusions to which we tentatively jumped when considering the lithium atom can be put as follows: Helium is chemically inert because its electrons form a closed shell, and lithium resembles hydrogen because each contains just one electron that is not in a closed shell. If only hydogen, helium, and lithium are taken into account, these conclusions are mere speculation, but the speculation can be checked by finding out what element has a closed L shell. Our table shows that it is neon, which is another inert gas! Moreover, after lithium, the next element that has just one electron not in a closed shell is sodium, which belongs to the same chemical family as lithium. These facts are strong support for the Exclusion Principle, and for the idea that chemical behavior is governed by the shell structure.

Turning our attention to the two halogens in the table, we see immediately that fluorine and chlorine each have seven electrons in their outer shell. In fact, comparing the elements from $_{11}$Na to $_{18}$A with those from $_{3}$Li to $_{10}$Ne, we see that those that lie in the same group in the Periodic Table have the same number of electrons in their outer shells. We conclude that *the chemical properties of an atom are determined by the arrangement of its electrons, particularly by the number of electrons in the outer shell* of the nonionized atom.

The arrangement of the electrons in atoms is therefore the basis of the Periodic Table. The periodicity in chemical properties springs from the existence of closed shells, which give rise to repetition in the numbers of outer electrons as one progresses through the table. The closed shells, in turn, are explained by the Exclusion Principle. Our faith in this principle is based on the perfect correlation among the principle, the facts of spectroscopy, and the Periodic Table.

53–5. The Structures of Some Heavier Atoms. The atoms at the beginning of the Periodic Table have illustrated the basis of atomic structure and its relation to chemical behavior. A brief discussion of the more complicated atoms has several points of interest. Although the facts are more complex, the ideas are the same.

Lithium and sodium are similar not only in their chemistry, but also in their spectra. The wavelengths present in the spectra are of course different, but the general patterns of lines are alike. Moreover, the lines are double, as are those of hydrogen. Helium, beryllium, and magnesium have spectra that resemble one another but differ markedly from the spectra of lithium and sodium. Their lines are either single or triple, never double. The spectroscopist can justly assume that the series of double lines come from atoms whose outer shell contains just one electron, and that spectra with single and triple lines signify two electrons in the atom's outer shell. Using such clues, it was possible after years of research to interpret any spectrum in terms of electron structure, and thus to decipher the structure of the complicated atoms.

The assumption that n and l have values as small as possible breaks down for atoms beyond argon. This is shown by the fact that the next atom, potassium ($_{19}K$), has a spectrum like that of lithium or sodium. This means that potassium has a single electron in its outermost shell. With potassium, therefore, the N shell, with $n = 4$, begins to be occupied even though the M shell, with $n = 3$, is not filled up. The spectrum of potassium atoms in a magnetic field shows that the outer electron is normally in an ellipse that has only one permitted value of tilt. It follows that $l = 0$. The spectrum of calcium shows that this orbit, which of course can hold two electrons provided they have opposite spins, is filled in the calcium atom ($_{20}Ca$). When the scandium atom ($_{21}Sc$) is built up, the twenty-first electron has to go into an unoccupied orbit, which could conceivably either be one for which $n = 4$ and $l = 1$, or else one for which $n = 3$ and $l = 2$. The spectrum of scandium decides in favor of the second possibility; the orbit that was spurned by the nineteenth and twentieth electrons is occupied by the twenty-first. The only "explanation" that can be offered is that the electrons go into the unoccupied orbit that entails the lowest energy.

The actual electronic configurations of all atoms have in recent years been worked out by studying spectra. As a result, Table 53–I can be continued as in Table 53–II.

TABLE 53–II

THE DISTRIBUTION OF ELECTRONS IN SOME HEAVIER ATOMS

Atomic Number and Symbol	K	L		M			N	
	$n = 1$	$n = 2$		$n = 3$			$n = 4$	
	$l = 0$	$l = 0$	$l = 1$	$l = 0$	$l = 1$	$l = 2$	$l = 0$	$l = 1$
$_{19}$K	2	2	6	2	6		1	
$_{20}$Ca	2	2	6	2	6		2	
$_{21}$Sc	2	2	6	2	6	1	2	
$_{22}$Ti	2	2	6	2	6	2	2	
$_{23}$V	2	2	6	2	6	3	2	
$_{24}$Cr	2	2	6	2	6	5	1	
$_{25}$Mn	2	2	6	2	6	5	2	
$_{26}$Fe	2	2	6	2	6	6	2	
$_{27}$Co	2	2	6	2	6	7	2	
$_{28}$Ni	2	2	6	2	6	8	2	
$_{29}$Cu	2	2	6	2	6	10	1	
$_{30}$Zn	2	2	6	2	6	10	2	
$_{31}$Ga	2	2	6	2	6	10	2	1
$_{32}$Ge	2	2	6	2	6	10	2	2
$_{33}$As	2	2	6	2	6	10	2	3
$_{34}$Se	2	2	6	2	6	10	2	4
$_{35}$Br	2	2	6	2	6	10	2	5
$_{36}$Kr	2	2	6	2	6	10	2	6

53–6. Long Periods, Transition Elements, and Subgroups. The most satisfying conclusion that can be drawn from Table 53–II is that it accounts for the first long period, and incidentally it shows why the transition elements form a special category. The long periods arise because there are so many permitted orbits outside the *K* and *L* shells. After $_{18}$A, one has to go all the way to $_{36}$Kr before there are again eight electrons outside a closed shell. This means going eighteen places in the Periodic Table before finding close resemblance in chemical properties. For a second instance, start with $_{13}$Al. Its unfilled shell contains two electrons for which $l = 0$, and one for which $l = 1$. When more electrons are added, there are so many permitted orbits that an unfilled shell like the one in $_{13}$Al does not arise before $_{31}$Ga. Therefore no element between aluminum and gallium can closely resemble aluminum in chemical behavior. Again eighteen elements intervene between two that have the same arrangement of outer electrons. This is why the long periods contain eighteen elements.

TABLE 53–III
THE ELECTRONIC CONFIGURATIONS OF THE ATOMS

I	II	III	IV	V	VI	VII	VIII		
1 H K1							2 He K2		
3 Li L1 K2	4 Be L2 K2	5 B L3 K2	6 C L4 K2	7 N L5 K2	8 O L6 K2	9 F L7 K2	10 Ne L8 K2		
11 Na M1 L8 K2	12 Mg M2 L8 K2	13 Al M3 L8 K2	14 Si M4 L8 K2	15 P M5 L8 K2	16 S M6 L8 K2	17 Cl M7 L8 K2	18 A M8 L8 K2		
19 K N1 M8 L8 K2	20 Ca N2 M8 L8 K2	21 Sc N2 M9 L8 K2	22 Ti N2 M10 L8 K2	23 V N2 M11 L8 K2	24 Cr N1 M13 L8 K2	25 Mn N2 M13 L8 K2	26 Fe N2 M14 L8 K2	27 Co N2 M15 L8 K2	28 Ni N2 M16 L8 K2
29 Cu N1 M18 L8 K2	30 Zn N2 M18 L8 K2	31 Ga N3 M18 L8 K2	32 Ge N4 M18 L8 K2	33 As N5 M18 L8 K2	34 Se N6 M18 L8 K2	35 Br N7 M18 L8 K2	36 Kr N8 M18 L8 K2		

TABLE 53–III *Continued*

37 Rb O1 N8 M18 L8 K2	38 Sr O2 N8 M18 L8 K2	39 Y O2 N9 M18 L8 K2	40 Zr O2 N10 M18 L8 K2	41 Nb O1 N12 M18 L8 K2	42 Mo O1 N13 M18 L8 K2	43 Tc O1 N14 M18 L8 K2	44 Ru O1 N15 M18 L8 K2	45 Rh O1 N16 M18 L8 K2	46 Pd N18 M18 L8 K2
47 Ag O1 N18 M18 L8 K2	48 Cd O2 N18 M18 L8 K2	49 In O3 N18 M18 L8 K2	50 Sn O4 N18 M18 L8 K2	51 Sb O5 N18 M18 L8 K2	52 Te O6 N18 M18 L8 K2	53 I O7 N18 M18 L8 K2	54 Xe O8 N18 M18 L8 K2		
55 Cs P1 O8 N18 M18 L8 K2	56 Ba P2 O8 N18 M18 L8 K2	57-71 Rare-Earth Metals *	72 Hf P2 O10 N32 M18 L8 K2	73 Ta P2 O11 N32 M18 L8 K2	74 W P2 O12 N32 M18 L8 K2	75 Re P2 O13 N32 M18 L8 K2	76 Os P2 O14 N32 M18 L8 K2	77 Ir P2 O15 N32 M18 L8 K2	78 Pt P2 O16 N32 M18 L8 K2
79 Au P1 O18 N32 M18 L8 K2	80 Hg P2 O18 N32 M18 L8 K2	81 Tl P3 O18 N32 M18 L8 K2	82 Pb P4 O18 N32 M18 L8 K2	83 Bi P5 O18 N32 M18 L8 K2	84 Po P6 O18 N32 M18 L8 K2	85 At P7 O18 N32 M18 L8 K2	86 Rn P8 O18 N32 M18 L8 K2		
87 Fr Q1 P8 O18 N32 M18 L8 K2	88 Ra Q2 P8 O18 N32 M18 L8 K2	89 *Actinon Metals							

*See page 456

TABLE 53–III *Continued*

Rare-Earth Metals	57 La	58 Ce	59 Pr	60 Nd	61 Pm	62 Sm	63 Eu	64 Gd	65 Tb
	P2 O9 N18 M18 L8 K2	P2 O8 N20 M18 L8 K2	P2 O8 N21 M18 L8 K2	P2 O8 N22 M18 L8 K2	P2 O8 N23 M18 L8 K2	P2 O8 N24 M18 L8 K2	P2 O8 N25 M18 L8 K2	P2 O9 N25 M18 L8 K2	P2 O9 N26 M18 L8 K2
66 Dy P2 O8 N28 M18 L8 K2	67 Ho P2 O8 N29 M18 L8 K2	68 Er P2 O8 N30 M18 L8 K2	69 Tm P2 O8 N31 M18 L8 K2	70 Yb P2 O8 N32 M18 L8 K2	71 Lu P2 O9 N32 M18 L8 K2				

Actinon Metals	89 Ac	90 Th	91 Pa	92 U	93 Np	94 Pu	95 Am	96 Cm	97 Bk
	Q2 P9 O18 N32 M18 L8 K2	Q2 P10 O18 N32 M18 L8 K2	Q2 P9 O20 N32 M18 L8 K2	Q2 P9 O21 N32 M18 L8 K2	Q2 P8 O23 N32 M18 L8 K2	Q2 P8 O24 N32 M18 L8 K2	Q2 P8 O25 N32 M18 L8 K2	Q2 P9 O25 N32 M18 L8 K2	Q2 P8 O27 N32 M18 L8 K2
98 Cf Q2 P8 O28 N32 M18 L8 K2	99 E Q2 P(?) O(?) N32 M18 L8 K2	100 Ct Q2 P(?) O(?) N32 M18 L8 K2	101 Mv Q(?) P(?) O(?) N32 M18 L8 K2						

The transition, or subgroup, elements in the first long period begin with scandium, $_{21}Sc$, and continue through zinc, $_{30}Zn$ (Article 40–2). The structures in Table 53–II explain the existence and the behavior of the transition elements. In the transition between $_{20}Ca$ and $_{31}Ga$, the structural change is a filling up of the next-to-the-outermost shell. The outer shells of these atoms contain two electrons, for the most part, although a few contain only one. Since the atoms have nearly the same outer structure, they have nearly the same chemical properties. When ionization removes the outer electrons, however, the outer structures of the resulting ions have appreciable differences. As a result, the ions of the transition elements have markedly different chemical behavior.

Tables 53–I and 53–II also explain why the transition elements fit into subgroups in the short form of the Periodic Table. What $_{13}Al$, $_{21}Sc$, and $_{31}Ga$ have in common is that each has three electrons that are not in closed subshells. In $_{13}Al$ and $_{31}Ga$, these three electrons are all in the outer shell, whereas in $_{21}Sc$ one of them is in an unfilled inner shell. This limited resemblance in atomic structure is the reason that the chemical behavior of scandium has a limited resemblance to that of aluminum or of gallium.

Similar distinctions, but not always identical ones, account for the subgroups in other columns of the Periodic Table. In $_{11}Na$, $_{19}K$, and $_{29}Cu$, a single electron lies outside of closed subshells. In $_{11}Na$ and $_{19}K$, however, the single electron lies outside of a shell of eight electrons, but in $_{29}Cu$ it lies outside of a shell of eighteen. Table 53–III is a Periodic Table that gives a tally of the electrons in each shell of the various atoms. Using this chart, you can see why gold and silver resemble copper, whereas rubidium and cesium resemble sodium.

53–7. The Rare-Earth Metals. Table 53–III shows the explanation for the rare-earth metals. After the *N* shell has eighteen electrons, it does not begin to acquire more until there are eleven electrons outside it, in the *O* and *P* shells. Then as the atomic number increases from 57 to 71, the *O* and *P* shells undergo hardly any change, while the *N* shell fills up. Since the chemical properties of an atom are determined largely by the outer electrons, elements 57 through 71 behave almost alike.

53–8. Iron and Magnetism. The extraordinary magnetic properties of iron arise from the fact that in the iron atom, $_{26}Fe$, a large majority of the electrons in the *M* shell happen to have their spins lined up in the same direction. None of the *M* electrons have $m_s = +\frac{1}{2}$, and only five have $m_s = -\frac{1}{2}$. Since each electron is a little magnet, their cooperative alignment makes the iron atom a magnet.

In view of the usefulness of magnetic machinery, it is fortunate that this exceptional alignment of spins occurs in iron rather than in platinum or fluorine.

Summary

The spectra of hydrogen and lithium have some similarity, although they are not at all like the spectrum of helium, which lies between hydrogen and lithium in the Periodic Table. To account for this fact, and for other resemblances among spectra, a hypothesis called the Exclusion Principle was put forward. This hypothesis states that no two electrons in an atom can have the same set of quantum numbers. It follows from the Exclusion Principle that not more than two electrons can be in the innermost orbit ($n = 1$), not more than eight electrons in the next set of orbits ($n = 2$), not more than eighteen in the next ($n = 3$), and so on. Sets of orbits having the same value of n are called shells. Sets of orbits with the same n and the same l are called subshells. When each of the possible orbits in a shell or subshell contains two electrons, the shell or subshell is said to be closed.

Our faith in the Exclusion Principle is based on its perfect correlation with the facts of spectroscopy and with the Periodic Table.

The number of electrons in the outermost shell of an atom can be determined experimentally by studying the pattern of lines in its spectrum. The Exclusion Principle accounts for the arrangement of the electrons in the interior shells, and the distribution of electrons in the outer shells is always consistent with the Exclusion Principle. This principle is a rule that is fundamental in the sense that it cannot (at present!) be explained in terms that are simpler. It enables us to correlate the findings of the spectroscopists, whose studies of spectra have shown how the electrons in each atom are arranged.

By comparing electronic arrangement with position in the Periodic Table, we find that the chemical properties of an atom are determined by the arrangement of its electrons; the most important factor is the number of electrons in the outer shell. In any one group in the Periodic Table, the main-group elements all have atoms with the same number of electrons in the outer shell. The transition elements, which form the subgroups in the short table, have atoms that differ chiefly in the population of the next-to-outermost shell.

The atoms of the rare-earth metals are alike (or nearly so) in the two outer shells, but they differ in an inner shell. Their similarity in outer structure accounts for their similarity in chemical behavior.

Iron atoms act as little magnets because a large majority of the electrons in the M shell of iron are lined up so that their magnetic fields augment one another.

Questions

1. What is the Exclusion Principle?
2. What is a shell? What is a closed shell?
3. Show how acceptance of the Exclusion Principle leads one to expect that lithium has one electron outside of a closed shell.
4. What spectroscopic and chemical facts support the idea that lithium has one electron outside of a closed shell?
5. What structural feature characterizes the alkali metals?
6. What structural feature characterizes the alkaline-earth metals?
7. What structural feature characterizes the halogens?
8. What structural feature characterizes the inert gases?
9. What structural feature characterizes the transition elements?
10. What structural feature characterizes the rare-earth metals?
11. In any group, how do the atoms in the subgroup resemble those in the main group? How do the main-group and subgroup atoms differ?
12. What accounts for the special magnetic properties of iron?
13. Can a closed shell of electrons act as a magnet?

54

X-RAYS AND THE STRUCTURE OF SOLIDS

Although x-rays were discovered in 1895, about the same time as radioactivity and the electron, discussion of them has been postponed until this chapter because they were not understood until after Bohr had invented his theory of atomic structure.

54–1. The Discovery of X-Rays (1895). A German physics professor named Roentgen discovered that in the neighborhood of a discharge tube, certain minerals will fluoresce, and photographic film will be affected as though by light, even though the light from the discharge tube is cut off by a screen of opaque paper. He found that these effects are caused by something that travels in straight lines, since an object interposed between the discharge tube and the photographic film will cast a sharp shadow (Figure 54–A). Therefore Roentgen ascribed the effect to rays of a type previously unknown, and he called them "x-rays."

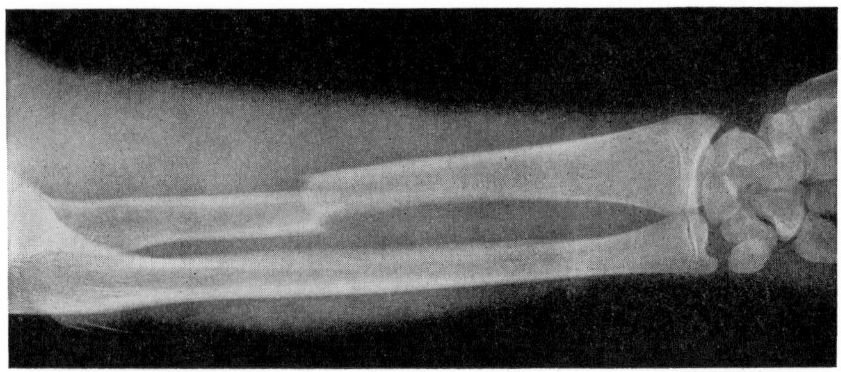

Eastman Kodak Co.

FIGURE 54–A. An x-ray shadowgram of a broken arm. The sharpness of the shadows is testimony that x-rays travel in straight lines; the nature of the shadows illustrates the fact that materials are less transparent to x-rays when they contain elements of higher atomic number, such as the calcium in bones.

Two of Roentgen's discharge tubes appear in Figure 54–B. He found that the x-rays emanated from a part of the discharge tube on which the cathode rays impinged; this and later investigations showed that x-rays

Deutsches Museum, Munich

FIGURE 54–B. Two of Roentgen's discharge tubes.

are produced when cathode rays collide with matter, i.e., when fast-moving electrons strike atoms. Discharge tubes intended for use as x-ray sources are usually made so that the cathode rays hit a massive anode, or "target," as shown in Figure 54–C.

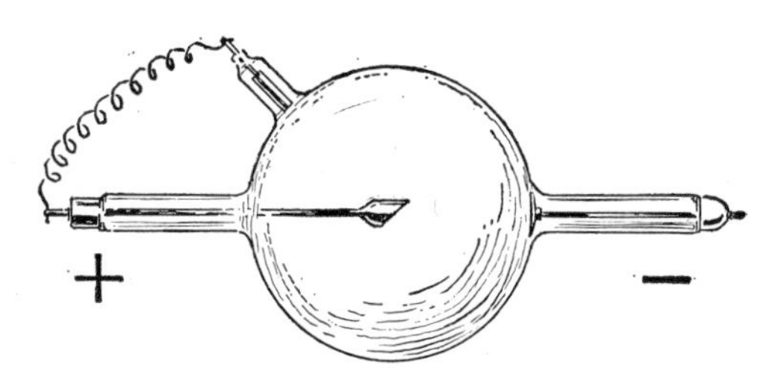

FIGURE 54–C. A discharge tube designed for generating x-rays. Electrons from the cup-shaped cathode converge to a small intense spot on the target, which attracts the electrons because it is connected to the anode.

X-rays have three properties by which they can be detected: they affect a photographic film; they cause fluorescence of certain substances; and they turn a gas into an electrical conductor. Quantitative measurements of the intensity of x-rays are commonly made by letting them ionize the air between two electrodes, and measuring the electrical conductivity of the air.

EXPERIMENT. The fact that x-rays do ionize the air through which they pass can be seen by charging an electroscope and observing that the charge leaks off if an x-ray tube is put in operation a short distance away.

Perhaps the most striking property of x-rays is that they pass rather freely through many things, for instance wood or flesh, that are opaque to light. They are strongly absorbed in materials with high atomic number, for example lead; they can therefore be confined to beams by letting them pass through holes or slits in plates of lead.

54–2. The Nature of X-Rays (1910). After more than a decade of uncertainty as to the nature of x-rays, it was proved that they are electromagnetic waves, of wavelength much smaller than that of visible light. The proof that x-rays are waves was accomplished by showing that they can undergo diffraction. Some Dutch physicists repeated the experiment of Grimaldi (Article 47–1), except that they used x-rays instead of light, and slits between metal blocks instead of pinholes in an opaque screen.

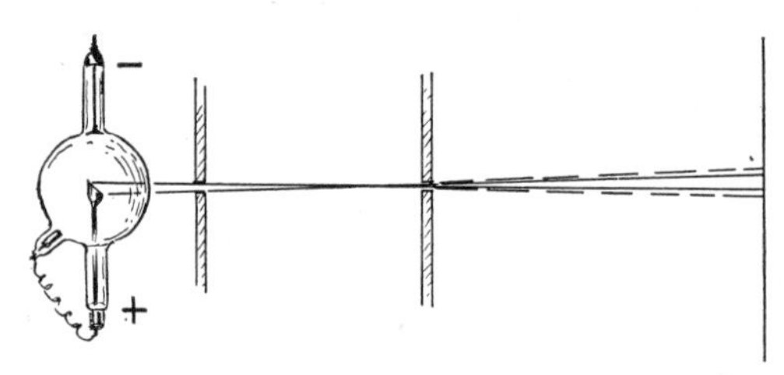

FIGURE 54–D. An experiment showing that x-rays can undergo diffraction, and hence that they consist of waves. The solid lines between the x-ray tube and the film mark the limits within which the rays could travel if there were no diffraction. The darkening on the film reveals that some energy arrives over a wider area, indicated by the dotted lines; there must therefore be some diffraction at the second slit.

Figure 54–D shows the scheme. When the x-rays coming through the second slit were detected with a photographic film, the film showed that the radiation spread out slightly when passing the edges of the slit. From the amount of spreading, it was estimated that the wavelength of the x-rays was about 4×10^{-11} m, or about one ten-thousandth of the wavelength of blue light.

Because the wavelengths of x-rays are so small, the amount of diffraction that they experience in passing through a slit is very small, and several previous experimenters had failed to detect it.

54–3. X-Ray Spectra. If x-rays strike a smooth metal plate at a very glancing angle, then instead of going through the plate they are reflected;

the plate acts like a mirror. If a fine grating of lines is scratched on the plate, the x-rays will be diffracted into a spectrum that can be photographed. Knowing the spacing of the ruled lines, one can calculate the wavelength of the radiation diffracted at any particular angle. The problem is entirely similar to the problem of using a ruled grating to measure the wavelength of visible light (Article 49–1). Since x-rays are electromagnetic waves, they travel with the same velocity as light and radio waves, and this velocity is well known (186,000 miles/sec, or 3×10^8 m/sec). Knowing the wavelength and velocity of the waves, it is easy to calculate their frequency from the relation

$$\text{Velocity} = \text{Wavelength} \times \text{Frequency}.$$

Photographic detection of the diffracted x-rays shows that they have a continuous spectrum, on which are superimposed intense lines. These lines have specific frequencies that depend on the kind of atoms that are being bombarded by the cathode rays. Figure 54–E reproduces one group of spectrum lines radiated by a tungsten target.

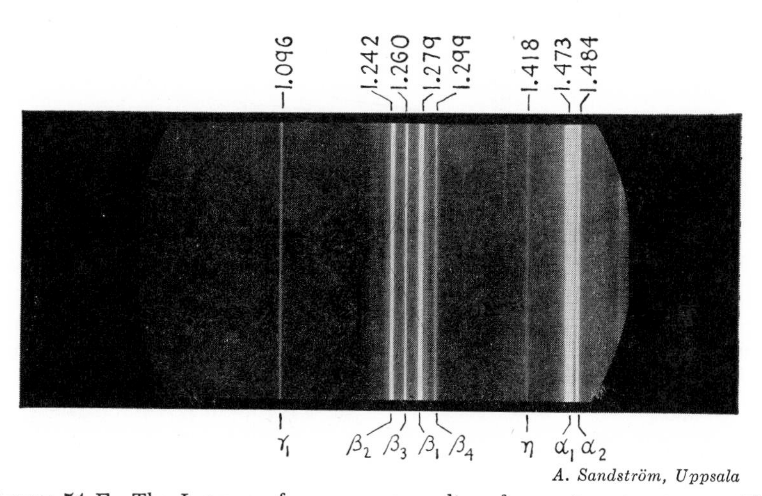

A. Sandström, Uppsala

FIGURE 54–E. The *L* group of x-ray spectrum lines from a tungsten target. These radiations arise when electrons jump from other orbits into *L*-shell vacancies in tungsten. Jumps from the *M* shell produce the α lines; jumps from the *N* shell, the β lines; and so on. The general brightness of the background is due to the continuous x-ray spectrum. The numbers are wavelengths, in units 10^{-10} meter.

Studies of x-ray spectra disclose the origin of the rays. The lines in the x-ray spectra are generated by a process much like the one that gives rise to the lines in the visible spectra of gases. The cathode-ray electrons are sufficiently energetic to knock electrons out of the inner shells of the atoms they strike, and other electrons from the outer shells fall into the vacancies thus produced. In making a transition from an outer shell to an inner one, an electron loses P.E., and this energy is converted into radiation. As in the case of visible spectra, the frequency of the radiation is determined by the amount of energy that is liberated when the electron moves from one shell to the other; the frequency has to satisfy the equation

$$\text{Energy liberated} = \text{Planck's constant} \times \text{Frequency}$$

or

$$E = h\nu.$$

Visible spectra are produced by electrons jumping from one outer orbit to another; x-ray spectra are produced by electrons jumping from an outer orbit, or an intermediate one, into a vacancy that has been created in an inner shell. The latter sort of jump involves a much greater liberation of energy. Consequently the x-rays have frequencies much higher, and wavelengths much smaller, than those of visible light. Figure 54–F illustrates the two situations.

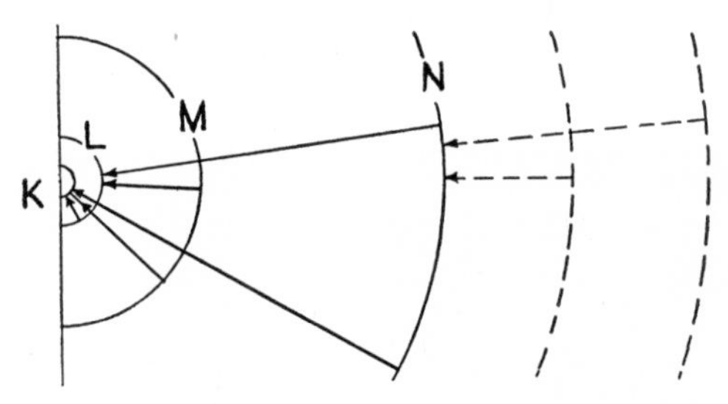

FIGURE 54–F. Electron jumps in x-ray and optical spectra, for the copper atom. The solid arcs, drawn to scale, represent shells that are normally occupied; the dotted arcs, not drawn to scale, represent shells that are normally not occupied. The jumps designated by solid arrows generate lines in the x-ray spectrum, whereas the dotted arrows represent electron jumps that give rise to ultraviolet or visible radiation.

The continuous x-ray spectrum is generated by the cathode-ray electrons as they are slowed down by passage through matter. This is in qualitative accord with Maxwell's theory that accelerated charges will produce radiation, but since this effect occurs on the atomic scale, the Maxwellian theory does not account for the quantitative details of the process. These details are accounted for by the new mechanics that will be mentioned in the next chapter.

54–4. The Structure of Solids. Our chief interest in x-rays is that they give detailed information about the arrangement of atoms in solid matter.

Consider a crystal of sodium chloride. We know that this substance,

NaCl, is formed by the combination of equal numbers of sodium and chlorine atoms. From the considerations discussed in Article 43–2, we also know the mass of a sodium atom and the mass of a chlorine atom. Therefore if we measure the mass of a crystal of sodium chloride, we can find out how many atoms entered into its composition.

The last sentence may seem awkward. Why not simply say, "We can find out how many atoms the crystal contains"? The answer depends on a fact that will be explained in the next section: actually we are sure that when sodium and chlorine atoms combine to form a crystal of NaCl, the crystal is composed of sodium and chloride *ions*, not atoms. Many other crystals also are collections of ions. On the other hand, some crystals are collections of atoms. Therefore a certain degree of care must be used in formulating statements about crystals. In the present chapter we shall dodge the difficulty by speaking of the atomic nuclei in the crystal, with the understanding that in some crystals the nuclei are surrounded by their full quota of electrons and are the centers of atoms, while in other crystals the number of electrons around each nucleus does not exactly compensate for the charge on the nucleus, which is therefore the center of an ion. In the next section, the distinction between the two kinds of crystals will be discussed at length.

As already mentioned, by simple operations we can find out how many atoms entered into the composition of a crystal of NaCl, and this gives us the number of atomic nuclei in that crystal. The natural faces of a crystal of NaCl are always perpendicular to one another (Figure 54–G), and it is therefore reasonable to assume that the nuclei in the NaCl crystal are stacked in a simple rectangular array. It is easily possible to measure the volume of a given crystal. Knowing how many atomic nuclei there are in a crystal whose dimensions have been measured, and assuming them to be equally spaced in a cubic array, it is a simple matter to calculate the distance between the nuclei in the crystal. It turns out to be about 10^{-10} m. The same kind of measurements and calculations applied to other crystals leads to results of the same order of magnitude. The result can be expressed a little differently by saying that the atoms or ions in a crystal are packed 10 billion to the meter, or 250 million to the inch.

It occurred to one of the leading German physicists about 1912 that the distance between the nuclei in a crystal is about the same as the wavelength of the x-rays, and that therefore a crystal should diffract x-rays in much the same way that a ruled grating diffracts visible light. Specifically, the fluctuating electric field in the x-radiation exerts fluctuating forces on the electrons grouped about the nuclei, setting the electrons into vibration. In this vibrating condition, the electrons experi-

(a)

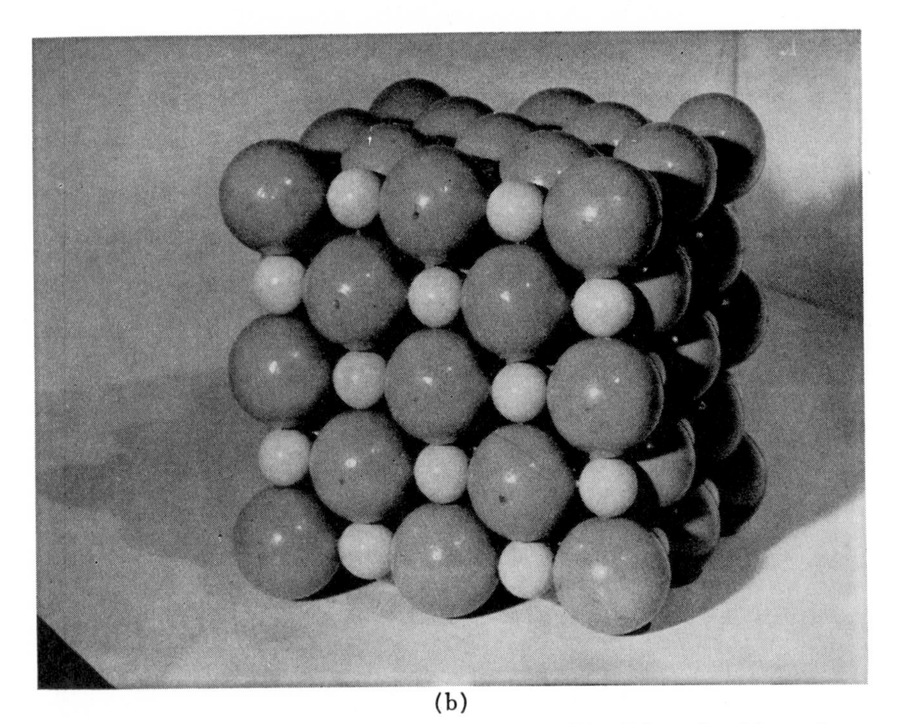

(b)

FIGURE 54–G. (a) Sodium chloride crystals (rock salt). (b) A plausible mechanical model of a sodium chloride crystal. X-ray studies show that this model is a correct one.

ence accelerations and therefore emit electromagnetic waves on their own account, as suggested by Figure 54–H. These waves, which are x-rays just like the original ones, spread out in all directions from each atom or ion and interfere with one another, in much the same way as the waves of visible light that come from the slits in a ruled grating. There is one important difference: the array of slits in a grating extends only in one direction, but the array of atoms or ions in a crystal extends in three dimensions.

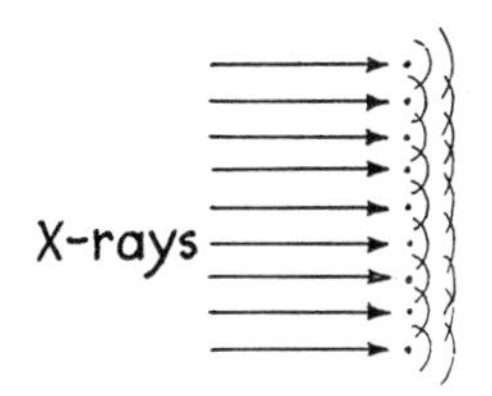

FIGURE 54–H. A layer of atoms responding to excitation by a beam of x-rays.

The mathematical analysis of three-dimensional diffraction is too complicated to be presented here. It shows that constructive interference can occur only in certain exceptional directions, and that therefore the diffraction pattern to be expected is a set of spots. The locations of these spots will depend on the arrangement of the nuclei in the crystal, and by studying the spots one can infer what kind of arrangement prevails in the crystal.

EXPERIMENT. The effect of a *two-dimensional* array of diffracting centers can be seen by viewing a tiny source of light through two gratings ruled on glass plates. Let the gratings be superimposed, with their rulings perpendicular, and held in front of the eye. An array of spots is seen. A different pattern is seen if one grating is turned so that the rulings are no longer perpendicular. By taking enough trouble, one could learn to judge the angle between the rulings, and hence the pattern of the diffracting centers, from the pattern of the spots.

The experimental arrangement for studying crystal structure by means of x-rays is sketched in Figure 54–I. The rays from an x-ray tube at the left (not shown) pass through holes in a pair of lead plates, so as to form a narrow beam of nearly parallel rays. This beam then strikes the

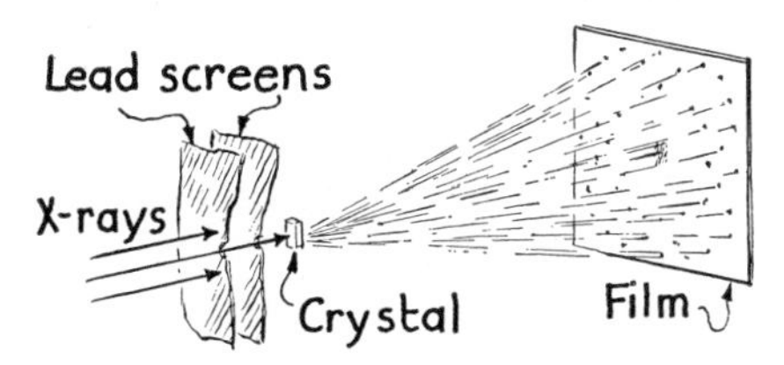

FIGURE 54–I. Recording the diffraction pattern of a crystal.

crystal, where it is diffracted in various directions. The diffracted rays fall on the photographic film and produce a pattern of spots, such as the one in Figure 54–J. The pattern indirectly divulges the arrangement of the atoms or ions in the crystal. Such experiments have verified the old suspicion that the regular geometry of crystals is due to a regular arrangement of their constituent particles. For example, the cubic crystals of NaCl actually do owe their form to the fact that their constituent

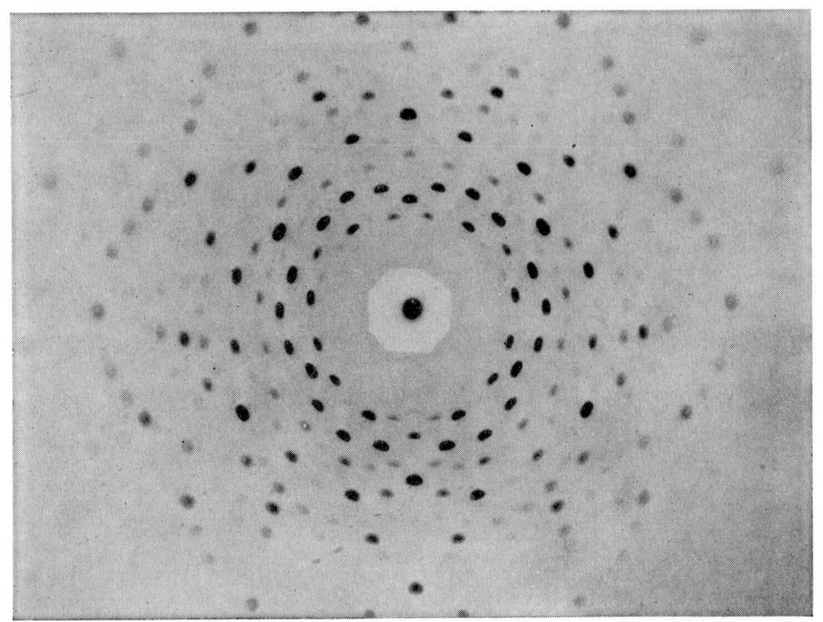

B. E. Warren, Massachusetts Institute of Technology

FIGURE 54–J. The diffraction pattern made by x-rays passing lengthwise through a crystal of quartz. Compare the symmetry of this pattern with the six-sidedness of the crystals in Figure 18–D.

particles are stacked in a rectangular array, like eggs in a crate, sodium alternating with chlorine (Figure 54–G). Many crystals have their atoms or ions arranged in more elaborate patterns. Figure 54–K shows a crystal of calcite, $CaCO_3$, and its internal structure.

SUMMARY

X-rays are generated by the impact of cathode rays on matter. They can be detected by the blackening they cause on a photographic film, by the fluorescence they produce in various salts, or by the electrical conductivity they produce in gases by the creation of ions. They pass with considerable freedom through many materials that are opaque to visible light.

The fact that x-rays are waves was shown by subjecting them to diffraction, first by means of very narrow slits and later by means of ruled gratings. They are in fact electromagnetic radiation like light, except that

(a)

(b)

FIGURE 54–K. (a) A crystal of calcite, a mineral form of calcium carbonate. (b) The structure of calcite, as revealed by x-rays. The black balls represent calcium ions. Each cluster of three white ones represents a carbonate radical, CO_3^{--}; the carbon atom is at the center of the radical and does not show in the model. Compare the slant of the dotted line, drawn through a row of calcium ions, with the slant of the crystal face in (a).

their wavelength is about one ten-thousandth as large. They arise from two causes. Some of them are generated because the cathode-ray electrons knock electrons out of inner shells of the atoms they strike, and when an electron from an outer shell falls into the vacancy it loses energy which escapes as electromagnetic radiation. These x-rays form line spectra that are characteristic of the atoms from which they come. Other x-rays are generated simply by slowing down of the cathode-ray electrons in their passage through the matter that they strike. These x-rays form a continuous spectrum.

From our point of view, the most interesting aspect of x-rays is the information they give us about the arrangement of atoms or ions in solids. By studying the diffraction of x-rays by crystals, one can unriddle the internal structure of the crystal.

Questions

1. Under what conditions are x-rays produced?
2. How can x-rays be detected?
3. How was it shown that x-rays are waves? Why is it to be expected that these waves are electromagnetic?
4. Describe the two ways in which x-rays originate.
5. To what sort of spectrum does each of the processes in Question 4 give rise? Account for the kind of spectrum by considering the nature of each process.
6. Outline the way that x-rays can be used to determine the arrangements of the atoms or ions in crystals.
7. About how far apart are the atoms or ions in a crystal?
8. Compare the spacing of atoms or ions in a crystal with the diameters of atoms as determined from measurements on gases (Article 51–3). Correlate the result with the fact that solids are not easy to compress.

Suggestion for Further Reading

L. Le Corbeiller, "Crystals and the Future of Physics," *Scientific American*, January, 1953, pp. 50–56. This genial bit of speculation about trends in physics includes some interesting factual material on the geometry of crystals.

> A striking discovery like that of the Röntgen rays acts much like the discovery of gold in a sparsely populated country; it attracts workers who come in the first place for the gold, but who may find that the country has other products, other charms, perhaps even more valuable than the gold itself.
>
> Sir J. J. Thomson (1909)

55

QUANTUM MECHANICS

Probability is the guide of life.
CICERO (*ca.* 50 B.C.)

The modified Bohr theory was highly successful in accounting for the details of the hydrogen spectrum, and in accounting qualitatively for the main features of the spectra of more complicated atoms. Quantitatively, however, the theory failed to account for the spectrum of even such a simple atom as helium. Calculations like the one in Article 51–3 were carried out for the case of helium, and the answers simply did not agree with the frequencies in the helium spectrum. By 1925, it was realized that Bohr's hypothesis II, which had already been elaborated in so many ways that it had lost its simplicity, could not be patched up to fit all the facts of spectra. Physics was in a jam; it got out by sliding out of some of its old garments.

55–1. The Wave Aspect of Matter. In 1924, a young Frenchman named de Broglie wrote a doctoral thesis containing a radical proposal. He pointed out that during most of the nineteenth century light had been explained entirely in terms of waves, but that later developments made it necessary to treat light as consisting of particles (photons). In diffraction experiments, light behaves like a wave; in the photoelectric effect, light behaves like particles. Heretofore, said de Broglie, we have always supposed that electrons behave like particles; perhaps our description of the atom is incomplete because the electrons behave in some respects like waves. In other words, de Broglie suggested that since light has two aspects, perhaps matter does also. This wild idea turned out to be correct.

Among the first to test de Broglie's hypothesis was J. J. Thomson's son. He passed a beam of fast electrons through a crystal and let them fall on photographic film. He obtained a pattern of spots, of the same kind as the patterns produced by x-rays. Figure 55–A shows the result of such an experiment. Instead of striking the film in just one spot, as a stream of bullets would, the electrons strike in many places, showing that they have undergone diffraction. Clearly, they behave like waves.

The wavelike behavior of electrons suggests the possibility that matter of any kind is most likely to be found in places where some kind of a wave has its maximum effect. This view has been confirmed by observing diffraction with beams of whole atoms, and even with beams of molecules.

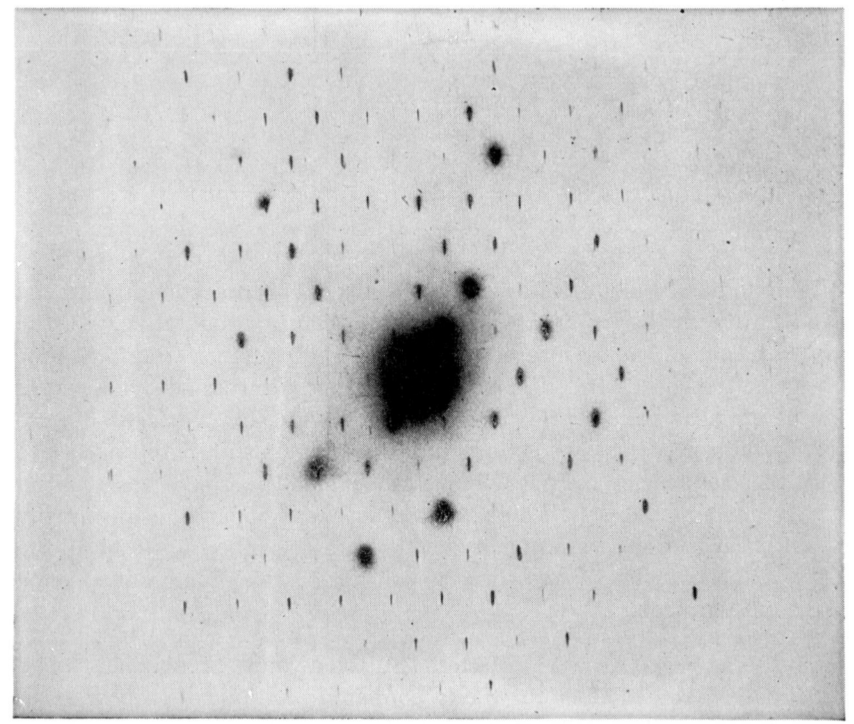

L. H. Germer, Bell Telephone Laboratories

FIGURE 55–A. The diffraction pattern made by electrons passing through a thin crystal of mica. Before striking the crystal, the electrons were in a single slim beam. The large central spot was made by electrons that passed through the crystal without being very much deviated; it resembles the point W in Figure 49–A.

55–2. The New Mechanics. The nature and behavior of "matter waves" were worked out in detail in the years around 1930, mainly by German theorists. (Bohr himself played a leading part, however.) Needless to say, the wave aspects of matter could be incorporated into the body of physics only by making drastic changes in the foundations of mechanics. For electrons, the wavelength of the matter waves is small,* and for more

* Figure 55–A shows that electrons are diffracted by the atoms in a crystal. They are therefore seen to have wavelengths comparable with the spacing of the atoms, i.e., about 10^{-10} m.

massive particles, it is smaller still. For a golf ball, the wavelength is so small that no diffraction can possibly be observed; the behavior of the golf ball can be described without taking waves into account at all. Newton's mechanics is therefore adequate for golf balls. Because of their small wavelength, even electrons exhibit diffraction effects only when experiments are conducted on a very fine scale. In the experiments on cathode rays that we discussed earlier, diffraction had no noticeable effect. The electrons experienced so little diffraction that they could be treated as simply as golf balls.

In an atom, we do have a small-scale situation. Therefore, in an atom the wave aspect of electrons becomes very important. Bohr's theory of the atom has had to undergo a major revision. His patched-up hypothesis II has been thrown out, his other hypotheses being retained without much change. The new theory is based on the following hypotheses:

I. In the atomic domain, Maxwell's electromagnetic theory is not valid.

II. In the atomic domain, Newton's mechanics is not valid. His Second Law of Motion, $F = ma$, can be replaced by

$$\frac{\partial^2\psi}{\partial x^2} + \frac{\partial^2\psi}{\partial y^2} + \frac{\partial^2\psi}{\partial z^2} = \frac{8\pi^2 m}{h^2}(V - E)\psi,$$

where ψ (psi) measures the strength of the wave associated with the electron. V is the P.E. of the particle, E is its total energy, and m is its mass.

III. Energy is radiated when the electrons in an atom change their arrangement, or "configuration," to one that has a lower energy. The frequency of this radiation is given by

$$h\nu = E_1 - E_2,$$

where $h\nu$ is the energy of the photon, E_1 is the energy of the electrons in their initial configuration, and E_2 is their energy in the second configuration.

The complicated equation, called the "wave equation," is included in these pages only for exhibit. Working with it is a job for a skilled theoretician.

Note that the wave equation describes *only the wave* associated with the electron. You can never be quite sure, therefore, where the electrons in the atom are. All you can do is make assertions about their positions-on-the-average. The implications of this fact are described in Article 55–3; we mention it here because it accounts for the new wording of hypothesis III, which has to be stated in terms more general than those used before.

55–3. The Quantum Mechanical Description of the Atom. Unlike ordinary algebraic equations, the wave equation has a great diversity of solutions for the quantity ψ. Each solution is characterized by a specific value for E, the energy of the atom. The predicted frequencies of the spectrum lines come from these permitted values of the energy, through hypothesis III. The principle here is the same as in the older theory (Article 51–3), but energies found from the wave equation give the correct frequencies even for complicated spectra.

Because it supersedes the old Newtonian mechanics when the production of light quanta (photons) is under discussion, the new physics based on the wave equation is usually called *quantum mechanics.* Sometimes it is called "wave mechanics," because it takes into account the wave aspect of matter.

In the older theory, based in part on $F = ma$, the quantum numbers n, l, and m_l had to be introduced quite arbitrarily (Articles 51–3, 52–1, and 52–2). When the wave equation is used, however, these integers appear in the solutions in an entirely natural way. Consider first a hydrogen atom. Using the wave equation, one finds how the quantity ψ varies in the region near the nucleus. In the solution are integers n, l, and m_l, which are subject to certain restrictions. The integer n can have any positive value; l can be any integer between 0 and $n - 1$, inclusive; and m_l can be any integer between $-l$ and l, inclusive. These are just the restrictions that were put on the quantum numbers n, l, and m_l in the older theory. The new theory has the advantage that the quantum numbers turn up automatically.

Each set of quantum numbers gives one solution. In the new theory, however, this solution does not confine the electron to a particular path. Each solution describes a distribution of ψ in the space around the nucleus. When the wave equation was first discovered, the meaning of ψ was not at all clear. It surely had to do with the strength of the electron wave, but nobody was sure just what that meant. Before long, however, it was realized that ψ tells what the chances are of finding the electron in a given place. If ψ has a large value for some point in space, then the electron is likely to be in that place. This interpretation of ψ discloses the outstanding feature of quantum mechanics: it deals in probabilities, not in certainties.

The easiest way to understand quantum mechanics is by thinking about the diffraction of electrons. If a single electron is shot at a thin crystal, the wave equation can give the probability that the electron will be going in any specified direction when it emerges. If the experiment were tried, the electron might go in some rather improbable direction, so quantum mechanics would be of little help. An actual experiment, however, would normally be done with a *beam* of cathode rays, containing billions of electrons. Here probability is an adequate guide to what will actually be observed. Many electrons will go in the directions that have high probability; only a few will go in the directions that have small probability. The theory can therefore predict the pattern the electrons will make when they strike a film placed behind the crystal (Figure 55-A).

Knowing how ψ for an electron is distributed around the nucleus of a hydrogen atom, we know the relative chances that the electron will be in various places. Different solutions of the wave equation, involving dif-

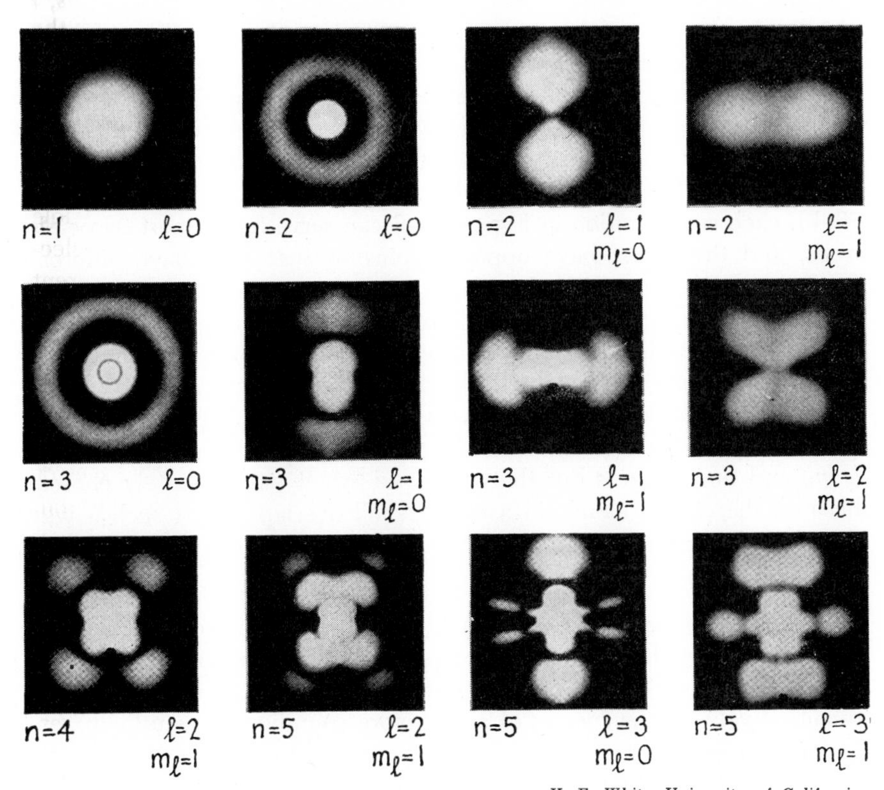

H. E. White, University of California

FIGURE 55-B. Some electron orbits in hydrogen, according to quantum mechanics. The charge cloud is simulated in these photographs by a time exposure of a spinning paper model. The scale is not the same for all of the photographs; the charge cloud is larger for large values of n.

ferent values for the quantum numbers, also involve different distributions of ψ. The chances of finding an electron in a given place, therefore, depend on what the values of the quantum numbers are. Figure 55-B illustrates the quantum-mechanical description of the hydrogen atom for several sets of quantum numbers. The description says the electron is more likely to be in some places than in others; or, what is the same thing, that the electron spends more time in some places than in others. The degree of whiteness in Figure 55–B indicates the relative amounts of time that the electron spends in various places.

The region in which the electron is likely to be is often called a *charge cloud.* The form of the cloud is specified by the quantum numbers, whose interpretation is broadly the same as in the older theory. The number n is a measure of the average distance of the electron from the nucleus, l specifies the shape of the cloud, and m_l specifies the orientation of the cloud. For $l = 0$, the cloud is spherical, and for larger values of l the clouds have projecting lobes.

It should be noted that the last paragraph, and Figure 55–B, deal with the simplest atom, hydrogen. Atoms with more than one electron can be described fairly closely by a superposition of hydrogenlike charge clouds, one for each electron. Because of Pauli's Exclusion Principle (Article 53–1), each configuration in Figure 55–B can serve for at most two electrons, and they must have opposite spins so that they have different quantum numbers m_s. The building up of the complex atoms therefore follows the scheme discussed in Chapter 53. The only difference is that the quantum numbers describe charge clouds—probability distributions—instead of definite orbits.

The idea of a closed shell retains its old meaning. It is the entire set of electrons having a given value of n and using up all resulting values of l, m_l, and m_s. It turns out that the word "shell" is fortunately chosen, because the charge clouds in a closed shell overlap in just such a way that the lobes interlock and form a smooth spherical cloud that is indeed a shell.

55–4. The Success of Quantum Mechanics. In spite of its ability to explain the Periodic Table and the spectrum of hydrogen, Bohr's theory of the atom could not be considered a final one. It failed to account quantitatively for the spectra of atoms more complicated than hydrogen. Quantum mechanics succeeds. Each solution of the wave equation corresponds not only to a definite configuration of the electron cloud, but also to a definite energy. From these energies and hypothesis III (page 473), the frequencies of the spectrum lines can be predicted. The new theory agrees with the observed facts; it can even go further, and predict which lines in the spectrum will be bright, and which ones will be weak.

It is important to notice that although quantum mechanics does not commit itself about the path of an electron in an atom, it does commit itself to definite answers about all the properties of an atom that are actually observable.

Quantum mechanics would win acceptance with its success in the domain of spectra alone, but it takes care of other problems as well. Here we need mention only its unified treatment of matter and light. Before discovering the new mechanics, physicists were uncomfortable about light. In order to explain interference and diffraction, they had to assume that light consists of waves (Chapter 47). In order to explain the photoelectric effect, however, they had to assume that light behaves like particles (Chapter 50). Which was it—waves or particles? The new mechanics shows that matter can be described correctly in terms of waves *and* particles, and light fits the same scheme. Describing light or matter in terms of waves alone, or particles alone, is taking a view so restricted that it holds only in a limited range of circumstances.

55–5. Some Philosophical Implications of Quantum Mechanics. In 1895, it seemed that the laws of Newton and Maxwell were fundamental truths that would suffice to describe the universe. Half a lifetime later, physicists had seen these laws fail again and again, and had then built up a new conceptual scheme in which the laws of Newton and Maxwell were simply special cases. This was a very sobering experience. How had it happened, and how could similar fiascoes be avoided in the future? After a period of introspection, physics arrived at a better understanding of its task. The conclusions can be summarized as follows.

The proper business of science is the correlation of observed facts. The facts themselves are easily described in plain language, but the correlation is done in terms of abstract concepts. As an example, consider Young's pinhole experiment (Article 47–2). The facts are simple: light from some small source passes through two pinholes in an opaque screen; when the light strikes a second screen, it makes bright bands that are separated by dark ones. Complexity comes in when we try to correlate this fact with others, such as the distribution of light when only one pinhole is used instead of two. We invoke the concept of waves, and devise a theory of light that is brilliantly successful—up to a certain point. That point is the explanation of the photoelectric effect (Article 50–2), where the wave theory of light makes predictions that conflict with fact. For the photoelectric effect, we devise an explanation in terms of particles called photons. Then someone asks: Is light *really* waves, or is it particles?

There is no use in saying that light is really both waves and particles. Waves and particles are not capable of being the same thing. The trouble is that the concept "wave" and the concept "particle" were invented to describe events that have nothing to do with interference or the photoelectric effect. To say that light is "really" one or the other, or "really" both at once, is nonsense. Light is really light, and there is no reason why it should be exactly like something else.

In the last article, we said "Light can be described correctly in terms of waves and particles." This is not at all the same as saying that light *is* waves and particles. If a scientist has correlated observed facts in such a way that he can *describe correctly* what will happen in a new situation, he has done his part.

As soon as it is realized that correct description of fact is all one should ask of a theory, it is no longer a matter of distress that quantum mechanics deals only in probabilities. For massive bodies, the probability is overwhelmingly in favor of behavior in accord with Newton's Laws. For atoms or electrons, the probability is in favor of diversified behavior, but we ordinarily deal with such large numbers of atoms or electrons that a statistical prediction is all we need.

Quantum mechanics does have one shocking implication. If a beam of electrons passes through the regularly spaced atoms of a crystal, then, as we have seen, it is diffracted. Some electrons pass straight through; others go off at various angles, some angles being more probable than others. As long as we deal with a beam of electrons, theory can describe correctly, in advance, what the results will be. Now all the electrons in the beam are alike, they are all subject to the same influences, yet they do not all emerge along the same direction. Clearly, the familiar concepts of cause and effect do not apply.

A similar difficulty arises when the emission of alpha-particles is analyzed in terms of quantum mechanics. Just when an atom emits an alpha-particle is a matter of pure chance. There is no cause that makes one uranium atom emit an alpha-particle now, but makes another identical atom wait for a million years.

The breakdown of cause and effect in atomic systems has an interesting implication. In classical physics, you could predict the future behavior of a particle if you knew its present velocity and the forces that were going to act on it. These forces would be exerted by the gravitational, electric, or magnetic fields of other particles. Imagine an ideally intelligent person who would be given the present position and velocity of every particle in the universe. In principle, he could calculate the future motion of each particle under the forces exerted on it by the others. Even though the actual calculation would be too complicated for anybody to carry out, the laws of physics certainly implied that the future of the universe is completely determined by its state at present. The universe was a machine; all its parts, including men, could merely go through their predestined motions. Physics left no room for free will. All this is changed by the new mechanics. The universe is still composed of particles, but many of the particles are electrons, and electrons as individuals are very unpredictable. Quantum mechanics therefore liberates the future from complete bondage to the past. No murderer can plead Newton's Laws as the cause of his crime, nor can any physicist, however skilled at calculation, tell for certain which assemblage of particles will win the next Presidential election.

SUMMARY

When the Bohr theory was applied to atoms more complex than hydrogen, it gave incorrect values for the frequencies of the spectrum lines. Something was clearly wrong with the fundamental concepts with which the theory worked. About 1925 it was suggested as a guess, and later discovered by experiment, that the electron has the attributes of a wave. The wave effects appear only in small-scale phenomena, because the wavelength of the electron is very small. Other forms of matter also exhibit wavelike behavior, but even for a single atom the wavelength is so small that the effects can be observed only with difficulty.

The wave aspect of material particles can be incorporated into mechanics by replacing Newton's equation $F = ma$ with a more complicated expression called the wave equation. Physics based on the wave equation is called quantum mechanics or wave mechanics.

Quantum mechanics presents a picture of the atom that differs considerably from the picture based on Bohr's original theory. Nevertheless, the quantum numbers and the Exclusion Principle, and consequently the theory of the Periodic Table, remain as before. In the new theory, the quantum numbers appear as a natural result of the wave equation, instead of being introduced by special assumptions. The new theory correctly accounts for all the observable properties of even the complex atoms. Some of its most interesting implications lie in the domain of philosophy.

QUESTIONS

1. Describe an experiment that brings into prominence the fact that electrons behave like waves.
2. Why is the wavelike behavior of matter not a part of everyday experience?
3. What is the significance of the quantity ψ in the equation that is the quantum-mechanical equivalent of Newton's Second Law of Motion?
4. How does quantum mechanics modify the physical picture of the atom that was presented in the chapters preceding this one?
5. With regard to spectra, in what way is quantum mechanics superior to the original Bohr theory?
6. What is now considered to be the legitimate aim of a physical theory?

SUGGESTIONS FOR FURTHER READING

Erwin Schroedinger, *Science and Humanism* (New York: Cambridge University Press, 1951). This simple little essay, by one of the inventors of quantum mechanics, treats mainly the impact of quantum mechanics on our views of matter. (It denies any connection between physics and free will.)

Banesh Hoffmann, *The Strange Story of the Quantum* (New York: Harper & Bros., 1947). A light-hearted but instructive account of the development of quantum mechanics.

GENERAL VIEW OF SECTION VIII

Air at low pressures will conduct electricity if it is in a strong electric field. The effect is studied by means of partially evacuated glass vessels called discharge tubes. From the cathode of a tube operating at low pressure come rays called cathode rays, which can be detected by the fluorescence they produce. By deflecting these rays in electric and magnetic fields, Thomson showed that they are streams of negatively charged particles. Moreover, he showed that the charge-to-mass ratio of the particles is larger than that of the hydrogen ion, which had been inferred from experiments on electrolysis. From this relationship and the fact that the particles pass easily through metal foils, he concluded that the particles are less massive, and smaller, than atoms. Since the particles are the same no matter what material the cathode is made of, he concluded that the particles, which are called electrons, are actually parts of atoms. Ions are atoms that have more or less than their normal quota of electrons, and the quantum of charge is the charge carried by an electron.

By observing the motion of charged oil droplets in electric and gravitational fields, Millikan showed that the quantum of charge is 1.60×10^{-19} coulomb. Combining this figure with measurements made in electrolysis experiments, we can find the masses of hydrogen atoms and other atoms, and can then find the number of molecules in a mole. This turns out to be 6.02×10^{23}, a number so large as to be almost unimaginable.

The charge-to-mass ratio of ions can be measured by deflecting the ions in electric and magnetic fields. This technique yields a new and important piece of information: atoms that are alike chemically are not necessarily alike physically. Atoms that are chemically the same, but that differ in mass and therefore in physical structure, are called isotopes. A related piece of new information is that the atomic weights of individual isotopes are very nearly integers, which suggests that atoms are all built up from a common set of building blocks.

Some atoms, e.g., uranium and radium, are found to be unstable. Some give off doubly charged helium ions (α-rays), some give off very fast electrons (β-rays), and some give off γ-rays, which turn out to be electromagnetic radiation of very short wavelength.

By observing the deflections of α-rays as they passed through very thin foils of various metals, Rutherford and his students showed that all of the positive charge of an atom, as well as nearly all of its mass, is concentrated in a minute core called the nucleus, whose volume is only about a billionth of the volume of the atom. They showed further that the charge on the nucleus, if expressed in quanta instead of in coulombs, is equal to the atomic number, which is the serial number showing the position of the atom in the Periodic Table. For example, the aluminum nucleus carries a charge of 13 quanta, a gold nucleus carries a charge of 79 quanta, and a uranium nucleus, 92 quanta. The number of electrons in the electrically neutral atom is equal to the number of quanta of charge carried by the nucleus, and is therefore equal to the atomic number. Since atomic number relates to position in the Periodic Table, it is clear that the chemical properties of an atom depend on the number of electrons that normally surround its nucleus. The chemical properties of course depend ultimately on the nuclear charge, but the nuclei are relatively so far apart, and are so well screened from one another by their complements of electrons, that the chemical activities of atoms must depend directly on the interactions of their electrons.

The final key to chemical behavior was found in the study of the light emitted by atoms. Light moves through space as an electromagnetic wave, and it spreads out after passing through a narrow slit. If many parallel slits are lined up side by side, to form what is called a grating, then the waves coming from the various slits will in most places be out of step and cancel one another. There will be some places, however, where the waves from successive slits are out of step by just one wavelength, and in these places the waves from all of the slits will augment one another, producing relatively bright light. Just where this brightness occurs will depend in a calculable way on the wavelength of light, and therefore the wavelength of light can be measured by observing where the brightness falls. It is found that each color corresponds to a different wavelength, and that each atom, when it is in a hot gas, emits light at specific wavelengths which are different for each kind of atom. By studying the wavelengths that are emitted by each atom, one can infer how the electrons in the atom are arranged about the nucleus.

The basic relation between the emitted light and the electrons can be stated most simply in terms of the frequency, rather than the wavelength, of the light. The relationship is expressed in the equation

$$\text{Change in energy of electrons} \propto \text{Frequency of light}$$

or

$$E_1 - E_2 = h\nu,$$

where h is Planck's celebrated constant, and ν is the frequency of the light. This relationship is based on Einstein's photon theory of light, which holds that light energy comes in packets, or photons, and that the energy of each photon is $h\nu$. The hypothesis was introduced by Einstein in order to account for the photoelectric effect, which was not explainable by Maxwell's purely wave theory of light.

From the observed frequencies of the light emitted by the hydrogen atom, the simplest of atoms, Bohr and others were able to devise a set of rules about the ways in which an electron in an atom can move. These rules are characterized by the employment of four numbers, called quantum numbers, which serve to specify the motion of each electron in an atom. The motions that can occur in the more complicated atoms, which contain more than one electron, obey Pauli's Exclusion Principle, which says that no two electrons in an atom can have the same motion. A handier but less pictorial statement of the principle is that no two electrons in an atom can have identical quantum numbers.

Within the limits set by the Exclusion Principle, the electrons will tend to take up the motions that involve the smallest allowable energy. Generally speaking, these will be the motions in which the electron is as near as possible to the nucleus; this means that for each electron the quantum number called n will have a value as small as possible.

The Exclusion Principle permits only two electrons for $n = 1$, eight for $n = 2$, eighteen for $n = 3$, etc. Therefore as we go to higher atomic numbers, we find that the shells or layers of electrons fill up and new ones farther from the nucleus have to be started. We find a correlation between the number of electrons in the outer shell and the chemical properties of the atom. From spectroscopic data, one can find the actual distribution of electrons in the various shells even in the complicated atoms where the simple rule mentioned above is not reliable; the correlation between the chemical properties of the atom and its electron configuration is perfect. Since new shells have to be started periodically as the atomic number gets bigger, the periodicity of chemical properties is explained.

IX

Chemical Binding

Until the beginning of the present century, chemists studied chemical reactions without having any satisfactory theory as to why the reactions occur at all. The science was based on a tremendous record of laboratory experiences that had not yet been successfully fused together to yield an explanation of why the various atoms behave as they do. The central problem of chemistry could be stated in the form: "What causes chemical binding?" or, in other words, "What makes atoms enter into chemical union?" This problem was not solved until the period between the two World Wars, because it had to wait until the structure of the atoms had been unveiled by the researches discussed in the last section.

It has been found that there are several forms of chemical binding. After a brief discussion of each form, we shall observe how the chemical behavior of the various atoms depends on their structure. Then we can go on and apply this new knowledge to the study of substances and reactions that are important in everyday affairs.

56

CHEMICAL BINDING

> The underlying physical laws necessary for the mathematical theory of a large part of physics and the whole of chemistry are [now] completely known.
>
> DIRAC (1929)

As soon as Rutherford had shown that atoms consist of nuclei surrounded at relatively large distances by electrons (Chapter 46), chemistry stood in a clearer light. The nuclei do not come so close together as the electrons do; moreover, the nuclei are electrically screened from one another by the charge on the electrons. It was therefore evident that chemical union must come from interaction of the electrons. Working from this clue, a few chemists were able to make a good beginning on the explanation of chemical binding. They deduced the existence of shell structure in atoms. Later this structure was explained, through the discovery of quantum numbers and Pauli's Exclusion Principle. Our discussion of binding will deal only with the mature theory.

56–1. The Stable Octets. The most exceptional chemical behavior is that of the inert gases; they do not enter into chemical reactions at all. What is it about their electron configurations that makes them inert?

Helium has two electrons; both of them are in the *K* shell, which is therefore closed. Neon, the next inert gas, has ten electrons all told, two in the *K* shell and eight in the *L* shell. Both shells are therefore closed. One might suspect that an inert gas is one whose atoms have all their electrons in closed shells. This rule does not work, however; argon has only eight electrons in its outermost shell, which is the *M* shell, capable of holding eighteen electrons. Going on to krypton, the next rare gas, we find that it too has eight electrons in its outermost shell, and the same turns out to be true for the other inert gases, xenon and radon. The essential structural feature of the inert gas atoms is therefore apparent: Except for helium, which has but two electrons, the inert-gas atoms are the ones with eight electrons in their outermost shells.

In this chapter we shall see that chemical activity can be attributed to a transfer or a sharing of electrons. A chemically inert atom, then, must be one that will not engage in a transfer or sharing of its electrons. Since the chemically inert atoms are the ones that have eight electrons in their outer shells, it follows that atoms with eight electrons in their outer shells will neither transfer nor share their electrons. Hence a shell containing eight electrons must have a special degree of stability. An arrangement of eight electrons in a shell is consequently called a *stable octet.*

56–2. Ionic Binding. We have noticed heretofore that some atoms, for example sodium, tend to form positive ions, while others, like chlorine, tend to form negative ions. This behavior can now be understood in terms of the stable octets. Sodium normally has one electron in its M shell, and its L shell has eight electrons (Table 53–III). By losing its outermost electron, sodium can get a stable octet as its outer shell. Having lost the electron, it will be a positive ion. Chlorine, on the other hand, has seven electrons in its outer shell. It can acquire a stable octet by picking up an extra electron and becoming a negative ion.

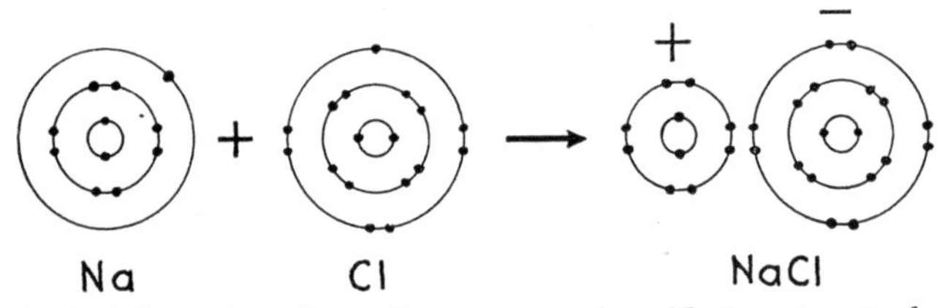

FIGURE 56–A. The union of a sodium atom and a chlorine atom to form an ion pair. (The circles are conventional symbols for the shells; they do not represent orbits.)

Suppose now that a sodium atom and a chlorine atom come together. They can both get stable octets in their outer shells if the chlorine atom captures an electron from the sodium atom. When this happens, we have a positive ion and a negative ion, and these attract one another electrically to form an ion pair which is a molecule of sodium chloride. Figure 56–A is a schematic representation of the reaction. The difference between the energy of the separated atoms and the energy of the ion pair is given off as heat.

If many of these ion pairs are brought together, at a low enough temperature so that they are not moving too fast, then they can group themselves into a regular array and form a crystal of NaCl. This crystal, which is found to be cubic in its structure, is like the mechanical model in Figure 54–G.

It is to be noted that when the ions aggregate to make a crystal, they are not paired off to form molecules. Each sodium ion has six chloride ions as equally close neighbors. In a crystal of this sort, therefore, molecules in the ordinary sense do not exist. The whole crystal is a vast "supermolecule." (It is for this reason that reference to molecules of solid NaCl or other salts has been avoided in the previous chapters.) In crystals that are composed of ions, each ion is repelled by all other ions of the same charge, but attracted by all ions of the opposite charge. Since the ions close to it are of opposite charge, the attractions have the upper hand over the repulsions and the crystal holds together. Moreover, since each ion can attract as many oppositely charged ions as happen to be in the neighborhood, there is no limit to the size that the crystal, or supermolecule, can attain.

The type of chemical binding that has just been described is called *ionic* binding. It gives a satisfactory explanation of the formation of many compounds, notably salts, bases, and metallic oxides. In the solid state, these compounds form ionic crystals. In the liquid state, the ions have enough energy so that the binding cannot hold them to fixed positions; the ions move about with considerable freedom. If an electric field between two electrodes is set up in the liquid, the ions migrate to the electrodes. Some metals, notably magnesium and aluminum, are prepared on an industrial scale by electrolysis of a molten salt or oxide.

If a molten salt is raised to a high enough temperature to vaporize it, the ions that go into the gaseous state pair off to form molecules.

56–3. Covalent Binding. There are obvious and important cases of chemical combination in which ionic binding cannot exist. Consider for example the hydrogen molecule, H_2. Since the innermost shell of an atom is closed when it contains two electrons, and since the inertness of helium shows that this closed shell of two has a special stability, we might be tempted to think that if two H atoms were put together, then one would gain an electron from the other to form a stable closed shell of two. Such an event, however, would leave the other atom stripped down to the bare nucleus. Intuitive guessing and mathematical calculation both show that in order to effect such a severe redistribution of the electrons, work would have to be done. Therefore the process cannot occur spontaneously. If the molecules were artificially constructed in this way, they would come apart of their own accord, because by doing so they could lose P.E. Nevertheless, we know that H atoms do combine to form stable H_2 molecules; these must be held together by some other force than that between ions.

The force that binds the H atoms to one another is only in part an electrostatic one. In larger part it is a new kind of force that we have not studied yet—one that arises naturally in terms of the new mechanics, although it has no place in the older mechanics based on Newton's Laws. If two hydrogen atoms are close enough so that their charge clouds overlap, then each electron will be to some extent associated with both nuclei. The new mechanics predicts that this sharing of the two electrons by the two nuclei will, if the electrons have opposite spins, produce a force of attraction. If the electron spins are aligned in the same direction, then there will be a repulsion between the two atoms. Therefore, *the two hydrogen atoms coalesce into a hydrogen molecule by sharing a pair of oppositely spinning electrons.* Figure 56–B is an artist's representation of a hydrogen molecule.

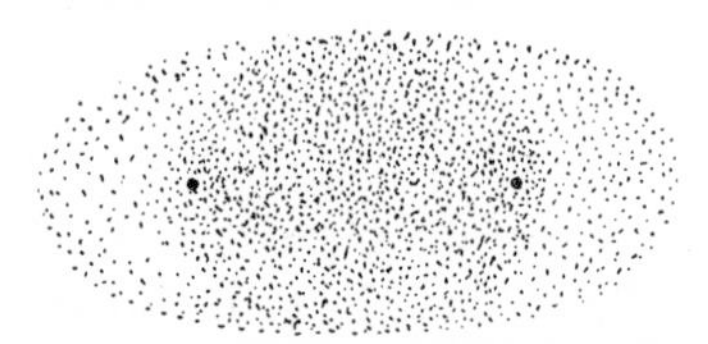

FIGURE 56–B. A charge-cloud representation of a hydrogen molecule. The electrons spend most of their time in the region between the two nuclei; the positively charged nuclei are bound together by the negative cloud between them.

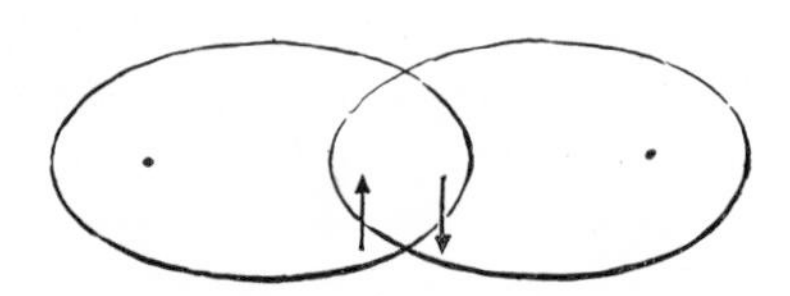

FIGURE 56–C. A diagrammatic representation of a hydrogen molecule.

The chemical bond formed by the sharing of oppositely spinning electrons is called the *covalent* bond.* One of its important attributes can be illustrated by considering what happens if a third atom of H is brought into the neighborhood of two others that are bonded together in a molecule. Except for the orientation of the electron spin, all H atoms are alike, when they are not "excited" (given extra energy) by high temperatures or by the hurly-burly of an electric discharge. To avoid a mathematical analysis based on the quantum numbers, we can resort to the schematic diagram of Figure 56–C. The two electrons in the H_2 molecule must have their spins oriented oppositely, in order to form the covalent bond. If a third atom were to join the molecule, so as to form H_3, then the molecule would contain three electrons in the same state of motion except for spin, and two of them would have the same direction of spin. This would violate the Pauli Exclusion Principle, and it does not happen. We see that *an atom of hydrogen can be bound to only one other atom of hydrogen.* There is consequently a very definite limit to the size of a molecule of hydrogen: it can contain two atoms and no more. Note the difference between this situation and the indefinitely large size of a sodium chloride crystal.

* One of the foremost American chemists suggested about 1916 that a shared pair of electrons acts as a chemical bond. The idea was confirmed and clarified about 1930 by the application of quantum mechanics to chemical situations.

Covalent binding, binding due to sharing of electrons, does not always lead to diatomic molecules, although in most cases it does lead to molecules that are restricted as to size. Consider the very important case of carbon. Carbon has four electrons outside of a closed shell of two; these four electrons can all be shared with other atoms. If four H atoms are

FIGURE 56–D. A model showing the structure of diamond.

brought near a C atom, the C can share an electron with each of the four H atoms, but not with more than four. We can therefore have CH_4, but not CH_5. This limit explains why C has a valence of at most 4. Because of the special stability of a shell containing eight electrons, carbon usually has a valence equal to 4, which gives it four pairs in its outer shell.

Atoms bound by covalent forces can form indefinitely large crystalline aggregates (as opposed to the limited aggregates exemplified by H_2) provided the atoms have several sharable electrons. For example, each carbon atom can share electrons with four others, so any number of them can congregate in a crystalline array. It is in this way that carbon atoms band together to form a diamond. X-ray studies show that the structure of diamond is that of the model in Figure 56–D, in which each ball represents a carbon atom. A stretched-out model of the basic pattern appears in Figure 56–E. Notice that each carbon atom is bound to four

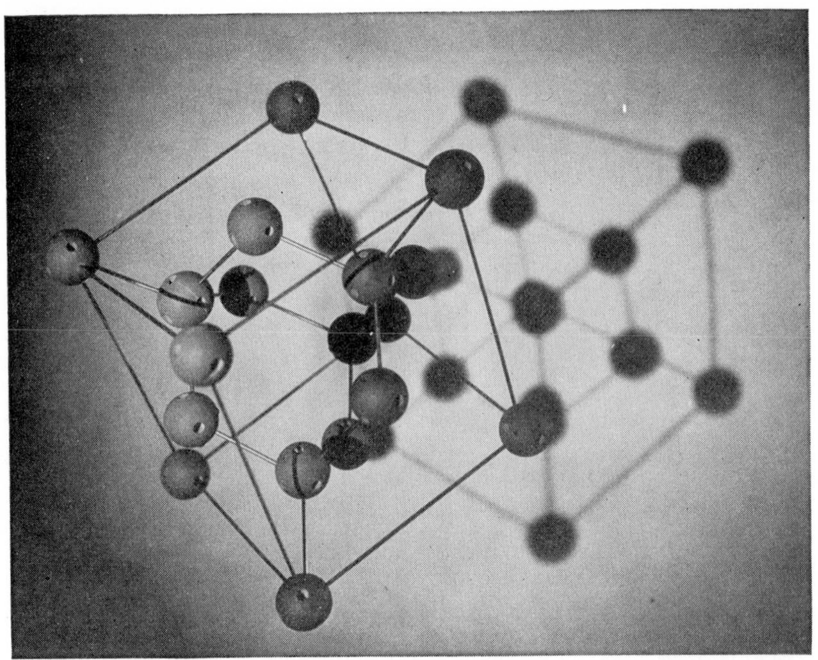

National Bureau of Standards

FIGURE 56-E. An expanded model of the diamond structure, showing the basic pattern.

FIGURE 56-F. The structure of graphite.

others that are in symmetrical positions around it. The over-all pattern is closely related both to the cube and to the hexagon.

Carbon can also exist as graphite, the material used as the "lead" in pencils. The properties of graphite are very different from those of diamond, and the difference in properties arises from a difference in structure. In graphite, the carbon atoms form layers of hexagonal rings, as in the model in Figure 56–F. As a result of its layered structure, graphite has a flaky character that makes it useful as a lubricant and as a writing material. In contrast, diamond, with its rigid lattice, is the hardest material known.

56–4. Metallic Binding. Neither ionic nor covalent binding can account for the structure of metals. Ionic binding is out of the question because metal atoms form ions that have charges all of the same sign. Covalent binding of the sort just described is impossible because a metal atom has only one, two, or three electrons to offer, and it would need to get a share in seven, six, or five additional electrons to form an octet. Nevertheless, at ordinary temperatures metal atoms do congregate in the solid state. What holds them together?

The metallic atoms are the atoms with many unfilled orbits in their outer shells, and their binding is based on this peculiarity. As a specific example, consider copper. The diffraction of x-rays by copper shows that this metal, like many others, has the structure represented by the model in Figure 56–G. Each atom has twelve nearest neighbors—four below, four alongside, and four above. To simplify the problem of binding, suppose that thirteen copper atoms come together in this way, in otherwise empty space. They will have a total of thirteen outermost electrons, or enough for six shared-pair bonds. If one atom is in the center, it can at any instant form a shared-pair bond with at most half of its twelve neighbors. Since the atoms are all alike, the bonds have the same probability of binding together any pair of atoms, and they can move from pair to pair.

The central atom in our group will therefore not be bonded to the same neighbors all of the time. It will have to share its electron equally among its twelve neighbors, by contributing the electron to each of them for one-twelfth of the time. If more copper atoms join the group, then each atom except the outside ones will have twelve near neighbors, and it will be bonded to each of them by one-twelfth of the shared-pair bond.

The difference between metallic binding and covalent binding lies in the building of stable octets. When carbon forms four shared-pair bonds, it acquires a stable octet, and it can enter into no new bonds. When a metal forms shared-pair bonds among its own atoms, there are so few sharable electrons that no atom will ever get a stable octet, except by chance and for a short time. Each atom will be able to enter into new bonds whenever chance makes them available.

From what we have said about the bonding, there is no reason why each copper atom should not share electrons with dozens of others. There is a limit, however, and the limit is set by geometry. If spheres of the same size are packed together as tightly as possible, each one can have

FIGURE 56–G. The structure of copper.

only twelve nearest neighbors. Their arrangement is that in Figure 56–G. Some metals have structures that are less closely packed, so that each atom has fewer close neighbors, but the general aspects of the binding are the same for all.

Metals are distinguished from other substances by the fact that they are good conductors of electricity when in the solid state. This property is now easy to explain; since the metallic bond does not result in the filling of stable octets, the binding electrons can move from atom to atom with great freedom. When a potential difference exists between two regions in a metal, such as the two ends of a wire, the electrons drift toward the region of higher potential. This drift of electrons constitutes an electric current.

The structure of metals also accounts for another of their typical properties, the ease with which they can be deformed without breaking. In metals whose structure resembles the model in Figure 56–G, the layers of atoms can slide over one another without ever causing a very violent disruption of the structure. Moreover, the interatomic attachments are individually weak and adaptable, because each arises from a shared-pair bond that is in being for only part of the time. Metals that have this structure are therefore capable of being rolled into thin sheets or drawn into wires; prominent examples are gold, silver, copper, and aluminum.

56–5. Hydrogen. To see how hydrogen fits into the chemical scheme, we may first summarize the general behavior of the other elements. Aside from the inert gases, they fit into three categories.

1. Except for hydrogen, atoms with one, two, or three electrons in the outer shell tend to lose these electrons and become positive ions. These atoms are the metallic ones.
2. Atoms with five, six, or seven electrons in the outer shell tend to acquire enough electrons to make a stable octet. They may take these electrons from metallic atoms and form ionic bonds, or they may share electrons and form covalent bonds. These atoms are the nonmetallic ones.
3. Atoms with four electrons in the outer shell seldom form ions; they are in general limited to covalent binding.

Hydrogen is exceptional because it has a unique electronic structure. It has only one electron in its outer shell, but it needs to gain only one electron to make a closed shell. Hydrogen usually enters into covalent binding, although its compounds with the most active metals are ionic. In its modes of binding, therefore, hydrogen acts as a nonmetal, but because it has only one electron in its outer shell, it can form positive ions.

Summary

Most of the phenomena of chemistry depend on the stability exhibited by shells containing eight electrons. Eight electrons in a single shell form what is called a stable octet; a pair of electrons in the *K* shell behaves in much the same way. With the exception of helium, which has only the pair of *K* electrons, all of the inert gases have stable octets in their outermost shells.

The two principal types of chemical binding are the ionic and the covalent ones. In ionic binding, a metallic atom achieves a stable outer shell by giving away one or more electrons from its outermost shell, while a nonmetallic atom builds its outermost shell into a stable octet by adding to its electron cluster. Thus the atoms both become ions, oppositely charged, and attract one another. At ordinary temperatures the ions usually congregate in a regular array to form a crystal, each ion being held in place by the attraction of its neighbors.

In covalent binding, stable octets in the outer shells are achieved by a sharing of electrons. The number of atoms that can enter into a combination of this kind is usually small, as it is for example in H_2 and CH_4. These small groups are called molecules. In some cases unlimited numbers of atoms can be held together by a network of covalent bonds; diamond is an example.

The atoms in a metal are held together by what is called metallic binding. Each atom contributes one or more electrons to form shared-pair bonds, each bond being shared with a number of neighboring atoms. Because metals have so few electrons in their outer shells, a bond in a metal is not confined to a specific pair of atoms. The mobility of the bonds is a mobility of electrons, and the motion of electrons is responsible for the electrical conductivity of metals.

There is a very satisfying correlation between the properties of a material in bulk and its structure on an atomic scale.

The chemical peculiarities of hydrogen are accounted for by the fact that its atom has only one electron, yet needs only one more to make a closed shell.

Questions

1. What evidence supports the belief that eight electrons in a shell constitute an especially stable grouping?
2. Describe ionic binding.
3. What class of elements is likely to form positive ions? What class of elements is likely to form negative ions? What kinds of compounds, therefore, are likely to depend on ionic binding?
4. Describe covalent binding.
5. State an instance in which covalent binding gives rise to diatomic molecules, and another in which covalent bonds hold together a molecule that contains more than two atoms. Under what conditions can covalent binding give rise to crystals?
6. What is the connection between Pauli's Exclusion Principle and the formation of molecules?
7. Describe metallic binding.
8. When copper is in the solid state, how many shared-pair bonds does each atom engage in, on the average? How many electrons does each atom then have in its outer shell, on the average? Show that the number of neighbors that a copper atom is bound to is limited by geometry, and not by the Exclusion Principle.
9. Correlate the typical metallic properties of deformability and electric conduction with the nature of the metallic bond.

57

MORE ABOUT CHEMICAL BINDING

The greatest part of the affections [properties] of matter . . . seems to depend on the motion and the contrivance of the small parts of Bodies.

BOYLE

Chapter 56 has described the three principal types of chemical binding—ionic, covalent, and metallic. Broadly speaking, the ionic bond unites metal to nonmetal; the covalent bond unites nonmetals to nonmetals, and the metallic bond unites metallic atoms to one another.

The ionic bond arises from the transfer of an electron from one atom to another, to form a pair of oppositely charged ions. Since each ion has an electric field extending in all directions, it can attract many ions of the opposite charge. Consequently, at room temperature, the typical ionic compound is a crystal. The covalent bond arises from the sharing, by two atoms, of a pair of electrons that have opposite spin. This bond operates between two atoms, and the typical covalent compound is one in which the atoms are bound into small clusters called molecules. When an atom can form several covalent bonds, as carbon can, it can enter into a crystalline structure in which all of the bonds are covalent. Metallic binding resembles covalent binding, but it is in a class by itself because metallic atoms have so few outer electrons that they can never form as many shared-pair bonds as the Exclusion Principle permits. The bonds they can form are limited only by geometrical crowding, and therefore (over a broad range of temperatures) metals are crystalline solids.

This chapter will deal first with the structure of covalent molecules, and then will explain how these molecules are bound together to make liquids or solids.

57–1. Symbolism. As we have seen, the chemical behavior of an atom depends primarily on the number of its electrons that lie outside of closed shells or stable octets. For chemical purposes, drawings like Figure 56–A show unnecessary detail. A more convenient symbolism is one that shows only the name of the atom, or ion, and the number of electrons in its outer shell. This scheme represents atoms of hydrogen, sodium, nitrogen, and chlorine thus:

$$\mathrm{H}\cdot \qquad \mathrm{Na}\cdot \qquad \cdot\overset{..}{\underset{\cdot}{\mathrm{N}}}\cdot \qquad \cdot\overset{..}{\underset{..}{\mathrm{Cl}}}:$$

A typical reaction that forms an ionic compound is described by:

$$\mathrm{Na}\cdot + \cdot\overset{..}{\underset{..}{\mathrm{Cl}}}: \rightarrow \mathrm{Na}^{+} + :\overset{..}{\underset{..}{\mathrm{Cl}}}:^{-}$$

The equation for a typical reaction that produces a covalent compound, say $3H_2 + N_2 \rightarrow 2NH_3$, takes the form

$$\mathrm{H}:\mathrm{H} + \mathrm{H}:\mathrm{H} + \mathrm{H}:\mathrm{H} + \overset{..}{\mathrm{N}}:::\overset{..}{\mathrm{N}} \rightarrow \mathrm{H}:\overset{\mathrm{H}}{\underset{\mathrm{H}}{\overset{..}{\underset{..}{\mathrm{N}}}}}: + \mathrm{H}:\overset{\mathrm{H}}{\underset{\mathrm{H}}{\overset{..}{\underset{..}{\mathrm{N}}}}}:$$

This mode of description is so cumbersome that it is seldom used for writing equations, but it is useful for depicting molecules in a way that describes their structure. Such a diagram for a molecule gives more information than a mere formula, say NH_3, which tells nothing about which atoms are bonded to which. Other examples of the representation are:

$$:\overset{..}{\underset{..}{\mathrm{Cl}}}:\overset{..}{\underset{..}{\mathrm{Cl}}}:$$

Chlorine, Cl_2

$$\begin{array}{ccc} & :\overset{..}{\mathrm{Cl}}: & \\ :\overset{..}{\underset{..}{\mathrm{Cl}}}: & \overset{..}{\underset{..}{\mathrm{C}}} & :\overset{..}{\underset{..}{\mathrm{Cl}}}: \\ & :\underset{..}{\mathrm{Cl}}: & \end{array}$$

Carbon tetrachloride, CCl_4

$$\begin{array}{cccc} & \mathrm{H} & & \overset{..}{\mathrm{O}}: \\ \mathrm{H}: & \overset{..}{\underset{..}{\mathrm{C}}} & : & \mathrm{C} \\ & \mathrm{H} & & \underset{..}{\overset{..}{\mathrm{O}}}:\mathrm{H} \end{array}$$

Acetic acid, $HC_2H_3O_2$ or CH_3COOH

For most purposes, such diagrams can just as well be simplified by using a line like a hyphen to represent a shared-pair bond. Two such lines represent two pairs of shared electrons, which form what is called a *double bond.* In some molecules, one pair of atoms shares three pairs of electrons; this *triple bond* is designated by three lines. An example of each case:

$$\begin{array}{c} \mathrm{H} \\ | \\ \mathrm{H{-}N{-}H} \end{array}$$

Ammonia, NH_3

$$\begin{array}{ccc} \mathrm{H} & & \mathrm{H} \\ & \diagdown\;\;\diagup & \\ & \mathrm{C{=}C} & \\ & \diagup\;\;\diagdown & \\ \mathrm{H} & & \mathrm{H} \end{array}$$

Ethene, C_2H_4

$$\mathrm{N{\equiv}N}$$

Nitrogen, N_2

These collections of symbols are called *structural formulas.* They are in widespread use.

57–2. The Determination of Molecular Structure. Information about molecular structure can come to us by many routes, of which we shall mention only a few.

Today, perhaps the most important guide to molecular structure is our knowledge of what is possible. Whether the binding is ionic or covalent can be determined by seeing whether the compound, when molten, is a conductor of electricity. If the binding is ionic, there must be a donor and a recipient of electrons, in order that atoms may become ions. If the binding is covalent, there must be a sharing of electron pairs. On the basis of these ideas alone, we may arrive at the structural formula for carbon tetrachloride, for example. The liquid is an insulator; therefore, the binding must be covalent. The necessary sharing of electrons would not be possible if the chlorine atoms were bound to one another in a lump, with carbon on the outside. Nor would the sharing be possible if the chlorine atoms were arranged in a row, with the carbon atom at one end. The only plausible structure is the one in the diagram above.

Before the understanding of bonds could reach its present state, scientists had to have experimental knowledge about a variety of molecular structures. One of the simplest ways to get such knowledge was to let substances of known composition (but perhaps unknown structure) react with one another. It was fair to assume that if, in a variety of reactions, a certain set of atoms appears both in the reactants and in the products, then that set of atoms is bonded together. The sulfate radical, SO_4, is an example; we may fairly assume that in any sulfate, there is a sulfur atom bonded to four oxygen atoms. Furthermore, if the radical ion is to have a negative charge of two quanta, the group of five atoms must contain two electrons obtained from some other atom or atoms.

Considerations of the same sort give a clue to the structure of acetic acid, $HC_2H_3O_2$. This compound has one hydrogen atom that is attached weakly, as we know from the fact the compound is an acid with a univalent radical. The other three hydrogen atoms are part of the acetate radical; they must be bound differently from the one that comes loose in solution. The actual structure of the molecule can be inferred in this case, as in many others, from the ways in which it can be built up in the laboratory from simpler molecules whose structure is known. The structural formula of the molecule appears on page 496.

Of the several physical phenomena that can be used for determining molecular structure, only two need be mentioned here. One is the diffraction of x-rays, which is capable of giving the same kind of information about molecules that it gives about crystals (Article 54–4). The other is the spectrum of the molecule. Molecular spectra are far more complex than atomic spectra. In atomic spectra, the radiated energy comes from the jumping of electrons from one orbit to another. In molecular spectra, there are other possibilities as well; the atoms in the molecule can vibrate with respect to one another, and the molecule can rotate in many ways. Each possible vibration or rotation has its own characteristic energy, and changes in rotation or vibration involve the emission or absorption of radiation that has a characteristic frequency. The spectral lines due to vibrations and rotations identify groups of atoms, and hence the grouping of atoms in a molecule may be studied by deciphering the spectrum of the molecule. The lines in one of the spectra in Figure 49–D are characteristic of the aluminum monoxide molecule, AlO.

57–3. Radicals. Before going further into the question of molecular structure, we may pause to consider the structure of radicals. The sulfate ion, as was mentioned above, consists of a sulfur atom, four oxygen atoms, and two extra electrons that give it its charge. It is easy to see that these members can form a stable group by sharing electrons thus:

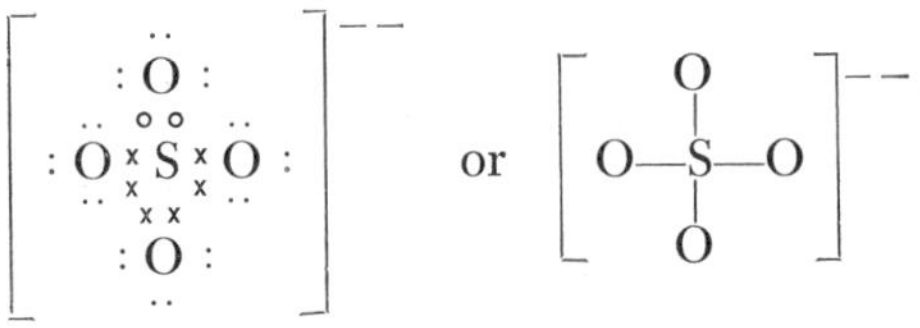

```
 ┌      ..       ┐--             ┌     O     ┐--
 │    : O :      │               │     |     │
 │  ..  o o  ..  │               │           │
 │ : O x S x O : │       or      │  O—S—O    │
 │  ..  x   x .. │               │     |     │
 │      x x      │               └     O     ┘
 │    : O :      │
 └      ..       ┘
```

The electrons are actually indistinguishable; the diagram designates them by different marks simply as an aid in keeping score.

A few radical ions have positive charge. The most important of these is ammonium, NH_4^+, which is formed when a hydrogen ion takes over a share in two previously unshared electrons in ammonia, NH_3:

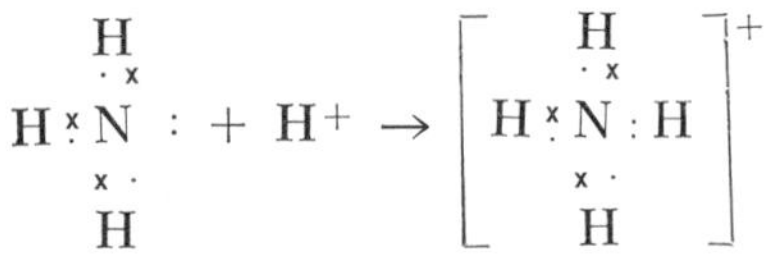

```
     H                       ┌    H      ┐+
     · x                     │    · x    │
   H x· N  :  +  H+  →       │ H x· N : H │
     x ·                     │    x ·    │
     H                       └    H      ┘
```

It has long been known experimentally that each radical has a characteristic charge and valence, and that a radical ion in solution loses its existence when it loses its charge. The structure of radicals makes these facts easy to understand. A definite excess or deficiency of electrons is needed in order that the atoms in the radical may have outer shells that are stable octets.

Radical ions enter into ionic compounds in the same way that other ions do. For example, anhydrous copper sulfate, $CuSO_4$, forms crystals that are regular arrays of copper ions, Cu^{++}, and sulfate ions, SO_4^{--}.

57–4. The Arrangement of Atoms in Space. From molecular spectra, and from the patterns formed by diffracted x-rays, it is possible to learn not only which atoms in a molecule are bonded together, but also how the atoms are arranged in space. Theory, as well, is now an aid in this inquiry. We shall make here only a few remarks on the subject, and they will be expressed in terms of theory, although it is to be understood that they are backed up by experimental evidence. In many cases, the experimental evidence is older than the theory.

Recall that quantum mechanics describes an isolated atom as a nucleus surrounded by a charge cloud. What we call an orbit is a specific cloud pattern. The pattern is spherical for $l = 0$, but when l is not zero, then the pattern has lobes, or tufts, or ears, as shown in Figure 55–B. In the normal state of the hydrogen atom and the inert-gas atoms, the charge clouds of the individual electrons fit together to make a spherical cloud. In

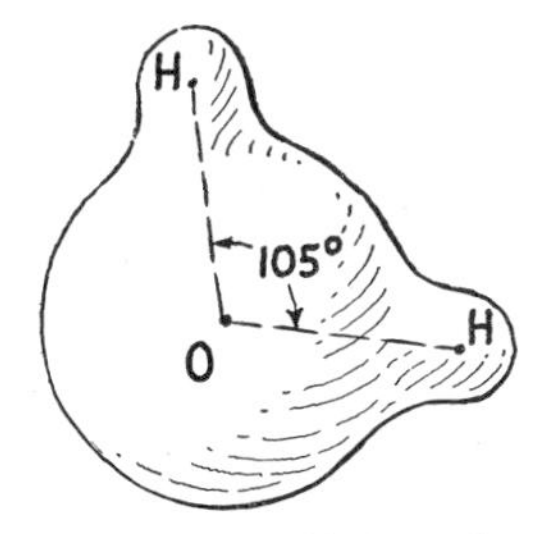

FIGURE 57–A. The water molecule.

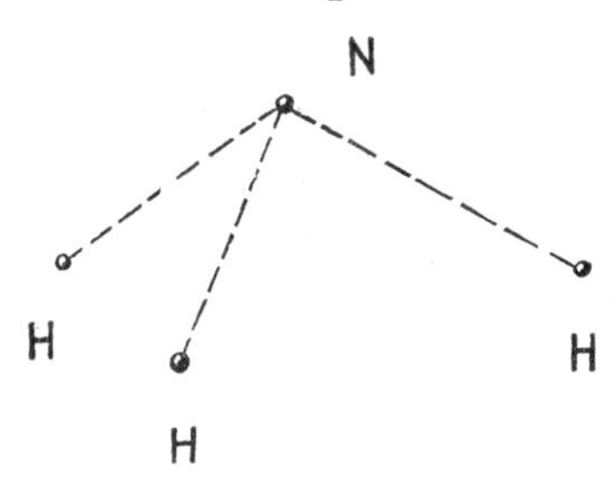

FIGURE 57–B. The nuclei in the ammonia molecule.

atoms that have more than two electrons outside of a stable octet, the outer part of the charge cloud will have lobes protruding in certain directions. What we call a sharing of electrons is an overlapping of the charge clouds of two atoms. Now the atoms that commonly enter into covalent binding are, for the most part, atoms with more than two electrons, and it is just these atoms that have lobes on their charge clouds. Since these lobes have definite directions, we may expect the covalent bonds to act in definite directions.

As an example of directed bonds, consider the bonds in water, H_2O. In oxygen, the two orbits with vacancies lie at right angles to one another. Likening the atom to the earth, we can say that one orbit has lobes at the poles, while the other has lobes on the equator. When two hydrogen atoms share these orbits, the hydrogen nuclei would be near, say, the north pole and the equator of the oxygen atom, were it not that the hydrogen nuclei repel one another. The internuclear repulsion modifies the shapes of all the orbits, and the two orbits containing shared pairs spread apart so that the two bonds form an angle of about 105°. The relative positions of the nuclei are shown in Figure 57–A; the electrons form a thick, rounded padding around the nuclei.

In ammonia, NH_3, the hydrogen atoms form shared-pair bonds with three orbits that are all perpendicular to one another when the nitrogen atom stands alone. Repulsion between the hydrogen nuclei spreads the bonds a little. As a result, the ammonia molecule has the skeleton indicated in Figure 57–B. The three hydrogen nuclei form the triangular base of a pyramid, and the nitrogen nucleus lies at the summit.

57–5. Dipoles. Thus far, we have been speaking as if any bond were either entirely covalent or entirely ionic. We have spoken as if an electron had to be attached exclusively to one atom, or ion, or else had to be shared equally by two atoms. Actually, the covalent bond and the ionic bond are idealizations; when two unlike atoms are bound together, the idealization does not correspond exactly to nature.

Consider a molecule of water. Here, an oxygen atom shares electrons with two hydrogen atoms. From the data on atomic volumes (like those in Figure 39–A), we know that atoms of hydrogen and of oxygen have nearly the same size.* Therefore, we are justified in expecting that when oxygen and hydrogen share an electron, oxygen will get the bigger share, since its nucleus has the bigger charge. If oxygen does get a major share of the electron, the covalent bond will have a partially ionic character, because the oxygen atom will have a slight surplus of negative charge, and the hydrogen atom will have a slight deficit of negative charge. As we shall see in a moment, there is factual support for this concept of a bond that is intermediate between a strictly covalent bond and a strictly ionic one.

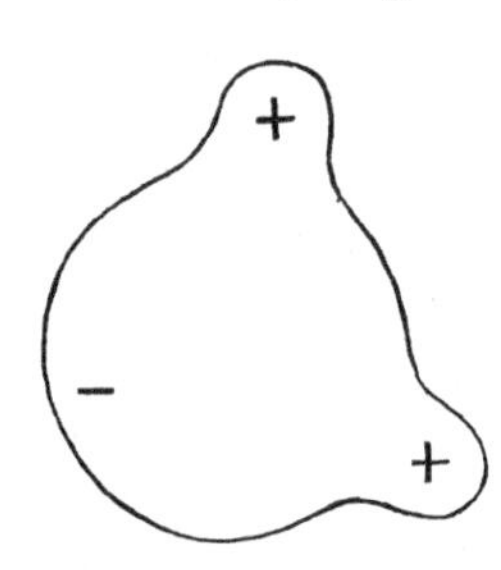

FIGURE 57–C. The distribution of charge in a water molecule.

Accepting the theoretical argument that has just been given, we can see that the water molecule must have an interesting electrical property. The uneven distribution of electrical charge in the molecule, which is depicted in Figure 57–C, will give the molecule a negative end and two positive ends. For many purposes, it is convenient to speak as if the water molecule had simply a positive end and a negative end. Such a distribution of charge is called a *dipole,* a dipole being a pair of equal and opposite charges that are close together. Molecules that act as dipoles are called *polar* molecules.

There is some very direct evidence that water molecules are polar. Consider two parallel plates, close together, one being connected to the ground and the other to the stem of an electroscope (Figure 57–Da). Put a large positive charge on the upper plate. The charge will distribute itself on the plate and on the electroscope; consequently the leaf of the

* The reason is that, although oxygen has two shells of electrons and hydrogen has only one, the larger charge on the oxygen nucleus draws in the electrons to such an extent that the L shell in oxygen has about the same size as the K shell in hydrogen.

electroscope will stand well out from the stem. Negative charge will be drawn from the ground to the lower plate. If now the space between the plates is filled with pure water, the electroscope leaf will drop instantly, although pure water is such a poor conductor that charge can leak between the plates only slowly. The drop of the leaf shows that charge runs from the leaf to the plate; it does so because of the polar character of the

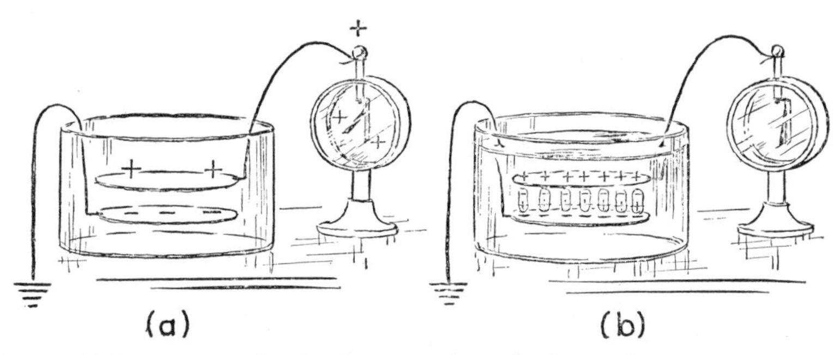

FIGURE 57–D. Water molecules between charged plates affect the distribution of charge, thereby giving evidence that the molecules are dipoles.

water molecules. Figure 57–Db shows how the presence of the dipoles traps charge on the upper plate; the dipoles turn in the electric field so that their negative ends point preponderantly toward the positive plate, and the attraction of the oriented dipoles draws charge away from the electroscope. From experiments resembling this one, the dipole character of water and many other substances was known even before the nature of chemical binding was fully understood.

Water has the polar property in a conspicuously large degree, but all unsymmetrical molecules are to some extent polar. Ammonia (Figure 57–B) is an example. Symmetrical molecules, for instance Cl_2, are not polar.

57–6. The Binding of Molecules into Solids. So far, we have accounted for only three kinds of solids: metals, ionic crystals, and crystals that are formed by three-dimensional networks of covalent bonds, as diamond is. These categories do not account for the solid state of water, carbon dioxide (dry ice), or a host of other substances that can exist as solids if their temperature is relatively low.

There is a force that comes into prominence in the liquid and solid states of any substance. The charges in any atom produce an electric field in its immediate neighborhood, and this electric field alters the relative positions of the charges in any other atom that happens to be close by. The distorted atoms become dipoles, much as the metal cylinder does in Figure 28–G. The positive end of one dipole attracts the negative end of another, so that there is a force of attraction between neighboring atoms, even though their net charge is zero. This attraction occurs even when the atoms are members of different molecules, and it can bind molecules together into a liquid or a solid. It is to such binding that the liquid and solid states of oxygen must be ascribed. Since oxygen is a liquid or a solid only at low temperatures, we conclude that the force of attraction between its molecules is far weaker than the covalent force that binds two oxygen atoms into a molecule.

Polar molecules attract one another because of the force just described, and they also attract one another by virtue of the fact that the molecules themselves are dipoles. Polar molecules can therefore aggregate into liquids or solids at higher temperatures than nonpolar molecules can. It is chiefly for this reason that water remains liquid at a higher temperature than oxygen does.

These forces of attraction that act between molecules are called "van der Waals attractions," after the nineteenth-century Dutch physicist who was among the first to study them. A mathematical treatment of the forces shows that, other things being equal, the van der Waals forces are stronger between larger molecules. Thus it is to be expected that the intermolecular attractions will be larger in bromine than in chlorine, and that they will be even larger in iodine. This accounts for the fact (Article 38–4 and Table 38–I) that at room temperature, chlorine is a gas, bromine is a liquid, and iodine is a solid.

57–7. Ice. Water, in the form of ice, affords one of the most interesting examples of the binding of molecules to form a solid. X-ray studies show that the oxygen atoms in ice are arranged in space like the carbon atoms in a diamond (Figures 56–D and 56–E). The binding, however, cannot be the same in ice as it is in diamond. Ice is a molecular crystal, held together by dipole forces between its molecules. The positive end of the dipole is actually a two-pronged fork, because there are two hydrogen atoms in the molecule. In ice, each of the prongs attracts the negative end of another water molecule. Figure 57–E shows the pattern assumed by such molecules in an idealized two-dimensional case. Each of the six molecules in the figure has one positive lobe that binds that molecule to the next one, and it has another positive lobe that could engage another molecule, which could engage two more, and so on to build up a two-dimensional chain of indefinite size. The actual three-dimensional arrangement of the water molecules in ice appears in Figure 57–F. The open character of the pattern explains why water expands when it freezes into ice, and the repeated six-sided ring of molecules

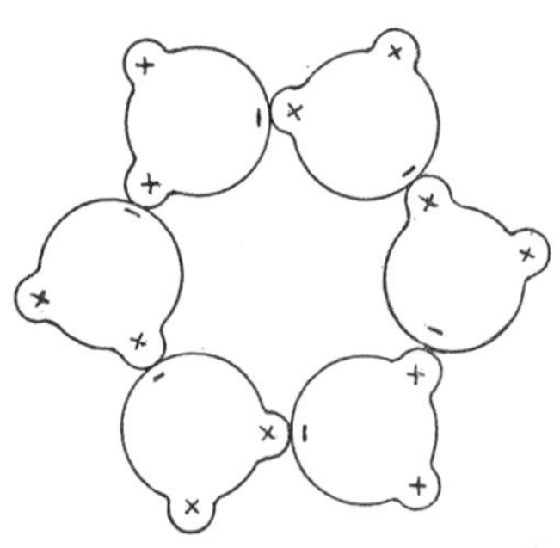

FIGURE 57–E. A ring of water molecules.

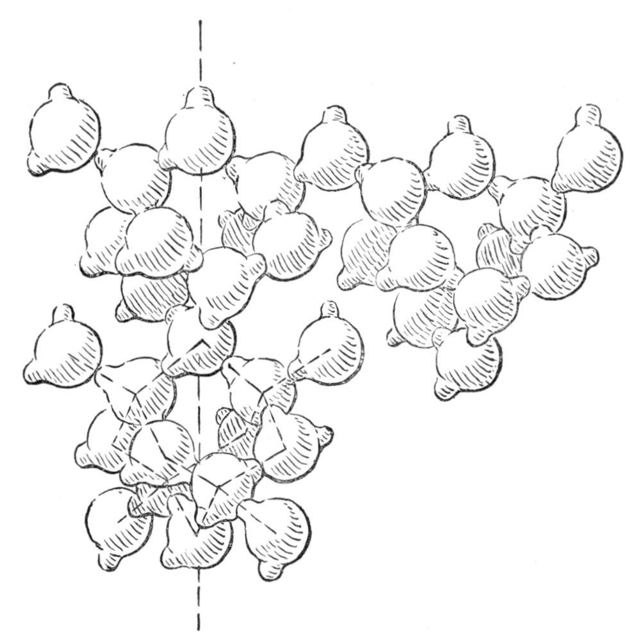

FIGURE 57-F. The structure of ice.

is the framework that regulates the shapes of the snow crystals in Figure 18-C.

SUMMARY

Molecular structure is investigated by many methods; among them are chemical reactions, molecular spectra, x-ray diffraction, and the application of bonding theory. These techniques disclose which atoms are bonded together and how they are arranged in space. The spatial arrangement of the atoms is governed mainly by the positions of lobes in their charge clouds.

Nonmetallic radicals are groups of atoms that are bound together by sharing some of their own electrons and one or more additional electrons. The additional electrons give the radical ion its negative charge. Positively charged radical ions are formed when atoms with sharable electrons share them with positive ions. In either case, a definite charge is needed if the structure is to be a stable one.

In the covalent binding of atoms that are not alike, the shared electrons are not shared equally by the two atoms. The atoms with the larger share in the electrons have a slight negative charge, and the other atoms have a slight positive charge. Many molecules are therefore dipoles, a dipole being a pair of equal and opposite charges that are close together. Such molecules are called polar molecules.

The binding of molecules into liquids and solids often depends on dipole forces that are called van der Waals attractions. These forces exist even between nonpolar molecules, because the electric field of any atom affects the distribution of charge in any other atom that is close to it. The van der Waals forces are stronger, however, in the case of polar molecules.

Questions

1. Using dots to represent electrons, write diagrams for the structure of a molecule of water, a molecule of iodine, and a molecule of methane, CH_4.
2. Using the conventional lines to represent covalent bonds, write structural formulas for chlorine, carbon tetrachloride, acetic acid, and carbon dioxide. (Its spectrum shows that carbon dioxide is a symmetrical molecule.)
3. Draw diagrams to show the sharing of electrons in (a) the perchlorate ion, ClO_4^-; (b) the nitrate ion, NO_3^-. (The nitrate ion has a double bond.)
4. Identify three procedures that can lead to knowledge of how the atoms in a molecule are arranged.
5. What is a dipole?
6. What is a polar molecule?
7. Name one polar molecule, and explain why it is polar.
8. What forces are responsible for the aggregation of covalent molecules into liquids and solids?
9. Account for the fact that at room temperature, methane (CH_4) is a gas, but carbon tetrachloride (CCl_4) is a liquid.
10. Account for the fact that at $-10°$ C, H_2O is a solid, whereas CCl_4 is a liquid.
11. Judging from the diagrams on page 496, how would you expect the freezing point of (pure) acetic acid to compare with that of carbon tetrachloride?

58

ATOMIC STRUCTURE AND CHEMICAL BEHAVIOR

Now that an understanding of chemical binding has been reached, it is easy to see why elements of the same chemical type do not all have exactly the same chemical behavior. This chapter will show how the structure of their atoms accounts for individual differences among the elements. Then it will explain the role of water in solutions and in hydrates.

58–1. The Chemical Activity of Metals. In Article 27–6, we saw that the metals can be ordered into a series such that each metal is chemically more active than those below it. Since then, we have learned that the metallic atoms are those that have only a few electrons in their outer shells. Furthermore, chemical activity as a metal depends on the formation of positive ions through the loss of these outer electrons (Article 56–2). It follows that the most active metals are those that most readily lose electrons.

In the Periodic Table, metallic character in the main groups increases as we go toward the left in a period, or toward the bottom in a group. For example, the order of activity in the second short period is Na > Mg > Al, and the order of activity in Group I is Cs > Rb > K > Na > Li. These rankings are easily accounted for by considering the structures of the respective atoms. Take first the change as we progress to the right in the table. From their atomic numbers, we know that the nuclei of the atoms have positive charge as follows: Na, 11 quanta; Mg, 12; Al, 13. The outer electrons, in each case, lie in the *M* shell ($n = 3$). Because of the larger charge on the nucleus, the *M* shell is smaller in Al than it is in Mg or in Na; the additional charge on the nucleus draws the shells in closer. Because the *M* electrons are closer to the nucleus and are attracted by a larger nuclear charge, they are more firmly bound in Al than they are in Na. Mg forms an intermediate case. For the same reasons, the outer electrons in Si are bound more firmly than in Al; the energy required to remove them is so great that the ion Si^{++++} is never formed in chemical reactions. The proof of this statement lies in the fact that silicon is never found in a strictly metallic role. The same considerations apply even more strongly to phosphorus, sulfur, and chlorine, the other elements in the second short period. The situation is much the same in other periods.

Somewhat similar reasons govern the increase in metallic activity as we go downward in a main group in the Periodic Table. Consider Group I. Potassium, a member of the group, has a nuclear charge of 19 quanta, and it has eighteen inner electrons. Here and in all the other atoms of alkali metals, there are enough inner electrons to neutralize the charge on the nucleus, except for a single quantum. Therefore the part of the nuclear charge that acts on the outer electron is about the same for all of the alkali metals. The major difference between these metals lies in the distance of the outer electron from the nucleus. The outer electron in Li is in the L shell ($n = 2$). In Na, the corresponding electron is in the M shell ($n = 3$); in K, the corresponding electron is in the N shell ($n = 4$); in Rb, it is in the O shell ($n = 5$), and in Cs, it is in the P shell ($n = 6$). As we go down through the group, the outer electron is farther and farther from the nucleus, as we can verify from the data on atomic volumes (Figure 39–A). Since in each case the outer electron is exposed to nearly the same effective charge on the nucleus, and the distance from the nucleus is greater in the heavier atoms, it is the atoms at the bottom of the group that can most easily lose their outer electrons, and the order of activity is Cs $>$ Rb $>$ K $>$ Na $>$ Li.

The radii of atoms can be found by measuring atomic volumes or by measuring the distances between atoms in metals or in covalent compounds. Atomic radii can also be calculated, by using wave mechanics to find the most probable positions of the outer electrons. (Recall our calculation of the radius of the hydrogen atom, Article 51–3.) The results of some measurements appear in Table 58–I.

58–2. Nonmetallic Activity. Nonmetallic atoms enter into chemical union by gaining electrons from other atoms, either to become ions or to form shared-pair bonds. The considerations that make for activity as a nonmetal are therefore just the reverse of those that make for activity as a metal. Nonmetallic activity is furthered by a small outer shell, and by a big net charge on the nucleus and inner electrons that form the core of the atom. Nonmetallic activity therefore increases as we go to the right in any period of the Periodic Table, and it increases as we go upward in any main group. Thus, Cl is more nonmetallic than S or Br, but less nonmetallic than F.

58–3. The Sizes of Ions. We have seen that metallic or nonmetallic activity depends strongly on the size of the outer shell of the atom in

TABLE 58–I

THE RADII OF SOME ATOMS AND IONS *

(The unit of measurement is the angstrom unit, 10^{-10} m.)

Li	1.23	Be	0.89	C	0.77	O	0.74	F	0.72
Li^{+}	0.60	Be^{++}	0.31			O^{--}	1.40	F^{-}	1.36
Na	1.57	Mg	1.36	Si	1.17	S	1.04	Cl	0.99
Na^{+}	0.95	Mg^{++}	0.65			S^{--}	1.84	Cl^{-}	1.81
K	2.03	Ca	1.73	Ge	1.22	Se	1.17	Br	1.14
K^{+}	1.33	Ca^{++}	0.99			Se^{--}	1.98	Br^{-}	1.95
Rb	2.16	Sr	1.91					I	1.33
Rb^{+}	1.48	Sr^{++}	1.13					I^{-}	2.16

* After Pauling.

FIGURE 58–A. Models of sodium chloride and cesium chloride.

question. In all matters of ionic binding, the size of the outer shell of the *ion* is also of importance.

A few simple effects make the size of an ion different from the size of the corresponding atom. Consider first the nonmetallic, or negative, ions. They are formed when an atom acquires one or more extra electrons in its outer shell. The electrons in the outer shell all repel one another; hence the shell expands when the atom turns into a negative ion. Negative ions are therefore larger than the corresponding atoms.

A metallic atom becomes a positive ion by losing one or more outer electrons. In the cases of simple ionic binding, the metallic atom loses all of the electrons in its outer shell. The metallic ion is therefore smaller than its parent atom.

The radii of ions have been found from x-ray studies of the crystals formed by ionic compounds. A few of these radii appear in Table 58–I. Notice that only the largest of the positive ions in the table is as big as the smallest of the negative ions.

Ionic size is one of the major factors that govern the structure of any ionic crystal. As an example, Figure 58-A shows models of sodium chloride and cesium chloride crystals. Although they are both alkali halides, the two substances have different crystal structures. The reason is that the cesium ion is about the same size as the chloride ion, whereas the sodium ion is much smaller.

You will recall that fluorides are somewhat different from the other halides; the small size of the fluoride ion is largely responsible for the special behavior of the fluorides.

58–4. Water as a Solvent. The behavior of water as a solvent is governed by the structure of the water molecule (Articles 57–4, 57–5). The clue to the subject is that water is a good solvent for ionic substances, but is not a good solvent for most covalent compounds. This fact, coupled with the polar structure of the water molecule, suggests that electric forces are at work when a substance dissolves in water. We may attribute the dissolving of an ionic compound to an attack of the water dipoles on the ions at the edges and corners of a crystal. Figure 58–B is an artist's sketch of the situation. The negative ends of some water dipoles become attached to positive ions of the crystal. The attractive forces that hold the ion in the crystal are in some cases overcome; the ion becomes surrounded by water molecules and wanders off into solution. Likewise, negative ions in the crystal become attached to the positive ends of water molecules, and go into solution. Some ionic compounds do not dissolve in water; these are compounds in which the interionic attractions are too strong to be overcome by the attack of the water dipoles.

The breaking up of a salt as it goes into solution does not agree exactly with Arrhenius' idea of the process. Unaware of the ionic structure of solid salts, he thought (Article 37–1) that a solid salt consisted of molecules, and that a solution of the salt contained molecules and ions in equilibrium with one another. Actually, the solid salt is not molecular, and in solution the surrounding dipoles prevent the ions from pairing off to form molecules. In the case of salts, therefore, the effects that Arrhenius laid to incomplete dissociation have to be ascribed now to forces exerted on the ions by other ions (Article 37–3) and by the surrounding clusters of water dipoles.

FIGURE 58–B. Water dissolving an ionic crystal.

Water is not a good solvent for solids that are not ionic in structure. In the main, these solids are held together by van der Waals forces, and they dissolve better in solvents that have larger molecules, and exert larger van der Waals forces, than water does. As might be expected, however, water does dissolve some covalent compounds that have polar molecules. Sugar is an example.

58–5. Hydration and Hydrates. The attachment of water molecules to ions is called *hydration.* Ions of either charge become hydrated in solution, but the water molecules are attached more firmly to the positive ions than to the negative ones. There are two reasons for the difference. In the first place, the negative charge of the water dipole is concentrated on the oxygen atom, whereas the positive charge is distributed between two hydrogen atoms. Moreover, as Table 58–I shows, positive ions are generally smaller than negative ones. For both of these reasons, the interacting charges are more concentrated, so that they interact more strongly, in the case of positive ions.

When water evaporates from a solution of a salt, the ions form a crystal again (Article 34–2). When some salts crystallize from solution, the positive ions retain a cluster of water molecules. The substance so formed is a hydrate (Article 34–5).

As one should expect, the tendency to form hydrates is pronounced when the metallic ion is small or when its charge is more than one quantum. The salts of lithium commonly have hydrated forms. Salts of cesium, which is chemically similar but of larger ionic radius, rarely have hydrated forms. The bivalent and tervalent metals form hydrated salts more commonly than the alkali metals do, because their ions have more charge.

The role of the water molecules is not the same in all hydrates. In many, the metallic ion and a definite number of water molecules cling together as a large positive ion, and the crystal has a normal ionic structure. In some hydrates, water molecules fit into chinks in the crystalline framework, being held by van der Waals forces. Cupric sulfate pentahydrate, $CuSO_4 \cdot 5H_2O$, illustrates both of these possibilities. In this crystal, the Cu^{++} ion is surrounded by four water molecules, and the fifth water molecule fits between this hydrated ion and two of the SO_4^{--} neighbors.

Summary

The degree of activity of a metal is governed by the weakness of attachment of the outer electrons in its atoms. The binding of the electrons follows Coulomb's Law; electrons are less firmly bound when they are farther from the nucleus, and when the net attracting charge is smaller. In any main group in the Periodic Table, the elements at the bottom of the group are the most metallic because atomic size increases toward the bottom of the group, and the net charge attracting the outer electron is the same throughout the group. In any single period in the table, the outer electrons are closer to the nucleus, and are attracted by a bigger nuclear charge, in the elements toward the right of the table. These facts explain the gradations in activity as one moves vertically or horizontally in the Periodic Table.

In the chemistry of ionic compounds much depends on the sizes of the ions. Metallic ions are smaller than the corresponding atoms, whereas the ions of nonmetals are larger than their atoms. As a result, positive ions are generally smaller than negative ions.

The action of water as a solvent depends on electric forces of attraction between the water dipoles and the ions or dipoles of the solute. Substances with nonpolar molecules do not dissolve in water. Ionic or polar substances dissolve by virtue of attachments between the ions or dipoles and the water molecules. The substance is soluble in water if these attachments are stronger than the forces that hold the solid together.

Because of their small size, the charge on positive ions is relatively concentrated, and this makes for strong attachments between positive ions and water dipoles. An ion that has one or more water molecules attached to it is said to be hydrated. In solution, positive ions are practically always hydrated, and negative ones often are. The positive ions sometimes keep their retinue of water molecules when the solute crystallizes. The crystal is then a hydrate; in some hydrates, the water molecules enter the structure in other ways.

As now understood, the mechanism of solution does not exactly agree with Arrhenius' idea of the process. In the case of salts, the effects that Arrhenius laid to incomplete dissociation have to be ascribed now to forces exerted on the ions by other ions and by the surrounding clusters of water dipoles.

Questions

1. Explain the fact that cesium is a more active metal than sodium.
2. Explain the fact that magnesium is a less active metal than sodium.
3. Explain the fact that chlorine is more nonmetallic than iodine.
4. State a fact that in some measure accounts for the differences between fluorides and the other halides.
5. State what the following particles have in common, and arrange them in the order of their size: Mg^{++}, Na^{+}, Ne, F^{-}, Al^{+++}, O^{--}, N^{---}.
6. Explain why water dissolves salts more readily than it dissolves solids that are held together by van der Waals forces.
7. Which element in Group IV do you think is most likely to form positive ions that have 4 quanta of charge? Explain.
8. Try to account for the fact that cesium chloride is much more soluble in water than sodium chloride is.

59

OXIDATION—REDUCTION

Das System der Elektrizität wird das System der Chemie werden. und umgekehrt.

RITTER (1798)

The interplay of electricity and chemistry has come to notice in connection with electric cells, electrolysis, and ionic binding. Further consideration of this subject makes possible a unified theory of a large variety of reactions that might at first seem to have little in common. Here we shall sketch the broad outline of the theory, and shall then see how it applies to the action of electric cells.

59–1. Oxidation–Reduction. The early chemists, who were much interested in oxides, gave the name "oxidation" to the union of a substance with oxygen (Article 25–6). The reverse process, the removal of oxygen from a compound, they called "reduction." Some examples of reduction appeared in Article 27–7.

As chemical knowledge grew, it became clear that combination with oxygen was not fundamentally different from certain other reactions. A candle will burn in chlorine, and in Article 38–4 there are some examples of metals and other substances that react with chlorine in much the same way that they react with oxygen. One example is the reaction of copper with chlorine, which resembles the reaction of copper with oxygen. Not only are the phenomena similar, but also the equations that describe them are similar:

$$2Cu + O_2 \rightarrow 2CuO$$

$$Cu + Cl_2 \rightarrow CuCl_2$$

In both cases, the copper is uncombined before the reaction, and after the reaction it has a valence of 2. Its valence can therefore be regarded as being increased from 0 to 2 by reason of its combination with oxygen or chlorine. The term "oxidation" therefore came into use in a broadened sense, in which it meant an increase in metallic valence. The reaction

$$Fe_2(SO_4)_3 + SnSO_4 \rightarrow Sn(SO_4)_2 + 2FeSO_4$$

is therefore regarded as an instance of the oxidation of the tin of stannous sulfate.

Modern ideas about chemical binding have made it useful to introduce the phrase *valence number.* The valence number of any element in a compound is the charge that ions of that element would have in the compound if the compound were completely ionic in character. In ionic compounds, the valence numbers are the charges on the ions. In covalent compounds, the valence number is merely an artificial aid, but it is often a useful one. The charge is to be measured in quanta. A positive valence number indicates metallic valence, and a negative one, nonmetallic valence. If an element is not in a compound, it is assigned a valence number of 0. In $FeCl_2$, the iron has valence number +2, and the chlorine has valence number −1; in Cl_2, the chlorine has valence number 0.

Since oxidation is an increase in metallic valence, oxidation involves an increase in valence number; the reverse process, reduction, involves a decrease in valence number.

It will be clear from a few examples that oxidation and reduction always occur together. Our first encounter with oxidation (Article 25–6) was with reactions like

$$2Mg + O_2 \rightarrow 2MgO \quad \text{and} \quad C + O_2 \rightarrow CO_2.$$

In the first, the valence number of magnesium changes from 0 to +2, and that of the oxygen changes from 0 to −2. In the second, the valence number of the carbon changes from 0 to +4, and that of the oxygen from 0 to −2. The magnesium and the carbon are oxidized in the reactions, and the oxygen is reduced. The reaction

$$CuO + H_2 \rightarrow Cu + H_2O$$

appeared in Article 27–7 as an example of reduction. It is equally an example of oxidation, since the copper of the CuO is reduced and the hydrogen is oxidized. In the equation above that involves the sulfates of iron and tin, the oxidation of the stannous tin is accompanied by reduction of the ferric iron. Further examples are unnecessary, because the physical interpretation of oxidation and of reduction will make it obvious that they must occur together. Reactions in which they occur are called *oxidation–reduction* reactions, or *redox* reactions.

The physical basis for a change in ionic valence is a change in ionic charge, and this change is effected by a transfer of electrons from one atom or ion to another. An increase in valence number implies an increase in positive charge, i.e., a loss of one or more electrons. Therefore, in the modern sense of the word, *oxidation is the loss of electrons.* Similarly, *reduction is the gain of electrons.* Since any electron lost by one atom or ion is gained by another, oxidation and reduction go together like opposite sides of the same coin.

59–2. Reactions in Solution. Although oxidation and reduction have some application in all branches of chemistry, these concepts have their greatest utility in the realm of the electrolytes, where binding is predominantly ionic. Redox reactions account for much of the chemistry of electrolytes in solution.

In Article 27–6, we noted as a fact that zinc will replace lead in a solution of lead nitrate. The changes in charge are shown by the ionic equation

$$Zn + Pb^{++} + 2NO_3^- \rightarrow Pb + Zn^{++} + 2NO_3^-.$$

The nitrate ion undergoes no change in the reaction, and it can be canceled out of the equation. It is profitable to divide the ionic equation into two parts that deal separately with the changes undergone by the zinc and by the lead. In the reaction, zinc atoms lose electrons and form zinc ions. This change, which is an oxidation, can be represented by the equation

$$Zn \rightarrow Zn^{++} + 2e.$$

The other aspect of the reaction is the reduction of lead ions to lead atoms:

$$Pb^{++} + 2e \rightarrow Pb.$$

These two equations are said to represent half-reactions. They may be added to give the ionic equation for the whole reaction:

$$Zn + Pb^{++} \rightarrow Zn^{++} + Pb.$$

The electrons are not entered in the last equation, because they would appear equally on both sides.

59–3. Electrolysis. In ordinary redox reactions, the oxidation and the reduction occur at the same place. In electrolysis, however, the two half-reactions occur separately at the two electrodes.

When a solution of copper bromide, $CuBr_2$, undergoes electrolysis, copper is deposited at one electrode and bromine is liberated at the other. The half-reactions are called "electrode reactions," because they occur at the electrodes. They are:

At the negative electrode $\quad Cu^{++} + 2e \rightarrow Cu$

At the positive electrode $\quad 2Br^- \rightarrow Br_2 + 2e.$

In the half-reaction involving copper, the electrons come from the negative electrode, where they are piled up in surplus by the action of the battery in the electric circuit. The other half-reaction gives electrons to the positive electrode, at which the battery maintains an electron deficit.

Chemically, electrolysis of copper bromide results in the decomposition of the substance into its elements. If the elements bromine and copper come into contact, they combine in an exothermic reaction:

$$Cu + Br_2 \rightarrow CuBr_2 + \text{heat}.$$

Therefore the reverse reaction will not occur unless energy is supplied; copper bromide does not decompose if left to itself. In electrolysis, the energy required to decompose the copper bromide is furnished by the battery:

$$CuBr_2 + \text{energy} \rightarrow Cu + Br_2.$$

Electric batteries or dynamos can be made to give an electron more energy than it could acquire in a chemical reaction. Therefore electrolysis can produce electron transfers that would not occur from purely chemical causes; in other words, electrolysis can promote chemical results that would not otherwise be attainable. For example, no chemical agent can capture an electron from the fluoride ion to form free fluorine. Free fluorine may be obtained, however, by the electrolysis of a molten fluoride, say NaF.

59–4. Electric Cells. Electrolysis is useful because it can bring about redox reactions that are endothermic, and that therefore could not occur of their own accord. There are many redox reactions, however, that are exothermic. We might expect that such reactions could be made to give energy to the electrons that take part in them, and that the energy of the electrons could be employed in an electric circuit. This idea is correct. Since the oxidation gives up electrons and the reduction takes them in, all we have to do is make them occur in different places, and then supply a wire so that the electrons given up at the place of oxidation can flow to the place where they are needed for reduction. The chemical energy set free in the exothermic reaction is given to the electrons, and it appears as electrical energy in the conducting circuit. The device that permits the oxidation and reduction to occur in separate places is called an electric cell (Article 30–3).

One simple redox reaction is the replacement of one metal by another in a solution of their salts. By telling us which of these reactions occur spontaneously, the replacement series (Table 27–I) tells us which ones are exothermic. Thus we see that the replacement of copper by zinc,

$$Cu^{++} + Zn \rightarrow Cu + Zn^{++},$$

is an exothermic redox reaction. The corresponding half-reactions are:

$$Cu^{++} + 2e \rightarrow Cu$$

$$Zn \rightarrow Zn^{++} + 2e.$$

The electric cell in Figure 59–A permits these two half-reactions to occur in different places, so that the chemical energy set free can be delivered to a flashlight lamp by the electrons. In the cell, each metal is surrounded

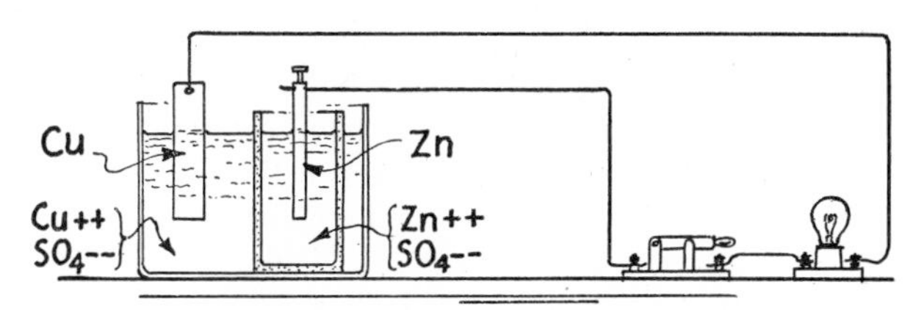

FIGURE 59–A. A simple electric cell.

by its ions in solution. The porous barrier prevents large-scale mixing of the solutions, but allows migration of ions to keep the solutions from becoming charged as a result of the electron transfer.

When the switch is open, each metal is in equilibrium with its ions in solution:

$$Zn \rightleftharpoons Zn^{++} + 2e$$

$$Cu \rightleftharpoons Cu^{++} + 2e.$$

When the metal contributes an ion to the solution, the two electrons remain on the electrode, which therefore acquires negative charge. Eventually this negative charge attracts positive ions from the solution at the same rate as the rate of solution of the metal, and equilibrium prevails. Since Zn atoms lose electrons more readily than Cu atoms do, the attraction required to produce equilibrium at the electrodes is greater for zinc than for copper. The zinc electrode therefore becomes more negative than the copper one. The difference in potential of the two electrodes is about 1 volt.

When the switch is closed, electrons accumulated on the zinc electrode can flow through the wire to the copper electrode, where the potential is higher. This flow of electrons destroys the equilibrium at the electrodes; zinc goes into solution and copper comes out. There will be an electric current in the lamp until the zinc all goes into solution as ions, or until there are no more copper ions to absorb the electrons at the copper electrode. The energy liberated in the chemical reaction is expended in the electric circuit.

59–5. The Dry Cell. Cells like the one in Figure 59–A were widely used in the nineteenth century, but they have now been supplanted by the so-called dry cell, which is more complicated to explain but more convenient to use. In this cell, depicted in Figure 59–B, the electrodes are a zinc can and a carbon rod. Between the electrodes is a layer of porous paper and a wet paste made of ammonium chloride, manganese dioxide, and water. The half-reactions at the electrodes are:

$$Zn \rightarrow Zn^{++} + 2e$$

$$2MnO_2 + 2NH_4^+ + 2e \rightarrow 2NH_3 + 2MnOOH.$$

At the negative electrode, zinc goes into solution, leaving electrons behind. At the positive electrode, ammonium ions have their charge neutralized if electrons are flowing to the carbon rod through the external circuit. The manganese dioxide reacts with the hydrogen that is detached when the ammonium ion is discharged. If this hydrogen were allowed to accumulate on the carbon electrode, it would impede the discharge of the ammonium ions. The ammonia molecules, being polar, become attached to zinc ions to form $Zn\ (NH_3)_4^{++}$. These ammonated ions are like hydrated ions, except that they involve ammonia dipoles instead of water dipoles. Since the cell liberates no gas, it can be sealed so that it will not spill or dry out.

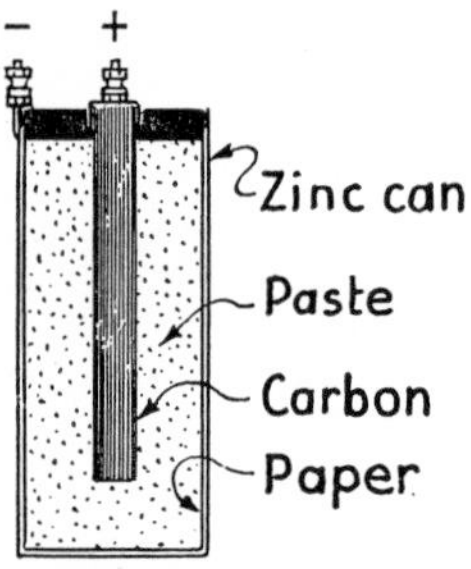

FIGURE 59–B. A dry cell.

Because the "fuel" it uses is zinc, the dry cell is not a cheap source of energy, but it is useful in flashlights and other devices where portability and safety are worth a price.

59–6. Storage Batteries. If energy is supplied by an electrical generator connected to the cell in Figure 59–A, the chemical reaction in the cell can proceed endothermically. The half-reactions at the electrodes are then the reverse of the spontaneous ones: zinc is deposited on the zinc electrode, and the copper goes into solution as ions. The energy thus stored in the cell can be used later by letting the cell operate exothermically.

A cell in which the redox reaction is reversible is called a "storage cell." The most common type is that used in automobile batteries. It is made by immersing in dilute sulfuric acid a lead plate and another plate consisting of a lead framework filled with lead dioxide. When the plates are connected externally by a conducting path, the following half-reactions take place exothermically:

At negative electrode $\quad Pb \rightarrow Pb^{++} + 2e$

At the positive electrode $\quad PbO_2 + 4H^+ + 2e \rightarrow Pb^{++} + 2H_2O.$

Both half-reactions produce Pb^{++} ions, which combine with SO_4^{--} ions from the solution to form on the plates a layer of lead sulfate. When both electrodes are lead sulfate, no further reaction occurs; the cell is "discharged." By connecting the cell to some source of electrical energy, however, the following half-reactions, which are endothermic, can be made to occur:

$$PbSO_4 + 2e \rightarrow Pb + SO_4^{--}$$

$$PbSO_4 + 2H_2O \rightarrow PbO_2 + SO_4^{--} + 4H^+ + 2e.$$

The cell therefore becomes restored to its original condition, which is called "charged."

The functioning of the cell is summarized by the equation:

$$Pb + PbO_2 + 2H_2SO_4 \underset{\substack{\text{(endothermic)}\\ \text{charging}}}{\overset{\substack{\text{discharging}\\ \text{(exothermic)}}}{\rightleftarrows}} 2PbSO_4 + 2H_2O.$$

In the charged cell, one electrode is lead and the other is lead dioxide; in the discharged cell, both electrodes are lead sulfate. Sulfuric acid is used up during the discharging process, but is remade when the cell is being charged.

EXPERIMENT. Let two clean lead plates be immersed in dilute sulfuric acid and connected to some source of direct current. One of the plates will become coated with lead oxide. The cell thus becomes charged, and it will light a flashlight bulb for a short time. The charging and discharging processes may be repeated at will.

SUMMARY

The words "oxidation" and "reduction" are used in a generalized sense to denote chemical changes in which there is a transfer of electrons. It is such transfers that cause changes in valence.

The valence number of an element in a compound is the charge that ions of that element have in the compound, or it is the charge that they would have if the compound were completely ionic. The charge is to be measured in quanta, so that the valence number is a small integer. If an element is uncombined, it is given valence number 0.

Oxidation, which is the loss of electrons, entails an increase in valence number. Reduction, which is the gain of electrons, involves a decrease in valence number. Since an electron lost by one atom or ion is gained by another, oxidation and reduction always occur together. Reactions in which they play a part are called oxidation–reduction reactions, or redox reactions. Such reactions account for much of the chemistry of electrolytes in solution.

A redox reaction can be considered in two parts, which deal separately with the changes undergone by the element that is oxidized and the one that is reduced. These parts are called half-reactions. In purely chemical reactions, they occur in the same place, but in electrochemical reactions, oxidation occurs at one electrode while reduction takes place at the other.

Redox reactions readily explain the facts of electrolysis and the behavior of electric cells.

Electrolysis reactions are those where oxidation and reduction occur in different places, one at each electrode, under the influence of electrical energy supplied from without. Electrolysis provides a means of promoting endothermic reactions.

Electric cells are devices for deriving electrical energy from exothermic redox reactions. The two half-reactions occur on different electrodes. If the electrodes are connected by a conducting path, charge flows through it as long as the reaction within the cell continues to deliver electrons to one electrode and remove them from the other.

Questions

1. What is the generalized meaning of "oxidation"?
2. What is the generalized meaning of "reduction"?
3. What is the valence number of an element in a compound? What is the valence number of an element in the uncombined state?
4. How are changes in valence number related to oxidation and reduction?
5. How is it that oxidation and reduction always occur at the same time? Give an example that illustrates the point.
6. With the emphasis on oxidation and reduction, describe the union of hydrogen gas with chlorine gas to form hydrogen chloride.
7. Write ionic equations for the half-reactions that occur when:
   (a) Copper replaces silver from a solution of silver nitrate.
   (b) Chlorine oxidizes stannous chloride to stannic chloride. In each case, state which half-reaction is the oxidation and which one is the reduction.
8. On page 514, there is an equation describing an oxidation of stannous ions and the accompanying reduction of ferric ions. Write the ionic equations for the corresponding half-reactions.
9. Write equations for the half-reactions that occur when fluorine is liberated by the electrolysis of molten sodium fluoride.
10. Sketch an electric cell that would use the reaction

$$2Al + 3Pb(NO_3)_2 \rightarrow 2Al(NO_3)_3 + 3Pb.$$

    Identify the positive and negative terminals of the cell.
11. If silver nitrate were used in place of the lead nitrate in the preceding question, would the cell produce a larger difference of potential, or a smaller one? How do you know?
12. Suppose that the cell in Figure 59–A, or a dry cell, maintains a current of 0.50 amp in an electric lamp for 2.0 hours. How many electrons would pass through the lamp? How many zinc ions would go into solution? What weight of zinc metal would be consumed?

60

THE MODERN VIEW OF ACIDS AND BASES

> But 'tis a common proof
> That lowliness is young ambition's ladder,
> Whereunto the climber-upward turns his face;
> But when he once attains the upmost round,
> He then unto the ladder turns his back,
> Looks in the clouds, scorning the base degrees
> By which he did ascend.
>
> *Julius Caesar*, II, i

According to the theory of Arrhenius, an acid is a hydrogen compound that furnishes hydrogen ions when dissolved in water (Article 37–5). Present knowledge of atomic and molecular structure gives us a much more detailed comprehension of hydrogen compounds than Arrhenius had. One result is a better understanding of acid behavior. Another result is a deeper insight into the relation of bases to acids, and into the role that the solvent plays in reactions that involve acids and bases.

60–1. Hydrogen Ions. We have already noted that salts are ionic compounds, and that a salt goes into solution through the attachment of its ions to water dipoles (Article 58–4). The presence of ions in a salt solution is therefore trivially easy to understand. Concerning acids, the story is not so simple. Hydrogen chloride, hydrogen fluoride, sulfuric acid, and in fact acids in general, are not conductors of electricity when they are in the liquid state. This fact shows that their bonding is covalent, not ionic. Nevertheless, water solutions of these substances do conduct electricity, which indicates that there are ions in the solutions. Electrolysis of hydrogen chloride solution liberates hydrogen and chlorine at the electrodes; we therefore conclude that the solution of hydrogen chloride contains hydrogen ions and chloride ions. This ionization of a covalent compound arises from the unique character of the hydrogen ion.

Since the hydrogen atom has but one electron, a hydrogen ion, when not attached to anything else, is just a bare nucleus. This lack of a charge cloud means that the hydrogen ion is much smaller than the ion of any other element. Because of its exceptionally small size, a hydrogen ion is especially subject to hydration (Article 58–5). The attraction between a hydrogen nucleus and a water dipole is so strong that it can break the covalent attachment of hydrogen to chlorine or to many other atoms or atomic groups. Hence it is that acids, although they are covalent compounds, can furnish hydrogen ions when in water solutions.

When it is in water, the hydrogen ion, like almost any other positive ion, is hydrated. As a reminder of the hydration, the hydrated hydrogen ion is often called the *hydronium ion* and designated by H_3O^+; although such a reminder seems hardly necessary, there are times when it is convenient.

In the light of modern knowledge, therefore, the Arrhenius conception of an acid (Article 37–5) can be restated as follows: An acid is a substance whose molecules can transfer hydrogen nuclei to water molecules.

60–2. Brönsted Acids. About 1900, a few chemists started to pay increasing attention to reactions that occur in solvents other than water. They found that many substances dissolve readily in liquid ammonia and that ionic reactions occur in this solvent in much the same way as in water solutions. There are many parallels between reactions in ammonia and reactions in water. Nitrogen compounds have the same prominence in "ammonia chemistry" that oxygen compounds have in "water chemistry." Perhaps the most fundamental resemblance between the two solvents is their self-ionization:

$$2H_2O \rightleftharpoons H_3O^+ + OH^-$$

$$2NH_3 \rightleftharpoons NH_4^+ + NH_2^-.$$

Reactions in hydrogen sulfide (H_2S) and in acetic acid ($HC_2H_3O_2$) also received extensive study. It soon became clear that water, for all its cheapness and convenience, had no good claim to a key role in chemical theory. Why should an acid be defined in terms of the transfer of a hydrogen nucleus to a *water* molecule? A definition, if meaningful, cannot be wrong. It can, however, be inconvenient, and chemists felt the need of a broad definition of "acid" that would not hamper them in discussions of solvents like ammonia or acetic acid. Brönsted, one of Bohr's fellow-professors at Copenhagen, suggested in 1923 that the term "acid" be applied to any molecule or ion that can act as the donor of a hydrogen nucleus. Brönsted acids include all of the substances that are ordinarily called acids. Ions such as H_3O^+ and NH_4^+ are also Brönsted acids, since each can give away a hydrogen nucleus.

60–3. Brönsted Bases. Brönsted's definition of an acid was only a modest extension of classical ideas, but he went on to propose a wholly new meaning for the word "base."

In the classical sense, set forth by Arrhenius, a base is a hydroxide that, when in solution, furnishes hydroxide ions (Article 37–5). Bases, when molten, are conductors of electricity; this means that a base is an ionic compound. With respect to structure, therefore, bases are like salts. Bases are in a class by themselves because they react with acids to form water. A typical neutralization reaction is that of sodium hydroxide with hydrochloric acid in water:

$$Na^+ + OH^- + H^+ + Cl^- \rightarrow H_2O + Na^+ + Cl^-.$$

The sodium and chloride ions play no part in the reaction, and they need not be included in the equation, which can just as well be written:

$$H^+ + OH^- \rightarrow H_2O.$$

Brönsted pointed out that the essential feature of a neutralization reaction in water is the transfer of a hydrogen nucleus from an acid molecule to a water molecule and thence to a hydroxide ion, to form a second water molecule. He urged that the definition of "base" be extended to include any molecule or ion that can accept a hydrogen nucleus. According to his definition, the reaction just discussed involves two bases. One is the water molecule that takes a hydrogen nucleus from the hydrogen chloride molecule. The other base in the reaction is the hydroxide ion (not sodium hydroxide), which takes the hydrogen nucleus from the hydronium ion.

Brönsted's suggestion has much to recommend it. For centuries, chemists have regarded acids and bases as being in some sense chemically opposite. A strong acid and a strong base are both very corrosive substances, but when they are mixed together in the right proportions, the resulting solution is relatively noncorrosive. Moreover, acids and bases have exactly contrary effects on litmus and other vegetable dyes (Article 26–4). Brönsted made the oppositeness of bases and acids a matter of definition: An acid is a donor of hydrogen nuclei, and a base is an acceptor of hydrogen nuclei.

Among the Brönsted bases are H_2O, NH_3, and all negative ions, including, of course, OH^-.

60–4. Reactions between Brönsted Acids and Brönsted Bases. By Brönsted's definitions, acid behavior is of the form

$$\text{Acid} \rightarrow \text{Hydrogen nucleus} + \text{Base},$$

and basic behavior is of the form

$$\text{Hydrogen nucleus} + \text{Base} \rightarrow \text{Acid}.$$

In practice there must be something to supply the hydrogen nucleus in the lower equation and that something is, by definition, another acid.

When this acid has given up the hydrogen nucleus, the product left behind is a base. Similar considerations apply to the upper equation. In either case, therefore, the reaction has the form

$$(\text{Acid})_1 + (\text{Base})_2 \rightarrow (\text{Base})_1 + (\text{Acid})_2.$$

A pair of concrete examples will make this matter clear:

$$\underset{\text{Acid}_1}{HCl} + \underset{\text{Base}_2}{H_2O} \rightarrow \underset{\text{Base}_1}{Cl^-} + \underset{\text{Acid}_2}{H_3O^+}$$

Here H_2O, acting as a base, takes a hydrogen nucleus from HCl, which plays the role of an acid; the result is the ion H_3O^+, which is an acid because it could give up its hydrogen nucleus, and Cl^-, which could accept one. Similarly,

$$\underset{\text{Acid}_1}{HCl} + \underset{\text{Base}_2}{NH_3} \rightarrow \underset{\text{Base}_1}{Cl^-} + \underset{\text{Acid}_2}{NH_4^+}$$

In this second example, no water is involved, and the product is a pair of ions that constitute a salt; it is apparent that the Brönsted approach to acids and bases is much more general than the classical one.

It is clear from the examples, as well as from mere thought, that when an acid molecule has given up a hydrogen nucleus it has changed into a base, because it can take a hydrogen nucleus back again when suitable conditions prevail. A Brönsted acid and base are called *conjugate* if they are related by the transformation

$$\text{Hydrogen nucleus} + \text{Base} \rightleftharpoons \text{Acid}.$$

Table 60–I lists some Brönsted acids and their conjugate bases.

TABLE 60–I

SOME BRÖNSTED ACIDS AND THEIR CONJUGATE BASES

Acid (↑ Stronger)	Base (↓ Stronger)
Acetonium ion, $CH_3COOH_2^+$	Acetic acid, CH_3COOH
Perchloric acid, $HClO_4$	Perchlorate ion, ClO_4^-
Hydrogen chloride, HCl	Chloride ion, Cl^-
Sulfuric acid, H_2SO_4	Bisulfate ion, HSO_4^-
Hydronium ion, H_3O^+	Water, H_2O
Bisulfate ion, HSO_4^-	Sulfate ion, SO_4^{--}
Acetic acid, CH_3COOH	Acetate ion, CH_3COO^-
Ammonium ion, NH_4^+	Ammonia, NH_3
Water, H_2O	Hydroxide ion, OH^-
Ethyl alcohol, C_2H_5OH	Ethoxide ion, $C_2H_5O^-$
Ammonia, NH_3	Amide ion, NH_2^-

There are several points of interest in Table 60–I. In the first place, some molecules and ions appear both as acids and as bases. This situation is not entirely new; even in the Arrhenius theory, water had to be considered as both an acid and a base. If a substance is capable of acting as either an acid or a base, its actual behavior will depend on its environment. Water acts as a base when it accepts a hydrogen nucleus from hydrogen chloride, but it acts as an acid when ammonia is dissolved in it, in which case it gives up hydrogen nuclei to form the ions NH_4^+ and OH^-.

It would be more in accord with modern thought to use "acid" as an adjective instead of a noun, and to say "X shows acid behavior" instead of "X is an acid." Such usage sometimes occurs, but it is still usual to say that certain substances are acids.

Table 60–I ranks Brönsted acids and bases in a certain order. Any acid in the list will lose a hydrogen nucleus more readily than the one below it. Therefore the acids at the top of the list exhibit acid behavior more strongly than the ones below them. For example, since HCl loses a hydrogen nucleus more readily than H_3O^+ does, the equilibrium

$$HCl + H_2O \rightleftharpoons H_3O^+ + Cl^-$$

will prevail only when the ions on the right far outnumber the molecules on the left. According to Arrhenius, the "strong" acids are those that undergo nearly complete ionization in water. They are the ones that lie above H_3O^+ in Table 60–I. The conceptions of Brönsted are therefore in accord with those of Arrhenius, as far as acids are concerned, but the Brönsted scheme goes much further: it applies to ionization of acids not only in water but also in other solvents; for example, in sulfuric acid, acetic acid, or ammonia.

The great difference between the conceptions of Arrhenius and of Brönsted lies in the realm of bases. Brönsted pointed out that the hydroxide radical is in no way unique, except in relation to water. In water solutions, the hydroxide ion is the conjugate base of the solvent molecule. When an acid is dissolved in water, there is a formation of H_3O^+ ions, and these ions are responsible for the acid properties of the solution. The addition of a soluble hydroxide introduces OH^- ions, which combine with the H_3O^+ ions and thus eliminate them. The acid behavior of the solution is thereby decreased, and perhaps entirely neutralized. If an acid is dissolved in ammonia, it can be neutralized by adding NH_2^- ions.

A strong Brönsted base is one that has a great affinity for hydrogen nuclei. It is apparent that if a Brönsted acid is strong, its conjugate base will be weak, because the acid could not readily lose hydrogen nuclei if the base had a strong tendency to hold them.

60–5. The Acid–Base Scheme of Lewis (1923). Brönsted's system of acids and bases rests on the unique properties of the hydrogen atom, which is the only one in which the loss of an electron leaves the nucleus bare. A Brönsted acid is one in which a hydrogen nucleus is weakly bound by electrons that it shares with some other atom. The hydrogen nucleus can transfer from the acid to another molecule or ion (the base) in which there is an electron pair that can be shared. The great American chemist Lewis proposed that the concepts of acid and basic behavior be extended to include any reactions in which there is an exchange of shared pairs. A Lewis base is any molecule or ion having a pair of electrons that it can share. A Lewis acid is any molecule or ion that can accept a share in a pair of electrons. This system finds its chief use in chemical situations that are more complex than the ones that we have discussed in this book. A single example, however, may be of interest; it shows hydrogen chloride in the role of a Lewis base:

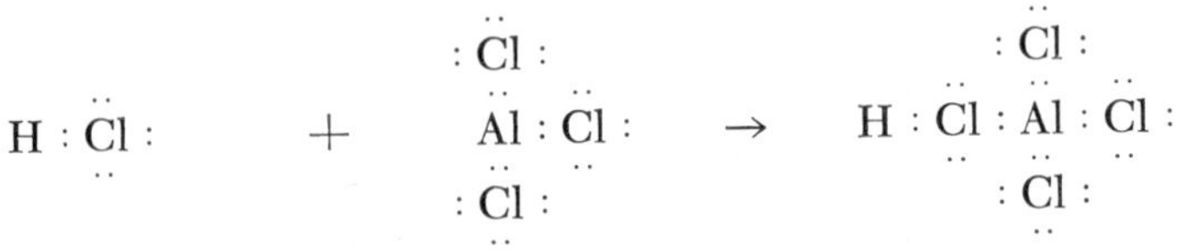

$$\mathrm{H : \underset{\cdot\cdot}{\ddot{Cl}} :} \qquad + \qquad \begin{array}{c} \mathrm{:\ddot{Cl}:} \\ \mathrm{\underset{\cdot\cdot}{\ddot{Al}} : \underset{\cdot\cdot}{\ddot{Cl}} :} \\ \mathrm{:\underset{\cdot\cdot}{Cl}:} \end{array} \qquad \rightarrow \qquad \begin{array}{c} \mathrm{:\ddot{Cl}:} \\ \mathrm{H : \underset{\cdot\cdot}{\ddot{Cl}} : \underset{\cdot\cdot}{\ddot{Al}} : \underset{\cdot\cdot}{\ddot{Cl}} :} \\ \mathrm{:\underset{\cdot\cdot}{Cl}:} \end{array}$$

Donor (Lewis base) — Acceptor (Lewis acid)

60–6. The Uses of Acid-Base Schemes. From the theoretical point of view, it is very satisfying to extend the conception of an acid or a base to make it as comprehensive as possible. Which acid–base scheme one uses in practice will depend on what one is doing. The Arrhenius scheme is correct as far as it goes, but it does not go very far. When supplemented by current knowledge about atomic structure, the Arrhenius scheme is adequate for understanding what happens in water solutions. The Brönsted scheme has the advantage of applying equally well when the solvent is not water, or even when there is no solvent. The Lewis scheme, which is even more comprehensive, finds its principal use in the chemistry of carbon compounds.

Summary

Acids are covalent compounds that become ionized through the transfer of a hydrogen nucleus. Hydrogen is unique because its atom is the only one that has no charge cloud left when it has lost one electron. The ionization of acids in water comes about because their molecules lose hydrogen nuclei, which become hydrated hydrogen ions (hydronium ions). An acid, in the classical sense of Arrhenius, is a substance whose molecules can transfer hydrogen nuclei to water molecules.

Interest in solvents other than water led to the Brönsted definition of an acid: An acid is any matter whose molecules or ions can transfer hydrogen nuclei to other molecules or ions. Brönsted defined a base to be any matter whose molecules or ions can accept a hydrogen nucleus.

He pointed out that in water solutions, a hydroxide ion owes its importance to the fact that by acquiring a hydrogen nucleus, it turns into a solvent molecule. In solvents other than water, the hydroxide ion has no special significance.

In the Brönsted scheme, acids and bases are defined by the relation

$$\text{Hydrogen nucleus} + \text{Base} \rightleftharpoons \text{Acid}.$$

Two molecules or ions that satisfy this relation are said to be conjugate; each acid has its conjugate base, and vice versa.

Lewis acids are molecules, atoms, or ions that can acquire a share in a pair of electrons, and a Lewis base is a molecule, atom, or ion that has a pair of electrons that it can share.

The acid–base scheme of Arrhenius is satisfactory only with respect to water solutions. The Brönsted scheme, which is as simple as that of Arrhenius, is superior because it applies even when the solvent is not water. The more comprehensive scheme of Lewis extends the acid–base concept to reactions that do not involve hydrogen. Its chief use lies in the chemistry of carbon compounds.

Questions

1. Account for the fact that acids, which are covalent compounds, form ions when dissolved in water.
2. In what respect does an ion of hydrogen differ from other ions encountered in solutions?
3. State Brönsted's definition of an acid and of a base.
4. How does the Brönsted conception of an acid differ from the classical conception that was formulated by Arrhenius?
5. Why is the Brönsted acid–base scheme an improvement on the classical one?
6. Explain the special significance of the hydroxide ion.
7. Write equations to describe the production of ions when each of the following is dissolved in water: nitric acid, acetic acid, sulfuric acid. (Use two steps in the last one.)
8. Compare an acid–base reaction, in the sense of Brönsted, with an oxidation–reduction reaction.
9. How do the so-called strong acids differ from other acids?
10. By reference to Table 60–I, write equations for the ions that are produced when (a) acetic acid is dissolved in sulfuric acid, no water being present; (b) acetic acid is dissolved in liquid ammonia, no water being present. In each of the resulting solutions, what ion is the Brönsted acid?
11. Discuss the ions in a water solution of sodium acetate. What effect do you think the solution would have on litmus paper?
12. How does the Lewis conception of an acid resemble that of Brönsted? How do the two differ?

61

THE HYDROCARBONS

The difference of Bodies may depend meerly upon that of the schemes whereinto their Common matter is put.

BOYLE

Any survey of a modern science would be incomplete if it included no examples of applied science. Many of the physical principles we have studied have useful applications that are obvious and familiar, but so far our discussion of chemical behavior has been on a somewhat abstract level. To strike a balance, it will be proper to discuss some of the technological aspects of chemistry. We are now in a fine position to do this meaningfully, because you have an understanding of molecular structure. You know how molecules are formed, and how their structure can be investigated. This knowledge is basic to any appreciation of chemical technology, because the fitness of a product for industrial or domestic use depends very much on its physical properties, and, as the next few chapters will show, the physical properties of a substance are determined by its structure.

Of the substances that are familiar through household use, the overwhelming majority are compounds of carbon. In order to be dealing with a limited and coherent topic, we shall confine our attention to this class of compounds.

Carbon has such distinctive chemical properties that the study of its compounds forms a recognized profession in itself. It is called "organic" chemistry, because it began with substances that had some connection with living organisms. Until 1828, it was thought that these substances could be formed only by the life processes of plants or animals. In that year, however, a professor in Berlin synthesized one of them (urea) in the laboratory. For the next century, Germany led the world in organic chemistry; activity in the science is now more widely diffused, with the United States playing a leading part.

Carbon owes its exceptional position in chemistry to a combination of two factors: it can form four shared-pair bonds per atom, and the bond between two carbon atoms is stronger than most bonds between like atoms. These two qualities enable carbon to make up the framework of notably large and varied molecular structures. About half a million different compounds of carbon are now described in the chemical literature, as against only three or four thousand compounds of all other elements together.

The *hydrocarbons* are the compounds that contain only carbon and hydrogen. They come chiefly from two raw materials, petroleum and coal. The carbon skeleton of the molecule may be a simple, or "normal," chain, a branched chain, or a ring structure.

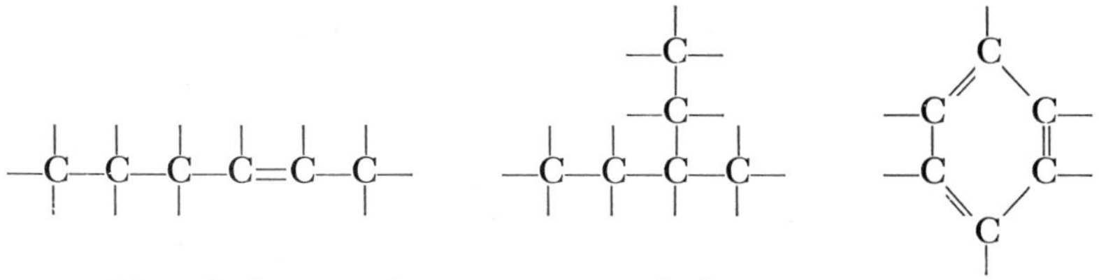

Normal Chain — Branched Chain — Ring Structure

In these diagrams and in those that follow, all valence bonds of carbon represent attachment to hydrogen, unless otherwise indicated.

Chain Hydrocarbons

The four bonds of a carbon atom suffice to attach it to at most four other atoms. The carbon atom may be attached to only three or two other atoms, if the bonds are double or triple ones. It is useful to distinguish the compounds containing multiple bonds from those that contain only single bonds. Compounds that have no multiple bonds in their structure are called *saturated*; the others are *unsaturated*.

61–1. Saturated Chain Hydrocarbons. Saturated chain hydrocarbons may have structures like those in Figure 61–A. It is easy to see that the

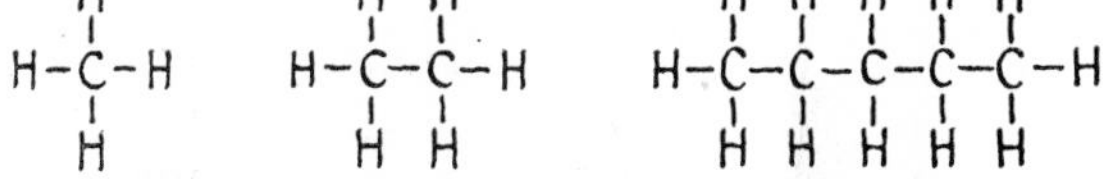

```
  H          H H            H H H H H
  |          | |            | | | | |
H-C-H      H-C-C-H        H-C-C-C-C-C-H
  |          | |            | | | | |
  H          H H            H H H H H
```

FIGURE 61–A. Some saturated simple-chain hydrocarbons: methane, ethane, and pentane.

formula for any of them has the form C_nH_{2n+2}, where n is some integer. A whole series of such compounds exists; Table 61–I gives the names, formulas, freezing points, and boiling points of the first few members of the series, which is called "the methane series."

TABLE 61-I

SOME SATURATED HYDROCARBONS

Name	Formula	Freezing Point	Boiling Point
Methane	CH_4	−184° C	−161° C
Ethane	C_2H_6	−172	− 88
Propane	C_3H_8	−190	− 42
Butane	C_4H_{10}	−135	− 0.5
Pentane	C_5H_{12}	−132	36
Hexane	C_6H_{14}	− 94	69
Heptane	C_7H_{16}	− 91	98
Octane	C_8H_{18}	− 57	126
Nonane	C_9H_{20}	− 54	150
Decane	$C_{10}H_{22}$	− 31	174
Hexadecane	$C_{16}H_{34}$	18	287
Tetracosane	$C_{24}H_{50}$	51	324

At room temperature, the first four members of the methane series are gases, and the next few are liquids; at about the sixteenth member, hexadecane, they become solids. The melting points, as well as the boiling points, increase as the molecules get larger, because of the increase in van der Waals attractions.

Standard Oil Co. of New Jersey

FIGURE 61-B. A catalytic-cracking plant.

Methane and ethane are constituents of natural gas, and they are much used as fuel in the home and in industry. Propane and butane are sold as bottled gas for rural use. Pentane, hexane, and heptane find industrial use as solvents. Gasoline consists mostly of octane and its immediate neighbors in the series, and the slightly larger molecules, up to about hexadecane ($C_{16}H_{34}$), form the bulk of kerosene. As the molecules get larger, the chain hydrocarbons go successively through the light fuel oils, the light and heavy lubricating oils, the light and heavy greases, and the paraffin waxes.

When they are heated at high pressure in the absence of air, the large hydrocarbon molecules break up into smaller ones, with some carbon left over. This process is called "cracking"; the presence of a suitable catalyst permits hydrogen atoms to be added to the molecular fragments, so that no carbon is left over. By allowing the refineries to turn less valuable hydrocarbons into gasoline, catalytic cracking more than doubles our supply of this fuel. It is carried out in apparatus like that in Figure 61–B. By varying the cracking process, the oil chemist can foster the production of other useful substances that are not abundant in crude oil.

61–2. Isomers. In inorganic chemistry, molecules that have the same formula usually have the same structure. Among the carbon compounds, it is normal to find several different structures that fit a given formula. Even though their formula is the same, substances with different structures have different properties, and they have to be classified as different substances. Compounds that have the same formula and different structures are called *isomers*. As an example, consider the possible pentanes. Their formula is C_5H_{12}, and their structures are:

```
                                  |                         |
                                 —C—                       —C—
   |  |  |  |  |            |  |  |  |                |  |  |
 —C—C—C—C—C—              —C—C—C—C—                  —C—C—C—
   |  |  |  |  |            |  |  |  |                |  |  |
                                                         —C—
                                                          |
```

As the number of carbon atoms increases, the number of possible isomers goes up very rapidly. In order to keep track of them, a vocabulary has had to be invented.

61–3. Nomenclature of the Chain Hydrocarbons. The International Union of Chemistry has agreed on a systematic vocabulary that is used in organic chemistry throughout the world. A few simple rules govern the naming of chain hydrocarbons. The stem of the name indicates the number of carbon atoms in the chain. The stems for the simplest compounds are remnants of an older nomenclature: *meth–* indicates one carbon atom; *eth–*, two; *prop–*, three; *but–*, four. Stems designating the longer chains are named after the Greek (or, rarely, Latin) numbers: *pent–* indicates five carbon atoms in the chain; *hex–*, six; *hexatetracont–*, forty-six.

To the stem is attached an ending that designates the degree of saturation in the chain. For a saturated chain, the ending is *–ane*. Thus we have methane, pentane, hexatetracontane, as examples of chain hydrocarbons with no multiple bonds.

Each hydrocarbon has a related radical, which resembles the hydrocarbon but has one less hydrogen atom. One carbon atom of the radical has an unshared electron that can form a bond with some other atom. The radical is designated by the ending *–yl* attached to the appropriate stem:

CH_4	methane	$—CH_3$	methyl
C_2H_6	ethane	$—C_2H_5$	ethyl
C_3H_8	propane	$—C_3H_7$	propyl

When the skeleton of a hydrocarbon is a branched chain, the substance has two names. The first is formed in the manner just described. This name does not differentiate isomers from one another. The other name affords a complete description of the molecule. Its ending is the name of the longest normal chain, formed according to the rules given above. To this part of the name are prefixed the names of the side chains. The points of attachment of the side chains are specified by giving serial numbers to the carbon atoms in the main chain; the appropriate number is prefixed to the name of each side chain.

The system is much less complicated to use than it is to describe. A few examples, the isomers of pentane, will make it clear:

```
                                    |                      |
                                  —C—                    —C—
 |  |  |  |  |                    |  |  |  |              |  |  |
—C—C—C—C—C—                    —C—C—C—C—              —C—C—C—
 |  |  |  |  |                    |  |  |  |              |  |  |
                                                         —C—
                                                           |
```

Normal pentane, a chain of five carbons, with no additional groups.

A butane with a methyl group on the second carbon. Hence its full name is 2-methylbutane

A propane with two methyl groups on the second carbon. Its full name is 2,2-dimethylpropane, because it is a chain of three atoms with two methyl groups added, and both of them are on the second carbon of the propane chain.

The full name of a compound is a description of its structure; given the name, we can easily write down the structural formula. For example, the name 2,2,4-trimethylpentane implies a chain of five carbon atoms with three methyl groups added, two on the second carbon in the main chain and one on the fourth. Therefore the structural skeleton is

```
      |     |
     —C—   —C—
  |   |  |  |   |
 —C—C—C—C—C—
  |   |  |  |   |
     —C—
      |
```

The substance is one of the octanes. Actually, it is the one upon which the octane rating of gasolines is based.

61–4. Unsaturated Chain Hydrocarbons. The unsaturated chain hydrocarbons are the ones that contain at least one double or triple bond between carbon atoms. There are many series of such substances, of which a few will be of interest in what follows.

The chain hydrocarbons that have just one multiple bond, and that a double one, are designated by the ending *–ene.* The first member of the series is ethene, the second is propene, and so on, the group as a whole being called "the ethene series."

```
H       H              H  H     H
 \     /               |  |    /
  C=C               H—C—C=C
 /     \               |       \
H       H              H        H
 Ethene                Propene
```

If a chain hydrocarbon has one triple bond, and no other multiple bonds, it is designated by a name ending in *–yne.* The only member of this series that is of general interest is ethyne, called commercially by its older name, acetylene. It is widely used as a fuel in welding operations and as a starting substance in the manufacture of other organic compounds.

When a chain hydrocarbon contains one or more multiple bonds, it is often desirable to state where they are. The full name of the substance contains numbers that designate the position of any multiple bonds in the chain.

```
                                                  |
                                                 —C—
 |   |   |   |                |  |                |  |
—C—C=C—C—         —C≡C—C—C—         —C≡C—C—C—
 |           |                |  |                |  |
  2-butene              1-butyne           3-methyl-1-butyne
```

The *dienes* are chain hydrocarbons that contain just two double bonds.

```
 |   |   |   |
—C=C—C=C—
```

The only one that will interest us has the structure —C=C—C=C—. Often it is simply called "butadiene," although properly speaking it is 1,3-butadiene because bonds 1 and 3 are the double ones.

61–5. Addition. Through the conversion of a double bond to single ones, an unsaturated hydrocarbon can take on more hydrogen until it becomes saturated. A simple example is the conversion of ethene to ethane:

$$\begin{array}{ccccccccc} & \mathrm{H} & \mathrm{H} & & & & \mathrm{H} & \mathrm{H} & \\ & | & | & & & & | & | & \\ \mathrm{H}- & \mathrm{C} = & \mathrm{C} & -\mathrm{H} & + \ \mathrm{H}-\mathrm{H} \ \rightarrow & \mathrm{H}- & \mathrm{C} - & \mathrm{C} & -\mathrm{H} \\ & & & & & & | & | & \\ & & & & & & \mathrm{H} & \mathrm{H} & \end{array}$$

Energy has to be supplied to break one member of the double bond, but the formation of bonds with the added hydrogen atoms liberates somewhat more energy. The over-all reaction is therefore exothermic; once it has been started, it can operate as a self-sustaining reaction (Article 27–8). The rate of reaction is faster in the presence of a catalyst that aids in the dissociation of the hydrogen.

Reactions like this one, which result in the addition of hydrogen to a hydrocarbon, are simply called *addition* reactions. They form one of the best indications of the presence of multiple bonds. It is easy to form a mental picture of an addition reaction. Energy given to an unsaturated molecule may go into a change in the electron configuration, such that the electrons in a shared-pair bond cease to be shared.

$$\begin{array}{ccccccc} \mathrm{H} & & \mathrm{H} & & \mathrm{H} & & \mathrm{H} \\ & \diagdown \ \diagup & & & & \diagdown \ \diagup & \\ & \mathrm{C} \vdots \mathrm{C} & & + \text{energy} \rightarrow & & \mathrm{C} : \mathrm{C} & \\ & \diagup \ \diagdown & & & & \diagup \cdot \ \cdot \diagdown & \\ \mathrm{H} & & \mathrm{H} & & \mathrm{H} & & \mathrm{H} \end{array}$$

When that happens, each carbon atom can form a new shared-pair bond with a hydrogen atom if hydrogen is available.

$$\begin{array}{ccccccccc} & \mathrm{H} & \mathrm{H} & & & & \mathrm{H} & \mathrm{H} & \\ & | & | & & & & | & | & \\ \mathrm{H}- & \mathrm{C} - & \mathrm{C} & -\mathrm{H} & + \ 2\dot{\mathrm{H}} \ \rightarrow & \mathrm{H}- & \mathrm{C} - & \mathrm{C} & -\mathrm{H} \ + \ \text{energy.} \\ & \cdot & \cdot & & & & | & | & \\ & & & & & & \mathrm{H} & \mathrm{H} & \end{array}$$

Instead of taking on more hydrogen, unsaturated molecules can combine with one another. This process, the union of similar simple molecules to form a more complex one, is called *polymerization*. The complex molecule is called a *polymer*. Two ethene molecules, one of them "activated" by the rupture of a shared-pair bond, can combine thus:

$$\begin{array}{ccccccccc} & \mathrm{H} & \mathrm{H} & & & & \mathrm{H} & \mathrm{H} & \\ & | & | & & & & | & | & \\ \mathrm{H}- & \mathrm{C} - & \mathrm{C} & -\mathrm{H} & & \mathrm{H}- & \mathrm{C} - & \mathrm{C} & -\mathrm{H} \\ & \dot{\uparrow} & \dot{\uparrow} & & \longrightarrow & & | & \diagdown & \\ & \mathrm{H} & \mathrm{H} & & & & \mathrm{H} & & \mathrm{H} \\ & \cdot\cdot & | & & & & & \diagdown & | \\ \mathrm{H}- & \mathrm{C} = & \mathrm{C} & -\mathrm{H} & & & \mathrm{H}- & \mathrm{C} = & \mathrm{C}-\mathrm{H} \end{array}$$

The resulting aggregate contains a double bond, so the process can occur again to attach a third molecule, again to attach a fourth, and so on indefinitely. The resulting polymer is *polyethene,* a widely used plastic. There are many other plastics that are polymers.

61–6. Rubber. Natural rubber is a polymer of 2-methyl-1,3-butadiene. The simplest synthetic rubber is made by polymerizing butadiene. The following diagrams show the structures of the butadiene molecule in its ordinary state and in the activated state:

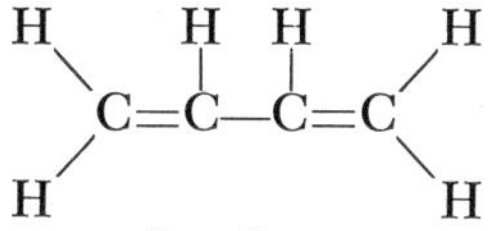

Butadiene

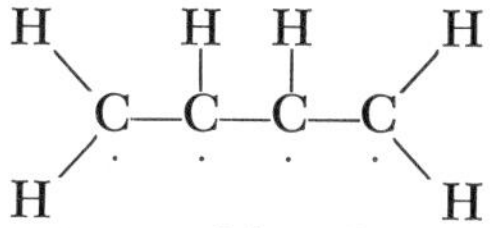

Activated butadiene

After activation, the two carbon atoms in the middle of the chain form another bond with each other, and the carbon atoms on the ends of the chain form single bonds with similar atoms in other molecules. There results a chain like the one in the next diagram, in which the erstwhile butadiene skeletons are marked off with dotted lines.

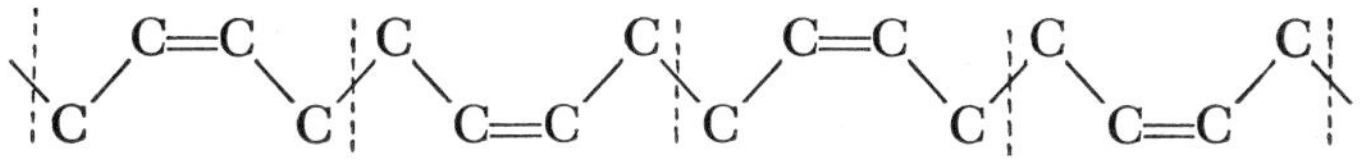

Part of a long chain of carbon atoms in synthetic rubber made from butadiene.

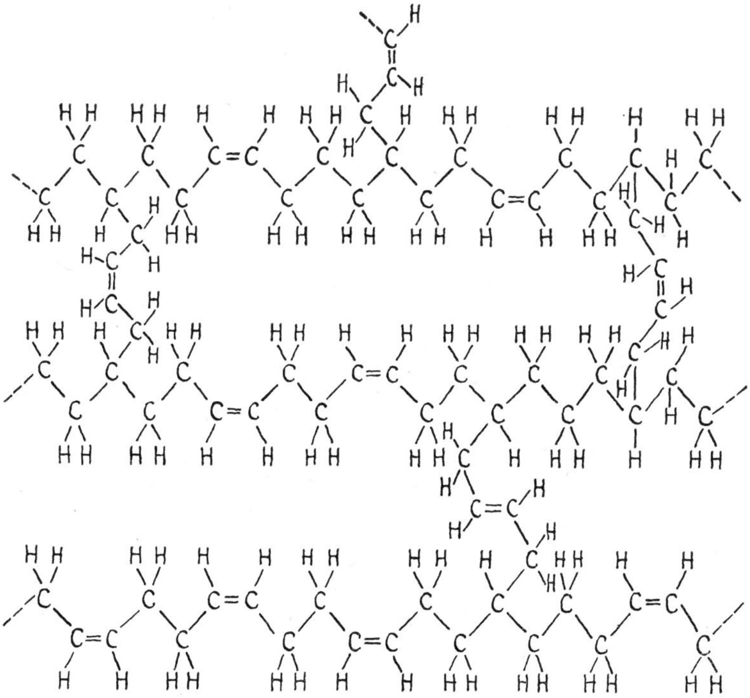

FIGURE 61–C. The structural plan of butadiene rubber.

It is believed that some molecules form cross-links that are attached here and there at places where there would otherwise be double bonds. The resulting polymer is like Figure 61–C. The long chains and occasional cross links make a structure that is flexible and elastic.

The strength and hardness of rubber are increased by the process called "vulcanizing," which incorporates sulfur into the rubber. The function of the sulfur is apparently to form more cross links between the chains, thus tightening up the whole structure.

Aromatic Hydrocarbons

Although there are many kinds of ring skeletons, the ones that are of most general interest have rings like the one on page 529. This ring, which has six carbon atoms with alternating double bonds, is called the *benzene ring.* Hydrocarbons built on the benzene ring are called the *aromatic* hydrocarbons. In the past they have come mainly from coal, through the process of destructive distillation, which involves heating the coal in the absence of air. Through catalytic-cracking processes they are now also available from petroleum.

The ring structures, like the chains, form series of compounds that have some general formula in common. We shall deal here only with a few aromatic substances that will be useful in the chapters that follow.

61–7. Some Simple Aromatic Hydrocarbons. The simplest aromatic hydrocarbon is *benzene,* which may be regarded as a fundamental framework that forms the basis for a host of other aromatic compounds. It was discovered by Faraday. The structural formulas for benzene and another simple aromatic compound are:

```
          H                            H
          |                            |
          C                            C
        // \                         // \
    H—C      C—H                 H—C      C—CH3
      |      ||                    |      ||
    H—C      C—H                 H—C      C—H
        \\  /                        \\  /
          C                            C
          |                            |
          H                            H
       Benzene                      Toluene
```

Toluene can be regarded as related to benzene through the replacement of a hydrogen atom by a methyl radical. Both are widely used as solvents.

The structural formulas show double bonds in the rings, but it has long been known that the bonds in the rings do not behave like the ones in unsaturated chains. The rings are exceptionally stable structures. In most reactions, they behave as units; the double bonds in a ring do not easily become activated.

To simplify the structural diagrams, it is customary to represent benzene by a hexagon, ⬡, which stands for the ring of carbon atoms with alternate double bonds and with a hydrogen atom attached to each carbon. If something other than hydrogen is attached, it is shown explicitly in the diagram. Thus, toluene is represented by ⬡—CH_3.

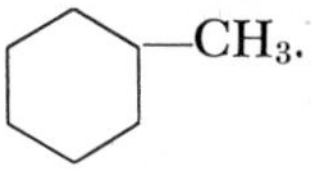

Ring compounds can be built up from benzene in two ways: some or all of the hydrogen atoms on the ring may be replaced by more complex groups ("substitution"), and the rings may join together by sharing sides ("condensation"). Toluene is an example of the first kind of elaboration. The second kind has as its simplest exemplar the substance naphthalene, ⬡⬡, from which moth balls are made.

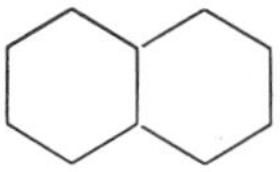

61–8. Aromatic Isomers. When more than one hydrogen atom on a benzene ring is replaced, by substitutions, we need a way to specify their locations. It will be sufficient here to consider the naming of compounds in which there have been just two substitutions on the ring. An example will make the nomenclature clear.

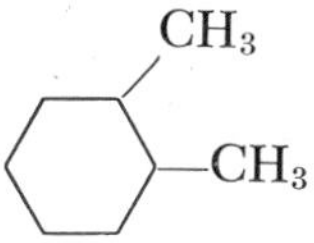

CH_3 CH_3 — *o*-xylene

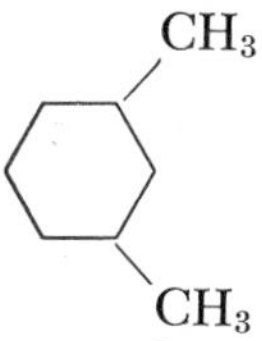

CH_3 CH_3 — *m*-xylene

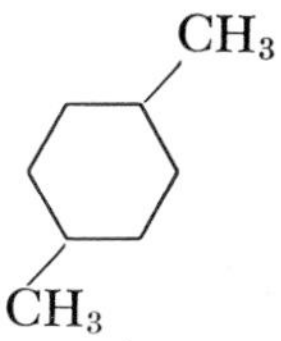

CH_3 CH_3 — *p*-xylene

In all such cases, there are three possible isomers, and they are distinguished by the prefix *ortho-*, *meta-*, or *para-*, depending on whether the substituted groups on the ring are adjacent, separated by one carbon, or opposite. This nomenclature applies to all substituted benzenes, not only to the pure hydrocarbons. Thus paradichlorobenzene, a popular moth-repellant, has the structure

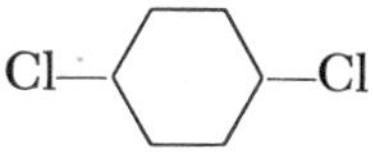

Cl—⬡—Cl

Summary

Organic chemistry is the study of carbon compounds. The compounds that contain only carbon and hydrogen are called hydrocarbons; in some, the carbon skeleton is a chain, and in others the skeleton contains one or more rings. The chain compounds are classified as unsaturated or saturated, depending on whether or not any multiple bonds are present.

Among the chain hydrocarbons, there are many series of compounds that have the same general structure but differing numbers of carbon atoms. Except in the simplest chains, the same assortment of carbon and hydrogen atoms can join together in more than one way; the compounds so formed are called isomers.

In the names of chain compounds, there is a stem that designates the number of carbon atoms in the chain. The stems meth–, eth–, prop–, but–, pent–, hex–, and so on, indicate one, two, three, four, five, six, and so on, atoms of carbon in the chain. The bonding system in the chain is shown by the ending of the name: –ane stands for a saturated chain; –ene indicates the presence of one double bond; and similarly for other possible chains. There is a concise system for the naming of isomers.

In the series of saturated hydrocarbons, the members with low molecular weight are used as gaseous fuels in domestic and industrial heating. At ordinary temperatures, the members with somewhat longer chain skeletons are liquids; they are used as gasoline, fuel oil, and lubricating oils. The still more complex members make up the heavy greases and the paraffins.

In the unsaturated chains, the multiple bonds can be converted into single ones by adding atoms to the molecule. The conversion of multiple bonds to single ones also makes possible the bonding of one molecule to another similar one; this process, called polymerization, is the basis for many plastics, including natural and synthetic rubber.

The aromatic hydrocarbons are built on a ring of six carbon atoms with alternating double bonds. The simplest aromatic hydrocarbon is benzene, which can be regarded as forming the foundation of all other aromatic compounds. The others may be related to benzene by substitution or by condensation. The substituted compounds are those in which some other atom or radical takes the place of a hydrogen atom in the benzene structure. A condensed compound is one in which there are two or more rings, and each ring shares two carbon atoms with another ring.

Questions

1. Compare the structures of branched chains and aromatic rings with the structures of diamond and graphite (Article 56–3).
2. State two properties of the carbon atom that enable it to form the basis of an extraordinarily large number of compounds.
3. Distinguish between saturated and unsaturated chain compounds, and give the structural formula for one example of each. Why is "saturated" an appropriate term?

4. The formula C_nH_{2n+2} covers any saturated chain hydrocarbon, if n is an integer chosen to fit the particular substance in question. Using this formula, write an equation to represent the burning of gasoline. (One of the products is carbon dioxide.)
5. Draw structural formulas and give the full names for the isomers of hexane.
6. Why can there not be a substance that the rules of nomenclature would name "methene"?
7. Draw the structural formulas for ethyne and 1,2-butadiene.
8. Show that the formula for members of the ethene series is C_nH_{2n}, where n is any integer.
9. Draw structural formulas for a pentene and a pentadiene. Give the full name for each.
10. Why is it unnecessary to designate the position of the double bond in ethene or in propene?
11. Draw the structural formulas for as many butyl radicals as you can.
12. Draw structural formulas for 1,3-pentadiene and 2,3-dimethylhexane.
13. Point out some relations between the structures and the properties of various organic substances.
14. What is responsible for the similar properties of natural and synthetic rubber?
15. Draw a sketch that shows the structure of the plastic called "polystyrene." Styrene has the structural formula

H
C=C
H H

16. How are benzene, toluene, and xylene related?
17. What do the prefixes *ortho-*, *meta-*, and *para-* signify in respect to a ring compound?
18. Draw the structural formula for naphthalene, showing each atom.

Suggestion for Further Reading

James Bryant Conant and A. H. Blatt, *The Chemistry of Organic Compounds* (New York: Macmillan Co., 1952). Chapters 1 and 21 of this college textbook cite simple examples of how chemical evidence gives clues to the structure of an organic compound.

62

HYDROCARBON DERIVATIVES

Looking upon Chymistry in the gross, as a Discipline subordinate to Physiques, even Mechanical Philosophers may justly, in my opinion, think favourably of it, since, whatever Imperfections, or, if they please, Extravagancies there may be in the Principles and Explications of Paracelsus or other Leading Artists, these faults of the Theoretical part may be sufficiently compensated by the Utilities that may be derived from the Practical part.

BOYLE

It is not uncommon for an organic compound to have a structure like that of some hydrocarbon, except that in one or more places where the hydrocarbon has a hydrogen atom, the other compound will have a different atom or a group of atoms. A compound that can thus be related to a hydrocarbon is called a *hydrocarbon derivative.* Paradichlorobenzene,

TABLE 62–I

SOME HYDROCARBON DERIVATIVES AND THEIR FUNCTIONAL GROUPS

Class	Functional Group
Alcohols and Phenols	—OH
Ethers	—O—
Acids	$-C\begin{matrix} \nearrow O \\ \searrow O-H \end{matrix}$ (—C(=O)—O—H)
Esters	$-C\begin{matrix} \nearrow O \\ \searrow O- \end{matrix}$ (—C(=O)—O—)
Aldehydes	$-C\begin{matrix} \nearrow O \\ \searrow H \end{matrix}$ (—C(=O)—H)
Amines	$-NH_2$

mentioned in Article 61–8, is an example. This chapter will consider some of the other hydrocarbon derivatives that have a significance in everyday life.

62–1. Functional Groups. Any hydrocarbon derivative has two important aspects; one is its carbon skeleton, and the other is the feature of its composition that differentiates it from a hydrocarbon. In simple cases, this feature is a single atom or group, which is called a *functional group* because it plays a major part in determining the chemical behavior of the compound. The functional groups form a basis for classifying the hydrocarbon derivatives. A few of the important classes of derivatives are listed in Table 62–I, together with the functional groups that identify them.

62–2. Alcohols and Phenols. The alcohols are among the simplest and most instructive hydrocarbon derivatives. They have an —OH group in place of one of the hydrogen atoms in a chain hydrocarbon. There are two that are particularly worth considering:

```
     H                 H  H
     |                 |  |
  H—C—OH            H—C—C—OH
     |                 |  |
     H                 H  H
```

Methanol (methyl alcohol) Ethanol (ethyl alcohol)

The alcohols and other hydrocarbon derivatives take their names from the parent hydrocarbon. The formal names of the alcohols are made up by adding *-ol* to the stem that characterizes the parent, but they often are called by older names.

Methanol (methyl alcohol) is also known as "wood alcohol," since it used to be obtained mainly by the destructive distillation of wood. It is now produced in large quantities by the direct union of hydrogen with carbon monoxide, in the presence of a catalyst. The equation for the reaction is

$$2H_2 + CO \rightarrow CH_3OH.$$

Methanol is much used as a solvent for shellac and other varnishes, and it plays an important part in the manufacture of other organic compounds. When taken internally, it is highly poisonous, causing blindness or death.

Ethanol (ethyl alcohol, or "grain alcohol") is produced mainly from the fermentation of glucose ($C_6H_{12}O_6$), a sugar found in grains, potatoes, and fruits. The reaction, which is catalyzed by certain substances called "enzymes" that are produced by yeast cells, may be represented by the equation

$$C_6H_{12}O_6 \rightarrow 2C_2H_5OH + 2CO_2.$$

Besides forming the basis of social life in some communities, ethyl alcohol has extensive industrial uses. In Europe, it is not uncommonly used as a fuel.

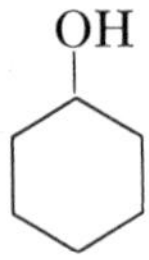

OH
|
(benzene ring)

Phenol

The *phenols* are compounds that have an —OH group on an aromatic ring. Only the simplest one, *phenol,* will be of interest in what follows. This substance, also known as "carbolic acid," comes from the destructive distillation of coal. In very dilute solution in water, it is a useful antiseptic. It is one of the starting materials for the production of many dyes and drugs, and also of certain plastics. To satisfy the demand for phenol for these purposes, it is now being synthesized from petroleum.

Because the —OH group is polar, methanol and ethanol are liquid at room temperature, where methane and ethane are gaseous. Similarly, phenol is solid, whereas benzene is liquid.

62–3. Acids. The organic acids contain the functional group $-C\begin{smallmatrix} \diagup\!\!\diagup O \\ \diagdown OH \end{smallmatrix}$, which is called the "carboxyl" group. Substances containing this group are acids because the hydrogen of the group can be donated (as a nucleus) to basic substances. The reaction between an organic acid and a metallic hydroxide is of the form

$$Na^+ + OH^- + RC\begin{matrix} \diagup\!\!\diagup O \\ \diagdown OH \end{matrix} \rightarrow \left[RC\begin{matrix} \diagup\!\!\diagup O \\ \diagdown O \end{matrix} \right]^- + H_2O + Na^+.$$

Here R stands for any hydrocarbon radical (Article 61–3).

One of the simplest and best-known organic acids is ethanoic acid (CH_3COOH), so called because its carbon skeleton is that of ethane. In this country it is nearly always referred to by its older name, *acetic acid.* It can be formed by oxidation of ethyl alcohol:

$$\begin{matrix} & & H & & H & & \\ & & | & & | & & \\ H & - & C & - & C & - & OH \\ & & | & & | & & \\ & & H & & H & & \end{matrix} + O_2 \rightarrow H_2O + \begin{matrix} & & H & & \\ & & | & & \\ H & - & C & - & C\begin{matrix} \diagup\!\!\diagup O \\ \diagdown OH \end{matrix} \\ & & | & & \\ & & H & & \end{matrix}$$

This is the reaction that makes wine or cider turn to vinegar; it is a process that occurs in nature with the help of enzymes produced by certain bacteria.

The acids derived from the chain hydrocarbons are called "fatty acids," because they are related to fats. Among them are *palmitic acid* (hexadecanoic acid, $C_{15}H_{31}COOH$), *stearic acid* (octadecanoic acid, $C_{17}H_{35}$-$COOH$), and *oleic acid* (9-octadecenoic acid, $C_{17}H_{33}COOH$), which will be of interest in connection with soaps and fats.

Simple examples of acids with aromatic structures are *benzoic acid* and *o*-hydroxybenzoic, or *salicylic*, acid. The latter is interesting because it has two functional groups; it is both an acid and an alcohol.

$$\text{C}_6\text{H}_5\text{—C}\overset{\text{O}}{\underset{\text{OH}}{\diagdown}}$$

Benzoic acid

$$\text{C}_6\text{H}_4(\text{OH})\text{—C}\overset{\text{O}}{\underset{\text{OH}}{\diagdown}}$$

Salicylic acid

62–4. Esters. When an acid reacts with an alcohol, one of the products is water; the other is called an *ester*. If the acid is an organic one, the reaction has the form

$$RCOOH + R'OH \rightarrow RCOOR' + H_2O,$$

where R and R′ are hydrocarbon radicals. As the example shows, the esters of organic acids consist of two hydrocarbon radicals joined through the functional group $\text{—}\overset{\text{O}}{\overset{\|}{\text{C}}}\text{—O—}$. The reaction is often carried out in the presence of sulfuric acid, which removes the water by hydration, thereby preventing the reaction from running backwards.

Experiment. About 0.5 g of pentanol (amyl alcohol) and a like amount of concentrated acetic acid may be mixed with a few drops of concentrated sulfuric acid and warmed for a few minutes in a test tube. After the addition of water and enough sodium hydroxide to neutralize the excess acid, an oil rises to the surface. The oil, which has a powerful banana-like odor, is the ester pentyl acetate, known commercially as amyl acetate and popularly as *banana oil*. It finds extensive use as a solvent in lacquers, including fingernail polish.

Esters are named by reference to the alcohol and the acid from which they derive. Thus we have pentyl acetate, ethyl nitrate, methyl salicylate.

Salicylic acid, being both an acid and an alcohol, can enter into the formation of an ester by playing either role. When it acts as an alcohol and reacts with acetic acid, the resulting ester is salicyl acetate, better known as *aspirin*. When salicylic acid acts as an acid and reacts with methyl alcohol, the resulting ester is methyl salicylate, which is *oil of wintergreen*. This substance exemplifies the fact that esters are responsible for most of the odors of fruits and flowers.

Experiment. About 0.5 g of salicylic acid will react with methyl alcohol under conditions like those in the last experiment. The resulting ester has the odor of wintergreen.

62–5. Amines and the Sulfa Drugs. The amines are compounds in which hydrocarbon radicals take the place of one or more of the hydrogen atoms in the ammonia molecule. We shall consider only the so-called primary amines, in which just one of the hydrogens in an ammonia molecule is replaced by a hydrocarbon radical. They are characterized by the functional group —NH_2. Examples are:

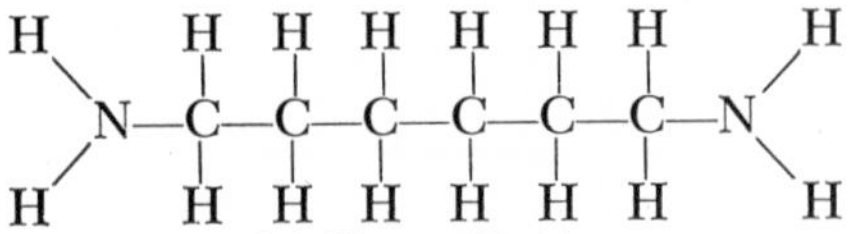

1,6-Hexanediamine

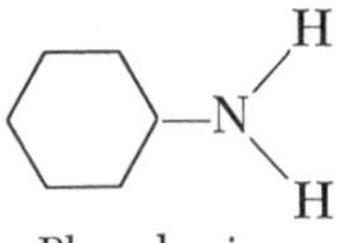

Phenylamine

Some of the amines with chain structures will be of interest in the next chapter. Phenylamine,* or aniline, which comes from coal tar, is a starting material for the manufacture of many dyes. *Sulfanilamide* and *sulfapyridine,* of the famous group of sulfa drugs, are phenylamine derivatives.

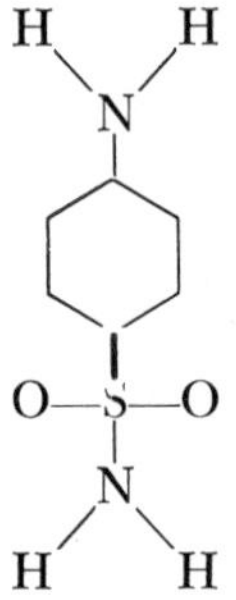

Sulfanilamide
(*p*-aminobenzenesulfonamide)

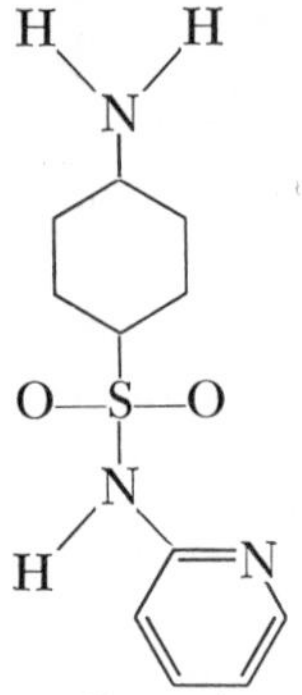

Sulfapyridine

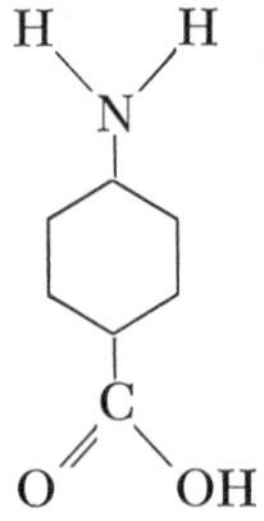

p-Aminobenzoic acid

It is believed that the antibacterial action of the sulfa drugs results from their structure. As the diagrams show, sulfanilamide and sulfapyridine have a structural resemblance to *p*-aminobenzoic acid, which is a nutrient for bacteria. Because of the resemblance, the drugs are taken in by the bacterium along with its natural food. The drug and the acid do differ in their chemical behavior, however, and the difference costs the bacterium its life.

62–6. Some Familiar Plastics. Many of the commonly encountered plastics are made by combining formaldehyde with phenol or with urea. *Formaldehyde* is the common name of oxomethane; it is the simplest and most important of the aldehydes.

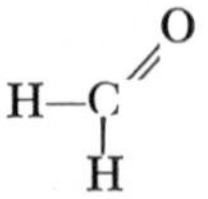

Oxomethane
(formaldehyde)

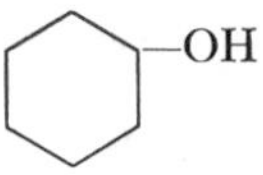

Phenol

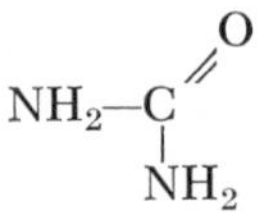

Urea

* The *phenyl* radical is the aromatic radical —C_6H_5, which arises when one hydrogen atom is removed from benzene.

When phenol reacts with formaldehyde, the double bond in formaldehyde turns into two single ones that link together two of the phenol rings. The result is water and a set of linked rings that form indefinitely large molecules; these large molecules constitute a plastic. The reaction is sketched in Figure 62–A.

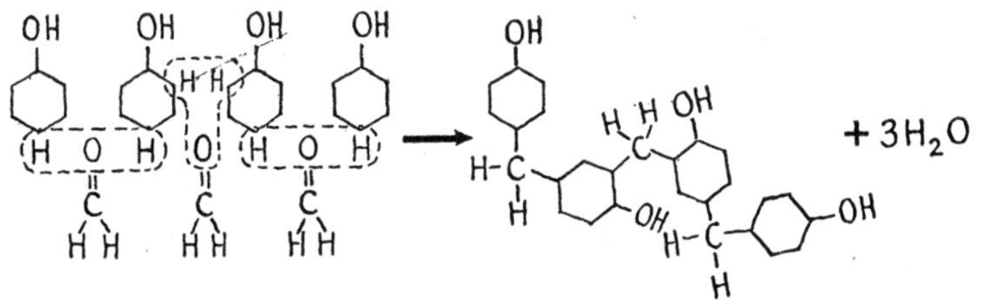

FIGURE 62–A. Molecules of phenol (upper row on left) react with molecules of formaldehyde (lower row on left) to form a plastic and water.

Products ranging from sticky liquids to hard solids may be obtained by varying the conditions of the reaction and the proportions of the ingredients. One of the most widely used phenolic plastics is called *Bakelite*.

By a similar reaction, formaldehyde can react with urea to form long chains, as shown in Figure 62–B. Using a larger proportion of formaldehyde leads to

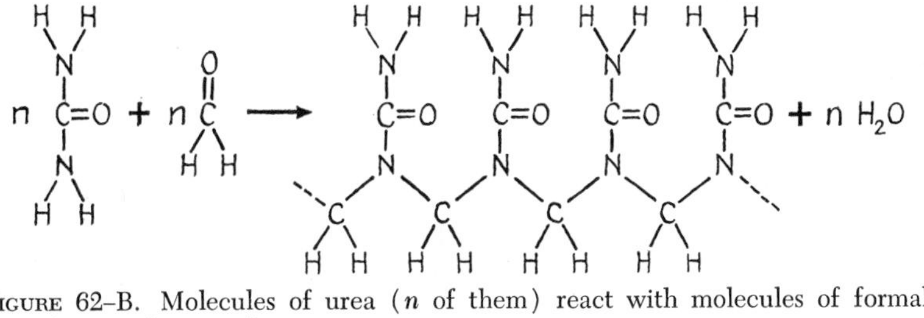

FIGURE 62–B. Molecules of urea (n of them) react with molecules of formaldehyde to form a plastic and water.

the formation of cross links by some of the amine ($—NH_2$) groups, and a more rigid structure results. The hard, shiny plastic thus produced is suitable for tumblers, cups, combs, and similar articles.

62–7. Some Other Hydrocarbon Derivatives. We may close this chapter with a brief description of two complicated hydrocarbon derivatives that everyone has heard of, D.D.T. and T.N.T. The first initials stand for *dichlorodiphenyltrichloroethane*, the second for *trinitrotoluene*. It is easy to see why these compounds are popularly known by simplified names. Note, however, that the popular names give no idea of what the substances are like, whereas the chemical names actually describe the molecular constitution of the compounds.

The complete description of D.D.T. is given by its full name, 1,1,1-trichloro-2,2,-bis(*p*-chlorophenyl)ethane, where "bis" is used instead of "di" because the group in parentheses is a complex one. The full name of T.N.T. is 2,4,6-

trinitrotoluene; to understand its significance, one must know that the prefix "nitro" stands for the functional group $—NO_2$. From the names, we see that the structures are:

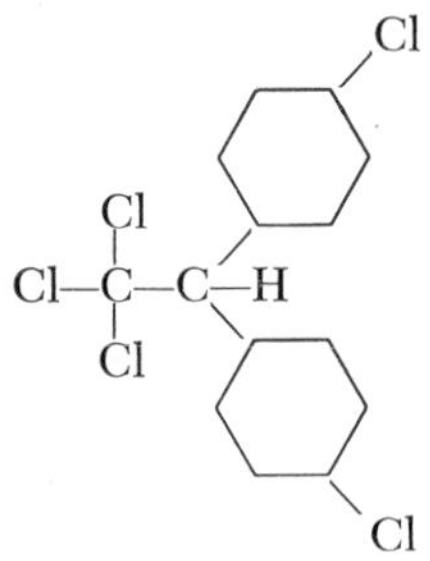

D.D.T.
1,1,1-trichloro-2,2-bis(*p*-chlorophenyl)ethane

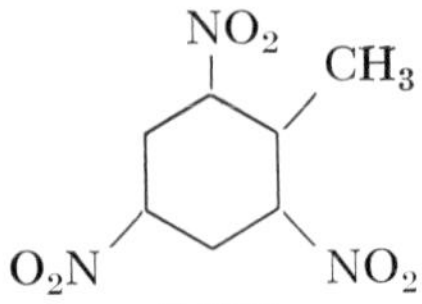

T.N.T.
2,4,6-trinitrotoluene

Like all chemical explosives, T.N.T. contains a large amount of molecular potential energy, which can be converted into molecular kinetic energy. When a molecular breakdown is initiated by a strong shock, some of the oxygen atoms in the T.N.T. molecule pair off with carbon atoms to form carbon monoxide, and the rest of the oxygen atoms find hydrogen partners and form water. As a result, many molecules of gases (CO, H_2O, and N_2) are formed from each molecule of T.N.T. Moreover, the temperature rises greatly, because molecular P.E. is turned into molecular K.E. If the decomposition occurs in a confined space, the increases in the number of molecules and in the temperature cause a tremendous pressure to develop almost instantly, and an explosion results.

Summary

A hydrocarbon derivative is a substance whose molecule is like that of some hydrocarbon, except that in the derivative, some other atom or group takes the place of at least one of the hydrogen atoms in the hydrocarbon molecule.

The classification of hydrocarbon derivatives is based on the atoms or groups that distinguish the derivative from its parent hydrocarbon. Derivatives containing an —OH group are called alcohols and phenols; those containing the group —COOH are called acids, and so on. These substituted groups are called functional groups, because they have an important influence on the behavior of the molecule.

The alcohols are useful chiefly as solvents. Esters, which derive from the reaction of an alcohol with an acid, are responsible for most of the odors of fruits and flowers.

The amines are compounds in which hydrocarbon radicals take the place of one or more of the hydrogen atoms in the ammonia molecule. In the primary amines, the functional group is $—NH_2$. Some of the sulfa drugs are among the many amines that have a bearing on living organisms.

Questions

1. Draw structural formulas for palmitic acid and stearic acid.
2. Draw the structural formula for oleic acid.
3. Explain the alternative name for salicylic acid that is given in the text. Which name do you think is better? Why?
4. Explain how the names 1,6-hexanediamine and *p*-aminobenzoic acid describe the structures of the respective molecules, which are depicted in the text.
5. How is the structure of an alcohol related to the structure of water?
6. Contrast esters with salts.
7. Draw the structural formula for aspirin (salicyl acetate).
8. Draw the structural formula for oil of wintergreen (methyl salicylate).
9. Why is formaldehyde particularly suited to entering into reactions that form plastics?

Suggestion for Further Reading

L. A. Greenberg, "Alcohol in the Body," *Scientific American,* December, 1953, pp. 86–90.

63

FATS, CARBOHYDRATES, AND PROTEINS

The stomach is the true alchemist.
PARACELSUS (*ca.* 1530)

The most important organic compounds are those that constitute our food. These fall mainly into three classes: fats, carbohydrates, and proteins. Other members of the same classes have become important adjuncts of our daily life. It is interesting to see how the useful properties of these materials are related to molecular structure.

FATS

The fats are oily or greasy substances that come from animal or vegetable sources. They are esters, and this fact distinguishes fats from the oils and greases that come from petroleum.

63–1. The Structure of Fats. Esters are related to acids and alcohols in somewhat the same way that salts are related to acids and bases (Article 62–4). The esters that constitute natural *fats* are derived from an alcohol called *glycerol* and one of the acids like palmitic, stearic, or oleic.*

$$\begin{array}{c} \text{H} \\ | \\ \text{H—C—OH} \\ | \\ \text{H—C—OH} \\ | \\ \text{H—C—OH} \\ | \\ \text{H} \end{array} \qquad \begin{array}{c} \text{H} \quad\quad \text{O} \\ | \quad\quad\;\; \| \\ \text{H—C—O—C—}C_{15}H_{31} \\ | \\ \text{H—C—OH} \\ | \\ \text{H—C—OH} \\ | \\ \text{H} \end{array} \qquad \begin{array}{c} \text{H} \quad\quad \text{O} \\ | \quad\quad\;\; \| \\ \text{H—C—O—C—}C_{17}H_{35} \\ | \quad\quad\;\; \text{O} \\ | \quad\quad\;\; \| \\ \text{H—C—O—C—}C_{17}H_{35} \\ | \quad\quad\;\; \text{O} \\ | \quad\quad\;\; \| \\ \text{H—C—O—C—}C_{17}H_{35} \\ | \\ \text{H} \end{array}$$

Glycerol (1,2,3-propanetriol) — Glyceryl 1-monopalmitate — Glyceryl tristearate

* *Waxes* are esters derived from other complex alcohols and the long-chain fatty acids.

These acids, whose formulas are given in Article 62–3, are members of the group called "fatty acids" because of its relation to the fats. They are long-chain compounds with a carboxyl group on one end of the chain. Glycerol (popular name, glycerin) is the alcohol formed by putting an —OH group on each of the carbon atoms in a propane skeleton. Because of its three —OH groups, it is capable of forming fats that contain one, two, or three acid radicals per molecule.

63–2. Sources of Fats. Among the principal sources of fats are tallow, lard, cottonseed oil, palm oil, and olive oil. All of these consist of palmitates, stearates, oleates, and other similar esters, in varying proportions. The animal fats, including butter, consist largely of palmitates and stearates, with some oleates and little else. The vegetable oils contain a larger fraction of oleates, and they also contain esters of other unsaturated fatty acids. "Oils" are distinguished from fats only in being liquid at room temperature or thereabouts, by reason of their higher content of unsaturated substances. The esters of the unsaturated acids have lower melting points than those of the saturated acids.* By adding hydrogen atoms to the unsaturated molecules, it is possible to convert the relatively cheap vegetable oils into solid fats, which are preferred as ingredients for cooking. This process is carried out on a large scale; most of the brand-name shortenings are made from vegetable oils.

63–3. Soap. Any ester will react with sodium hydroxide; the products are the alcohol and the sodium salt of the acid to which the ester is related. If the acid is one of the long-chain fatty acids, its sodium or potassium salt is called a *soap.*

Soap made commercially comes from tallow or from hydrogenated vegetable oils. It is a mixture of sodium salts of fatty acids, mostly the palmitate and the stearate. A reaction for the production of soap is of the form:

$$\underset{\text{Glyceryl tristearate}}{C_3H_5(OOC{-}C_{17}H_{35})_3} + 3NaOH \rightarrow \underset{\text{Glycerol}}{C_3H_5(OH)_3} + \underset{\text{Sodium stearate}}{3C_{17}H_{35}COONa}.$$

The by-product, glycerol, is used in the manufacture of many conveniences, among them inks, cosmetics, cigarettes, and dynamite.

CARBOHYDRATES

The carbohydrates are hydrocarbon derivatives in which the only elements are carbon, hydrogen, and oxygen. They are characterized by the

* The carbon skeleton of a normal-chain compound is not straight, but zigzag. The C—C—C bonds form an angle of 111°; the bonds C—C=C make an angle of 124°. The presence of a double bond therefore causes an irregularity in the zigzags, and consequently hinders the unsaturated molecules from nestling closely together. This effect reduces the strength of the intermolecular forces, making the melting point lower than it would be if all the bonds were single ones.

presence in each molecule of many —OH groups and, usually, an aldehyde group (—CHO) or a ketone group ($>C{=}O$). The carbohydrates that are of greatest general interest are the sugars, the starches, and cellulose, all of which come from plants.

63–4. Sugars. The simplest carbohydrates are called *sugars*; the two principal classes contain six and twelve carbon atoms per molecule. In each class there are many isomers, and these vary in sweetness. Ordinary table sugar, known as *sucrose,* is an isomer of $C_{12}H_{22}O_{11}$. Its structural formula is:

```
                                                          H
                                                          |
                                                       H—C—OH
                                                          |
           OH              OH                          O—C—H
           |               |                          /    |
       H—C————————————————C—H                        /     |
          /                 \                       /      |
   H—C—OH             H—C————————O————————C         |
          \                 /                  /   \       |
       H—C————————————————O                  /     \  H    |
          |                            H—C—H        \ |    |
       H—C—OH                            |           C—C—OH
          |                              OH          |  |
          H                                          OH H
```

Sucrose

Evidence for the structure of sucrose comes from the fact that a molecule of sucrose will react with a molecule of water to produce one molecule of each of the simpler sugars, *glucose* ($C_6H_{12}O_6$) and *fructose* ($C_6H_{12}O_6$), whose structures are:

```
                                                              H
                                                              |
                                                           H—C—OH
                                                              |
       OH               OH                                 O—C—H
       |                |                                 /    |
   H—C————————————————C—H                                /     |
      /                  \                               /      |
H—C—OH             H—C—OH                   HO—C         |
      \                  /                         /  \       |
   H—C————————————————O                          /    \      |
      |                                      H—C—H     \ H   |
   H—C—OH                                     |         \|   |
      |                                       OH         C—C—OH
      H                                                  |  |
                                                         OH H
```

Glucose Fructose

Note how simply a molecule of sucrose can react with one of water to produce glucose and fructose. Our digestive juices contain an enzyme that promotes this breakdown.

The sucrose we use comes from sugar cane or from sugar beets; maple sugar is impure sucrose. Fructose (fruit sugar) and glucose (grape sugar) are present in fruits. In the presence of certain enzymes, they decompose to form carbon dioxide and ethyl alcohol; this process, called "fermentation," is the basis of winemaking and brewing.

Glucose is of special interest because it is the principal fuel on which the human body runs. The body may get the glucose directly, or by the breakdown of sucrose, or by the breakdown of starch.

63–5. Starch. Starch occurs especially in the seeds of plants and in tuberous roots, as in rice, wheat, corn, and potatoes. It is made up of carbon, hydrogen, and oxygen in proportions given by the formula $(C_6H_{10}O_5)_n$, where n may range from perhaps 50 to several thousand. Since starch molecules are not all exactly the same, starch is not a definite substance, but a class of substances.

Starch is of interest because it is one of the basic human foods. Under the action of the digestive juices, the starch molecules break down into fragments that react with water and form glucose, $C_6H_{12}O_6$, which enters the blood stream. Through a variety of intermediate steps, the body oxidizes glucose and converts the liberated energy into heat or work. The over-all reaction is

$$C_6H_{12}O_6 + 6O_2 \rightarrow 6CO_2 + 6H_2O + \text{energy}.$$

The conversion of starch to glucose is also carried out industrially, by heating starch and water, at high pressure, with a catalyst. The reaction produces "corn syrup":

$$\underset{\text{Starch}}{(C_6H_{10}O_5)_n} + \underset{\text{Water}}{nH_2O} \rightarrow \underset{\text{Glucose}}{nC_6H_{12}O_6}.$$

63–6. Cellulose. *Cotton* fibers are nearly pure cellulose; the substance occurs in a less pure state in the woody parts of all plants. Like starch,

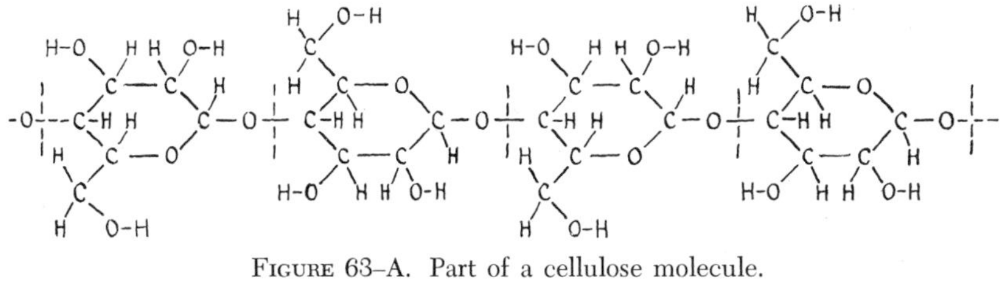

```
                    H  O-H                                     H  O-H
                     \/                                         \/
  H-O   H H  O-H      C             H-O   H H  O-H               C
     \ /   \ /       / \               \ /   \ /                / \
 |    C --- C   H   | H   C --- O   |   C --- C   H         | H   C --- O          |
     /       \ /    |    /        \     /       \ /         |    /         \       |
-O-|--C-H H    C-O-|-- C-H H        C-O-|- C-H H   C-O-|-- C-H H           C-O-|--
 |     \  /      /  |       \    /  \   |   \  /     /      |       \     / \     |
   H    C --- O     |        C --- C   H  H  C --- O        |        C --- C   H
        /                  /  \  / \         /                      /   \ / \
       C              H-O    H H  O-H       C                  H-O    H H  O-H
      / \                                  / \
     H   O-H                              H   O-H
```

Figure 63–A. Part of a cellulose molecule.

it has the molecular formula $(C_6H_{10}O_5)_n$, but the arrangement of the atoms is not the same in cellulose as it is in starch. Cellulose consists of long chains in which each link is closely related to glucose. The difference is that one —OH group on each side of the glucose ring is replaced by —O—; the oxygen bonds join adjacent rings to one another. The cellulose molecule consists of several hundred rings joined end to end (Figure 63–A). Starch consists of rings that are nearly the same as the rings in cellulose, but in starch the rings form branched chains. The differences in their molecular architecture make cellulose and starch behave quite differently. The cellulose molecules pack together to make long crystalline fibers, and many of the uses of cellulose depend on its fibrous structure. Cotton yarn is the simplest example.

Paper is essentially a mat of entangled cellulose fibers. The cellulose comes from wood, straw, or cotton or linen rags. The raw materials are treated mechanically and chemically to remove other substances. Then the cellulose, which has been hydrated by soaking in water, is flowed onto a wire or cloth screen and dried. Some of the water of hydration remains in the paper, where it forms bridges between chains. Bleaches, sizings, fillers, and dyes are used to give properties that suit the cellulose mat to particular uses.

63–7. Cellophane and Rayon. Cellulose treated with sodium hydroxide will react with carbon disulfide to form a cellulose compound that is soluble in sodium hydroxide. The viscous solution so obtained is called "viscose"; when treated with dilute acid to neutralize the hydroxide, viscose reverts to cellulose. The process is useful because it changes the grouping of the cellulose molecules, thereby changing the physical properties of the material. When viscose is forced through a narrow slit into an acid bath, the cellulose takes the form of thin sheets, called Cellophane. If a tiny nozzle is used instead of a slit, the cellulose forms a fine smooth thread that bears a resemblance to silk. The thread is called *viscose rayon.*

Another kind of rayon, *acetate rayon,* is an artificial fiber made of the acetate ester of cellulose. The cellulose acetate is dissolved in acetone (CH_3COCH_3) and sprayed continuously through a fine nozzle into a stream of warm air. The solvent evaporates quickly, leaving a thread of cellulose acetate. In sheets, cellulose acetate serves as the base of photographic film.

Proteins

The proteins are complex substances that contain nitrogen as well as carbon, hydrogen, and oxygen. Some of them also contain other elements, notably phosphorus and sulfur. Their complexity can be judged by their molecular weights, which range from about 30,000 to 1,000,000 or more. They are essential parts of every living cell. As food, they provide material for the rebuilding of body tissue. Their structures are not known, but when boiled with a dilute acid they all react with water to form some much simpler compounds called *amino acids.* This relation to the amino acids is what differentiates proteins from other substances.

63–8. Amino Acids. The compounds known as amino acids are those hydrocarbon derivatives that contain the functional group of an amine and also that of an acid. The structural formulas for two simple ones and a more complex one are:

```
    H    O               H  H    O
    |   //               |  |   //
 H—C—C              H—C—C—C
    |   \                |  |   \
    N    OH              H  N    OH
   / \                     / \
  H   H                   H   H
   Glycine                 Alanine
(aminoethanoic acid)   (2-aminopropanoic acid)
```

```
      I              I
       \              \          H  H    O
        ___            ___       |  |   //
 HO—<     >—O—<     >—C—C—C
        ‾‾‾            ‾‾‾       |  |   \
       /              /          H  N    OH
      I              I             / \
                                  H   H
```

Thyroxine
(2-amino-3[4{3,5-diiodo-4-hydroxyphenoxy}3,5-diiodophenyl]-propanoic acid)

Thyroxine is made in man by the thyroid gland. Lack of iodine in the diet causes a deficiency of thyroxine in the body, resulting in goiter, which is an enlargement of the gland.

The carboxyl group in one amino acid molecule may combine with the amine group of another to form a larger molecule, with water as a by-product.

```
HO    H    H             HO    H    H
  \   |   /                \   |   /
   C—C—N        +           C—C—N        →
  //  |   \                //  |   \
O     H    H             O     H    H
   Glycine                  Glycine

              HO    H       O  H     H
                \   |       ‖  |    /
                 C—C—N—C—C—N        + HOH.
                //  |  |       |    \
              O     H  H       H     H
                    Glycylglycine            Water
```

Since the product of such a reaction is also an amino acid, the process of enlargement can be continued indefinitely. Substances built up in this way are called "peptides." In the presence of an acid and water, the *peptide linkage,* —CONH—, reacts with water to form the groups —COOH and —NH_2; the peptide breaks down into amino acids. This reaction is of course just the reverse of the type shown in the last diagram.

When a protein is treated with water and an acid, it breaks down into simpler molecules, many of which are amino acids. We conclude that proteins are constructed largely of amino acid units bound together by peptide linkages. Not much more is known as yet about the structures of proteins, but the problem is under attack from many sides. When we know how the living organism manages to reproduce such very complicated molecules, we shall probably have a much better understanding of the life process itself.

63–9. Silk and Nylon. The natural proteins have a wide range of properties. Muscle tissue, fingernails, hair, skin, and egg white are all made of proteins. *Silk* is a mixture of proteins secreted as a fiber by the silkworm. When it has been treated for use as yarn, it is nearly a pure substance. When heated with an acid and water, this substance breaks down into amino acids, mostly glycine and alanine. X-ray studies show that the fiber contains a recurring atomic group which is presumably a peptide linkage. The molecules of the fiber are believed to be long chains, a section of which may have the form:

```
      H      O  H     CH3 H     O  H     CH3 H     O
      |      ‖   \   /    |     ‖   \   /    |     ‖
      N      C     C      N     C     C      N     C
    /  \   /  \  /  \   /  \  /  \  /  \   /  \   /  \
        C      N      C      C      N     C      C
      /  \     |      ‖    /  \     |     ‖    /  \
     H    H    H      O   H    H    H     O   H    H
```

Molecules with structure like this are clearly suited to the formation of fibers.

Nylon is an artificial material whose resemblance to silk is based upon its molecular structure. It is made by forming peptide linkages between molecules of a diamine and those of a diacid. The structures of molecules of these types are:

```
H    H  H  H  H  H  H    H        HO    H  H  H  H    OH
 \   |  |  |  |  |  |   /           \   |  |  |  |   /
  N—C—C—C—C—C—C—N                    C—C—C—C—C—C
 /   |  |  |  |  |  |   \           //  |  |  |  |   \\
H    H  H  H  H  H  H    H        O     H  H  H  H    O
     1,6-Hexanediamine                Hexanedioic acid
```

The formation of a peptide linkage between the diamine and the diacid produces water and an amino acid, and the amino acid molecules can combine to form a peptide chain of indefinite length. The result is Nylon:

```
     H            H             H            H
     |            |             |            |
---N—(CH2)6—N             N—(CH2)6—N
                  |             |            |
                  C—(CH2)4—C               C—(CH2)4—C---
                  ‖             ‖            ‖            ‖
                  O             O            O            O
```

When molten, Nylon is pressed through a fine nozzle while cooling, so that it forms a thread, which is then put under tension and stretched to several times its original length. The stretching straightens out the curled-up molecules, aligning them in a fibrous array, and the van der Waals forces keep them in that condition. The fiber is much like silk, but it is cheaper and more durable. Nylon is a vivid example of the organic chemists' ability to custom-build molecules whose structure results in materials that fill specific needs.

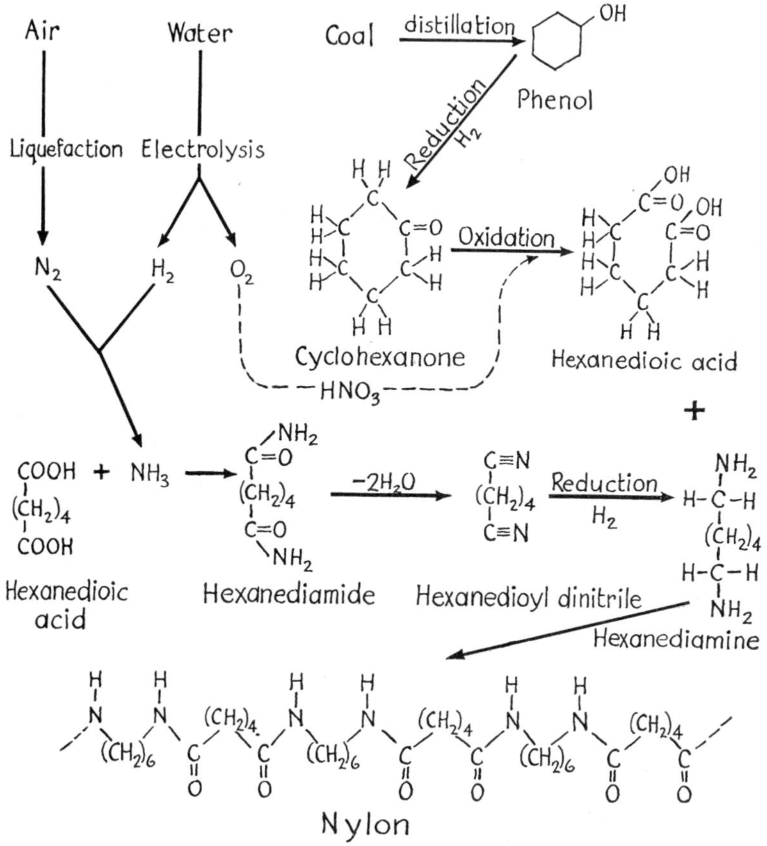

FIGURE 63–B. The synthesis of Nylon from air, water, and coal.

Nylon may be made from coal, water, and air. The first step is to get phenol (Article 62–2) by destructive distillation of the coal. Hydrogen, from water, is added to the ring to form cyclohexanone (Figure 63–B), which is then oxidized to break the ring and produce hexanedioic acid. Treating part of the acid with ammonia replaces the —OH groups in the acid by amine groups, —NH_2, making hexanediamide, which can be used to make hexanediamine. This last substance reacts with the acid that has been kept, and the product is Nylon.

Summary

Fats are esters related to glycerol on the one hand and on the other hand to acids derived from the chain hydrocarbons. We get them from animals and plants. They are used as foods and as raw material for the manufacture of soap. Commercial soap is mostly sodium palmitate and sodium stearate.

The carbohydrates are certain hydrocarbon derivatives that contain only carbon, hydrogen, and oxygen. The simplest of them are called sugars. Starch and cellulose are carbohydrates with molecules that consist of many sugar units bound together. Man's digestive system can break down the starch into a sugar, glucose, that the body uses as fuel. The cellulose molecule is a long chain of sugar units, and because of their structure, cellulose molecules can pack together to form fibers. Cotton yarn and paper exploit the fibrous structure of cellulose. Cellophane and one type of rayon are made by rearranging the cellulose molecules in a way that destroys the fibrous structure.

Amino acids are those hydrocarbon derivatives that contain the functional group of an amine and also that of an acid. They can react with themselves or with one another to form more complex amino acids, a process of enlargement that can be continued indefinitely. The smaller amino acid units are in such cases held together by the functional group —CONH—, which is called the peptide linkage. When treated with water in the presence of an acid, the peptide linkage breaks down.

Because treatment that breaks down a peptide linkage will break down proteins and yield amino acids, proteins are believed to be built up from amino acid units held together by peptide linkages. The structure of proteins is at present a lively subject of research, because they play a vital part in living organisms.

Silk is a fairly simple protein material with a fibrous structure. Nylon consists of smaller man-made molecules that have an architecture similar to that of silk.

Questions

1. What are fats?
2. How are fats related to an alcohol?
3. What are the fatty acids? Name two of them, and state how these two differ.
4. How are vegetable oils made into solid fats for use in the kitchen?
5. How is the existence of cotton fibers related to the structure of cellulose molecules?
6. What is a peptide linkage? How is it related to the amino acids? How is it related to the proteins?

7. Give a brief chemical characterization of: (a) soap, (b) waxes, (c) table sugar, (d) corn syrup, (e) paper, (f) Cellophane, (g) viscose rayon, (h) acetate rayon, (i) silk, (j) Nylon.
8. The solubility of table sugar in water indicates (Article 58–4) that this sugar has polar molecules. To what groups in the sugar molecule can this polar character be attributed? Name another class of substances whose molecules contain this same group. Are familiar members of this class soluble in water?

Suggestions for Further Reading

E. Slosson, *Creative Chemistry* (New York: The Century Co., 1920). Although out of date in its details, this simple book on industrial chemistry is still one of the best.

W. Haynes, *Cellulose: The Chemical that Grows* (Garden City, N. Y.: Doubleday & Co., 1953). An account of the industrial exploitation of cellulose.

L. Pauling, R. B. Corey, and R. Hayward, "The Structure of Protein Molecules," *Scientific American*, July, 1954, pp. 51–59. Superbly illustrated.

Wäre die Natur in ihren leblosen Anfänge nicht so gründlich stereometrisch, wie wollte sie zuletzt zum unberechenbaren und unermesslichen Leben gelangen? *

GOETHE

* If Nature in her lifeless beginnings were not so essentially geometrical, how could she hope to achieve incalculable and immeasurable Life?

64

ENERGY AND LIFE

> Another interesting conclusion is, that the animal frame, though destined to fulfil so many other ends, is as a machine more perfect than the best contrived steam engine—that is, is capable of more work with the same expenditure of fuel.
>
> JOULE (1847)

At various times in our discussion of the world of inanimate things, we have seen that changes in those things can be correlated with changes in energy. We are now in a position to consider also the relations between energy changes and living organisms.

64–1. Photosynthesis. Simple experiments show that plants take water from the ground and carbon dioxide from the air, and convert them into carbohydrates. Oxygen is given off as a waste product. When a carbohydrate burns, it combines with oxygen, and the reaction produces water and carbon dioxide. This latter reaction liberates heat; since this one is exothermic, the reverse reaction that goes on in the plants must be endothermic. Taking sucrose as a typical carbohydrate found in plants, we have:

$$C_{12}H_{22}O_{11} + 12O_2 \underset{\text{Plant grows}}{\overset{\text{Sugar burns}}{\rightleftharpoons}} 12CO_2 + 11H_2O + \text{energy}.$$

These considerations show that in order to build a carbohydrate from carbon dioxide and water, the plant must take in energy. The source of this energy is indicated by the fact that plants will not grow without light. Since light supplies the energy that enables the plant to build carbohydrate molecules, the process is called *photosynthesis*. Although it has been the subject of a great deal of experimental study, photosynthesis has not yet been reproduced in the laboratory, and no trusted theory for the process exists. One thing that seems certain is that the electromagnetic energy of the light is absorbed and converted into chemical energy through the action of chlorophyll, $C_{55}H_{72}O_5N_4Mg$, the green coloring matter in the plants. The complexity of the whole process can be appreciated by noting the complexity of the structural formula for the chlorophyll molecule, in Figure 64–A.

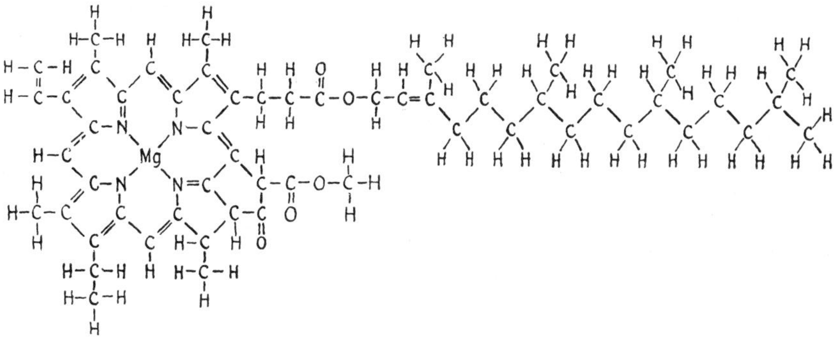

FIGURE 64–A. The chlorophyll molecule.

64–2. Food as Fuel. If we measure what goes into a man and what comes out, we find that the most important chemical change is the disappearance of oxygen and of food consisting largely of carbon and hydrogen, and the appearance of carbon dioxide and water. Very broadly speaking, therefore, the chemical change in man is the reverse of that in a plant.

In a day, a resting man takes in about 1.5 kg of water and 0.7 kg of oxygen, and gives out 2.4 kg of water and 0.8 kg of carbon dioxide. He therefore produces H_2O and CO_2. These products are just what we would get by burning hydrogen and carbon in oxygen. We can calculate the fuel value, in calories, of the hydrogen and carbon the man consumes, and we can put him in a box and measure the amount of heat he gives off. If the man is resting, and not putting on or losing fat, then the heat he gives off is found to be equal to the fuel value of the food he uses up. The heat a resting man gets from the fuel, he gives to his surroundings.

If a man is working, in the mechanical sense, then he needs more fuel. A resting man needs about 2000 calories per day, while a manual laborer may need 5000. In our brief discussion of steam engines (Article 16–3), we mentioned that when heat is converted into work, other heat has to be discarded. The ratio between the work obtained and the total heat put in is called the "efficiency" of the engine. We can measure the efficiency of a man, considering him as an engine, and we find that (from this point of view at least) a man is a very satisfactory contrivance. He has an over-all efficiency, when working hard, of about 25 percent, which is better than most steam engines. As animals go, however, men are not exceptionally efficient; the efficiency of a horse is just about as good.

An animal, of course, is not a steam engine. He is a chemical engine, and a very complicated one. We cannot go into the physiological question of how the body turns heat into work, but it will be interesting to look at the over-all energy situation.

Consider first the source of our personal energy, i.e., our food. All of this energy comes from green plants. Sometimes we eat the plant, sometimes we feed the plant to an animal and then eat him, but it comes to the same thing. We are, in a very real sense, parasites.

By photosynthesis, the plant converts carbon dioxide and water into sugars and other organic substances, and into oxygen which is given off to the air. The energy for this endothermic transformation comes from sunlight. The man or animal that eats the plant reverses this change; he combines sugar or other organic material with oxygen from the air and produces carbon dioxide and water. In doing so, he extracts some of the energy that the plant got from the sunlight. The sun is therefore the source of our personal energy. Plants collect the energy from sunlight and convert it into chemical energy that our bodies can put to use.

64–3. Energy and Agriculture. The power that the sun delivers to the earth is enormous, averaging about 750 watts, or about 1 horsepower, per square yard of the earth's surface. This means that in a day an average of 65 million joules, or 15 thousand calories, is delivered to each square yard of the earth's surface. The total solar energy falling on New Hampshire in one growing season, if all converted into food energy, would provide enough fuel to keep the whole world's population fed for a year.

Of course the plant does not actually convert radiation into food very efficiently. About 3 percent of the radiant energy that strikes wheat is used to construct organic molecules, but only a fraction of the organic matter is edible grain. In terms of usable calories per acre of crop, the following yields are typical:

Wheat ....1.6 million calories/acre
Potatoes ......3.0 million calories/acre
Rice ....3.6 million calories/acre.

Rice is therefore a particularly appropriate crop for a densely populated country.

To grow an acre of wheat in China takes a man 26 days' work, during which he uses 90 thousand calories. The yield is 1.6 million calories, or nearly 20 times as much as the energy he used to cultivate the crop. In the United States, a man has to work only 1.2 days and consume only about 4 thousand calories in order to produce an acre of wheat yielding 1.6 million calories. Of course, he also has to put fuel in his tractor, and may spend a larger *total* of energy than the Chinese does, but he spends less *human* energy. In our society, one man engaged in agriculture can, on the average, feed several other men, who are then able to devote their time to industrial or intellectual pursuits, and to a striving for improvement and progress.

Energy also plays an important part in the relation of man to domestic animals. We know that fuel value is not the only criterion by which food must be chosen. We may therefore want to use our green plants for pasturage and convert them into protein foods, such as milk or beef. The resulting fuel yields per year are, roughly speaking:

Milk ....0.7 million calories/acre
Beef ....0.1 million calories/acre.

These figures must be compared to 3 or more million calories per acre obtainable from two crops of grain, and they go far to explain the high cost of roast beef. To give the whole world as much meat as we eat in the United States would involve at least doubling the acreage devoted to grazing. Unless extremely radical changes in agricultural practice are forthcoming, this would mean an intolerable reduction in the amount of land devoted to crops. Therefore an abundant supply of meat for all people is at present impossible.

Animals are useful not only for food, but also for doing work. As mentioned earlier, the horse works with an efficiency of about 25 percent. Unfortunately, he has to stand in the barn doing nothing all night, and while there he still burns hay (although at a reduced rate) to keep himself warm. His efficiency over a 24-hour period is consequently only about 10 percent. This is at least as good as the efficiency of a tractor, and the horse has the additional advantage of being able to repair himself with no industrial outlay for spare parts. The thermodynamics of the ox is even more favorable, and in poor countries people use oxen, or sometimes the still more efficient water buffalo. In the United States, however, gasoline is so cheap compared with hay and oats that the tractor, in spite of its small efficiency, is more economical than the horse for most agricultural purposes. If the tractor had to run on alcohol made from crops, the horse would probably be better. The scheme for industrializing Asia by alcohol fuel from crops can be immediately dismissed, since the land will scarcely grow enough to feed the people.

One important change in these considerations may be just over the horizon. Man could be freed from dependence on his inefficient and uncertain agriculture if he could reproduce first in the laboratory, and then on an industrial scale, the process of photosynthesis that chlorophyll accomplishes in plants. Great efforts in this direction are being made, and we may hope for the day when the behavior of chlorophyll is understood and imitated by man, so that the sun's energy can be converted into enough food for all.

64–4. Sources of Industrial Energy. Energy for our mechanical or industrial processes comes mainly from coal, petroleum, or waterfalls. The coal is simply old plants that got their energy from the sun. Petroleum is the remains of plants or animals whose energy came from the sun. Waterfalls depend on water that was vaporized and raised to high altitude by heat from the sun. In fact, it is easy to show that all of our usable energy comes from the sun. Or at least it did until very recently. In 1942 a way was found to get usable energy from a terrestrial source: uranium atoms. The questions of where the sun gets its energy, and why uranium atoms can release energy, lead us into the realm of nuclear physics.

Summary

The Conservation of Energy applies to animate as well as inanimate processes.

The energy we use for supporting life and industry comes, in one way or another, from the sun.

Suggestions for Further Reading

Pei-Sung Tang, "Helios and Prometheus: A Philosophy of Agriculture," *Scientific Monthly,* vol. 58, pp. 169–75 (March, 1944). A provocative article on food production; the source of many of the data quoted in this chapter.

E. Taschdjian, "Problems of Food Production," *Bulletin of the Atomic Scientists,* vol. 7, pp. 209–13 (August, 1951).

O. P. Pearson, "The Metabolism of Humming Birds," *Scientific American,* January, 1953, pp. 69–72. The same issue of this journal contains an article entitled "Trace Elements" that deals with an aspect of nutrition that this book has passed over.

E. Borek, *Man, The Chemical Machine* (New York: Columbia University Press, 1952).

GENERAL VIEW OF SECTION IX

Knowing how the electrons in different atoms are arranged, we have been able to lay out a systematic explanation of chemical behavior.

The elements with eight electrons in the outermost shell are the inert gases. Their inertness shows that an outer shell of eight electrons is an exceptionally stable arrangement. It is called a stable octet. The metals are those atoms that have only a few electrons (one to three) in their outermost shells; the nonmetals are those atoms whose outermost shells contain nearly enough electrons to form a stable octet.

Nonmetals combine with metals mainly by ionic binding, and they combine with other nonmetals by covalent binding. Metallic atoms combine with one another by pooling their outer electrons; the metallic bond is somewhat like a covalent one, but in a metal the shared electrons are mobile, because the atoms do not have enough outer electrons to form as many bonds as the Exclusion Principle allows.

Once the principles of chemical binding are understood, the relations among the chemical elements all fall into place on the basis of electronic structure. Valence, the formation of radicals, the degree of chemical activity, the process of solution, and the existence of transition elements and rare earths, all cease to be mysteries.

The role of electrons in chemical binding explains the connection between chemistry and electricity. The dual process of oxidation and reduction is simply a transfer of electrons from one substance to another. The chemical reactions produced by electric currents, and the production of electric currents by chemical means, follow as logical consequences. Application of the new ideas to electrolytes has aided in a sweeping revision of Arrhenius' theory of ionization. As a result, we have new and more satisfactory concepts of the nature of an acid and of a base.

New clarity in the chemical concepts brings new unity to chemical practice. We have discussed in particular the interpretation of physical properties in terms of chemical structure. Organic chemistry has provided many examples of how the uses of a substance are related to the structure of its molecules. With our present understanding of chemical binding, new substances can be formed, almost at will, to fill specific needs.

These chapters close our study of the interplay of atoms. Looking back, we see that lines of experimental evidence arose in many fields of science and converged to delineate the world of atoms. The basic concepts of atomic science are drawn from various branches of physics, but the area of chemistry served as a vital testing ground. The two formerly distinct sciences are, in principle, now united.

Although much interesting research on details has yet to be done, the general aspects of atomic behavior seem now to be well understood. Possibly no really major revisions will be needed. Tucked away inside each atom, however, there is a nucleus, for which at present there is scarcely any theory at all. In nuclear science there are many experimental facts, however, and also much mystery, much opportunity, and much danger. We shall therefore devote our last section to this scientific frontier.

X

The Atomic Nucleus

A brief discussion of radioactivity in Chapter 45 revealed the fact that some atoms emit alpha-, beta-, and gamma-rays. The alpha-rays are doubly charged helium ions. They must come from the nucleus of the emitting atom, because the nucleus is the seat of all of the positive charge, and most of the mass, of an atom. The fact that a nucleus can emit an alpha-particle indicates, of course, that nuclei are not indivisible. They are composed of parts, and the nature of the parts affords a topic for investigation. It has turned out to be a very exciting one. In spite of its appearing at first sight to be a quest far removed from the world of affairs, nuclear research has already had a substantial effect on medicine and war, and it shows promise of providing man with an important source of energy for industrial purposes. To a student of the liberal arts, it is interesting also because it forms one of the present-day frontiers of physical science. Much that is interesting and even spectacular is known, but much has yet to be explained.

65

TRANSMUTATIONS

Chapter 45 introduced the phenomenon of radioactivity. One of the early researches on the behavior of alpha-rays led to the discovery of the atomic nucleus (Chapter 46), and in tracing the results of the discovery we have strayed away from radioactivity. We now return to the subject.

65–1. Natural Transmutations. Remember that various elements near the end of the Periodic Table, for example uranium and radium, spontaneously emit charged particles. The beta-particles are electrons, and the alpha-particles are doubly charged helium ions, which means that they are helium nuclei. Suppose that radium chloride is carefully purified and then bottled up in a closed vessel. Since the radium gives off alpha-particles (helium nuclei), we expect that after a few months there will be a detectable amount of helium in the vessel along with the radium chloride. The helium is indeed there (Article 45–6), but *one also finds another element* that was not originally present. This element, called radon, is a chemically inert gas like helium or argon. Physically, however, it is not inert; it is radioactive. It gives out alpha-particles on its own account. These alpha-particles can be distinguished from those of radium by the fact that they are ejected with higher velocity and therefore travel farther in air before being brought to rest. The presence of these alpha-particles affords a sensitive test for the presence of radon.

The transformation of the metal radium into the inert gas radon is a type of change that was long thought to be impossible. It is changing one element into another element. The changing of one element or atom into another is called a *transmutation* or *disintegration.* The fact that it occurs in nature was discovered about 1900 by Rutherford. His later discovery that the atom has a nucleus, whose charge determines the chemical behavior of the atom, made possible an understanding of transmutation.

If an alpha-particle comes out of an atom, it must come out of the nucleus, because outside of the nucleus there is nothing but electrons. Now, when a nucleus loses an alpha-particle, it loses 2 quanta of positive charge and therefore becomes a different nucleus. For example, if a radium nucleus with a charge of 88 quanta loses an alpha-particle, the nucleus that remains behind has a charge of only 86 quanta. The latter nucleus therefore has a normal quota of eighty-six electrons around it, and it belongs in the eighty-sixth box in the Periodic Table. In short, *the act of emitting an alpha-particle changes the radium atom into a different kind of atom,* namely radon. Notice that the eighty-sixth box in the Periodic Table does fall in Group VIII; the theory of transmutation is therefore in conformity with the experimental fact that radon is a chemically inert gas.

Not all radioactive nuclei emit alpha-rays; some emit beta-rays, which are electrons. If a nucleus emits an electron, then it loses a negative charge of 1 quantum. This is the same as gaining a quantum of positive charge, so the nuclear charge increases by 1 quantum, thereby increasing the atomic number by one unit and moving the atom to the next box in the Periodic Table. The fact that such transmutations are actually found to occur shows that, at least in some cases, beta-rays come from the nucleus. For example, one of the isotopes of bismuth (atomic number 83) is a beta-ray emitter. When it emits a beta-particle, this atom changes to polonium (element 84).

We can summarize these facts by saying that the transmutations involving loss of alpha-particles move the atom two places to the left in the Periodic Table, and transmutations involving the emission of a beta-particle (electron) from the nucleus move the atom one place to the right in the table.

65–2. Nuclear Nomenclature. Recall (Article 44–3) that a given element may, and usually does, have several kinds of atoms. The mass spectrograph shows that nature provides ten kinds of tin atoms, differing

---

Ernest Rutherford, a New Zealander, was one of Thomson's first research students at the University of Cambridge. Like many British scientists before and since, he made a professional reputation in one of Britain's dependencies, and then returned to the mother country. At 27, he was research professor at McGill; some years later, he returned to England as professor of physics at the University of Manchester, and after World War I he succeeded Thomson at Cambridge. In each of his posts, he developed vigorous and productive schools of research. Public recognition brought him a knighthood (1914) and a peerage (1931). For his work on radioactivity, he received the Nobel prize in chemistry (1908).

By courtesy of the Cavendish Laboratory, Cambridge University

LORD RUTHERFORD OF NELSON
(1871–1937)

in mass. These atoms all have nuclear charges of 50 quanta, and hence all have fifty electrons for their normal quota, and all behave alike chemically. The differences in these isotopes are due to differences in their nuclei, because their electron systems are identical. Consequently, isotopes are of fundamental interest to the nuclear scientist.

In order to state clearly and concisely just which kind of nucleus we are talking about, we can put after the chemical symbol for the atom a number showing its mass. This number, called the *mass number*, is obtained by measuring the relative mass of the atom on a scale such that the principal isotope of oxygen has a relative mass of just 16 (Article 44–3), and then rounding off this mass measurement to drop the decimal places. For example, hydrogen has an atomic mass of 1.008, and its mass number is 1; the only isotope of sodium that is found in nature has an atomic mass of 22.997 and its mass number is 23. These atoms can therefore be designated H^1 and Na^{23}. The various isotopes of tin have the symbols Sn^{112}, Sn^{114}, Sn^{115}, and so on.

Although this system designates a nucleus unambiguously, a further elaboration of the symbols is often convenient. To save a reader from having to look at a Periodic Table to see how much charge is on the Sn nucleus, we can use the atomic number of tin as a prefix to the symbol. Then the symbols for the isotopes just mentioned become ${}_{50}Sn^{112}$, ${}_{50}Sn^{114}$, ${}_{50}Sn^{115}$, and so on. Similarly, the principal isotopes of sulfur are designated by ${}_{16}S^{32}$ and ${}_{16}S^{34}$. This system of symbols is particularly useful for discussing transmutations.

65–3. Radioactive Series. Within a few years after the discovery of radioactivity, it was established by tedious chemical and physical analysis that most radioactive atoms found in nature can be grouped into three series. Since these series are basically similar, only one needs to be discussed in detail.

Over 99 percent of the uranium atoms on the earth are ${}_{92}U^{238}$. They emit alpha-particles and are thereby transmuted into atoms with atomic number 90 and atomic mass 234. (The alpha-particle, being a nucleus of ${}_{2}He^{4}$, carries away four units of mass.) Since element 90 is thorium, the new atom is an isotope of thorium and has the symbol ${}_{90}Th^{234}$. When the first work on radioactivity was done, however, the existence of isotopes, and even of nuclei, had not yet been discovered; the atom into which uranium was transmuted was therefore given a name of its own. It was called Uranium X_1, to designate both its kinship with uranium and its unknown character. This unceremoniously created atom is itself unstable, and it, too, flies apart. One fragment is a beta-particle (electron) and the other is a new atom of another substance called Uranium X_2, which in the light of our present knowledge we see must be an isotope of element 91. This is an element we have never had occasion to mention: proto-

TABLE 65-I

THE RADIUM SERIES

Modern Name	Original Name With Emission and Half-Life
$_{92}U^{238}$	Uranium I
	α ↓ 4.5×10^9 years
$_{90}Th^{234}$	Uranium X_1
	β ↓ 24 days
$_{91}Pa^{234}$	Uranium X_2
	β ↓ 1.1 minutes
$_{92}U^{234}$	Uranium II
	α ↓ 250,000 years
$_{90}Th^{230}$	Ionium
	α ↓ 80,000 years
$_{88}Ra^{226}$	Radium
	α ↓ 1620 years
$_{86}Rn^{222}$	Radon
	α ↓ 3.8 days
$_{84}Po^{218}$	Radium A
	α ↓ 3.0 minutes
$_{82}Pb^{214}$	Radium B
	β ↓ 26.8 minutes
$_{83}Bi^{214}$	Radium C
	β ↓ 19.7 minutes
$_{84}Po^{214}$	Radium C′
	α ↓ 1.6×10^{-4} second
$_{82}Pb^{210}$	Radium D
	β ↓ 22 years
$_{83}Bi^{210}$	Radium E
	β ↓ 5.0 days
$_{84}Po^{210}$	Polonium
	α ↓ 138 days
$_{82}Pb^{206}$	Lead

actinium. The new atom has nearly the same mass as the old, so it can be designated $_{91}Pa^{234}$. (The loss of an electron reduces the weight of an atom by only a tiny fraction of a mass unit.) The train of transmutations continues, as in Table 65–I, until the atom has turned into an isotope of lead, $_{82}Pb^{206}$. This atom is *stable,* i.e. nonradioactive.

TABLE 65–II

THE THORIUM SERIES

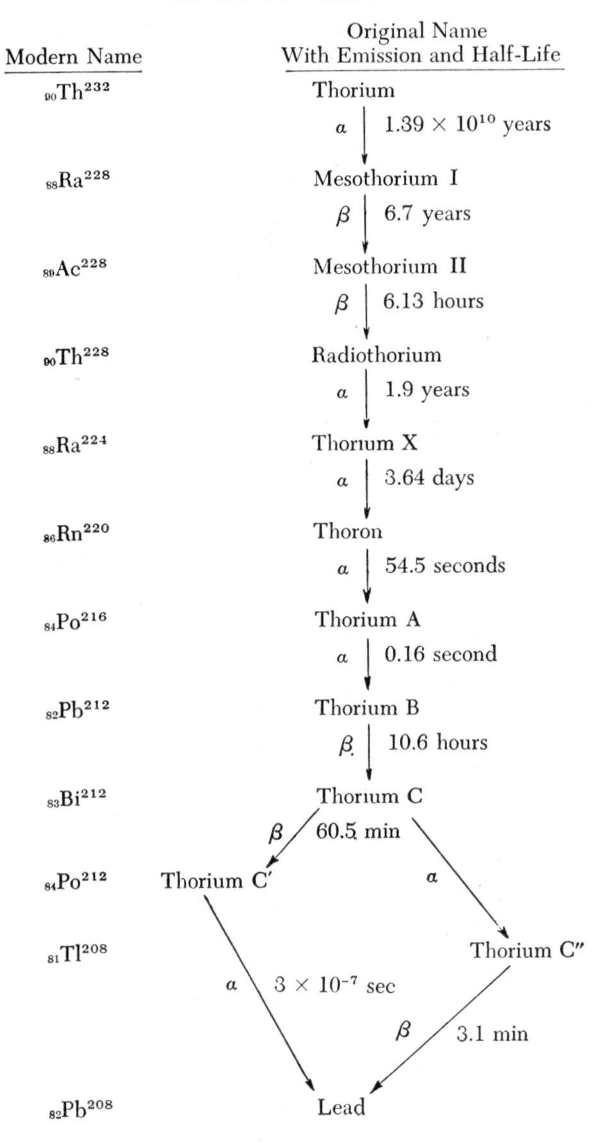

Modern Name	Original Name	Emission and Half-Life
$_{90}Th^{232}$	Thorium	α ↓ 1.39×10^{10} years
$_{88}Ra^{228}$	Mesothorium I	β ↓ 6.7 years
$_{89}Ac^{228}$	Mesothorium II	β ↓ 6.13 hours
$_{90}Th^{228}$	Radiothorium	α ↓ 1.9 years
$_{88}Ra^{224}$	Thorium X	α ↓ 3.64 days
$_{86}Rn^{220}$	Thoron	α ↓ 54.5 seconds
$_{84}Po^{216}$	Thorium A	α ↓ 0.16 second
$_{82}Pb^{212}$	Thorium B	β ↓ 10.6 hours
$_{83}Bi^{212}$	Thorium C	60.5 min; β → Thorium C′, α → Thorium C″
$_{84}Po^{212}$	Thorium C′	α 3×10^{-7} sec → Lead
$_{81}Tl^{208}$	Thorium C″	β 3.1 min → Lead
$_{82}Pb^{208}$	Lead	

The second series starts from another isotope of uranium, ${}_{92}U^{235}$, and has as its ultimate member another isotope of lead, ${}_{82}Pb^{207}$. The third series springs from thorium, ${}_{90}Th^{232}$, and ends in a still different isotope of lead, ${}_{82}Pb^{208}$. It is shown in Table 65–II.

In these series, alpha-emission is slightly more common than beta-emission; a few atoms can emit either kind of particle.

65–4. The Half-Life. Consider again a flask containing a purified sample of radium chloride. The radium transmutes into radon. Therefore if a man puts 1.00 gram of radium atoms in a flask, and fifteen years later purifies the radium salt again to remove the products of transmutation, he will find that there is less than a gram of radium in the flask. Experiment shows that there will be only 0.99 g of radium left; in the course of the fifteen years about 1 percent of the radium has been transmuted into radon. In another fifteen years about 1 percent *of what is left* will have turned into radon. At this rate, how long will it take for half of a radium sample to turn into radon? The problem cannot be done by simple arithmetic, but any statistician could determine, from the experimental information given, that half of the radium would be gone in about 1600 years. The time required for half the atoms of a radioactive isotope to undergo transmutation is called the *half-life* of the isotope.

Radioactive half-lives vary from substance to substance. Half of a sample of radon disappears in a little less than 4 days, but the half-life of ${}_{92}U^{238}$ is over 4 billion years. Very long and very short half-lives cannot be measured by weighing the purified substance at different times. Weighing is unnecessary in any case, because the amount of substance present is accurately indicated by the rate at which it gives out alpha- or beta-particles. (Alpha-particles, and with some refinements the beta-particles also, can be counted by scintillations; other methods will be discussed in a later chapter.) If at some time a sample of radon gives out a million alpha-particles per second, and 4 days later it gives out only half a million alpha-particles per second, then one can safely conclude that the half-life of radon is 4 days.

The measurement of very long and very short half-lives is carried out indirectly. By measuring how much radon is in equilibrium with a gram of radium, one can find mathematically the ratio of their half-lives, and therefore the half-life of radium. If the radium and the radon are in equilibrium, then radium is turning into radon at the same rate that radon is turning into something else. In other words, the radium and the radon are transmuting at the same rate. But the rate at which a substance transmutes is proportional to the amount of the substance present, and is inversely proportional to the half-life. (The shorter the half-life, the more rapid the transmutation.) Therefore, knowing the amount of radon that exists in equilibrium with a known amount of radium, and knowing the half-life of radon, one can calculate the half-life of radium by a simple proportion. In uranium-bearing rocks, there is radium in equilibrium with the uranium. The same procedure can therefore be applied to discover the half-life of uranium.

The half-lives of the members of the radium and thorium series are shown in Tables 65–I and 65–II. Figure 65–A is a graph of the decline in a population of radon atoms over the course of three weeks. Other radioactive populations decline in the same way, except that the time scale is longer or shorter, according as the half-life is longer or shorter. This decline in population is called *radioactive decay.*

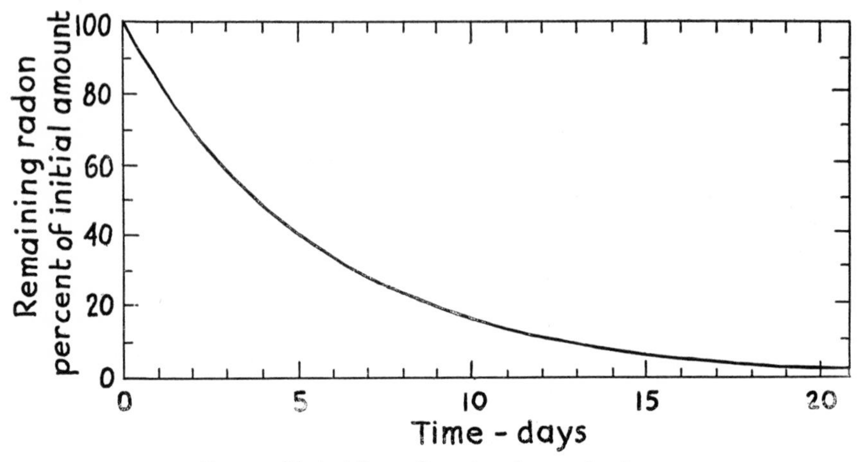

FIGURE 65–A. The radioactive decay of radon.

65–5. The Age of the Earth. Uranium, after successive transmutations, eventually turns to lead. If the uranium is in a rock, then as time goes on the lead content of the rock increases, and the uranium content decreases. The transmutation of the uranium into lead proceeds at a known rate: half of the uranium will turn to lead in 4.5 billion years. If one supposes that when the rock was formed it contained no lead, then the age of the rock can be determined from a comparison of the number of lead atoms it now contains with the number of uranium atoms that are still left. If the rock were found by chemical analysis to contain equal numbers of Pb and U atoms, then half of the original supply of uranium would have been transmuted, and the rock must be 4.5 billion years old.

Actually, in all rocks that have been tested, the uranium atoms outnumber the lead atoms. The ratio of these two atomic populations indicates an age of about 2 billion years for the oldest rocks that have been analyzed. The earth is certainly older than these rocks, so it is more than 2 billion years old.

65–6. Nuclear Collisions. After studying the passage of alpha-particles through metal foils, and thereby discovering the nucleus, Rutherford turned his attention to the passage of alpha-particles through hydrogen and other light elements. He reasoned that the nucleus of a light atom would rebound violently from an encounter with an alpha-particle. Using the Law of Conservation of Momentum (Article 7–2), he calculated what must happen when an alpha-particle makes a head-on collision with a hydrogen nucleus. He found that the hydrogen nucleus would be impelled forward with more velocity than the alpha-particle originally had. He could therefore expect that a hydrogen nucleus, so struck, would travel farther in the gas than the alpha-particle would have gone. Hence, the hydrogen nucleus could be distinguished from the alpha-particle.

To investigate nuclear collisions, Rutherford used the apparatus in Figure 65–B. Even simpler than his gold-foil setup, it consisted of a box with a fluorescent screen at one end and a source of alpha-particles on a movable support inside. The box could be filled with hydrogen or any other gas. The observer watched the scintillations caused by the alpha-particles striking the screen, then he gradually moved the source farther from the screen. Rutherford found that when the box was filled with hydrogen, the alpha-particles, which were very numerous, would strike the screen until the source was about 0.25 meter away. Moving the source farther away did not stop the scintillations entirely, however. There were some particles that could travel as far as 1 meter in the hydrogen. These long-range particles must be hydrogen nuclei that had been impelled forward by the alpha-particles. The experiment thus confirmed Rutherford's hunch as to the observability of collisions between alpha-particles and other nuclei.

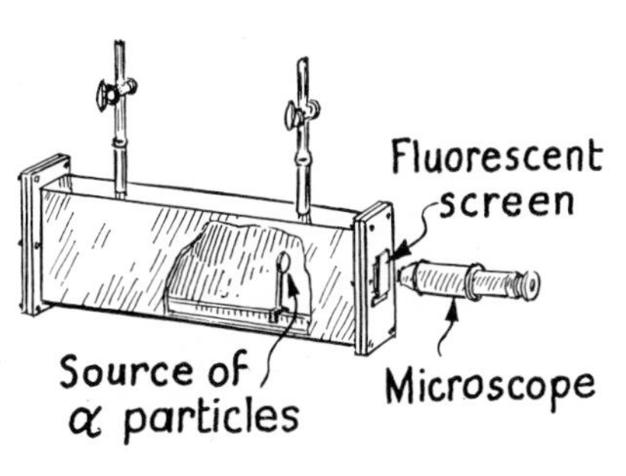

FIGURE 65–B. Rutherford's apparatus for studying nuclear collisions.

65–7. Artificial Transmutation (1919). If a tennis ball collides with a basketball, the basketball will be set in motion, but it will not go so fast as the tennis ball did. Similarly, if an alpha-particle collides with a heavier nucleus like that of nitrogen, the nitrogen nucleus will rebound with a velocity smaller than that of the alpha-particle. (This conclusion is in accord with the Law of Conservation of Momentum.) A nitrogen nucleus impelled by the impact of an alpha-particle will therefore not travel so far in the gas as the alpha-particle would have gone if it had escaped making a collision.

Nevertheless Rutherford filled his box with nitrogen to see what did happen, and he found that long-range particles are produced by collisions in nitrogen as well as in hydrogen. He found that a few particles hit his fluorescent screen when the source was 0.28 m away, although the alpha-particles could travel only about 0.07 m in the nitrogen. The long-range particles must have started out moving faster than the alpha-particles, so they must be less massive; Rutherford decided that they were hydrogen nuclei. He then showed that when deflected in a magnetic field, they really behaved like hydrogen nuclei. After eliminating every other conceivable possibility (for example, that the hydrogen nuclei came from traces of water vapor in the nitrogen), he was forced to assume that the hydrogen nuclei were knocked out of the nitrogen nuclei. The loss of a hydrogen nucleus entails loss of a quantum of charge, and the nitrogen nucleus must therefore have been transmuted into some other kind of nucleus. Rutherford had accomplished the feat of *artificial transmutation.* His experiment marked the beginning of man's control over the atomic nucleus.

Summary

The emission of an α- or β-particle changes the charge on a nucleus and therefore converts an atom into a chemically different one. This process is called transmutation.

To distinguish different isotopes from one another, the chemical symbol for an atom is often supplemented by the mass number of the particular isotope under discussion. The mass number is the nearest whole number that expresses the relative mass of the atom, on a scale for which 16 corresponds to the principal isotope of oxygen. The mass number comes after the chemical symbol: U^{238}, He^4.

Although the atomic number of an atom is implied by its chemical symbol, the number is often stated explicitly, as a matter of convenience: ${}_{92}U^{238}$, ${}_{2}He^4$.

An important characteristic of a radioactive substance is its half-life. This is the time required for half of the atoms in a sample of the substance to undergo transmutation.

Alpha-particles are sufficiently small and energetic to be able to make actual collisions with other nuclei. Rutherford discovered that if nitrogen is bombarded with alpha-particles, then the collision can knock a hydrogen nucleus out of the nitrogen nucleus. The nitrogen nucleus thus has its charge altered, and it therefore becomes the nucleus of an atom different from nitrogen. In brief, the nitrogen is transmuted into a different element.

Questions

1. What is transmutation?
2. Give an example of transmutation and describe how it occurs.

3. When an alpha-particle is emitted from a nucleus, how does the atomic number of the residual nucleus differ from the atomic number of the original nucleus?
4. If the nucleus of an atom emits a beta-ray, how is the change in that atom related to the Periodic Table?
5. Describe the scale of atomic masses. What is the mass number of an atom?
6. How is the mass number of an atom affected by the emission of an alpha-particle from the nucleus?
7. How does the emission of a beta-particle affect the mass number of the emitting atom?
8. From what is said in the text, show that Uranium X_2 must be an isotope of element 91.
9. What is a radioactive series?
10. What is meant by the half-life of a radioactive substance?
11. Describe Rutherford's experiment on the passage of alpha-particles through hydrogen. What was the significance of the experiment?
12. Describe Rutherford's experiment on the passage of alpha-particles through nitrogen. What is the significance of the experiment?

66

THE APPARATUS OF NUCLEAR PHYSICS

Most experiments in nuclear physics are studies of what happens when a nucleus is struck by another particle. The nuclear experimenter must therefore have ways of observing the nuclear particles, and he must have equipment for setting his nuclear projectiles into rapid motion. It will be best to devote a chapter to these tools, to clear the way for a discussion of nuclear experiments.

The Detection of Nuclear Particles

66–1. The Photographic Plate. The photographic process depends on a peculiar property of the silver halides. If exposed for a long time to light, they turn from white or cream to a very dark gray (Article 38–3). Investigation shows that in a silver halide crystal that has had prolonged exposure to light, some of the silver ions have been converted into silver atoms. The light therefore produces a chemical change in the silver halide crystal, a change involving reduction of the silver.

A photographic plate or film consists of a suspension of tiny silver halide crystals in gelatin that is spread on a glass plate or on a plastic film. If some parts of the plate are given a brief exposure to light, no visible effect is produced; but if the plate is then treated with a chemical reducing agent called a "developer," the silver halide crystals that have been exposed to light rapidly turn dark. For reasons that are not really understood, the developer acts most rapidly on those crystals that have been exposed to the most light. Presumably the light initiates a process of reduction, which is continued by the chemical action of the developer. After enough of the silver ions have been reduced to atoms by the developer, the remaining silver halide is removed by treating the plate with another solution called a "fixing bath." The tiny silver particles that remain behind make the gelatin layer more or less opaque in those parts that have been exposed to more or less light. The plate is then called a "photographic negative"; by shining light through it onto a second light-sensitive preparation spread on paper, and developing and fixing the paper, an ordinary photographic print can be made.

Our present interest in photographic plates springs from the fact that if a charged particle strikes a silver halide crystal, the silver in the crystal can be reduced by a developer just as if the crystal had been hit by light. The mechanism of the process is still obscure, but the effect is simple and useful. A charged particle passing through the layer of gelatin will leave a trail of developable crystal grains that give a record of its path; their

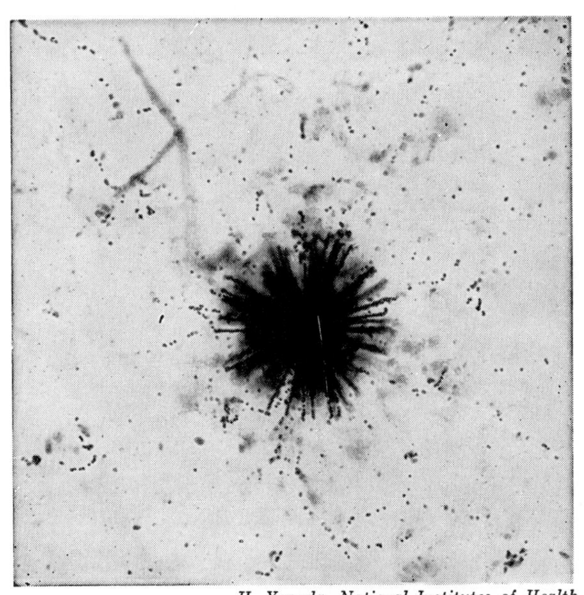

H. Yagoda, National Institutes of Health

FIGURE 66–A. Alpha-particle tracks in a photographic plate.

spacing depends on the charge, mass, and velocity of the particle. In general a slow particle makes a more pronounced track than a fast one does, and a heavy particle makes a more pronounced track than a light one. By making some tests with particles he knows all about, an experimenter can learn to identify particles from the tracks they make, and to judge their energy from the length of the track.

Figure 66–A is an enlargement from a photographic plate on which there was a speck of polonium. The dark rosette is a set of alpha-particle tracks radiating from the polonium. The actual length of each track is about 0.001 inch. Near the rosette is a trio of tracks from some radioactive atom that has undergone a succession of transmutations of the sort discussed in Article 65–3. The three tracks come from three successive alpha-particle emissions on the part of this atom. The tracks are out of focus because the microscope through which the enlargement was made was focused on the rosette, which is at a different depth in the gelatin.

66–2. The Cloud Chamber. In the days when Thomson was studying ions, one of his students found that under appropriate conditions water vapor can be made to condense on ions in the air. If water is put in a closed vessel, it will evaporate until an equilibrium sets in, with water molecules from the vapor rejoining the liquid just as fast as molecules of the liquid are evaporating. If the air space above the water is then suddenly expanded, the equilibrium is disturbed and some of the water vapor will condense on ions in the air if any are present.* The positions of the ions will therefore be marked by droplets of water. Because it depends on the condensation of water into droplets to form fog or cloud, the device is called a *cloud chamber.*

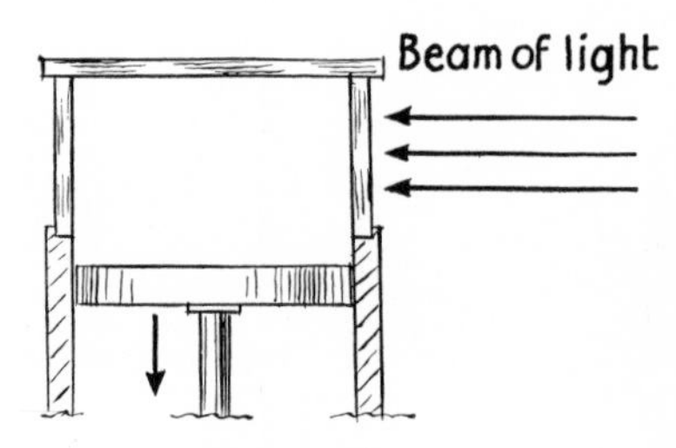

FIGURE 66–B. The elements of a cloud chamber.

In practice, a cloud chamber usually consists of a cylindrical vessel closed by a glass window at one end and a movable piston at the other, as in Figure 66–B. The volume of the chamber can be suddenly enlarged by a quick retraction of the piston, and the droplets on the ions can be viewed or photographed through the glass window. If an electron or other charged particle passes through the chamber, it ionizes the air along its path. If the chamber is expanded just after the ions are formed, the droplets formed on the ions clearly mark the path of the moving particle. The cloud chamber therefore enables us to observe and photograph the motions of individual subatomic particles. Rutherford called it "the most original and wonderful instrument in scientific history."

Figure 66–C shows two views of a five-inch cloud chamber in which a distintegration has just occurred. A beam of x-rays from a nearby machine passes through the center of the chamber, where its path is visible because of the ionization that the x-rays produce in the gas of the chamber. This cloud chamber contains an atmosphere of helium, and one of the $_2He^4$ nuclei has just been disrupted by a photon, in an event that is the nuclear equivalent of the photoelectric effect.

A mirror near the cloud chamber has served to give a view of the chamber from a different angle. By using the two pictures in an appro-

* The reasons for this behavior are now pretty well understood, but are too complex to be explained here.

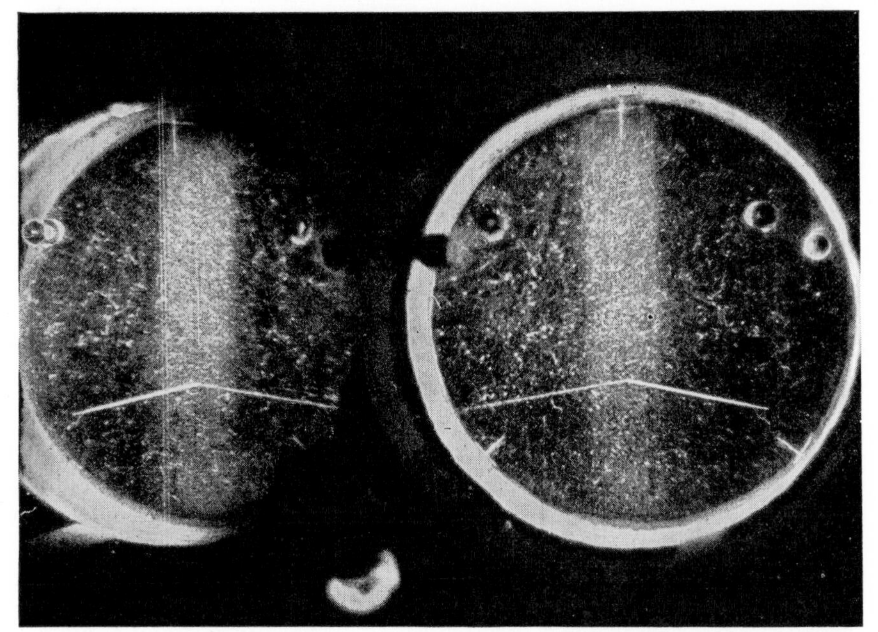

E. R. Gaerttner and M. L. Yeater, Research Laboratory, General Electric Co.

FIGURE 66–C. Tracks of nuclei in a cloud chamber.

priate viewer, the experimenter can make a three-dimensional study of the tracks.

66–3. The Geiger Counter. In many experiments it is not necessary to observe the paths taken by the subatomic particles; it is sufficient simply to count the particles. The device most frequently used for this purpose is a *Geiger counter*, named for its inventor. The counter is a sealed tube with two electrodes, one of which is a fine wire running along the axis of the tube. The other electrode is a metal cylinder that surrounds the wire. Often this outer electrode is the jacket of the counter, but the special glass-jacketed counter in Figure 66–D shows the construction more clearly.

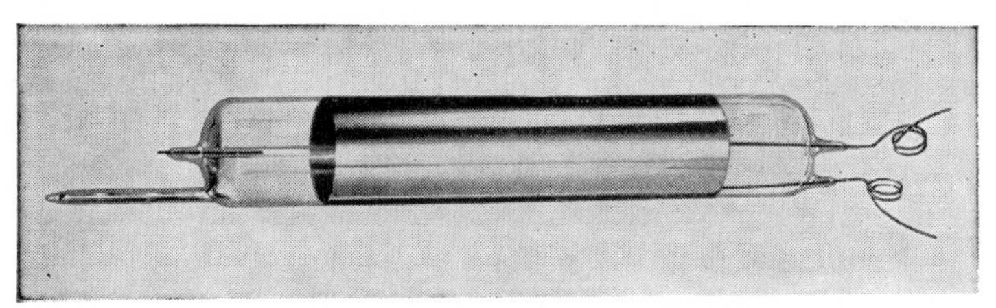

Radiation Counter Laboratories

FIGURE 66–D. A Geiger counter.

A battery or other device maintains a potential difference of about 1000 volts between the wire and the outer electrode. The potential difference is adjusted so that it is just insufficient to cause a spark. Then when a charged particle, say a beta-ray, passes through the chamber and creates a few ions, these ions are rapidly accelerated by the electric field between the electrodes. They are soon in such rapid motion that they too produce ionization, and the ions thus created produce still more ionization in the same way. Therefore the passage of a single charged particle through the counter tube can set off a multiplicative process that produces millions of ions and makes the gas in the tube a good conductor. The resulting current through the tube can be made to actuate a recording device. Several hundred particles per second can be counted in this way.

66–4. The Ionization Chamber. In a Geiger counter, the relatively few ions produced by the passage of an ionizing particle are multiplied by the action of the electric field. The current produced by the migration of so many ions is large enough to be easily detected. Although it is more difficult, it is sometimes desirable to collect only the ions created by the ionizing particles that are being studied. This can be done by using collecting electrodes differing in potential by only about a hundred volts, so that the ions are not accelerated fast enough to have a multiplying effect as in a Geiger counter. A box of gas with electrodes for ion collection without multiplication is called an *ionization chamber.*

A single particle passing through an ionization chamber produces so few ions that the current in the chamber is very small, but particles entering the chamber in a copious stream will produce so many ions that the current can readily be measured. It is even possible to detect the passage of single particles, by using very refined apparatus for detecting the current. Ionization chambers and Geiger counters are useful for detecting not only charged particles, but also x-rays and gamma-rays, because these rays create ions in the gas.

The Production of High-Speed Particles

At the end of his paper announcing the artificial transmutation of nitrogen (Article 65–7), Rutherford remarked: "The results as a whole suggest that, if α-particles—or similar projectiles—of still greater energy were available for experiment, we might expect to break down the nucleus structure of many of the lighter atoms." A charged particle can of course be given energy by letting it accelerate in an electric field, but using this method to produce particles more energetic than alpha-particles would require a potential difference of several million volts. Such high voltages were not available when Rutherford made his remark.

After the discovery that Newton's laws are not a valid guide to the behavior of subatomic particles, a Russian physicist named Gamow * applied the new mechanics to collisions of charged particles with nuclei. His theoretical analysis led to the conclusion that the chance of a projectile's penetrating into the nucleus depends strongly on the velocity of the projectile, but does not depend much on its mass. Therefore if transmutations are to be produced by particles accelerated in an electric field, easily accelerated particles are to be preferred. In particular, hydrogen nuclei will be preferable to the more massive helium nuclei (alpha-particles).

66–5. The Simple Accelerator. The first transmutations by means of artificially accelerated projectiles were made by researchers in Rutherford's laboratory (1930). The projectiles were hydrogen nuclei issuing from a canal-ray tube containing hydrogen. From the canal-ray tube they passed into a long evacuated tube containing at its far end an electrode maintained at an attracting potential of nearly a million volts.† In passing down this tube, the hydrogen nuclei acquired great speed, and proceeded headlong through a hole in the attracting electrode. They could then be used as the experimenter saw fit.

This accelerator of particles could not produce particles moving as swiftly as natural alpha-particles, but it could produce them in much more numerous supply. Since nuclear collisions are a matter of chance, a copious stream of projectiles greatly enhances the possibility of observing something interesting. Moreover, the velocity of the projectiles could be varied at will by adjusting the accelerating voltage. Some of the results obtained will be discussed in the next chapter.

Simple accelerators, based on the use of a very large potential difference between a source of ions and an attracting electrode, have in recent years been built on a larger scale, some of them being designed for operation at 5 million

* Gamow is mentioned here by name because he has since come to the United States and written a series of unsurpassed books on atomic science for the lay reader.

† The high potential was obtained by stepping up the ordinary lighting voltage by means of the device called an "electric transformer." This operates on the same principle as an induction coil (Article 48–1), except that the fluctuating magnetic field is produced by reversals ("alternations") of the current in the electromagnet, instead of by a mechanical interrupter. The possibility of using transformers is the chief reason for preferring alternating current to "direct" (nonreversing) current.

There is one complication when transformers are used; their output reverses periodically, or alternates, just as the lighting voltage does. To prevent the potentials on the accelerating tube from reversing, an additional tube, called a "rectifier," is put in the circuit. The rectifier tube has a high vacuum; the only charge-carrying particles in it are electrons from a filament that is kept so hot that electrons escape from it by virtue of their thermal motion. This device acts as a valve which passes current only when its hot electrode is at a lower potential than the cool electrode, so that the electrons are attracted toward the cool one. The valving action prevents voltage from being applied to the accelerating tube in the wrong direction.

volts or more. In most of them the high potential is built up not by transformers as in the earliest types, but by an ingenious scheme that involves spraying a charge on a motor-driven belt which carries positive charge to the high-potential terminal and dumps it there. Hydrogen ions, created in a discharge tube inside the terminal, escape into a long evacuated tube whose farther end is at the potential of the ground. The nuclear projectiles in the tube are accelerated to high velocity by the repulsion between their positive charge and the very large positive charge on the terminal. A device of this sort is called a

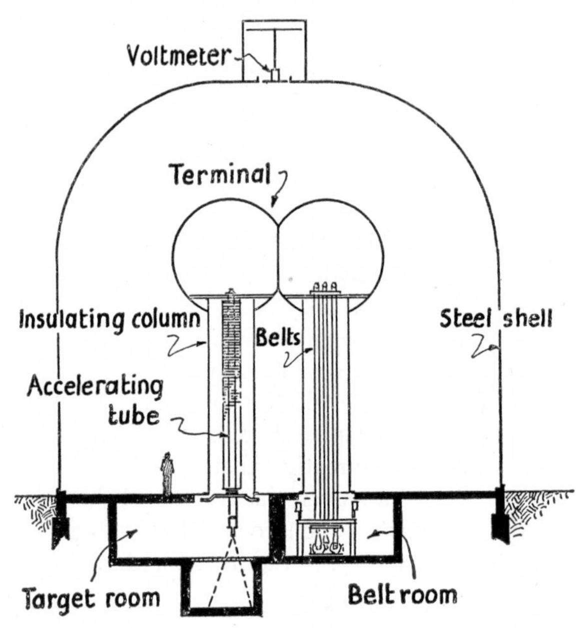

FIGURE 66–E. A simple accelerator using a Van de Graaff generator. Charge is carried to the terminal by the conveyor belts in one of the columns, and ions passing down the accelerating tube attain high velocity by reason of the force of repulsion between the charge on the terminal and the charge on the ions.

"Van de Graaff electrostatic generator," after its inventor. Figure 66–E is a sketch of an early model (1940). The terminal, supported on its two insulating columns, appears in Figure 66–F. One column contains the charging belts; the other, the accelerating tube. Figure 66–G shows some sparks generated in preliminary trials of the device at 2.5 million volts. More recent accelerators attain higher voltage in less space; to discourage sparking, they are enclosed in a tank of gas at high pressure.

66–6. The Cyclotron. The simple accelerator has the drawback that insulation problems are very troublesome when a potential difference of more than about a million volts is used. At about the same time that Rutherford's laboratory was building the first simple accelerator for nuclear bombardment, a more subtle device, called a *cyclotron*, was being developed at the University of California. The fundamental principle of this device is simple: instead of acquiring kinetic energy by a single passage through a huge potential difference, the particle acquires K.E. by passing many times through a modest potential difference, say 10,000

Massachusetts Institute of Technology

FIGURE 66–F. A Van de Graaff generator.

volts. Putting this simple idea into practice involves finding a way to make a particle pass through an electric field repeatedly, and always in such a direction that the field speeds up the motion.

The cyclotron consists of four principal parts: a source of ions, a source of high voltage, a pair of specially shaped electrodes, and a very large electromagnet. The two electrodes are hollow D-shaped metal cavities, called "dees," like two halves of a flat circular box that has been sawed apart along a diameter. The two electrodes are placed close together, but not in contact, and the source of ions is placed between them as in

Figure 66–H. The ions are usually formed by an electrical discharge in a suitable device. The dees, together with the ion source, are mounted between the poles of a magnet and connected to a source of high voltage, which will be described presently. The dees are usually at least 2 feet in diameter, and the magnet is proportionately large. Figures 66–I and 66–J are photographs of an early cyclotron and a more recent one.

Massachusetts Institute of Technology

FIGURE 66–G. When the high-voltage generator in Figure 66–F ran at too high a potential, it produced these 20-foot sparks.

When a positive ion issues from the source, it is attracted toward the negative electrode, and therefore moves into the negative half of the box (Figure 66–K). The electric field due to the opposite charges on the two dees is concentrated almost entirely in the gap between the dees; therefore an ion that is well inside one of the dees will not be subject to an electric field of any appreciable strength. The ion would move through the dee with uniform motion, except for the fact that the dees are between the poles of a magnet and the ion is therefore in a *magnetic* field. Like any other charged particle moving through a magnetic field, the ion will experience a force at right angles to its direction of motion, and will therefore move in a curved path which is an arc of a circle.

When it has moved through a semicircle, the ion will be back at the gap between the dees in Figure 66–K. If the potential of the dees had

Oak Ridge National Laboratory

FIGURE 66–H. The dees of a small cyclotron. The ion source is near the center of the slot between the dees, and the target to be bombarded is at the far end of the slot. When in use, this whole assembly is housed in an evacuated box.

remained steady while the ion was making its semicircular excursion, then the ion would be repelled by the opposite dee when it reached the gap, and it would lose all the velocity that it had gained in its original passage across the gap. The efficacy of the cyclotron depends on a simple trick: while the ion is coasting in its semicircular path inside the dee, the charges on the dees are reversed. Therefore when the ion reaches the gap after its excursion in the dee, the opposite dee has a negative charge and attracts the ion. The ion accelerates as it crosses the gap, coasts in the second dee in a larger semicircle because it is going faster than before, and reaches the gap again just in time to find that the direction of the electric field has again been reversed so that the ion is again accelerated by passage across the gap. Using mathematics and physical laws that are already familiar to us, we could easily prove that the faster the ion is moving, the larger the radius of its semicircular path. Therefore suc-

University of Rochester

FIGURE 66–I. A small cyclotron. Hydrogen nuclei acquire an energy of 7 Mev while spiraling outward to a radius of 1 foot. In the experiment under way here, they pass through the evacuated tube in the center of the picture to a chamber between the poles of the magnet at the left, whose field is used in the study of the effects that the hydrogen nuclei produce when they strike other nuclei.

cessive accelerations across the gap make the ion move in a path that spirals outward. The ion may be deflected out of its last semicircle, by a charged electrode installed on the rim of one dee, and then passed through a thin metal or mica window into the laboratory. The ion beam in Figure 66–L has an energy of 16.2 Mev when it emerges into the air, where it makes a luminous track 5 feet long. In the biggest cyclotrons, the ions go so fast that it is impractical to deflect them in this way; therefore the material to be bombarded by the ions is put right inside the dee.

University of Rochester

FIGURE 66–J. A large cyclotron. In front of the student and over his head are the coils of the magnet, which occupies most of the picture. With a dee diameter of 10 feet, the machine accelerates hydrogen nuclei to an energy of 250 Mev.

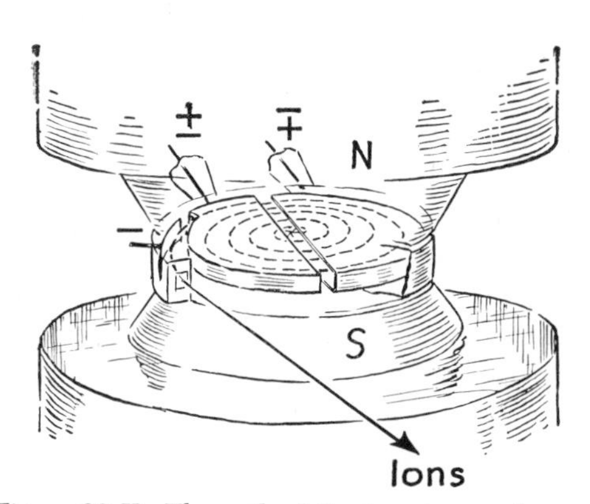

Figure 66–K. The path of the ions in a cyclotron.

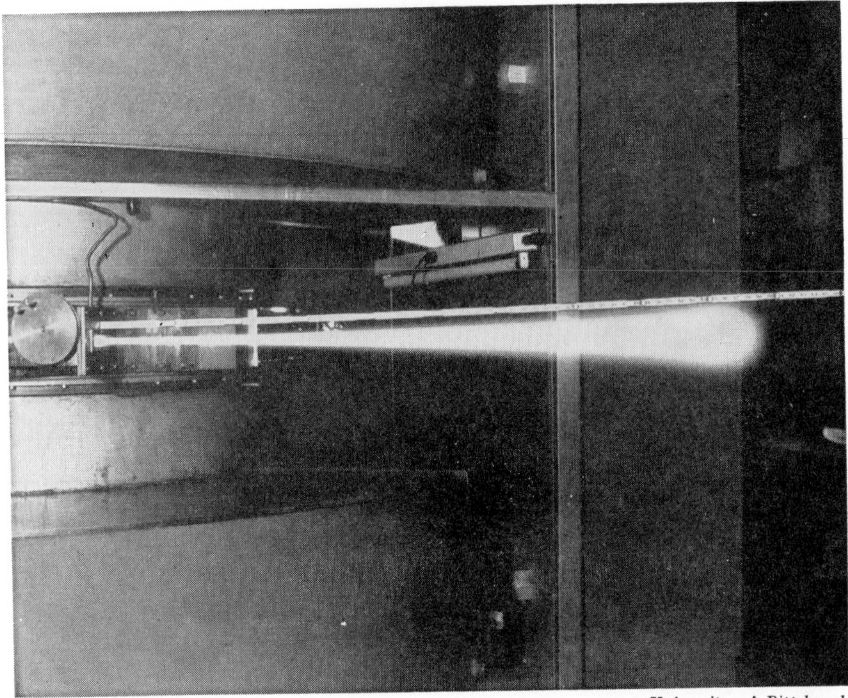

University of Pittsburgh

FIGURE 66–L. Ions emerging from a cyclotron. In use, the beam of ions strikes a target either just inside or just outside the cyclotron. Here the beam is being stopped only by the air; collisions with the atoms of the air ionize it and thereby render it luminous. The ruler above the beam shows that each of its particles travels 5 feet in the air while dissipating the 16 Mev of energy that it acquired in the cyclotron.

One question has been left unanswered: How can the charges on the dees be reversed at just the right times? In the chapter on electromagnetic waves, it was mentioned that radio waves are generated by making charge oscillate back and forth in an electric circuit. The same circuits that were developed for this purpose are used to place an alternating potential difference on the dees, the frequency of reversal of the voltage being chosen so that the time between reversals is just equal to the time that an ion spends in making its semicircular trip inside the dee.

The biggest cyclotrons in operation at present can give hydrogen nuclei an energy of 300 Mev. There are a few even larger accelerators, differing in detail from the cyclotrons but employing essentially the same principle. Figure 66–M depicts one of the largest, which accelerates hydrogen nuclei to an energy of a couple of billion electron-volts.

Brookhaven National Laboratory

FIGURE 66–M. One of the largest accelerators of nuclear particles. During acceleration, each ion makes millions of trips around an evacuated pipe set into the slot in the periphery of the doughnut-shaped magnet, which is 60 feet in diameter. The ion is accelerated in an electric field each time it goes around, until it has an energy of 2000 Mev or more, and then it is directed against a target. The dark cylinders that look like early cannon are pumps for evacuating the pipe, and the blocks of concrete in the foreground shield nearby workers from the radiation produced when the machine is operating.

SUMMARY

Nuclear charged particles can be detected by means of photographic plates, cloud chambers, Geiger counters, and ionization chambers. All of these devices (except perhaps the photographic plate) depend on ionization produced by the particles in the matter through which they pass. In the photographic plate and in the cloud chamber, the particles produce visible tracks.

High-speed nuclear particles can be produced by accelerating hydrogen or helium nuclei in electric fields. In the simple accelerator, the acceleration occurs in a single passage through a very large difference of potential. In a cyclotron, the acceleration occurs in repeated passages through a moderate difference of potential.

Questions

1. Describe how a photographic plate acts as a detector of nuclear particles.
2. Describe the construction and operation of a cloud chamber.
3. In what respect are a photographic plate and a cloud chamber alike?
4. Explain the construction and operation of a Geiger counter.
5. How does an ionization chamber differ in operation from a Geiger counter?
6. Describe a simple accelerator of nuclear particles.
7. What is the essential difference between a simple accelerator and a cyclotron?
8. Enumerate the four principal parts of a cyclotron, and describe the function of each one.

Suggestions for Further Reading

T. H. James, "Photographic Development," *Scientific American,* November, 1952, pp. 30–33. A clear and beautifully illustrated article on the photographic process.

R. A. Peck, Jr., and Paul Stelson, "Laboratory Exercise in Nuclear Emulsion Technique," *American Journal of Physics,* vol. 19, pp. 48–52 (1951). A discussion of equipment and procedures for observing nuclear tracks in photographic plates.

C. F. Powell and G. P. S. Occhialini, *Nuclear Physics in Photographs* (London: Oxford University Press, 1947). A superb collection of nuclear-track photographs.

67

THE FUNDAMENTAL PARTICLES

In Chapter 1, we noted Thales' concern with the question, "What is everything made of?" His answer was, "Water." Later Greeks had other answers. The Aristotelian elements, earth, air, fire, and water, eventually gave way to the equally ancient doctrine that everything is made of atoms, and that there is a considerable variety of them. Thomson and Rutherford discovered that the atoms themselves have parts—electrons and nuclei. Soon it was realized that the nuclei, too, consist of parts, because in radioactivity they emit charged particles. Electrons, however, are not known to consist of parts. We call them *fundamental particles,* by which we mean that they cannot (at present) be explained in terms of something simpler. The electron seems to be really one of the things that everything is made of. Other fundamental particles have been discovered more recently.

67–1. The Proton. Rutherford's experiment on the transmutation of nitrogen (Article 65–7) is interestingly related to the question of atomic masses. Ever since the discovery of isotopes (Article 44–3) it has been known that the masses of all atoms are very nearly integers, on the atomic mass scale. The simplest atom, hydrogen, has a mass near 1, helium has a mass near 4, chlorine atoms have masses near 35 and 37, and so on. Moreover, the mass of an atom is mainly the mass of the nucleus. The nuclear mass, therefore, is nearly equal to some whole number times the mass of a hydrogen nucleus.* One might at first conclude that other nuclei are groups of hydrogen nuclei. A moment's thought, however, shows that such a hypothesis is too simple; if a helium nucleus were an aggregate of four hydrogen nuclei, it would have a mass of 4 units, which is right, but it would also have a charge of 4 quanta. We know from the atomic number of helium that it has a nuclear charge of only 2 quanta.

* Here and in the rest of this article, we use "hydrogen nucleus" to refer to the nucleus of the common isotope of hydrogen, the one with mass near 1. Deuterium—hydrogen with mass near 2 (Article 44–3)—has a different nucleus.

After Rutherford had succeeded in knocking hydrogen nuclei out of nitrogen nuclei, he was convinced that hydrogen nuclei are constituents of all other nuclei, even though they are not the only constituents. The nucleus of H^1, since it has not been explained as consisting of parts, is a fundamental particle. It is commonly called the *proton*. ("Proton" is Greek for "the first one.")

67–2. The Neutron. As early as 1920, Rutherford supposed that nuclei are made of protons, together with other particles which he called *neutrons*, the neutron being an uncharged particle with a mass the same as that of the proton, or at least nearly the same.

It was obvious from the start that neutrons would be hard to detect, because they have no charge. When electrons or protons or alpha-particles pass through matter, their charges interact with the electrons in atoms that they encounter. Some of the electrons are knocked loose

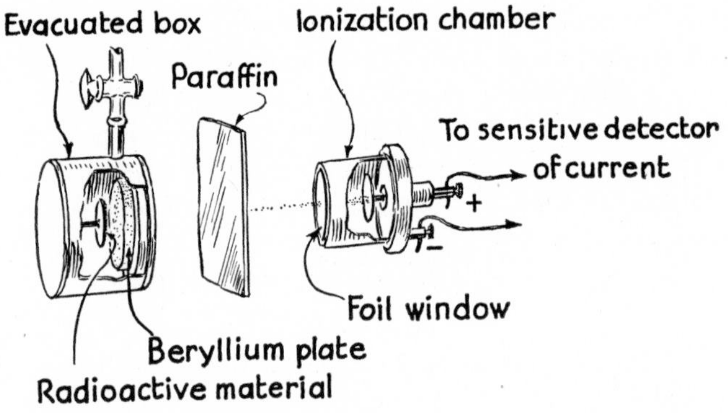

FIGURE 67–A. Apparatus used in the discovery of the neutron.

from their atoms, which therefore become ions. Hence the passage of a charged particle can be detected with a Geiger counter or an ionization chamber. If charged particles strike certain salts, e.g. zinc sulfide, they disturb the electrons in the salt in such a way that light is emitted; the impact of charged particles on the salt produces fluorescence. Neutrons pass through a material without appreciably disturbing its electrons and therefore without changing its properties. Neutrons will produce an observable effect only when they happen to collide with the nucleus of an atom. Because a nucleus is much smaller than an atom, nuclear collisions are relatively infrequent. For these reasons, neutrons are relatively unobtrusive particles.

Neutrons were finally discovered and identified in 1932 by one of Rutherford's collaborators. A year or so earlier some continental scientists, one of them a daughter of Mme. Curie, had observed that alpha-particles striking beryllium give rise to a very penetrating radiation. The radiation was so penetrating that the experimenters supposed it to be gamma-rays of extremely high frequency. Rutherford's protegé suspected that it might be the long-sought neutrons. To verify this guess, he put a beryllium disk in front of a source of alpha-rays, in an evacuated box. In front of the box he placed an ionization chamber. Figure 67–A shows the apparatus. One face of the chamber was made of thin aluminum foil, to

I. Hamouda, Zurich

FIGURE 67–B. Neutron-proton collisions in a cloud chamber. Neutrons, from a source above the top of the photograph, knock protons out of hydrogen atoms in the gas of the chamber. The protons, since they are charged particles, make visible tracks in the chamber. For this experiment, the forward-directed tracks (resulting from head-on collisions) extended for 10 cm, from which it was possible to infer a value of 3.6 Mev for the energy of the neutrons.

permit charged particles to enter the gas. When the chamber was placed in front of the beryllium, small bursts of ionization in the chamber showed that particles were coming into it.

Paraffin, chosen because it is a hydrocarbon and therefore contains an abundance of hydrogen atoms, was then interposed between the beryllium and the ionization chamber. The bursts of ionization in the chamber became much more frequent, showing that the radiation was knocking charged particles out of the paraffin. When the paraffin was replaced by a material rich in nitrogen, the bursts of ionization were larger. The particles causing the ionization were identified by the amount of ionization they produced, and by their respective ability to penetrate thin sheets of aluminum or gold.* The charged particles were found to be nuclei of hydrogen and nitrogen, respectively. Their velocities could be inferred from their penetrating powers. Having found their masses and velocities, the experimenter was able to calculate that they had been set in motion by particles whose mass is at least approximately equal to the mass of a proton.† The conclusion was that the neutron actually exists. Since it has a mass number of 1, and no charge, it can be designated by the symbol ${}_0n^1$.

Figure 67–B shows some tracks of protons that were knocked out of hydrogen atoms by a stream of neutrons passing through a cloud chamber. The neutrons themselves make no tracks, but some of them struck hydrogen nuclei in the water vapor or in the butane that had been pumped into the cloud chamber. Each such collision sets a proton in motion, and the protons make observable tracks.

67–3. The Detection of Neutrons. If a neutron makes a head-on collision with a hydrogen nucleus, then for momentum and energy to be conserved the whole energy of the neutron has to be passed on to the proton. A collision between a neutron and a heavier nucleus results in recoil of the neutron, and hence in only a partial transfer of energy from the neutron to the charged body. Therefore hydrogen is favored in the construction of neutron detectors.

Ionization chambers with a hydrogen-bearing solid in front of them, or with a hydrogen-containing gas such as butane inside of them, are still used for the detection of neutrons. One of the most widely used detectors of neutrons, however, is the photographic plate. The gelatin on the plate is rich in hydrogen. Neutrons traveling in the emulsion may therefore strike protons, which then hurtle forward in the emulsion and make a track that becomes visible when the plate is developed. The situation closely resembles that in Figure 67–B. Some neutrons make glancing collisions with the protons, and some of the recoiling protons pass out of the emulsion before coming to rest. Nevertheless a patient experimenter with a plate and a microscope can not only detect neutrons in this way, but also can use the length of the forward-directed proton tracks to find the energy of the neutrons.

67–4. Ideas About the Nucleus. The discovery of the neutron confirmed Rutherford's speculations about the constitution of the nucleus: nuclei

* The same amount of ionization can be produced by a light nucleus moving swiftly or by a heavier nucleus moving slowly, but the two cases can be distinguished because the light, swift particle has greater penetrating power. As in algebra, two sets of data are needed to solve for two unknowns, in this case the nature of the particle and its velocity.

† The calculation is based on Conservation of Momentum (Article 7–2) and on the assumption that kinetic energy, also, is conserved in the collision between the unknown particle and the hydrogen or nitrogen nucleus.

are made up of protons and neutrons. Since they are the building blocks from which nuclei are made, protons and neutrons are called *nucleons.*

The fundamental principle of nuclear structure is simple. The total number of particles is equal to the mass number of the nucleus (Article 65–2). $_1H^1$ has a single nucleon in its nucleus, and $_{16}S^{34}$ has 34 nucleons. Since the protons are the only charged particles in the nucleus, the number of protons is equal to the charge on the nucleus, expressed in quanta. This means that the number of protons is equal to the atomic number. Hence $_{16}S^{34}$ has 16 protons in its nucleus. If it has 34 nucleons and only 16 are protons, then the other 18 must be neutrons.

This principle shows that isotopes of the same element have the same number of protons in their nuclei, but different numbers of neutrons. For example, $_6C^{12}$ has 6 protons and 6 neutrons, but $_6C^{13}$ has 6 protons and 7 neutrons.

After digesting this simple principle, one may begin to wonder what holds a nucleus together. Surely it is not electrical forces that do so; a neutron has no charge, and the protons are all charged alike so that their electrical interactions are repulsions. Can the nucleus be held together by gravitational attractions? A short calculation based on Newton's Law of Gravitation (Article 8–2) shows that if a nucleus were held together only by gravitational forces, then it would come apart much more easily than it actually does. In entering the nuclear realm, therefore, we have uncovered the existence of some new kind of force, not gravitational and not electrical. Finding out about this force is one of the main problems in present-day physical science.

67–5. Cosmic Rays. Since about 1900, it has been known that a charge placed on a carefully insulated electroscope will gradually leak off through the air. This leakage shows that the air is to some extent ionized. At first the ionization was thought to be due entirely to the radiations from radioactive materials in the ground; to test this idea an electroscope was taken up in a balloon (1912). As was expected, the rate of leakage at first decreased as the electroscope was taken away from the ground. At higher altitudes, however, the leakage increased again. At 15,000 feet the charge leaked off several times as fast as it did on the ground. This increase was entirely contrary to expectation; it showed that there are more ions at high altitudes than there are near sea level, and that an ionizing agent must be entering the atmosphere from outside. Since the amount of ionization is about the same by night as by day, it must be caused by something else than the sun. Much patient research has shown that the ionization is caused by swiftly moving nuclei that come from outside the solar system. They are called *primary cosmic rays.* From the tracks they make in photographic plates carried to very high altitudes by balloons or rockets, it is known that most of the primary cosmic rays are protons, and that some are heavier nuclei. Their penetrating power shows that they have astonishingly high energies—often many billions of electron-volts.

High in the atmosphere, the primary cosmic rays begin to collide with atoms of the air. Just what happens is one of the very lively topics of research today, but one known result is that other energetic particles, many of them electrons and some of them heavier particles, come streaming through the atmosphere. These are called *secondary cosmic rays.*

67–6. The Positron (1932). By 1930 about all that was known of the cosmic rays was that they come from outside the solar system, and that some of them will pass through many feet of rock or even lead. Millikan realized that much might be learned by observing their tracks in a cloud chamber placed in a strong magnetic field. Such a chamber was built under his direction, and the young experimenter who carried out the work soon received a Nobel prize for his pains, because he discovered a new kind of particle.

Most of the tracks that appeared in the cloud chamber were the thin tracks that an experimenter recognizes as being caused by electrons. The tracks were curved, because of the force which a moving charge experiences in a magnetic field. There was nothing remarkable about most of these tracks, but the one in Figure 67–C was a find of prime importance. The particle that made this track passed through the lead plate in the center of the picture, and naturally in doing so it lost some velocity. For a charged particle moving across a magnetic field, the higher the velocity, the straighter the path. In Figure 67–C, the lower part of the track is less curved than the upper part. If the particle traveled faster on the lower side of the plate, it must have been traveling upward. The magnetic field in the cloud chamber was directed into the page. The rules in Article 32–3 therefore show that the charge on the particle was positive, even though the appearance of the track showed the experimenter that the mass of the particle is like that of an electron.

Particles like the one detected in Figure 67–C are now well known in the nuclear laboratory. They are called *positrons*, and they are fundamental particles. Except for having opposite charge, positrons are just like electrons, but positrons are less plentiful.

Much newer evidence (1955) indicates that there is also an *antiproton,* a particle that resembles the proton but has negative charge.

67–7. The Mesons (1937 and later). To analyze the cosmic radiation, many thousands of cloud-chamber photographs have been made. Some of the tracks cannot be ascribed to protons, electrons, or positrons. They

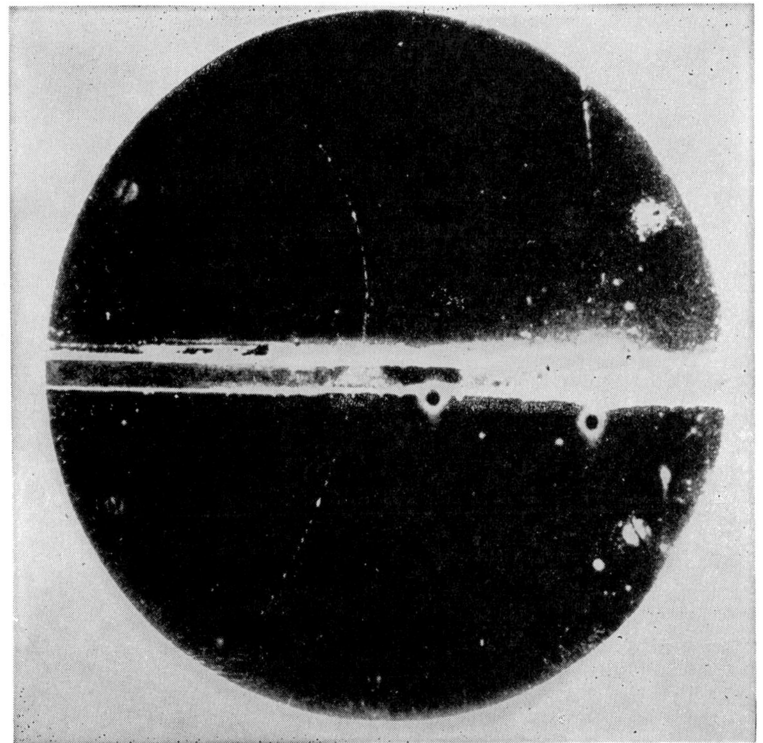

C. D. Anderson, California Institute of Technology

FIGURE 67-C. The cloud-chamber photograph that revealed the existence of positrons.

show the presence of other particles, called *mesons.* The most abundant types are π-mesons and μ-mesons, whose respective masses are 273 and 207 times as great as the mass of an electron.

The cloud-chamber photograph in Figure 67-D exhibits the tracks of two protons, two electrons, and a meson. Tracks *B* and *E* are characteristic of electrons. The electron in *B* was moving slower than the one in *E*, as we can tell from the fact that its path is heavier and more sharply curved. Tracks *A* and *C* are even heavier than track *B*, but *A* and *C* cannot have been made by slow electrons, because these tracks are too straight. These straight heavy tracks must therefore have been caused by a massive particle rather than by a slow one of little mass. They are characteristic tracks of protons.

Track *D* cannot be an electron track, because it is less curved than *E*, but heavier. It cannot be a proton track because it is lighter than *C*, but not so straight. It is the track of a meson.

By comparing the curvatures and the droplet populations of tracks D and E, it is possible to compare the mass of the meson with the mass of the electron. Similar measurements make it possible to distinguish π-mesons from μ-mesons.

A magnetic field bends some π-meson and μ-meson paths in one direction and others in the opposite direction, showing that the heavy and light mesons both have positive and negative varieties. There is also some evidence for neutral mesons.

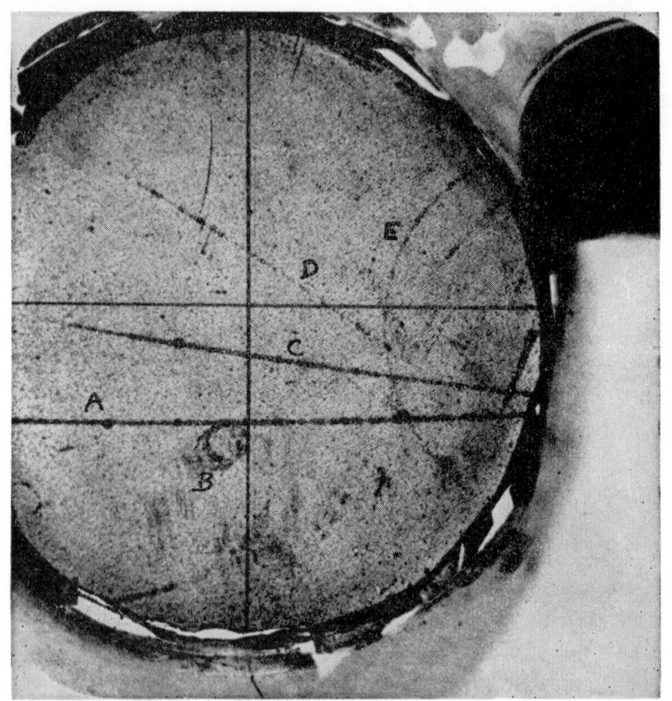

G. Ascoli, University of Illinois

FIGURE 67–D. Tracks A and C were made by protons, B and E by electrons, and D by a different charged particle, a meson.

Mesons are still mysterious particles. We know that they spring from the interaction of primary cosmic rays with matter. They can also be made in the laboratory, by bombarding nuclei with protons from the largest cyclotrons. What we do not know is how they fit into the general scheme of matter. It is strongly suspected that nucleons are bound to one another by sharing mesons, much as atoms are bound by sharing electrons. The copious supply of mesons from the new cyclotrons may soon improve our understanding of this question.

Summary

The ultimate constitution of matter is still unknown. Only a modest number of particles, however, cannot now be explained in terms of something simpler. These particles, of which the electron is one, are called fundamental particles.

Nuclei are made up of protons and neutrons, the protons being hydrogen nuclei and the neutrons being uncharged particles with about the same mass as protons. Neutrons and protons are both called nucleons.

Because neutrons have no charge, they do not interact significantly with atoms unless they happen to strike nuclei. This means that they can penetrate matter very readily, and it also means that they are hard to detect. They are detected by the effects that they produce when they do collide with nuclei.

Neutrons and protons both contribute to the mass of a nucleus, but only the protons contribute to its charge. The mass number of a nucleus is equal to the total number of nucleons in the nucleus, and the atomic number is equal to the number of protons in the nucleus. The numbers of protons and neutrons in a given nucleus are therefore easy to determine.

At present the chief problem in nuclear physics is the investigation of the force that binds nucleons together into a nucleus.

Primary cosmic rays are very energetic particles that come to the earth from space. Their interaction with nuclei in the air produces secondary cosmic rays. The secondary rays are varied in constitution. One constituent is the positron, a particle like the electron but positively charged; other constituents are negative, positive, and neutral mesons, which are heavier than electrons but lighter than protons. It may be that nucleons are bound to one another by sharing mesons, in somewhat the same way that atoms can be bound to one another by shared pairs of electrons.

Questions

1. What is a fundamental particle?
2. What is a proton?
3. What is a neutron?
4. What is a nucleon?
5. How do we know the number of nucleons in a given nucleus? How do we know how many of them are protons?
6. Give the numbers of protons and neutrons in the nucleus of each of the following atoms: ${}_1H^1$, ${}_1H^2$, ${}_2He^4$, ${}_7N^{14}$, ${}_9F^{19}$, ${}_{17}Cl^{35}$, ${}_{17}Cl^{37}$, ${}_{25}Mn^{55}$, ${}_{47}Ag^{107}$, ${}_{53}I^{127}$, ${}_{82}Pb^{208}$, ${}_{92}U^{238}$.
7. What are cosmic rays?
8. Describe the discovery of cosmic rays.

9. What is a positron?
10. How were positrons discovered?
11. What are mesons? How can they be detected?
12. What is the present tentative opinion as to what holds the nucleus together?
13. How can neutrons be detected?
14. Describe the discovery of the neutron.
15. The text states (page 598) that when a charged particle moves across a magnetic field, the higher its velocity, the straighter its path. By combining Newton's Second Law with the equations for the acceleration in uniform circular motion (Article 6–4) and for the force on a charged particle moving across a magnetic field (Article 42–1), find an equation that relates the radius of the path to the velocity of the particle. Show that this equation confirms the statement in the text.

Suggestions for Further Reading

Hans A. Bethe, "What Holds the Nucleus Together?" *Scientific American*, September, 1953, pp. 58–63. A qualitative discussion by one of the world's leading nuclear theorists.

C. D. Anderson, "The Positive Electron," *Physical Review*, vol. 43, 491 (1933). Reprinted in *Foundations of Nuclear Physics* (ed. R. T. Beyer; New York: Dover Publications, Inc., 1949). Anderson's first detailed account of his discovery of the positron.

68

NUCLEAR REACTIONS

For about a decade after Rutherford observed the transmutation of nitrogen under the impact of alpha-particles (1919), most of the physicists in the world remained busy with spectra and the electronic configurations of the various atoms. By 1930, the outsides of atoms were pretty well understood. Many of the most enterprising physicists then turned their attention to the insides of atoms, to the nuclei. The lore of transmutation developed rapidly.

68–1. A Typical Nuclear Reaction. When Rutherford first made an artificial transmutation, he did so by letting alpha-particles strike nitrogen nuclei (Article 65–7). The production of protons showed that a transmutation had taken place, but there was no conclusive evidence as to what the nitrogen had been transmuted to. Such evidence was supplied later by one of Rutherford's younger colleagues, who made the transmutation occur in a cloud chamber. One of the pictures he took is reproduced in Figure 68–A. Most of the tracks are made by alpha-particles from a bit of radioactive material (thorium C) placed in the chamber. One track ends in a fork; the forking point is the scene of a transmutation. The longer track is made by the proton that Rutherford already knew to be freed by the transmutation. The other tine of the fork is a short track, heavier than the track of an alpha-particle. It is made by the new nucleus formed in the transmutation. The alpha-particle has disappeared.

From the cloud-chamber photograph, we can learn exactly what the transmutation involves. The product of the transmutation, as we can see from the tracks, is just two particles, one of which is a proton. Call the other one x. Then we can describe the transmutation symbolically. Remembering that an alpha-particle is a helium nucleus, and that a proton is a hydrogen nucleus whose mass number is 1, we can write (Article 65–2)

$$_{7}N^{14} + {_2}He^{4} \rightarrow x + {_1}H^{1}.$$

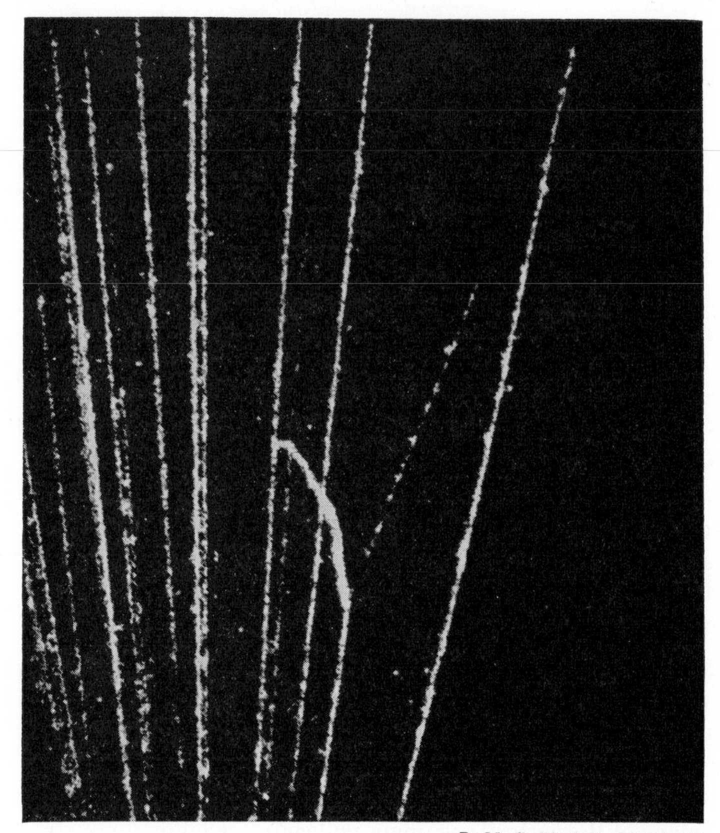

P. M. S. Blackett, Manchester

FIGURE 68–A. A cloud-chamber picture of a nuclear reaction.

Here we are writing the equation for a transmutation, or *nuclear reaction,* not a chemical reaction. Confusion with chemistry is avoided by letting the symbols include the charges and masses of the nuclei.

It is now easy to identify x, the new nucleus formed in the reaction. The reacting particles on the left have 9 quanta of charge $(7 + 2)$. Since charge is conserved, there must be 9 quanta of charge on the right; the proton has only 1, so x must have 8. Since x is a nucleus with a charge of 8 quanta, it occupies the eighth place in the Periodic Table. Therefore x is oxygen. Applying the same reasoning to the masses, we find that the mass number of x is 17. Hence the reaction is

$$_7N^{14} + {_2He^4} \rightarrow {_8O^{17}} + {_1H^1}.$$

68–2. Another Nuclear Reaction. Neutrons were discovered as products of the nuclear reaction that occurs when alpha-particles strike beryllium

(Article 67–2). The only isotope of beryllium that is found in nature is $_4Be^9$. Moreover, cloud-chamber studies have shown that when the bombarding particles have energies of only a few million electron-volts, then a nuclear reaction normally gives rise to just two product particles. The reaction discussed in the last article is therefore typical, in that there are two reactants on each side of the equation. With this knowledge, we can write out an equation for the reaction that produces neutrons when alpha-particles strike beryllium. It is

$$_4Be^9 + {}_2He^4 \rightarrow {}_6C^{12} + {}_0n^1.$$

68–3. Artificial Radioactivity (1934). Irene Joliot-Curie and her husband, the foremost French nuclear experimenter, have already been mentioned in connection with their near-discovery of the neutron. Continuing their study of the effects of alpha-particles on the nuclei of light elements, they soon did discover something else of great importance.

They directed alpha-particles, from polonium, against a bit of boron mounted in a cloud chamber. They found that the irradiated sample emitted neutrons, and that it also emitted charged particles whose tracks in the cloud chamber looked like tracks of electrons. On putting the cloud chamber in the field of a strong magnet, however, and observing the direction in which the particles curved, they found the particles to be positively charged. The particles were therefore identified as positrons (Article 67–6). The experimenters found to their astonishment that even after they stopped bombarding the boron sample with alpha-rays, the emission of positrons continued. They had therefore discovered a nuclear reaction that produces *artificial radioactivity.*

They offered a simple and correct interpretation of what was happening. They assumed that they had produced an artificial transmutation of boron by an alpha-particle. This reaction produced a neutron, as could be seen by the tracks made in the chamber by protons that were set in motion by some of the neutrons. In order to make the charges and masses balance, it was necessary to assume that $_7N^{13}$ was produced:

$$_5B^{10} + {}_2He^4 \rightarrow {}_7N^{13} + {}_0n^1.$$

They further assumed that the positrons came from the nitrogen. This was not unreasonable, even though the effect is not observed with ordinary nitrogen, because the nitrogen found in nature is not N^{13}; it consists of N^{14} and a trace of N^{15}. To see whether their new isotope of nitrogen was really responsible for the radioactivity, the experimenters bombarded boron nitride, BN, with alpha-particles, and then heated the sample with sodium hydroxide to form ammonia:

$$BN + 3NaOH \rightarrow Na_3BO_3 + NH_3.$$

The idea was that if the nuclear reaction was really turning some of the boron into a radioactive isotope of nitrogen, then this nitrogen would be carried away in the ammonia gas along with the ordinary nitrogen from the BN. They found that the radioactivity actually was handed over to the ammonia gas, and hence that they had guessed its source correctly.

When the ${}_7N^{13}$ emits a positron, it loses 1 quantum of charge and has a charge of 6 left. It then is a nucleus not of nitrogen, but of carbon. The loss of a positron entails no change in mass number, so the resulting nucleus is ${}_6C^{13}$.

The radioactive nitrogen is found to have a half-life of only about 10 minutes. Therefore if any of it ever existed in nature, it has all turned to carbon by now.

It is convenient to let the term "beta-ray" refer to the emission of either an electron or a positron from a nucleus, designating an electron by β^- and a positron by β^+. Using this symbolism, we can summarize the chain of events by the nuclear equation

$$
\begin{array}{l}
{}_5B^{10} + {}_2He^4 \rightarrow {}_7N^{13} + {}_0n^1 \\
\qquad\qquad\qquad\quad \searrow \text{10 min} \\
\qquad\qquad\qquad\qquad {}_6C^{13} + \beta^+
\end{array}
$$

68–4. "Tagged Atoms." Radioactive isotopes of many other light elements besides nitrogen have been made, by bombarding ordinary materials with nuclear particles. They have opened up a whole new realm of possibilities in structural chemistry and in biology, because they enable the researcher to distinguish certain (radioactive) atoms of an element from other (stable) atoms of the same element. For this reason, journalists refer to radioactive isotopes as tagged atoms. A few examples of their use may be of interest.

Research in organic chemistry, including the chemistry of living things, has received a valuable tool in C^{14}, a radioactive isotope made by bombarding N^{14} with neutrons. It can be used to make organic compounds, and *these particular carbon atoms* will be traceable by virtue of their radioactivity. For example, one can use them in a synthetic vitamin and then see what happens to them when an animal eats the vitamin.

One typical application of tagged atoms of carbon was made during a study of carbon monoxide poisoning. The people doing the research wanted to know whether carbon monoxide (CO) that enters the blood stream is converted into carbon dioxide (CO_2). Without the use of tagged atoms they could not tell whether it is or not, because of course carbon dioxide is always present in air exhaled from the lungs. They therefore made some carbon monoxide with radioactive carbon * and got a human subject to inhale it. Then they caught

* This work was done with C^{11}, made by bombarding B^{11} with protons from a cyclotron. The use of C^{14} in human subjects is inhibited by the fact that it has a half-life of thousands of years, and therefore could cause ionization in the body over a period so long that it might be dangerous.

the carbon dioxide exhaled by the subject and tested it for radioactivity. It was not radioactive; their work therefore showed that the body does not convert carbon monoxide to the dioxide.

The thyroid gland supplies the body with a hormone, thyroxine, whose molecule contains four atoms of iodine (Article 63–8). A small amount of iodine in the food is therefore necessary for the proper functioning of the thyroid gland, but sometimes the gland does not function properly even if it is supplied with iodine. A study was made of the rate of uptake of iodine by the gland in people with underactive, normal, and overactive thyroid function.

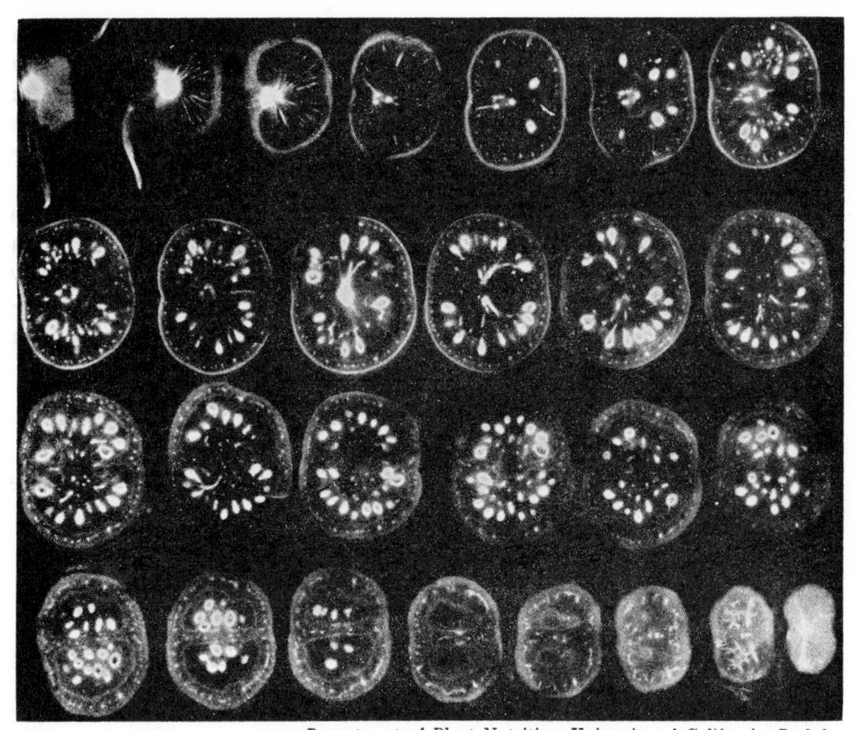

Department of Plant Nutrition, University of California, Berkeley

FIGURE 68–B. An autoradiograph showing the location of zinc atoms in a tomato. The work shows that zinc from the soil goes primarily into the seeds.

The subjects were fed small amounts of sodium iodide made from radioactive iodine manufactured with the help of a cyclotron. The thyroid gland is in the neck, and the amount of radioactive iodine in it could be determined by simply placing a Geiger counter against the patient's neck. It was found that the underactive glands took up almost none of the iodine; normal glands took up 3.5 percent of it over the course of a couple of days, and retained it without loss; and the overactive glands took up 14 percent within three hours, but did not retain it. Such studies throw valuable light on the gland and its disorders.

Tagged atoms are of use also to those who study plants. It has been known for some time that certain cultivated plants need soil in which there are traces of various metals. Figure 68–B was made by feeding radioactive zinc, $_{30}Zn^{65}$, to a tomato plant, and then letting thin frozen slices of one of the tomatoes lie on a photographic film. Beta-rays from the zinc atoms affected the film and made images of the slices; the picture shows that nearly all of the zinc in the tomato goes into the seeds. This conclusion could not have been reached easily by chemical means, since the total amount of zinc in the tomato was only about a millionth of a gram.

68–5. Energy in Nuclear Reactions. As might be expected, much can be learned from a quantitative study of the energy changes occurring in nuclear reactions. In an artificial transmutation, projectiles with a certain energy hit the nucleus, and other particles carry energy away from the scene. What about the energy balance: Is the reaction endothermic or exothermic?

Because chemical reactions normally liberate or absorb energy in the form of heat, the energies in chemical reactions are usually expressed in calories. In nuclear reactions, the energy liberated or absorbed is normally the kinetic energy of charged particles, and these energies can most conveniently be measured in millions of electron-volts (Article 45–5). It is a simple but very dull problem to compare an electron-volt with a calorie. The answer is

$$1 \text{ electron-volt} = 3.8 \times 10^{-23} \text{ calorie.}$$

Returning to Rutherford's first artificial transmutation, we can improve our description of the reaction by writing

$$_7N^{14} + {}_2He^4 + \text{K.E.} \rightarrow {}_8O^{17} + {}_1H^1 + \text{K.E.}$$

The velocities, and hence the kinetic energies, of the particles can be measured by making the reaction occur in a cloud chamber and measuring the curvature of the particle tracks when the chamber is in a known magnetic field. It is found that the total K.E. of the product particles is slightly less than the K.E. of the impinging alpha-particles; the reaction is endothermic.

As an example of an exothermic nuclear reaction, we can consider one of the reactions observed in Rutherford's laboratory when the first simple accelerator (Article 66–5) was put into operation. This accelerator would operate at differences of potential as high as 600,000 volts, or 0.6 million volts, and would therefore give protons a K.E. as high as 0.6 Mev. It was found that protons with K.E. as low as 0.2 Mev can produce transmutation of lithium. When these protons impinged on a lithium target mounted in a cloud chamber, pairs of identical particles were seen to emerge from the target, showing that the following reaction took place:

$$_3Li^7 + {}_1H^1 \rightarrow {}_2He^4 + {}_2He^4.$$

From the length of the alpha-particle tracks in the cloud chamber, it is found that each alpha-particle is ejected with a K.E. of 8.7 Mev, making 17.4 Mev for the pair. To take cognizance of the energy change involved, we can write the reaction in the form:

$$_3Li^7 + {}_1H^1 + 0.20 \text{ Mev} \rightarrow {}_2He^4 + {}_2He^4 + 17.4 \text{ Mev}.$$

This reaction is clearly exothermic, the energy released being 17.2 Mev.

It is interesting to compare the energy released by the "splitting" of lithium atoms with the energy released in some exothermic chemical reaction, for example the burning of hydrogen. When a mole of hydrogen combines with oxygen to form a mole of water, about 60 calories of heat are produced at the expense of chemical energy. The resulting mole of water contains about 6×10^{23} molecules of water (Article 43–3), so the amount of energy released by the formation of 1 molecule is 60 calories divided by 6×10^{23}. The amount is 10^{-22} calorie, or a little less than 3 electron-volts.

Comparing the 3 electron-volts released by the formation of a water molecule with the 17.2 *million* electron-volts released by the splitting of a lithium nucleus, we see that nuclear changes involve far more energy than chemical changes do. A chemical reaction can produce a useful amount of heat, because there are so many molecules in a mole, or even in a gram. Now, since a gram of lithium contains about 10^{23} atoms, the energy liberated if we could split all of them would be prodigious. Unfortunately, reactions like this show absolutely no promise for commercial purposes, because for each lithium atom that is split there are thousands of fast protons from the accelerator that are wasted because they do not score hits on any nucleus. Therefore, the energy obtained from the distintegrations is less than the energy that has to be supplied to the accelerator.

68–6. Masses in Nuclear Reactions. Thus far in dealing with the masses of various nuclei or atoms, we have used simply the mass numbers of the atoms, which express their relative mass merely to the nearest whole number. The mass spectrograph (Article 44–2) is capable of great accuracy; for example it tells us that the mass of the Li^7 atom is 7.0182 atomic mass units,* while that of the He^4 atom is 4.0039. Remembering Lavoisier's finding that in a chemical reaction the total mass of the products is equal to the total mass of the reactants, let us see whether the same law holds for nuclear reactions.

$$\begin{array}{ccccc} {}_1H^1 & + & {}_3Li^7 \rightarrow & {}_2He^4 & + \; {}_2He^4 \\ 1.0081 & & 7.0182 & 4.0039 & 4.0039 \\ \text{Total} = & & 8.0263 & \text{Total} = & 8.0078 \end{array}$$

$$\text{Discrepancy} = 0.0185 \text{ atomic mass units}$$

* One atomic mass unit is one-sixteenth of the mass of an atom of O^{16}. It is 1.66×10^{-27} kg.

Clearly the masses do *not* balance, some mass disappears in the reaction.*

Naturally we ask, "If mass disappears, what becomes of it?" The answer was supplied ahead of time by Einstein. About 1905, he set out to discover why light travels at the same speed in all directions on the earth, in spite of the earth's motion in its orbit. By a subtle and difficult line of reasoning, he was led to his famous theory of "relativity." One result was a revision of the concepts of space and time; another was the assertion that the inertia of a body is associated with the energy of the body, so that if a body loses energy, then its mass decreases. This conclusion was backed up experimentally by a German investigator who studied the deflection of swift electrons in a magnetic field. He showed that these electrons had a slightly smaller charge-to-mass ratio when they had more K.E.

One implication of Einstein's discovery is that mass is not an inherent property of a body, but that it should rather be regarded as a form of energy. He showed that a mass of m kilograms is equivalent to mc^2 joules, where c is the velocity of light in meters/second. This statement can be compressed into the now celebrated equation

$$E = mc^2.$$

Since c is very large (3×10^8 m/sec), one kilogram is equivalent to a very large number of joules (9×10^{16} joules).

The application of Einstein's equation to atomic affairs is complicated by our habit of expressing masses in atomic mass units rather than in kilograms, and expressing energies in Mev rather than in joules. A simple calculation, based on definitions given in various earlier chapters, shows that

$$931 \text{ Mev} = 1 \text{ atomic mass unit.}$$

In the light of Einstein's theory, we see that if the proton-lithium reaction liberates 17.2 Mev of K.E., then a certain amount of mass should disappear. Calling this amount x and using the last equation, we find

$$\frac{17.2}{931} = \frac{x}{1},$$

or

$$x = 0.0185 \text{ atomic mass units.}$$

This amount is just the "discrepancy" that we noted in the mass balance.† The proton-lithium reaction therefore verifies Einstein's conception of the

* This is why the phrase "chemical reaction" occurs in the Law of Conservation of Matter, Article 20–2.

† One might fear that the change of mass in a nuclear reaction would sometimes be so large that the mass numbers in the equation would not balance. This fear is not justified, however. To use up a whole unit of mass, the reaction would have to release 931 Mev of energy. Actual reactions do not release such a huge energy.

equivalence of mass and energy. It is typical of many nuclear reactions in which we can actually convert mass into mechanical or thermal energy.

In an exothermic chemical reaction, Einstein's theory asserts that mass disappears, but the energy changes in chemical reactions are so small that the loss of mass is not detectable.

In endothermic nuclear reactions, a measurable amount of mass is *created* at the expense of the K.E. of the bombarding particles. An even more startling creation of mass occurs in the cosmic rays and in some laboratory experiments. Here very energetic photons that come within the field of a nucleus can have their electromagnetic energy converted into mass by the formation of an electron and a positron. Figure 68-C

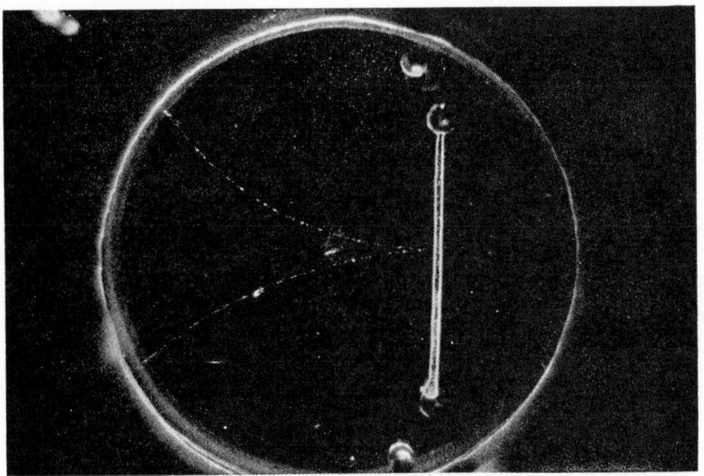

E. R. Gaerttner and M. L. Yeater, Research Laboratory, General Electric Co.

FIGURE 68-C. Electron-pair creation in a cloud chamber. Gamma-ray photons coming from the right strike a thin plate, in which occasionally one of them is converted into an electron-positron pair.

shows the cloud-chamber tracks of a pair of particles freshly created in this way. The cloud chamber is in a magnetic field which curves the paths of the particles; the opposite curvatures of the two tracks show that the particles have opposite charge. From the curvature and density of the tracks, it is concluded that the particles are an electron and a positron.

When a positron collides with an electron, the two can neutralize one another's charge and annihilate one another. Their mass is converted into electromagnetic (gamma-ray) energy. This annihilation is the reason that positrons are not commonly found, and it shows emphatically the need for revising the old idea that matter can neither be created nor destroyed.

68–7. More Violent Reactions. When the bombarding particle has an energy of many millions of electron-volts, the resulting reaction sometimes gives rise to more than two product particles. One such reaction, a very violent one, appears in the track-plate photograph in Figure 68–D.

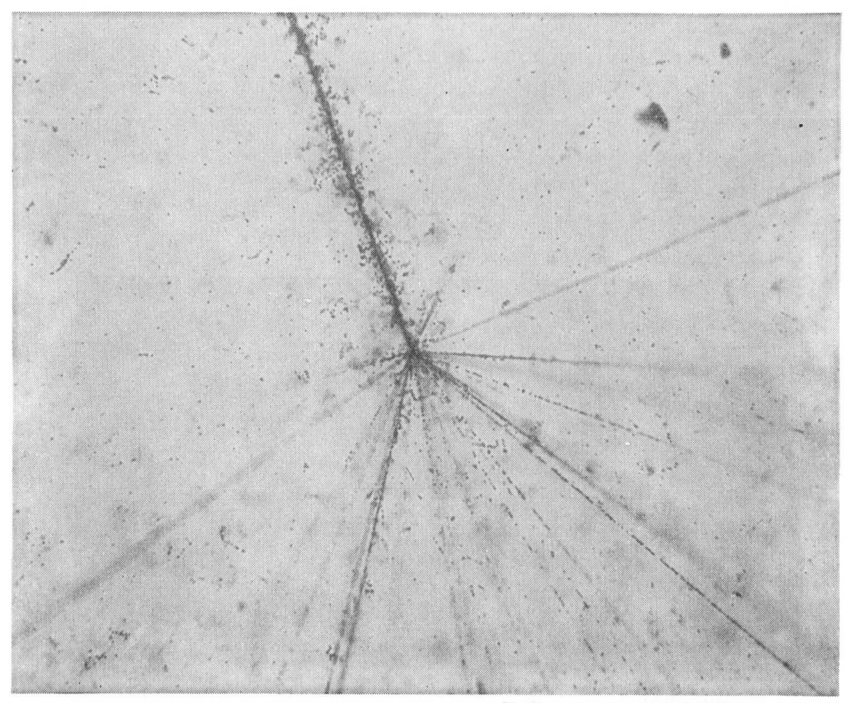

H. Yagoda, National Institutes of Health

FIGURE 68–D. A violent nuclear reaction, brought on by a nuclear collision at very high energy.

While this plate was held in the stratosphere by a balloon, a nucleus of iron made the heavy track and then hit a nucleus of silver or bromine in the gelatin. The collision caused a very serious disruption of the nuclei. From the energies of the fragments, one can infer that the iron nucleus had an energy of something like a billion electron-volts. Reactions like this cannot as yet be explained in detail by any theory.

SUMMARY

Experiments can give us enough information about a nuclear reaction so that we can describe it by means of an equation, if we invoke the conservation of charge and the approximate conservation of mass. In the equation, the charges must balance and the mass numbers must balance.

Some atoms, when bombarded with nuclear particles, turn into atoms that are radioactive. The artificial radioactive atoms usually emit electrons or positrons. Besides being of interest physically, they are useful as "tagged atoms," or "tracers," in chemical and biological research.

Studies of nuclear reactions have verified Einstein's assertion that mass should be regarded as a form of energy. In exothermic nuclear reactions, mass disappears and is converted into K.E. of the product particles. In endothermic nuclear reactions, K.E. is converted into mass. The energy equivalence E of a mass m is given by Einstein's equation $E = mc^2$. Energy changes in nuclear reactions may be accompanied by the creation or annihilation of particles.

It is believed that change of mass occurs, in principle, in chemical reactions, but the amount of change is too small to detect. The energy in a chemical reaction amounts to only a few electron-volts per molecule, in contrast to the energies of millions of electron-volts per nucleus in nuclear reactions.

Questions

1. Explain how Figure 68–A enables us to know what products resulted from Rutherford's transmutation of nitrogen with alpha-particles.
2. In an equation for a nuclear reaction, what quantities must balance?
3. Write equations for the following nuclear reactions:
   (a) Na^{23} is bombarded by protons, and neutrons are produced.
   (b) B^{10} is bombarded by neutrons, and alpha-particles are produced.
   (c) O^{16} is bombarded with protons, and fluorine is produced.
   (d) F^{19} is bombarded by nuclei of deuterium, H^2 (Article 44–3). Oxygen is produced.

   Assume in each case that the bombarding particle does not have enough energy to produce more than two product particles.
4. If the products of a nuclear reaction have more kinetic energy than the initial particles did, what can be said about the masses of the particles?

69

NUCLEAR BINDING

Nuclear physics is unclear physics.
CONTEMPORARY SAGE

Having discovered that molecules are composed of atoms, that atoms are composed of electrons and nuclei, and that nuclei are composed of protons and neutrons, atomic scientists have been faced with three fundamental problems:

What holds atoms together so that they form molecules?
What holds electrons and nuclei together so that they form atoms?
What holds protons and neutrons together so that they form nuclei?

We have seen that answers to the first two questions have been worked out very satisfactorily. The electrons are bound to the nuclei by electric attraction, and when we work out the details of this binding, we find that the electrons tend to congregate in shells that can accommodate definitely limited numbers of electrons. The tendency to fill these shells, either by a lending and borrowing of electrons (ionic binding) or by a sharing of electron pairs (covalent binding), accounts for the union of atoms to form either molecules or crystals. No such clear-cut answer to the third question exists as yet.

Our understanding of the atomic nucleus is probably as incomplete as the understanding of the solar system before the time of Newton, and the reasons are much the same in the two cases. Before Newton's day, nobody knew about the gravitational force, which makes the planets move as they do. Today, we know a very little about the forces that bind nucleons together to form a nucleus.

69–1. The Mass of the Neutron. In the interpretation of some experiments that bear on nuclear binding, the mass of the neutron is needed. The usual way of finding the mass of an atomic or subatomic particle is by deflecting it in magnetic and electric fields, to find its charge-to-mass ratio. Then, when the charge is known, the mass can be found. The neutron, having no charge, would experience no deflection in a mass spectrograph. The mass of the neutron must therefore be sought by other means. It can be calculated by finding a nuclear reaction in which the masses of the other particles are known and in which the kinetic energies can be accurately measured. The result of the best experiments is

$$\text{Mass of neutron} = 1.00897 \text{ atomic mass units.}$$

69–2. The Nuclear Force. Although there is as yet no satisfactory theory of nuclear binding, some generalizations about nuclei have been well established. The mere existence of nuclei shows that nucleons attract one another if they are close enough together. The forces that hold nuclei together cannot be electric attractions, because the only charges in the nucleus are positive. Gravitational attractions presumably exist in the nucleus, but the work required to break up a nucleus is about 10^{38} times as much as can be accounted for by Newton's Law of Gravitation. Because it seems unrelated to other kinds of force, the force of attraction between the nucleons is called the *nuclear force.*

The nuclear force differs quite fundamentally from the electrical and gravitational forces. Each of the latter forces is inversely proportional to the square of the distance between the interacting particles (Articles 8–2 and 29–1). If the distance between the particles is doubled, the electric or gravitational force drops to one-fourth of its previous value. There is clear evidence, however, that if the distance between two bound nucleons is doubled, then the nuclear force drops to almost nothing. The evidence comes from nuclear masses, which can be measured with a mass spectrograph (Article 44–2).

Two of the naturally occurring isotopes of oxygen are ${}_{8}O^{17}$ and ${}_{8}O^{18}$. They differ by one neutron. The neutron would have a mass of 1.00897 units if it were isolated, but in being attached to the O^{18} nucleus, it lost energy and therefore lost mass. The two isotopes have masses of 17.0045 and 18.0049 units; the difference, 1.0004 units, is the mass of the bound neutron. To extract a neutron from O^{18} would therefore demand a mass increase of $1.00897 - 1.0004 = 0.0085$ mass units, which is equivalent to 8 Mev of work.

Consider now two isotopes of platinum, ${}_{78}Pt^{194}$ and ${}_{78}Pt^{195}$. Their masses are 194.039 and 195.039 units, respectively. The difference is 1.000 units, so in this case the binding of the additional neutron causes a loss in mass amounting to $1.00897 - 1.000 = 0.009$ mass units, or just over 8 Mev of work.

It is very remarkable that a neutron is bound nearly equally in O^{18} and in Pt^{195}, because in O^{18} there are only seventeen other nucleons, whereas in Pt^{195}, there are nearly two hundred other nucleons. The conclusion is that the neutron is not attracted by all of the other nucleons in the nucleus, but only by its close neighbors. In other words, the nuclear force can extend only to very short distances. Two nucleons on opposite sides of the Pt nucleus do not attract one another noticeably, even though they are only about 10^{-14} meter apart. In fact, if these nucleons both are protons, then they will repel one another, because of their electric charge.

69–3. Nuclear Binding. Knowing that a nucleon is attracted only to its nearest neighbors, we can make a beginning on a theory of the nucleus. An important clue is found by studying the numbers of protons and neutrons in the various nuclei that occur in nature. Figure 69–A is a plot

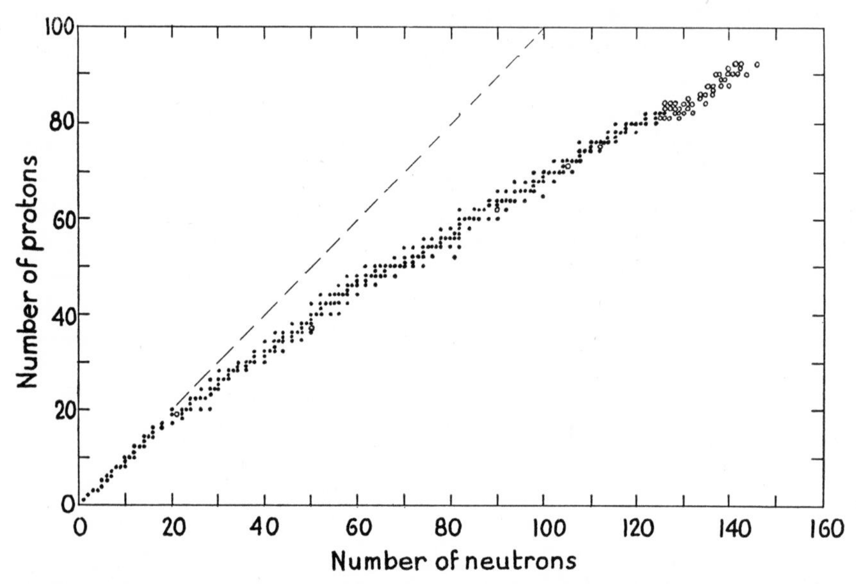

FIGURE 69–A. A plot of the numbers of protons and neutrons in the nuclei that are found in nature. The black dots represent stable nuclei, and the open circles, radioactive nuclei. The dashed line denotes the same number of neutrons as protons; the plot shows that the simplest nuclei have about as many neutrons as they have protons, but that in the more complex nuclei, the neutrons have a majority.

of these numbers. In the stable isotopes of the light elements, the mass number is about twice the atomic number. In other words, about half of the nucleons in a light nucleus are protons. These nuclei, therefore, contain equal or nearly equal numbers of protons and neutrons. Examples are ${}_2He^4$, ${}_3Li^6$, ${}_7N^{14}$, ${}_8O^{16}$, and ${}_{17}Cl^{35}$. In the heavier nuclei, however, the neutrons always outnumber the protons. For example, gold, ${}_{79}Au^{197}$, has 79 protons and $197 - 79 = 118$ neutrons.

The proportion of neutrons in the nucleus can be explained by assuming that Pauli's Exclusion Principle (Article 53–1) applies to the nucleons. It is believed that in the nucleus, as in the atom, only certain states of motion are possible. The Exclusion Principle prevents two identical particles from having the same motion. A proton and a neutron can have the same motion, because they are dissimilar particles. Some states of motion will be preferred, by virtue of their energy's being low. If each such state will accommodate a proton and a neutron, then protons and neutrons will tend to be present in equal numbers.

The composition of the heavy nuclei can be understood by taking into account the electric repulsions of the protons. Unless two protons are very close together, the nuclear force of attraction between them is overbalanced by the ordinary electric repulsions that the protons exert on one another by reason of their charge. Therefore a proton in a nucleus is attracted by the neighboring protons (and also by the neighboring neutrons), but it is repelled by the more distant protons. In a complicated nucleus like that of gold, many of the protons will be far enough apart to repel one another. This effect will disrupt the nucleus unless some "extra" neutrons are present to cement the protons together. As has been mentioned above, gold has 118 neutrons to go with its 79 protons. When nuclei contain about ninety protons, they are rickety structures no matter how many neutrons they contain, and they eventually come apart of their own accord. This we know from the fact that the elements near the end of the Periodic Table are radioactive. We can now interpret radioactivity in some detail.

69–4. The Origin of Alpha-Rays. The emission of alpha-particles is accounted for by assuming that two neutrons and two protons form a particularly stable combination, resembling in some way the favored grouping of eight electrons to form a stable octet. From the behavior of protons and neutrons in magnetic fields, it is known that they are tiny magnets. The Exclusion Principle would permit two particles with their north poles pointing in opposite directions to have motions that are otherwise identical (cf. the two oppositely spinning electrons allowed in each orbit, Article 53–2). Therefore two oppositely oriented neutrons and two oppositely oriented protons could form a group like a closed shell or a stable octet. Such a group (four nucleons, of which two are protons) would of course be an alpha-particle, ${}_2He^4$. It may well be that some of the nucleons in a nucleus are grouped into alpha-particles. At least it is not surprising that an exceptional combination like the alpha-particle should be ejected when a nucleus is unstable and has to unload a piece of itself.

69–5. The Origin of Beta-Rays. If nuclei are made of neutrons and protons, how can they emit electrons or positrons, as they do in beta activity? If there are no electrons or positrons in the nucleus, how can they come out? In this connection it is helpful to think of the emission of light by an atom. An atom does not carry the light around inside of it; the light is created at the moment of emission. It is created by atoms that are in an excited state, i.e. by atoms that can lose energy by rearrangement of their electrons. The beta-rays arise from a comparable situation in the nucleus.

In the discussion of artificial radioactivity (Article 68–3), it was mentioned that bombarding ${}_5B^{10}$ with alpha-particles, ${}_2He^4$, produces ${}_7N^{13}$. This nitrogen nucleus contains seven protons and only six neutrons. A nucleus with six protons and seven neutrons (${}_6C^{13}$) would have the same number of proton-neutron pairs (six) but the unpaired particle would be a neutron, while in ${}_7N^{13}$ it is a proton and is repelled by the other protons. Now, as we have seen, ${}_7N^{13}$ is a radioactive nucleus; it emits a positron and turns into ${}_6C^{13}$. This means that one of the protons has divested itself of its positive charge and turned into a neutron, and the charge has been carried off by the positron. We interpret the positron emission as an indication that a thirteen-particle nucleus has less P.E. if it has six protons than if it has seven. We attribute the difference to the mutual repulsion of the protons, which is less for six than for seven.

The emission of a negative beta-ray occurs when a nucleus can reach a state of lower energy by converting one of its neutrons into a proton. As an example, consider ${}_{83}Bi^{210}$, a member of the radium series (Table 65–I). It has 83 protons and $210 - 83 = 127$ neutrons. Of the neutrons, 83 will be paired with protons in the least energetic motions, but the rest of the neutrons will be distributed in states of motion that involve more energy. If one of them were a proton, there would be room for it in a less energetic state of motion. The nucleus can therefore lose energy if one of its neutrons turns into a proton; in order for this to occur without changing the amount of charge in the universe, a negative charge has to be created. The change is possible, and will eventually occur, because the resulting decrease in energy of the nucleus is sufficient to provide the mass of the electron. After the change, the nucleus still has 210 nucleons but now 84 of them are protons; therefore the nucleus is now that of polonium, ${}_{84}Po^{210}$.

Whether beta radioactivity can occur or not is dependent on the amount of energy that the nucleus would lose thereby. If the loss of energy is not sufficient to supply the mass of the electron or positron, in accord with the equation $E = mc^2$, then the change will not occur.

69–6. The Origin of Gamma-Rays. As a rule, the gamma-rays are emitted by nuclei that have been freshly formed, either by a radioactive change or by bombardment. In a freshly formed nucleus the nucleons may not have the motions that entail the lowest possible amount of energy. When they do settle into the states of motion that involve minimum energy, the spare energy is given off as electromagnetic radiation. The energy liberated by a rearrangement of the nucleons is much larger than the energy that is released by a rearrangement of the electrons in an atom. Therefore the gamma-ray photon will have much more energy than a photon of visible light. The frequency, given by $E = h\nu$, will be much greater for gamma-rays than for visible light, and the wavelength will be correspondingly smaller.

69–7. The Compound Nucleus. A hypothesis that helps to unify the various nuclear phenomena was put forward by Bohr in 1936.* The essential idea of the hypothesis is that when a nucleus is struck by a bombarding particle, this particle is temporarily incorporated into the nucleus and shares its energy with the other particles therein. In Bohr's words, "The energy is stored in a way resembling that of the heat motion of a liquid or solid body." After a short time (about 10^{-12} second), a considerable part of this "heat energy" may be concentrated in some particle near the surface of the nucleus. This particle (proton, neutron, or alpha-particle) can then escape from the nucleus. The ejection of a particle in an artificial transmutation can therefore be likened to the evaporation of a molecule from a drop of water.

The combination of the original nucleus and the captured particle is called a *compound nucleus*. One of the ways in which the hypothesis simplifies nuclear science can be seen by noting that many different situations can give rise to the same compound nucleus. All of these situations can therefore be expected to lead to the same result. As a concrete application of this idea, consider again Rutherford's bombardment of ${}_7N^{14}$ with alpha-particles, and the resulting formation of an ${}_8O^{17}$ nucleus (Article 68–1). In terms of the compound nucleus, the reaction should be written

$${}_7N^{14} + {}_2He^4 \rightarrow {}_9F^{18} \rightarrow {}_8O^{17} + {}_1H^1.$$

The same compound nucleus, ${}_9F^{18}$, could be formed by bombarding the common isotope of oxygen, ${}_8O^{16}$, with the nuclei of a heavy isotope of hydrogen, ${}_1H^2$. Bohr's hypothesis implies that this reaction, too, should result in the formation of ${}_8O^{17}$ and the setting free of a proton. It is found experimentally that this is indeed true:

$${}_8O^{16} + {}_1H^2 \rightarrow {}_9F^{18} \rightarrow {}_8O^{17} + {}_1H^1.$$

One of the fruits of Bohr's hypothesis is, therefore, the ability to predict how one reaction will go, on the basis of information about another reaction.

* After devising his theory of the hydrogen atom (1913), Bohr became professor of physics at Copenhagen. Just as Rutherford served as leader of the nuclear experimenters, so Bohr served for the atomic theorists. Advanced students from all parts of the world worked under his direction and became infused with his bold attitude toward physical problems.

Bohr's idea of the compound nucleus ties artificial radioactivity into the general scheme. Some reactions give rise to nuclei that are bound together firmly enough so that no particle in them can get enough energy to break loose. These nuclei may nevertheless be able to lose energy, and achieve still firmer binding, by changing a neutron to a proton or vice versa. Such changes may not occur immediately. When they do occur, they involve the emission of an electron or a positron; artificial radioactivity, therefore, is always β-activity. We have already (Article 68–3) met the example

$$_5B^{10} + {}_2He^4 \rightarrow {}_7N^{13} + {}_0n^1$$

$$\searrow \text{10 min}$$

$$_6C^{13} + {}_1e^0.$$

69–8. Shell Structure in Nuclei (1950). An interesting idea about nuclei has lately been developed by combing over the facts that were already known. It seems that there are nuclei that are in some way special, as the inert gases are special in the atomic realm.

One striking difference among the elements is the number of stable (i.e., nonradioactive) isotopes that the various elements possess. The average number of stable isotopes of an element is about three, but tin, $_{50}Sn$, has no less than ten stable isotopes. Calcium, $_{20}Ca$, has six, which is exceptional for such a light element. It seems that 50 protons and 20 protons are favored groups that tend to make nuclei stable.

A grouping of 50 neutrons or 20 neutrons is also especially favored. Among the nuclei found in nature, it is unusual for more than three or four kinds of nuclei to have the same number of neutrons. Nevertheless, there are six nuclei, $_{36}Kr^{86}$, $_{37}Rb^{87}$, $_{38}Sr^{88}$, $_{39}Y^{89}$, $_{40}Zr^{90}$, and $_{42}Mo^{92}$, that have 50 neutrons. There are five kinds of nuclei that have 20 neutrons. Moreover, experimenters have found that nuclei with 50 or 20 neutrons are exceptionally resistant to the removal of a neutron by gamma-ray bombardment. They also find that these nuclei have an exceptionally small tendency to capture additional neutrons. Similar evidence shows the special nature of nuclei with 82 protons, 82 neutrons, or 126 neutrons.

When these abnormalities were first recognized, nuclear scientists referred to 20, 50, 82 and 126 as "magic numbers," for lack of any theory that would explain the situation. Lately there has been a growing conviction that the magic numbers indicate the existence of a shell structure in nuclei. If a nucleus already contains 20 protons, then adding a new proton starts a new shell, which becomes completed when the total number of protons rises to 50.

By working back from the shell hypothesis, it is possible to assign quantum numbers to the nucleons. This assignment indicates that the first shell contains 2 like nucleons, the second 6, and the third 12. This makes a total of 20 particles in the first three shells. The next shell contains 30 particles, bringing the total to 50, and so on.

The work on shell structure in nuclei is undoubtedly not yet complete. What has already been done, however, gives promise of eventually clarifying nuclear physics in the same way that the understanding of electron shells has clarified chemistry.

69-9. Current Research. The problem of nuclear structure is in many ways more difficult than the problem of atomic structure. In the atomic problem, the electrons could safely be assumed to be bound to the nucleus by electric forces obeying Coulomb's Law. This law was already known, from experiments on large bodies. All information about the nuclear force, however, has to be obtained from experiments done with nucleons. Because the force is not known, these experiments are hard to interpret. Large new accelerators are opening a new range of energies to the experimenters, who hope to find new phenomena that give some clue to the forces that act.

The nucleons, as we have seen, exert forces only on their close neighbors. It seems that they may be able to enter into a limited number of bonds. This behavior suggests that nuclear binding may resemble covalent binding. One line of attack, which has been pressed with more vigor than success, is the hypothesis that nucleons are held together by a sharing of mesons, in much the same way that atoms can be held together by a sharing of electrons. All theories built on this hypothesis have been very complicated. What is worse, they have been in bad agreement with experimental facts. Very likely what is needed is some fundamentally new idea, an idea as new as those that Bohr started with when he made the first successful theory of the hydrogen atom.

Summary

The nucleons in a nucleus are held together by a force called the nuclear force. It is neither gravitational nor electric, and it decreases very rapidly as the distance between nucleons is increased. A nucleon is bound about as tightly in a small nucleus as in a large one; from this we infer that nucleons that are not close neighbors do not attract one another.

In the stable isotopes of the light elements, about half of the nucleons are protons and the other half are neutrons. In the heavier nuclei, the neutrons always outnumber the protons. Two particles can have the same motion only if the particles are not alike. In light nuclei, protons and neutrons are present in nearly equal numbers, in order that the states of motion entailing the least energy may each accommodate two particles, one a neutron and the other a proton. In heavier nuclei, the electric repulsion of the protons leads to instability unless most of the particles are neutrons. The heaviest nuclei, such as radium, are radioactive, because they contain so many protons that they are unstable no matter how many neutrons they have.

Alpha-particles consist of two protons and two neutrons, which can be expected to form a very stable combination like a stable octet of electrons. Alpha-particles can therefore escape as units from nuclei in which the proton repulsion is sufficiently large. These are almost always heavy nuclei like uranium and radium.

Negative beta-rays come from nuclei that can reach a state of lower energy by converting a neutron into a proton. Positive beta-rays come from nuclei that can decrease their energy by changing a proton into a neutron.

In nuclei that have been disturbed by radioactive change, or by bombardment, the nucleons may have motions that involve more than the least possible amount of energy. When the nucleons then settle into the states of motion that involve minimum energy, the excess energy can escape as the electromagnetic energy of a gamma-ray.

The study of nuclear reactions is simplified by Bohr's hypothesis of the compound nucleus. When a bombarding particle strikes a nucleus, the two combine to form a compound nucleus, which may disintegrate very soon. Bombardments that produce the same compound nucleus will result in the same products.

In the formation of nuclei, certain numbers of neutrons or protons are specially favored. The favored groupings result from the filling up of shells of nucleons, analogous to the shells of electrons which surround the nucleus. Learning more about these shells is one of the present goals of nuclear research. The major problem, however, is the nature of the nuclear force.

Questions

1. State an important difference between gravitational force and nuclear force.
2. Compare the binding of a neutron in an oxygen nucleus with the binding of a neutron in a platinum nucleus. What light does this comparison throw on the attractions between nucleons?
3. What accounts for the radioactivity of radium and the other elements near the end of the Periodic Table?
4. How does the Exclusion Principle favor the alpha-particle over other groups of nucleons?
5. Account for the emission of beta-rays by a nucleus.
6. Account for the emission of gamma-rays by a nucleus.

7. All of the fluorine found in nature is F^{19}, but F^{17} and F^{20} can be made in the nuclear laboratory. The latter two are radioactive. By comparing their neutron complements with that of F^{19}, decide what particle each of them emits when it decays. What nucleus results from each decay?
8. Summarize Bohr's compound-nucleus theory. How does it correlate nuclear reactions?
9. Using the hypothesis of a compound nucleus, write equations for the following reactions:
   (a) Carbon and protons are produced when neutrons strike N^{14}
   (b) Carbon and protons are produced when alpha-particles strike B^{11}.
10. Cite evidence for the existence of closed shells in nuclei.
11. What is the major goal of present-day nuclear research?

70

NUCLEAR FISSION AND ATOMIC BOMBS

One important type of nuclear reaction has yet to be discussed. In most of the reactions mentioned thus far, the compound nucleus releases one nucleon or electron, or perhaps an alpha-particle. Article 68–7 treats reactions in which the compound nucleus breaks up into a large number of small fragments. It is also possible for some compound nuclei to break up into two roughly equal parts. It is this kind of reaction that is used in the atomic bomb.

70–1. The Discovery of Fission (1939). In the large sense, the development of the atomic bomb began with the development of physical science. In the immediate (and not very important) sense, the development of the atomic bomb began in Italy in 1936. There Professor Fermi of Rome, considered by many to be the world's leading physicist, tried bombarding uranium with neutrons to see what would happen. Neutrons make fine projectiles to shoot at nuclei, because their lack of charge makes them capable of plunging into a nucleus without being slowed down or deflected by electrical repulsion.

The elements at the end of the Periodic Table were of special interest because, generally speaking, they are the naturally radioactive ones. To find out what makes the nucleus hold together, it must have seemed like a good idea to give some attention to the ones that do not hold together very well. Fermi had something further in mind, however. If he could get an extra neutron into uranium, perhaps the uranium nucleus would have such a surplus of neutrons that one of them would turn into a proton (Article 69–5). The nucleus would now have a charge of 93, and it would no longer be a nucleus of uranium. It would be the nucleus of a new, man-made, element.

The expected creation of a new element actually did occur. Other things happened, too, however, and it took several years to find out what was really going on. The problem of unraveling the details attracted a few workers in Germany; some of them soon proved by chemical analysis that when uranium was bombarded with neutrons, some of the uranium turned into barium (element 56) and other elements in the middle of the Periodic Table. Clearly the uranium nuclei were breaking up into two nuclei of nearly equal size. The breaking down of a heavy nucleus into nuclei of intermediate size has been called *fission* to distinguish it from ordinary transmutation, which involves merely the ejection of an alpha-particle or something simpler.

70–2. The Fission Process. Bohr quickly offered a correct explanation of the fission process. He had already pointed out (Article 69–7) that a transmutation can be likened to the evaporation of a molecule from a liquid droplet. He now proposed that a uranium nucleus that captures a neutron as in (a), Figure 70–A, is disturbed and deformed, and that the

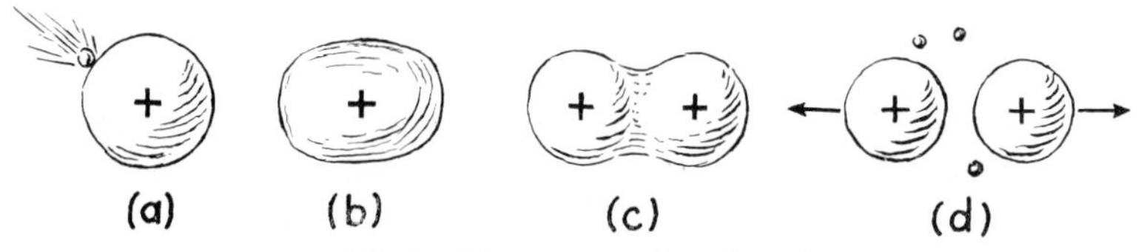

FIGURE 70–A. The process of nuclear fission.

mutual repulsions of the protons first distort it successively into shapes (b) and (c), and then tear it apart (d). The 92 protons in the original nucleus will be divided more or less evenly between the two large fragments in (d). These fragments will initially be very close together. They will therefore repel one another violently, and they will fly apart with much kinetic energy. It is very easy to calculate the loss of P.E., and the consequent gain in K.E., experienced by the fission fragments because of their electric repulsion; it turns out to be about 200 Mev. This figure is to be contrasted with the 1 to 10 Mev liberated in the more common type of nuclear reaction, and with the 10 *electron-volts* liberated by each molecule in an explosion of T.N.T. (Article 62–7).

Soon after the discovery of fission in 1939, Bohr came to America for some conversations with Einstein at Princeton. Of course he mentioned the discovery, and the news soon traveled to Columbia University, to which Fermi had moved because he did not see eye to eye with the Fascists in Italy. A group working with Fermi soon showed that the nuclei produced by fission actually do have kinetic energies of about 100 Mev each.

70–3. The Chain Reaction. Now examine the fission process in more detail. When ${}_{92}U^{238}$ is struck by a neutron, the compound nucleus is ${}_{92}U^{239}$. One possible product is barium, with 56 protons. The other fragment must have $92 - 56 = 36$ protons; it is therefore a nucleus of krypton. We have already noticed (Article 69–3) that heavy nuclei that are stable, or nearly so, are rich in neutrons. Therefore the number of neutrons present in the uranium nucleus is more than the two fragment nuclei require. For this reason, one or more neutrons may be set free by the fission, as in Figure 70–A (d). A typical fission reaction, then, is

$$_{92}U^{238} + {}_0n^1 \rightarrow {}_{92}U^{239} \rightarrow {}_{56}Ba^{145} + {}_{36}Kr^{92} + {}_0n^1 + {}_0n^1.$$

An equally possible fission is

$$_{92}U^{238} + {}_0n^1 \rightarrow {}_{92}U^{239} \rightarrow {}_{38}Sr^{96} + {}_{54}Xe^{140} + {}_0n^1 + {}_0n^1 + {}_0n^1.$$

The emission of neutrons in fission is of primary importance, because it has been found that under favorable conditions these neutrons can incite fission in other atoms of uranium, and this can be repeated indefinitely. A self-sustaining reaction of this sort is called a chain reaction (Article 27–8). Figure 70–B illustrates the multiplication of neutrons and fissions in a chain reaction. Here we are dealing with a very different situation from the artificial transmutation of, say, the lithium discussed in Article 68–5. There, thousands of protons had to be shot at the lithium target in order to score a hit on a lithium nucleus. The energy liberated by the transmutation was considerable, but the energy needed for accelerating the thousands of protons was far larger. Producing the transmutation involved a net expenditure of energy. In 1939, it seemed possible that somehow one could make a single neutron set off a chain reaction that would cause one fission after another. If this could be done, uranium might provide a *practical* means of liberating nuclear energy.

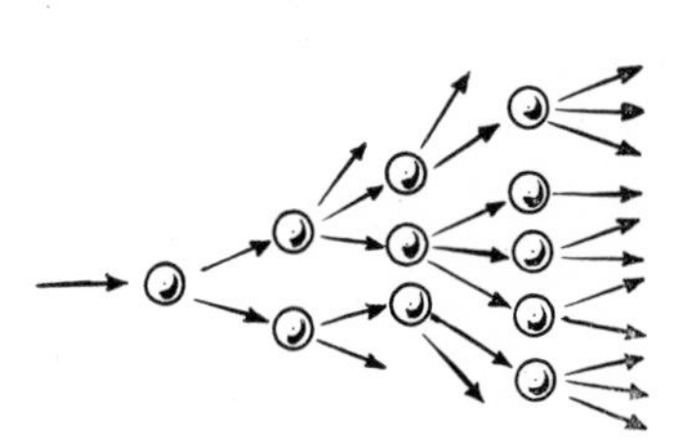

FIGURE 70–B. The beginning of a nuclear chain reaction in uranium. The spheres represent uranium nuclei; the arrows, neutrons. The medium-weight nuclei created by the fission process are not shown.

Scientists in many countries quickly took up the investigation of fission. It was found that the isotopes of uranium are not quite alike as regards fission: to produce fission of U^{238} the neutrons must be moving swiftly, but even slow neutrons can produce fission of U^{235}. The production of a chain reaction maintained by fast neutrons is difficult, because a neutron is likely to be slowed down by ordinary collisions without producing a fission. Therefore attention was focused on U^{235}, which can be split up by neutrons that have only the motion that is characteristic of room temperatures.

70–4. The Atomic Bomb (1945). A few months after the discovery of fission, war broke out in Europe. The refugee physicists at Columbia realized that Germany would attempt to exploit uranium for military

Oak Ridge National Laboratory

FIGURE 70–C. The wartime plant for separating the uranium isotopes by gaseous diffusion, at Oak Ridge, Tennessee. The length of the building is just under half a mile.

purposes. Early in 1940, they persuaded Einstein to use his prestige to interest President Roosevelt in the problem. Working first in universities under Government subsidies, and later in special colonies administered by the Army, American and foreign scientists showed that a chain reaction really can be produced, and that it can be used in bombs. Industrial firms operating under Government direction constructed vast plants for processing the fissionable material, and the first bombs stopped the war with Japan.

A great difficulty in using uranium as an energy source is that only about 0.7 percent of natural uranium is U^{235}; nearly all the rest is U^{238}. In order to make the first bombs, the isotopes had to be separated. This was done at first by using huge mass spectrographs which separated the two isotopes by deflecting them in a magnetic field (Article 44–2). It was found that the isotopes could also be separated by letting a gaseous compound of uranium (UF_6) diffuse through a series of porous barriers. As

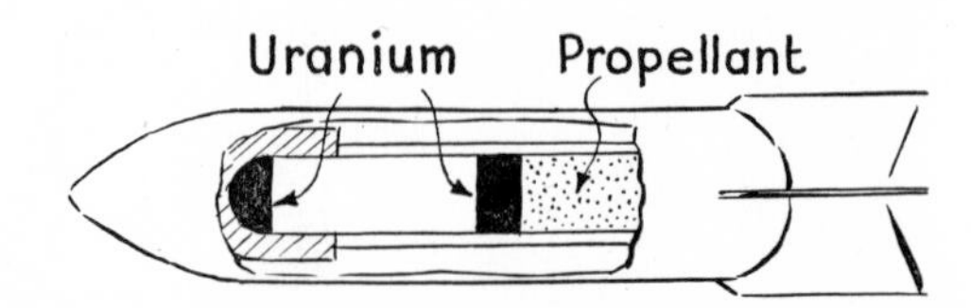

FIGURE 70–D. An artist's sketch of a uranium bomb. When the propellant is ignited, it drives one piece of U^{235} into contact with the other, and they explode.

in the experiment in Article 18–2, the lighter molecules are favored over the heavier ones in the passage through the barriers; after the gas has passed through a large number of barriers, the molecules containing U^{238} have mostly been sifted out. Carrying out this separation of isotopes on a large scale was a great industrial triumph. Figure 70–C gives an idea of the size of the plant required.

If a neutron strikes a small lump of U^{235} and produces a fission, the two or three neutrons produced by the fission are likely to escape from the lump before they strike other nuclei and produce more fissions. Under such conditions, a chain reaction will not occur. On the other hand, if a fission takes place in a sufficiently large piece of U^{235}, the neutrons produced are likely to strike uranium nuclei instead of escaping. There will then be a chain reaction, which occurs with explosive violence.

The uranium bomb is made by taking two or more pieces of U^{235}, each small enough to be harmless, and placing them together very suddenly so as to form a unit large enough to experience the chain reaction. The problem of making a bomb can therefore be broken down into three parts: separating the isotopes; calculating the maximum size for a harmless piece of U^{235}; and devising a mechanism that will, at the appropriate moment, put harmless pieces together to produce an explosion. The exact mechanism used is of course a secret, but the general plan is surely something like Figure 70–D.

The effect of the explosion is threefold. There is a tremendous evolution of heat and light, because temperatures of millons of degrees are developed. The heat causes the surrounding air to expand violently, thereby producing a prodigious gust of wind. This blast resembles those

Atomic Energy Commission

FIGURE 70–E. An A-bomb burst at Bikini in 1946. The ships are sizable naval vessels.

caused by ordinary bombs, but it is much more violent. During the explosion, there is also a terrific production of gamma-rays, which can cause serious illness and death. Finally, the fission fragments themselves are radioactive and have appalling possibilities as poisons. When taken into the body, they destroy the tissues by their ionizing effect.

The aerial photograph in Figure 70–E shows part of the column of water thrown up by a bomb exploded beneath the surface of the sea.

70–5. Nuclear Reactors. The atomic bomb, which should properly have been named a nuclear bomb, produces a nuclear reaction that proceeds more and more rapidly, until the fissionable material is either consumed or dispersed by the explosion. It is also possible to provide for a chain reaction that proceeds at a controlled rate, in a device called a *nuclear reactor.*

Fermi showed in 1942 that, by careful arrangement, a controlled chain reaction can be achieved with natural uranium. The difficulty hinges on the fact that U^{238}, the abundant isotope, can capture moderately fast neutrons and turn into U^{239}. To keep the chain reaction going, a neutron must either produce a fission before being slowed down by simple colli-

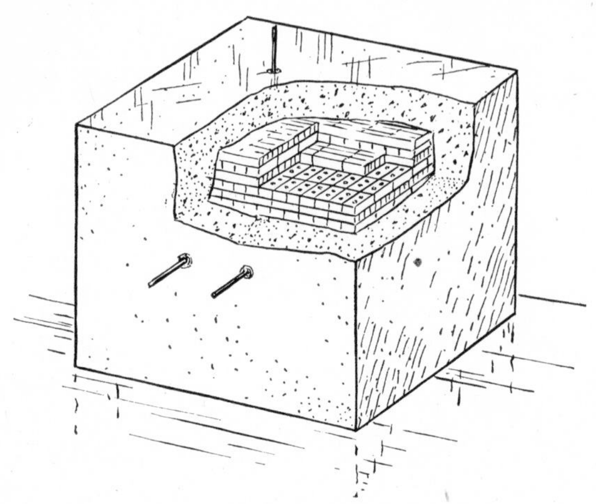

FIGURE 70–F. The structure of a nuclear reactor. The principal parts are: uranium rods or slugs imbedded in graphite bricks, graphite and concrete layers for shielding, control rods of neutron-absorbing material at the side, and a self-acting emergency control rod poised at the top.

sions, or else it must escape capture in U^{238} until it has been slowed down a great deal, at which time it can cause fission in U^{235}. Fermi proposed the use of an auxiliary substance, called a *moderator,* chosen so that it will slow neutrons down but will not capture them. Pure carbon is suitable as a moderator.

To make a reactor using natural uranium and a carbon moderator, the uranium is formed into rods and imbedded in graphite blocks. The blocks are stacked up like bricks, to form a cube several meters on a side. A neutron produced in one of the rods stands a good chance of escaping into the moderator, where it is slowed down by collisions until it simply shares in the thermal motion of its environment. As it wanders through the moderator, the neutron may eventually strike a rod of uranium, in which it can cause a fission of U^{235}. The essential parts of such a reactor are sketched in Figure 70–F; the exterior of an actual reactor appears in Figure 70–G.

If a chain reaction is to keep going at a steady rate, each fission must produce on the average exactly one new fission. On the average, each fission liberates 2.5 neutrons; the reactor must be made so that one of these neutrons produces a new fission, while the rest are captured or else escape from the reactor. The reaction can be controlled, or even stopped, by sliding into the reactor a rod of some material * that readily captures slow neutrons. This control rod is inserted just far enough to keep the reaction in balance.

Brookhaven National Laboratory

FIGURE 70-G. One face of a reactor that serves as a copious source of neutrons for experimental use.

The running of a reactor has three important results: the moderator is heated, U^{235} and a little U^{238} are converted into fission products, and U^{238} is converted into U^{239}. We shall consider these results separately.

70-6. Plutonium. Fermi's original interest in uranium had centered on the possibility that neutron capture by U^{238} might lead to the creation of a new element, number 93 (page 624). The unsuspected phenomenon of fission confused the first experiments, but element 93 actually was

* Usually cadmium.

created. Neutron capture in ${}_{92}U^{238}$ produces ${}_{92}U^{239}$, which later emits a β-ray and turns into element 93, which has been christened *neptunium,* Np. Neptunium is itself unstable, giving off a β-ray and turning into element 94, called *plutonium,** Pu. In symbols,

$$
{}_{92}U^{239} \xrightarrow[\beta^-]{23\ \text{min}} {}_{93}Np^{239} + {}_{-1}e^0
$$

$$
{}_{93}Np^{239} \xrightarrow[\beta^-]{2\ \text{days}} {}_{94}Pu^{239} + {}_{-1}e^0
$$

Plutonium is of great importance because it will fission under the action of slow neutrons. In this respect, it resembles U^{235}, the less common isotope of uranium. Plutonium has the great advantage, however, of being separable from uranium by *chemical* means. (You will remember that obtaining U^{235} for an atomic bomb was difficult, because U^{235} had to be separated from U^{238} by mass spectrographs or other devices that depend on the difference in mass.) The second bomb dropped on Japan was made with plutonium, which was made in a huge reactor constructed for the purpose at Hanford, Washington. Atomic bombs now being made presumably use plutonium rather than U^{235}.

70–7. Fission Products. The two atoms formed when a heavy nucleus splits are called *fission products.* Typical possibilities (page 626) are ${}_{56}Ba^{145}$, ${}_{54}Xe^{140}$, ${}_{38}Sr^{96}$, ${}_{36}Kr^{92}$. The heaviest stable isotopes of these elements are ${}_{56}Ba^{138}$, ${}_{54}Xe^{136}$, ${}_{38}Sr^{88}$, ${}_{36}Kr^{86}$. The fission products are overloaded with neutrons. In uranium, the neutrons greatly outnumber the protons. In the middleweight nuclei that are stable, the neutrons are only slightly more numerous than the protons. Therefore, the middleweight nuclei formed by splitting of uranium have too many neutrons for stability.

Their neutron excess makes the fission products highly radioactive. To some extent they are a nuisance, because they are copiously produced in a reactor and they are hard to dispose of. For certain purposes, however, they are very useful. They make intense sources of beta-rays and gamma-rays available for research or industrial purposes. Furthermore, radioactive isotopes of a very large variety of elements can be chemically extracted from the mixture of fission products. These isotopes open up wider possibilities for the use of "tagged atoms" (Article 68–4) in all kinds of research.

70–8. Useful Energy from Nuclear Reactors. The first nuclear reactors were built for studying the possibilities of chain reactions. Later, a very large reactor was built for making plutonium for bombs. The energy liberated by fission in these reactors heated the moderator, which when

* These elements have been named from analogy with the planets. The (known) planets most distant from the sun are Uranus, Neptune, and Pluto. Because of its sinister properties, there is much fitness in the linking of element 94 with Pluto, ruler of the dead.

necessary was cooled by running water. The large reactor for making plutonium generated enough heat to cause a noticeable rise in the temperature of the Columbia River.

As soon as the war was over, attention could be given to the problem of converting nuclear energy into useful work. Although the engineering details are far more complex, the problem very much resembles that of getting useful work from coal. Like the chemical energy of the coal, the nuclear energy of the uranium must first be converted into heat. Then the heat can be used to boil water for running a steam engine (Article 16–3). For some purposes, for example turning a ship's propeller, the work output of the steam engine could be used directly. For other purposes, the work would be needed at some distance from the reactor. In these cases, the steam engine would drive a dynamo, to convert the work into electrical energy; the energy could then be used by electric motors (Article 32–3) anywhere within a considerable distance. Figure 70–H is an artist's conception of a possible nuclear power plant.

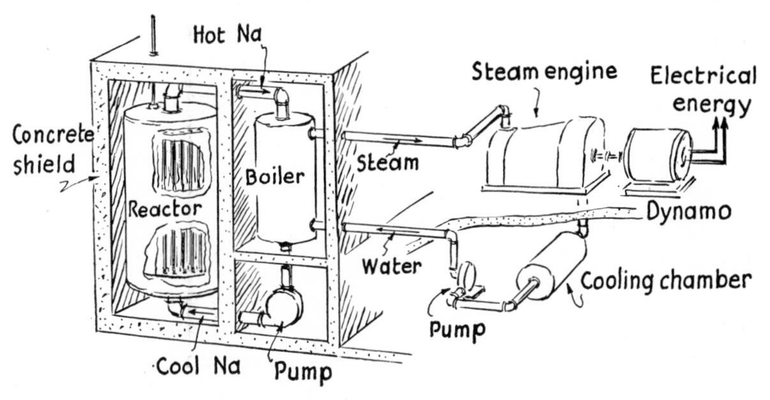

FIGURE 70–H. A nuclear power plant.

The future of nuclear energy for industrial purposes is very uncertain. A prime factor is that any uranium reactor produces not only heat, but also plutonium. Since plutonium can be used for making bombs, reactors are under close control by the various governments concerned. Moreover, the initial cost of a uranium power plant is very high. The great advantage of a nuclear reactor lies in the enormous amount of energy available from a small amount of uranium. A piece of natural uranium the size of a golf ball will liberate as much energy as about 1500 tons of coal. A reactor running on natural uranium requires a large amount of the metal fuel, but the fuel is used up very slowly indeed. One distinctive feature of nuclear reactors, therefore, is that one shipment of fuel will last a long time. Consequently, the cost of transporting the fuel is not an important factor. In countries, like Argentina, that have to import coal from distant mines, nuclear fuel would have a distinct economic advantage. Near a coal mine, however, present costs would give coal an advantage over uranium.

Prevailing international tensions make uranium and plutonium virtually unavailable for anything but military purposes. The first reactor that was built for producing useful power was installed in a United States submarine, which is presumably able to run for long periods without refueling. The extent to which uranium will replace coal and oil will depend on how much uranium is needed for military purposes, how much can be found, and how much it will cost. Uranium is not an especially rare element, but it usually occurs in low concentrations. Improved methods of winning uranium from low-grade ores will probably be devised. Until they are, uranium will remain scarce and costly.

Summary

Nuclear fission is the disruption of a heavy nucleus into two roughly equal parts. Fission is caused by the large electric repulsions that exist in heavy nuclei. The impact of a neutron can set the nucleus into vibration; it can then elongate, neck down in the middle, and come apart. The mutual repulsion of the parts causes them to fly apart with violence, acquiring an energy that is millions of times as large as the energy released by the disruption of an unstable molecule.

The fission process normally gives rise not only to the two middleweight nuclei, but also to one or more neutrons. Under proper conditions, these neutrons can produce new fissions, which produce new neutrons, and so forth. A self-sustaining reaction of this sort is called a chain reaction. It affords a practical means of liberating nuclear energy.

The isotope U^{235} is suited for a chain reaction, because U^{235} will fission under the impact of slow neutrons. To make the first atomic bomb, U^{235} was separated from U^{238} by huge mass spectrographs. Natural uranium will sustain a chain reaction in a device called a nuclear reactor, in which the neutrons are slowed down in some other material in order to reduce their chance of being captured by U^{238}. Those that are captured lead to the formation of a new fissionable element called plutonium, and those that escape capture keep the reaction going by causing more fissions of U^{235}. The rate of reaction can be controlled with a rod of some neutron-absorbing substance.

Plutonium, element 94, is useful for making bombs. It is better than U^{235}, because it can be separated from uranium by chemical treatment, which is much cheaper than the isotope separation that U^{235} requires.

The two atoms formed when a heavy nucleus splits are called fission products. They are radioactive, because they have an excess of neutrons. They are useful as cheap sources of beta- and gamma-rays, and as tagged atoms in many kinds of research.

In a reactor, much of the energy of the fission fragments turns into thermal motion. The reactor can therefore be used as a source of heat for running a steam engine and producing work. The work may be used on the spot, or it may be converted into electrical energy which can be used at a distance. The advantage of uranium as a fuel is that a large amount of energy can be obtained with only a small consumption of the fuel.

Questions

1. How does fission differ from the nuclear reactions discussed in earlier chapters?
2. What experimental fact led to the recognition of fission?
3. Describe fission in terms of Bohr's liquid-drop model of the nucleus.
4. As projectiles for the bombardment of nuclei, what advantage do neutrons have over protons and alpha-particles?
5. How is the emission of neutrons during fission related to the general principles of nuclear structure?
6. How is the emission of neutrons during fission related to the possibility of a chain reaction?
7. Describe the principle of the atomic bomb.
8. Why is energy released when fission occurs?
9. How does the energy released by fission of a uranium nucleus compare with the energy released by decomposition of a T.N.T. molecule?
10. What are the destructive effects that are associated with the explosion of an atom bomb?
11. Describe the construction of a nuclear reactor, and state what each part is for.
12. Explain the relationship of nuclear power plants, plutonium, and government supervision.

Suggestions for Further Reading

"The Atomic Bomb," *Life Magazine*, February 27, 1950, pp. 90–100.

H. deW. Smyth, *Atomic Energy for Military Purposes* (Princeton: Princeton University Press, 1945). The official report on the bomb project.

"First Central-Station Atomic-Power Plant," *Mechanical Engineering*, vol. 76, pp. 585–88 (July, 1954). A discussion of some of the engineering details of a reactor designed for producing power for lighting and industry.

71

COSMIC PHYSICS

Yet I doubt not through the ages one increasing purpose runs,
And the thoughts of men are widen'd with the process of the suns.
TENNYSON (1842)

In Chapter 64, it was pointed out that the sun is our primary source of energy. We are now in a position to discuss the origin of this energy.

71–1. Facts about the Sun. By means that have already been discussed in Articles 1–4 and 8–4, the following facts about the sun have been established. They show that solar affairs can be expected to differ considerably from terrestrial ones.

Diameter of Sun......110 earth diameters
Volume of Sun.......1,300,000 earth volumes
Mass of Sun.........330,000 earth masses

The distance from the sun to the earth is 93,000,000 miles (11,600 earth diameters). Therefore only a tiny fraction of the energy radiated from the sun is intercepted by the earth, but nevertheless each square meter of the earth's surface receives over a thousand joules per second. Using these two facts and some simple geometry, we can find that each square meter of the sun's surface radiates about 62 million joules per second, which is 62 million watts, or enough power to run 100,000 electric toasters. In order to radiate energy at this rate, the surface of the sun must be at about 6000° C.* It has been calculated that in order for the outside of the sun to be maintained at 6000° C in spite of its rapid loss of energy in radiation, the center of the sun must have a temperature of about 15 million degrees. Even at the relatively cool surface, the temperature is so high that molecules cannot exist, because they would be knocked apart by the violence of the collisions they would make with one another.

* The color given out by a hot body is also a clue to its temperature, as is well known. (A white-hot tungsten lamp filament is hotter than a red-hot stove.) The color of the sun verifies the conclusion that the sun's surface is at 6000°C.

Consequently *the energy given out by the sun cannot come from chemical reactions.*

Since it is so hot, the sun must be in a gaseous state. Moreover, in the interior the gas is completely ionized, because the thermal motion of the atoms is so violent that the electrons are all knocked off. The solar interior consists of bare nuclei and divorced electrons, all whizzing about at high speed.

71–2. Gravitational Contraction. Each part of the sun exerts a gravitational pull on all of the other parts, and the exterior therefore presses so heavily on the interior that the central portion of the sun is highly compressed. Although it is a gas, it is denser than lead.

It seems that the sun must have started out in life as a huge ball of cool gas at low pressure, and that it contracted because of the gravitational attractions that its parts exert on one another. The contraction compressed the gas, doing work on it and raising its temperature. In other words, gravitational P.E. was converted into heat. For a long time it was thought that this process would account for the sun's heat; after the pressure in the interior became great enough to support the outer regions, the sun would contract at a rate just sufficient to compensate for the cooling caused by loss of energy in radiation. Calculations on this basis showed that a modest rate of contraction would maintain the sun at its present temperature for many thousands of years.

After the discovery of the radioactive elements and their transmutation series, it became possible (Article 65–5) to estimate the ages of uranium-bearing rocks. These estimates show that the earth is over 2 billion years old, and the sun is certainly at least as old as the earth. The gravitational contraction cannot account for anywhere near all of the energy that the sun has radiated in such a long period, and therefore gravitational P.E. is not the principal source of the sun's energy, although it must be a contributing factor.

71–3. Nuclear Reactions in the Sun. In discussing the dynamical theory of gases, we found, in Article 18–2, an equation that gives the velocity of a gas molecule. At ordinary temperature the molecules in a box of air travel as fast as a pistol bullet—roughly a quarter of a mile per second. In spite of this high velocity, the molecule does not have a very impressive amount of K.E., because K.E. $= \frac{1}{2}mv^2$ and the mass of a molecule is not large. The average K.E. of a molecule at room temperature turns out to be only about 6×10^{-21} joule, or 0.04 electron-volt. At a temperature of 15 million degrees, however, a particle has on the average an energy of over a thousand electron-volts, and for a significant part of the time it has an energy of tens of thousands of electron-volts. The protons (hydrogen nuclei) in the solar interior are therefore moving fast enough to produce nuclear reactions. This was realized in a general way as early as 1929, but just what nuclear reactions went on was not at all clear. The problem was solved in 1938 by Bethe, a former German who is one of the leaders in American physics.

Bethe found that there are two sets of reactions that account for most of the energy liberated in stars. Under the conditions prevailing in the sun, the two sets of reactions are of about equal importance. They are called the *carbon cycle* and the *proton chain.*

The carbon cycle consists of the following reactions:

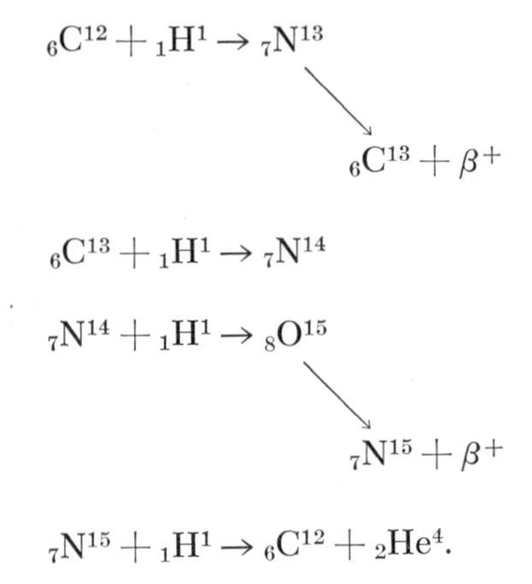

$$ {}_7N^{15} + {}_1H^1 \rightarrow {}_6C^{12} + {}_2He^4. $$

Note that each of the reactions produces a nucleus that is needed in the next reaction. The remarkable thing about this series of reactions is that the carbon and nitrogen are not used up. The net result of the whole series is that four protons disappear and a helium nucleus is formed, with two positrons as by-products. Hydrogen is the fuel; helium and positrons are the ashes. The carbon and nitrogen are merely catalysts, and they can go through the cycle again. The positrons are quickly annihilated by collision with electrons (Article 68–6), and the energy liberated by this destruction of matter can be counted as part of the energy released by the cycle. The material result of the reactions is therefore the conversion of four protons into a helium nucleus.

From a table of atomic masses, compiled by using a mass spectrograph, one finds that the mass of a helium nucleus is less than the mass of four protons. Therefore Bethe's cycle will convert mass into some other form of energy. To calculate the amount of energy liberated in the cycle, it is simply necessary to compute the amount of mass that disappears and then apply Einstein's mass-energy relationship, $E = mc^2$.

The mass of the four protons that go into the reaction is

$$ 4 \times 1.00759 = 4.03036 \text{ atomic mass units.} $$

The cycle creates an alpha-particle whose mass is 4.00277 a.m.u. The mass that disappears is

$$\begin{array}{r} 4.03036 \\ -4.00277 \\ \hline 0.02759 \text{ a.m.u.} \end{array}$$

Using Einstein's relation in the convenient form

$$931 \text{ Mev} = 1 \text{ a.m.u.},$$

we can easily find the energy equivalent of 0.02759 a.m.u. It is 25.7 Mev.

To find out the extent to which his cycle accounts for the energy liberated in the sun, Bethe calculated how many alpha-particles would be created in the sun each second, on the basis of spectroscopic data about the composition of the sun. Then he multiplied by 26 Mev, or an equivalent number of joules, to get the total energy generated per second by the carbon cycle in the sun. Then he compared this calculated rate of energy production with the rate at which energy is actually being radiated by the sun. Because conditions in the interior of the sun are not accurately known, the calculated rate of energy release can be only approximate, but it seems that something like half of the sun's energy comes from the carbon cycle. The rest comes from the proton chain.

The proton chain is simpler than the carbon cycle, but its over-all effect is the same. Since hydrogen is by far the most abundant element in the sun, collisions between protons are very frequent. There is a certain probability that when two protons collide, one of them will emit a positron and turn into a neutron, which will then pair with the proton to form a ${}_1H^2$ nucleus. Collision with another proton can convert this nucleus to ${}_2He^3$. Finally, a collision between two ${}_2He^3$ nuclei can produce ${}_2He^4$ and free two protons. The equations for the chain are:

$$\begin{aligned} {}_1H^1 + {}_1H^1 &\rightarrow {}_1H^2 + \beta^+ \\ {}_1H^2 + {}_1H^1 &\rightarrow {}_2He^3 \\ {}_2He^3 + {}_2He^3 &\rightarrow {}_2He^4 + {}_1H^1 + {}_1H^1. \end{aligned}$$

As in the carbon cycle, the net result is the conversion of four protons into an alpha-particle, with the liberation of energy.

By calculating the rates of reaction in the proton chain, it is possible to show that in a star like the sun, something like half of the energy production comes from the proton chain. Except for those that have used up most of their hydrogen, most of the stars have about the same composition as the sun. In those that are hotter than the sun, most of the radiated energy comes from the carbon cycle; in those that are cooler than the sun, the proton chain predominates.

71–4. The Hydrogen Bomb. Both the United States and Russia have found ways of bringing about on earth the release of energy by the fusion of hydrogen nuclei into a nucleus of some heavier element, presumably helium. The device for doing so is called a hydrogen bomb, a fusion bomb, or a thermonuclear bomb. Although the details are secret, a few generalizations may be made.

By means of a uranium or plutonium bomb (A-bomb), it is possible to produce on earth a temperature even higher than that of the sun's interior. The A-bomb can therefore be used to kindle a nuclear fuel that enters into a fusion reaction, such as might occur in a star. The A-bomb is limited in size, because each piece of plutonium in it must be small enough not to explode by itself (Article 70–4), and only a few pieces can be brought together when the bomb is set off. A fusion bomb, however, is subject to no such limitation; it can be made as big as you please, because it will not explode until it is heated.

It seems fairly certain that fusion bombs (H-bombs) do not employ the proton chain, because the first reaction in that chain proceeds too slowly. The bomb, being small, loses its heat much faster than the sun does; the bomb must therefore use a reaction that proceeds quickly. The heavier isotopes of hydrogen are suited to this purpose. One of these isotopes, ${}_1H^2$, known as deuterium, occurs in nature (Article 44–3). The other, ${}_1H^3$, is called "tritium." Since it is radioactive, with a half-life of only 12 years, tritium is not found in nature, but it can be made by letting deuterium sit in a uranium reactor and absorb neutrons. Two reactions that may be useful in bomb-making are:

$$ {}_1H^3 + {}_1H^2 \rightarrow {}_2He^4 + {}_0n^1 + 17 \text{ Mev} $$

$$ {}_1H^3 + {}_1H^3 \rightarrow {}_2He^4 + {}_0n^1 + {}_0n^1 + 11 \text{ Mev.} $$

Since a fusion reaction will maintain itself only at a temperature of millions of degrees, it is hard to see how it could be run on the earth as a source of industrial power. So far, it has been used only for making H-bombs. There is little published information about the performance of such bombs, but it seems safe to assume that any weapon using an A-bomb as a mere detonator must be a very potent device indeed.

71–5. The Origin of the Elements. Within the past few years, our understanding of atoms has progressed so far that it is now possible to consider scientifically the problem of how the elements came into being. Our hopes of solving this problem rest on two simple facts: The elements are present in about the same proportions throughout the universe, and the universe seems to have a definite, measurable age.

The relative abundance of the various elements in the earth's crust has been measured by direct chemical analysis. The relative abundance of elements in other parts of the universe can be estimated from a study of the spectra of stars. The results show that, with a few exceptions that are easy to account for, the elements are distributed in about the same way in all parts of the universe.

Hydrogen and helium are by far the most plentiful elements, except on small bodies like the earth where the gravitational pull has been too weak to restrain them from escaping into space. As a rule, lighter elements are more plentiful than heavier ones, up to atomic weights of about 100. Elements with atomic weights greater than 100 all have roughly the same cosmic abundance, about 10^{-10} as great as that of hydrogen.

Stellar spectra also give us a way of measuring the age of the universe. They imply that about 4 billion years ago there was a great cataclysm that marked the beginning of the universe as we know it. This conclusion rests on a phenomenon that we have not yet discussed. Although the spectrum of an element in a star is almost the same as the spectrum that that element exhibits in the laboratory, there normally is one difference: the lines in the stellar spectrum all have a very slightly larger wavelength. This shift in wavelength is what we should expect to observe if the source of light is moving away from us. The distance between crests of the light wave would then be the normal distance plus the distance that the source moves in the time interval between crests. From the amount of the shift, we can infer the velocity of the source.

There are two very remarkable things about the wavelength shift that is observed. In the first place, the wavelengths of the spectral lines of nearly all stars are greater than the normal values observed in the laboratory; nearly all of the stars must therefore be moving away from the earth. Since it seems unlikely that the earth has a favored position in the universe, we conclude that all of the stars are moving away from one another. In other words, *the universe is expanding.* Moreover, the shift in the spectrum is greater for the more distant stars.* Indeed, the shift is found to be proportional to the distance of the star. This relation implies that the velocity of the star is proportional to its distance from the earth. Turning the relation around, we see that the stars are at a distance that is proportional to their velocity, which is exactly what would be observed if the stars had all started out simultaneously from a single point! Since no other explanation of the spectral shift seems plausible, the shift seems to indicate that the stars are, in effect, fragments from some cosmic explosion that occurred when all the matter in the universe was concentrated in one relatively small volume. Figure 71–A shows how the argument would apply to a small-scale situation. The stellar velocities and distances indicate that the Beginning occurred about 4 billion years ago.

* The distance of a "nearby" star can be determined by measuring the apparent change in its position as the earth moves around its orbit. When the distance is known, the actual luminosity can be inferred from the apparent brightness of the star. Fortunately, among the stars whose distance can be measured, there is a close correlation between the luminosity and the color. The same correlation is assumed to apply to the more distant stars; by observing their color, the astronomer infers their luminosity. Then he measures their apparent brightness with a photoelectric cell attached to his telescope. He can then calculate how far away the star must be in order for its intrinsic luminosity to produce the observed brightness at the earth.

One can imagine that the elements might not be as old as the universe, but the evidence indicates that they are. If U^{238} and the shorter-lived U^{235} were created in the same amounts, then their ratio would achieve its present value (140:1) in just about 4 billion years. The present relative abundances of other radioactive isotopes, also, suggest that the elements were created about 4 billion years ago.

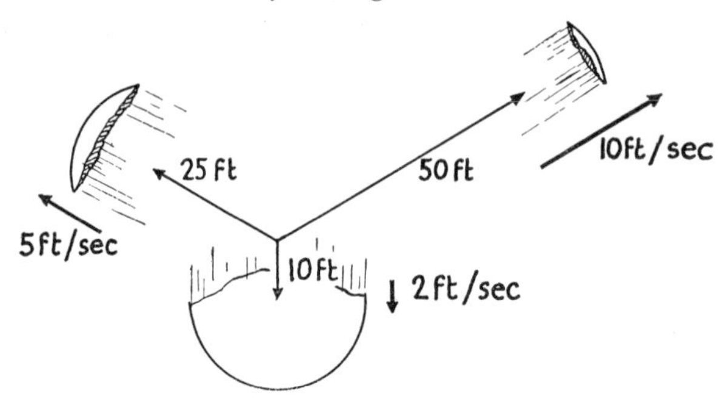

FIGURE 71–A. Fragments after an explosion. From the distances and velocities in the figure, we can infer that the fragments started from the same place 5 seconds previously. Similar considerations, on a vast scale, apply to the universe.

There are several theories about the origin of the elements, and as yet it is not possible to say that one is right and the others are wrong. A theory proposed by Gamow is the one that has had the best success in accounting for the relative abundance of the various elements. Gamow and his followers assume that just after the universe started to expand, about 4 billion years ago, all of the matter in the universe was an intensely hot ball of elementary particles, largely neutrons. During the expansion, some of the neutrons turned into protons. As the temperature fell, neutrons and protons joined together to form nuclei. A nucleus would be likely to grow by capturing more neutrons. If it acquired too many, some of them would turn to protons by emitting electrons. After that, the nucleus could capture more neutrons, and thus continue to grow.

Since the neutron-capturing tendencies of many nuclei have been measured in the laboratory, it is possible to calculate the relative abundance of the elements that would be formed by Gamow's neutron-capture process. His theory draws strong support from the fact that it predicts relative abundances that are in fairly good accord with the observed values. The actual calculations are extremely complex. One interesting feature of the theory is the rapidity of the process. The calculations show that the nuclei began to form a few minutes after the expansion started, and that the creation of the elements took about half an hour.

71–6. The Present Frontiers of Atomic Science. Although the broad aspects of atomic science have now reached a gratifying state of maturity, there is plenty of work still to be done. We do not yet know what holds the nucleus together. The number of fundamental particles is embarrassingly large; one of the most romantic branches of science is the attempt to understand the relations of these particles to one another, and to find out whether some or all of them are really the ultimate stuff of which the universe is made. Many physicists and chemists are at work on the more immediately practical problem of how to employ nuclear energy for useful purposes, either constructive or destructive.

In the more prosaic realm of atoms, molecules, and ions, the general principles outlined in the previous sections of this book are being used in the study of materials that have useful or exceptional properties. One important goal is a more detailed understanding of matter in the solid state, especially in the form of alloys or of slightly impure compounds. The organic chemists continue to unravel the structures of more and more complex substances, and to contrive new compounds for the satisfaction of practical needs. Other chemists are studying the rates at which reactions occur, and how catalysts influence these rates. In general, except in nuclear affairs, atomic science is in a state of assimilating the recent advances in theory and seeing how they apply to particular substances. The thrill of the unknown now reaches its highest pitch in the study of the subnuclear particles on the one hand, and of the universe as a whole on the other.

Summary

Gravitational attraction has compressed and heated the interior of the sun to such a high temperature that the atoms have been broken down into electrons and bare nuclei. Because of the high temperature, the protons have enough energy to produce transmutations. In a cycle of reactions involving nuclei of carbon, nitrogen, and oxygen, protons are used up and alpha-particles are created. The over-all result is exothermic; it involves the destruction of mass and the production of heat. Some of the sun's energy comes from this cycle of reactions, and some comes from the building up of alpha-particles directly from protons.

The reactions that keep the sun hot will continue for a reassuringly long time, because the only nuclei that are actually used up are the protons, and the supply of hydrogen in the sun is still very large.

Release of energy by the fusion of hydrogen nuclei has also been accomplished on the earth, by using a fission bomb to heat the hydrogen.

It is believed that the atoms as we know them were formed by nuclear reactions that occurred in matter hotter than the stars. The spectra of the stars indicate that the stars are receding from one another—the universe is expanding. Their present positions and velocities suggest that the stars are fragments thrown out by a great explosion that occurred about 4 billion years ago. To date, the most successful theory of the origin of the elements is based on the hypothesis that all of the matter in the universe was once a compact and intensely hot ball of fundamental particles, largely neutrons. As this aggregate expanded, it cooled, and the particles slowed down so that they could combine with one another to form nuclei. Many of the neutrons turned into protons and electrons. The theory, which accounts fairly well for the relative abundance of the various kinds of atoms, estimates that the formation of the elements took place in about half an hour.

Questions

1. Explain how gravitation can produce a high temperature in the interior of a star.
2. Why are we sure that gravitational P.E. is not the sole source of the energy radiated from the sun?
3. Why is it appropriate to apply the adjective "thermonuclear" to the processes that release energy in the sun?
4. Without describing the specific reactions and without using equations, formulate in a few sentences a description of the carbon cycle.
5. What do the carbon cycle and the proton chain have in common? How do they differ?
6. Describe the operation of the hydrogen bomb.
7. In what respect does the reaction in a hydrogen bomb resemble reactions that heat the sun?
8. Write the equation for the production of tritium by bombardment of deuterium with neutrons.
9. What is the evidence that the universe is expanding?
10. Summarize Gamow's theory of the origin of the elements.
11. A chain reaction involving fission can occur in material that is at room temperature, whereas the fusion reaction occurs only at high temperature. Correlate this difference with the fact that fission is induced by neutrons, whereas the particles that induce fusion are charged.

Suggestions for Further Reading

G. Gamow, *The Birth and Death of the Sun* (New York: Viking Press, 1945; Mentor Books [paper-bound], 1952). A very readable presentation of some of the most interesting aspects of nuclear physics and astrophysics.

L. N. Ridenour, H. A. Bethe, R. F. Bacher, and R. E. Lapp, "The Hydrogen Bomb," *Scientific American*, March, April, May, June, 1950. Although this article, in four parts, was published several years ago, it is still the best general reference on the subject.

G. Gamow, "Half an Hour of Creation," *Physics Today*, August, 1950. A qualitative summary of Gamow's theory of the formation of the atoms.

F. J. Hargreaves, *The Size of the Universe* (West Drayton, Middlesex, England: Penguin Books [Pelican Book A193], 1948). This fine exposition of one of its major problems is a good introduction to modern astronomy.

Fred Hoyle, *The Nature of the Universe* (New York: Harper & Bros., 1951). Lectures that formed a highly successful series of broadcasts in Great Britain. They describe one of the alternatives to the cosmic theory described in this chapter.

GENERAL VIEW OF SECTION X

After the arrangement of electrons around the nucleus had been explored through the study of spectra and the development of quantum mechanics, physicists turned their attention to the nucleus itself. Rutherford had already achieved an artificial transmutation in 1919, and the radioactivity that occurs in nature had been a subject of study for several decades.

By building accelerators to provide ample supplies of swift nuclear particles, experimenters have been able to study a host of nuclear reactions. As a result, we know that nuclei are built up of two fundamental particles, the proton and the neutron. Possibly these particles are held together by sharing another type of particle called a meson. An understanding of nuclear binding is the major goal of today's research in nuclear physics.

Experiments with transmutation have shown that Einstein's idea embodied in the equation $E = mc^2$ is correct: Mechanical and thermal energy can actually be created at the expense of mass. Many simple transmutations are highly exothermic, and the fission reaction is even more exothermic. The energy released in exothermic chemical reactions is of the order of 1 to 10 electron-volts per molecule. In many transmutations, the energy release is about 10 million electron-volts per nucleus, and each fission releases about 200 million electron-volts. Fission is important because it produces particles that can produce more fissions, so that a chain reaction is possible. At the high temperatures found in stars, some ordinary nuclear transmutations can lead to self-sustaining reactions.

Attempts to construct a theory of the nucleus have as yet had little success. Visible progress in nuclear science has for the most part been limited to the making of observations and measurements. Many teams of gifted scientists are building and using huge machines to accelerate subatomic particles and produce nuclear reactions. The quantitative data are piling up, as they did when Brahe spent his life in painstaking observation of the planets. It is to be hoped that a Kepler and a Newton will soon arrive to synthesize a theory from the mass of data.

Through the fission bomb and the fusion bomb, even our present meager understanding of nuclei is imperiling the very existence of Western Civilization. It is significant that this development, based on the conversion of mass to energy, was presaged as a philosophical abstraction in 1905 by Einstein, a man whose whole life was strongly motivated by pacifism. There has recently been a demand that scientists direct their activities toward goals that are socially desirable, or at least safe. In looking back over this section, or indeed over the whole book, the reader can easily see that no scientist can foretell the social consequences of his discoveries. In time of war or other crisis, the scientist can turn technologist and use available knowledge for predictable ends. In his normal role of explorer, however, all that the scientist can do is give his fellow men a deeper understanding of their environment, and of themselves.

Appendix

APPENDIX

I. The Elements That Are Found in Nature

Element	Symbol	Atomic Number	Atomic Weight
Actinium	Ac	89	227
Aluminum	Al	13	26.98
Antimony	Sb	51	121.76
Argon	A	18	39.944
Arsenic	As	33	74.91
Barium	Ba	56	137.36
Beryllium	Be	4	9.013
Bismuth	Bi	83	209.00
Boron	B	5	10.82
Bromine	Br	35	79.916
Cadmium	Cd	48	112.41
Calcium	Ca	20	40.08
Carbon	C	6	12.010
Cerium	Ce	58	140.13
Cesium	Cs	55	132.91
Chlorine	Cl	17	35.457
Chromium	Cr	24	52.01
Cobalt	Co	27	58.94
Copper	Cu	29	63.54
Dysprosium	Dy	66	162.46
Erbium	Er	68	167.2
Europium	Eu	63	152.0
Fluorine	F	9	19.00
Gadolinium	Gd	64	156.9
Gallium	Ga	31	69.72
Germanium	Ge	32	72.60
Gold	Au	79	197.2
Hafnium	Hf	72	178.6
Helium	He	2	4.003
Holmium	Ho	67	164.94
Hydrogen	H	1	1.0080
Indium	In	49	114.76
Iodine	I	53	126.91
Iridium	Ir	77	193.1
Iron	Fe	26	55.85
Krypton	Kr	36	83.80
Lanthanum	La	57	138.92
Lead	Pb	82	207.21
Lithium	Li	3	6.940
Lutetium	Lu	71	174.99
Magnesium	Mg	12	24.32
Manganese	Mn	25	54.93

Element	Symbol	Atomic Number	Atomic Weight
Mercury	Hg	80	200.61
Molybdenum	Mo	42	95.95
Neodymium	Nd	60	144.27
Neon	Ne	10	20.183
Nickel	Ni	28	58.69
Niobium	Nb	41	92.91
Nitrogen	N	7	14.008
Osmium	Os	76	190.2
Oxygen	O	8	16.000
Palladium	Pd	46	106.7
Phosphorus	P	15	30.975
Platinum	Pt	78	195.23
Polonium	Po	84	210
Potassium	K	19	39.100
Praseodymium	Pr	59	140.92
Protoactinium	Pa	91	231
Radium	Ra	88	226.05
Radon	Rn	86	222
Rhenium	Re	75	186.31
Rhodium	Rh	45	102.91
Rubidium	Rb	37	85.48
Ruthenium	Ru	44	101.7
Samarium	Sm	62	150.43
Scandium	Sc	21	44.96
Selenium	Se	34	78.96
Silicon	Si	14	28.09
Silver	Ag	47	107.880
Sodium	Na	11	22.997
Strontium	Sr	38	87.63
Sulfur	S	16	32.066
Tantalum	Ta	73	180.88
Tellurium	Te	52	127.61
Terbium	Tb	65	159.2
Thallium	Tl	81	204.39
Thorium	Th	90	232.12
Thulium	Tm	69	169.4
Tin	Sn	50	118.70
Titanium	Ti	22	47.90
Tungsten	W	74	183.92
Uranium	U	92	238.07
Vanadium	V	23	50.95
Xenon	Xe	54	131.3
Ytterbium	Yb	70	173.04
Yttrium	Y	39	88.92
Zinc	Zn	30	65.38
Zirconium	Zr	40	91.22

II. Man-Made Elements Not Found in Nature

Element	Symbol	Atomic Number
Technetium	Tc	43
Promethium	Pm	61
Astatine	At	85
Francium	Fr	87
Neptunium	Np	93
Plutonium	Pu	94
Americium	Am	95
Curium	Cm	96
Berkelium	Bk	97
Californium	Cf	98
Einsteinium	E	99
Centurium	Ct	100
Mendelevium	Mv	101

INDEX

Page numbers in italic type designate definitions or biographical notes.